Science in Elementary Education

Science in Elementary Education

PETER C. GEGA
San Diego State College

John Wiley & Sons, Inc.
New York · London · Sydney

To Dale, Chris, and Suzanne

Preface

This is a book on how to teach science in elementary schools. It should be especially useful in related college and in-service courses.

The book has two main parts. Part I introduces the basic things teachers need to know: how science is organized in elementary schools, strategies and tactics of science teaching, evaluation methods, how to get and use materials, how to plan lessons. Part II *applies* these methods in many different ways, within the typical subject-matter fields of elementary science.

The twelve chapters (or "units" as we shall call them) of Part II are the heart of this book. They contain specific, model lesson plans, arranged in teaching sequences that encourage children to learn through the development of their own critical thinking skills. These skills are clearly identified as they are used within each lesson. An understandable subject-matter exposition before each sequence of lessons provides the background needed to teach the sequence confidently and successfully.

There are four units each at the primary-, intermediate-, and upper-grade levels—enough material to make up most of a year's work at each level. Overlapping has been purposely planned. Adjustments in vocabulary, teacher assistance, and so on will enable all of these units to be taught at other levels.

The detailed nature of Part II may make someone who browses briefly through this book think that persons will use it in a "cookbook" way—that is, without adjusting and replanning for individual classes. I have found the opposite to be true. When there is substantial teaching of theory beforehand, carefully arranged details are seen as examples of principles previously presented, rather than prescriptive items to be blindly imitated. The deepened learning that results sets the stage for personal innovation and departure from routine.

I am greatly indebted to the following persons for help received during the preparation of this book: Douglas L. Baker, James E. Crouch, Norman F. Dessel, Avery H. Gallup, Charles F. Harbison, Edward W. Huffman, Fay Landweer, Orlando J. Lupone, Richard Madden, Claude F. Merzbacher, Frances I. Schalles, Richard E. Servey, John A. Spangler, Margaret V. Spengler, Lillian K. Spitzer, Blakemore E. Thomas, and Gerhard Wolter; and to Cyrus W. Barnes and Eugene C. Lee, who read the manuscript.

Thanks also go to The New Jersey State Department of Education for questions on page 3, adapted from the publication *Teaching Science* (1958);

and to the following persons and institutions for the photographs that appear on the pages indicated: A. Devaney, Inc. (page 242); Allyn & Bacon, Inc. (page 180); The American Museum of Natural History (pages 142, 264, 270, 292, 293, 294, 335, 360); B. M. Shaub (pages 292 and 293); David D. Pascoe and The La Mesa-Spring Valley School District (page 395); Don Cravens (page 412); Don. L. Chamberlin, Dean Jones, J. Fred Wilson, and The San Diego Unified School District (frontispiece, pages 9, 33, 44, 46, 65, 68, 70, 82, 84, 90, 101); Eastman Kodak Co. (pages 156 and 180); ESSA photos (page 323); Ewing Galloway (page 106); Ginn and Company (page 318); Henry Groskinsky, Silver Burdett Company (page 130); Hugh Spencer (page 374); James Industries, Incorporated (page 135); John M. Huffman, Henry R. McCarty, and The Department of Education, San Diego County (pages 25, 75, 78, 81, 87, 89); Lick Observatory, The University of California (page 328); Litton Industries (page 309); Myles J. Adler (page 180); Soil Conservation Service (page 279); Suzanne Szasz (pages 2, 66, 79, 363); The United States Department of Agriculture (pages 282 and 283); United States Geological Survey (page 288); and The United States Weather Bureau (pages 206, 323, 309).

Finally, many thanks go to my wife, Dale Gega, for her valuable and considerable assistance from the beginning through the end of the manuscript.

San Diego   Peter C. Gega
January, 1966

Contents

Part II: *Applications of Science Teaching Methods*

Unit

Science in Elementary Education

Part I

Introduction to
Science Teaching Methods

CHAPTER 1

Science in Elementary Education

When you were a child, you and all the other boys and girls wanted to know a great deal about the natural world around you. Children still do. Sooner or later, they will ask questions like:

"How do birds get in the egg?"
"Why doesn't a spider get stuck in its web?"
"How can you tell the difference between a boy and a girl tree?"

and

"Where does the dark come from?"
"What makes the wind blow?"
"Why is dirt different colors?"

and

"What makes water wet?"
"How does the picture get on television?"
"Where does smoke go?"

If you had asked these questions as a child, how thoughtfully would your teachers have handled them? Would you have been able to explore such a wide scope of knowledge? Or was learning more restricted? Were you guided to think through some problems for yourself? Or were answers always given? The ways in which your teachers worked with children depended greatly on their notions of good teaching in elementary science. The same truism applies today with you.

It would be convenient to state exactly what ideas are now most valued and practiced by teachers; but this is hard to do. For one thing, some ideas in the field have a disturbing way of not hanging on very long. Besides, no one knows accurately how much of what people say is actually put into practice. In spite of this, several broad contrasts in the teaching of elementary science have become apparent since 1930 or so. Although the older approaches are fading away their traces can still be found, perhaps in thousands of classrooms, and often in subtly changed forms.

HOW SCIENCE TEACHING IS CHANGING

Elementary science used to be considered a form of "nature study." There was much pressing of leaves and flowers, collecting of rocks, observation and sketching of trees, and observation of birds, for example. The object was to appreciate the beauty and wonder of the natural environment, as contrasted with the man-made environment. Often coupled was the thought that children's minds were not yet ready for "real" science study; this would be taken up later, and after the proper appreciation of nature was gained.

But over the years, teachers have come to realize that children can learn in any area of science, from astronomy through zoology. Difficulty of learning appears less related to the topic than to the complexity of the ideas studied. When necessary, this complexity can be adjusted to the mental ability of the learner. Moreover, appreciation of the natural world can now be gained as well or better through activities which are more intellectually stimulating than nature study. Understanding can be produced without the mysticism or exaggerated reverence for nature which often was a side effect of such teaching.

Teachers used to be concerned almost exclusively with the teaching of science information. They were concerned with teaching the results or *products* of scientific investigation. Progress was noted mostly by how much knowledge the pupil acquired at the end of a specific period of time, usually a term or year.

We are still concerned with the acquisition of knowledge. But there is now greatly increased interest in teaching science *processes* —that is, the ways of thinking scientists use in discovering and ordering knowledge. Most modern educators realize that for intelligent functioning it is at least as important to learn science thinking skills and attitudes (processes) as principles and facts of science (products).

At one time, it was common practice in the teaching of science to assign narrow topics by grade levels. In one school, for example, the frog was a third-grade topic, while birds held sway with first-grade teachers. Mastery of specific facts—the moon is 240,000 miles away, a spider has eight legs, and an insect has six—was the dominant theme. Often factual information within the topics studied was of a trivial nature, and unrelated to other portions of the curriculum. As a result, worrisome difficulties continually appeared. With rapidly increasing science knowledge, what should be left out? What included? Are insects more important than frogs? Why is so much forgotten by the children a short time after they have learned about the topic? Why is there so little application of science knowledge in daily living?

To construct workable solutions to these and other problems, interested persons began to re-examine how children learn. Increasingly educators began reasoning: Since children can profit from experiences in most areas of science, why not broaden the scope of study? Since science information is increasing so rapidly, why not dwell on the big ideas, or major principles,[1] of science? Because one-time topic teaching is soon largely forgotten, why not use a developmental approach? Some ideas can be repeated several times through the grades, but with increased complexity and in different contexts. These thoughts became some of the guidelines in use today.

As we have suggested, modern practices are not the result of educational thinking in just the last few years. A look at the 1932 and 1947 yearbooks of the National Society for the Study of Education[2] discloses the origins of much present thought and method. In addition, other educational organizations, such as the National Science Teachers Association, have continually emphasized curriculum development. Thus over the years there has been a continuous, though slow, transition toward more efficient practices.

Nevertheless, things are far from settled in science education. Since 1958 we have seen unparalleled activity in science course revision at all levels of precollege education. As the discovery of knowledge accelerates ever faster, there is mounting concern about the need to teach the truly fundamental ideas of science and ways to improve pupils' thinking abilities. How else can we achieve economy in learning? How else can we avoid teaching what is obsolete? These are the nagging questions. Study groups have formed everywhere to seek solutions, and it is the rare university or college whose personnel remain untouched by it all. The huge and unprecedented outpouring of money in support of these purposes from government and private foundations has been an important factor in this activity. So has the greatly increased participation of specialists in the science disciplines.

Although more and more attention to science education should do much to im-

---

[1] "Science principles," "big ideas," "laws," and "generalizations" are terms usually used interchangeably in elementary science education.

[2] National Society for the Study of Education, *A Program for Teaching Science, Thirty-First Yearbook,* Part I, Chicago: University of Chicago Press, 1932; and *Science Education in American Schools, Forty-Sixth Yearbook,* Part I, Chicago: University of Chicago Press, 1947.

prove the way science is taught, there is always danger of confusion when many voices are heard. Whom do we heed? Since this is a continual problem in education, it will be helpful to understand some of the factors that enter into the selection of what to teach.

FACTORS INFLUENCING WHAT WE TEACH

Much of our guidance for what to teach comes from the broad field of science itself. Although there are different specialties within the field, scientists have shown time and again that their knowledge is "all of a piece." It has become increasingly necessary for different specialists to work together in solving problems, as evidenced by the growth of such fused sciences as astrophysics, biochemistry, geophysics, and others. As scientists have developed generalizations they have shown how these relate to one another, and how they cut across traditional subject-matter lines. Even entire subsciences emerge that defy older classification. The best example is oceanography. Therefore, it is possible to select broad generalizations for teaching—those that have many applications in the lives of children.

Even little Bobby's broad generalization, "Things expand when they are heated" helps him to relate and explain such apparently different happenings as sidewalks buckling and cracking in hot weather, telephone wires sagging on a summer day, rocks rimming a campfire cracking open, and his mother's loosening of a tightly screwed jar lid by running hot water over it. His later understanding of more sophisticated statements of the same principle may involve molecular motion and coefficients of linear and cubical expansion. These refinements permit a more complete explanation of these events.

Because broad generalizations, and also skills, are so useful, it is tempting to increase their scope so that they apply to more and more phenomena. But there is always the question of when to stop. Explanations become continually more abstract and remote to the young mind as their "mileage" increases. As a teaching generalization or a technique more closely approaches the most advanced scientific model, it is less likely that children can learn it or will want to. To persist is simply to ask them to bite off more than they can chew.

In their efforts to teach broadly fundamental ideas or skills to children, some experimenters with science curricula have taken a learn-this-now, you-will-see-the-value-of-it-later approach. Even though a skill or a generalization may prove useful at some future time, this alone is not a sufficient reason to present it. It is important for children to maintain meaning throughout their studies and to see the purpose of what they are doing. In addition, they need to accomplish short-range goals as they head toward those farther away. To do otherwise cuts down pupil interest, understanding, and personal meaning in what is taught. Because they are relatively inexperienced, and intellectually as well as physically immature, children usually learn best when working with the concrete and semiconcrete, the limited theories, and the here and now.[3] This is most obvious and necessary with younger pupils, as primary teachers are quick to tell us.

There is a related point. Science for children usually includes some study of technological and other life applications of scientific principles—the telephone, airplane, vacuum cleaner, simple engines, and so on. Should we abandon study of these inventions for study of basic scientific ideas alone? After all, we are told, some inventions and other present applications of science may be around for only a short while.

Frequently, the best way to approach study of an important generalization is through some of the technological products that have resulted from it. Studying how something works becomes a convenient way for opening up study of far broader applications,

[3] David P. Ausubel, "Some Psychological Considerations in the Objectives and Design of an Elementary-School Science Program," *Science Education*, April 1963, pp. 278–284.

which results in mastery of the generalization. A curriculum that provides at least some of these applications is in touch with children's interests. It tends to keep study alive. And when applications are at hand in the everyday environment, so much the better. Their concreteness and accessibility may make them easy to work with. But these applications should be tied to important generalizations, otherwise much of their value is lost. Let us study the telephone and telegraph, for example, but while we are at it let us make sure that the ideas which made them possible—electromagnetism and change of energy forms—emerge as important learnings.

Then there are children's needs to be considered. As they develop, what must they understand about their bodies and the physical forces that govern their safety and play? What can we do to help them interpret now the things they want to know and need to know about their environment? What will they need to know as adults?

Usual sources of the science principles we teach have been textbooks, yearbooks of learned organizations, publications of national commissions, and education research projects. We have also relied upon these sources to provide us with methods of thinking that children can use as they discover or otherwise learn these principles.

Presently, increasing numbers of subject-area specialists are finding time to show us the important ideas and inquiry methods in their fields. There is no question but that these scientists and college teachers have identified many worthwhile ideas and process methods for teaching. Who is more aware of what is obsolete or current, important or unimportant, in scientific thought than the persons continually engaged in such thought? It is to be hoped that their contributions to elementary science curriculum development can continue indefinitely.

However, children are not "scientists," in spite of a few superficial similarities in curiosity and explanation-seeking behavior. Teaching statements of basic science principles must be modified to fit in with what we know about children's capacities. Ideas must be simplified, known interests and needs of children considered, and their physical coordination and dexterity weighed. What they can apply now and in the future must be assessed, as well as the other goals of early general education. Judgments about all these factors and more must enter into elementary-school science. The best science programs require a broad spectrum of talent. Besides the important role of scientists, contributions are needed from classroom teachers, psychologists, science educators, technicians, and professional writers. (The bibliography lists some noteworthy experimental programs.)

THREE FORMS OF TEACHING

Science in elementary education is likely to appear in three forms. Sometimes it is taught as a *basic program*, with a definite allocation of time. Sometimes it is *correlated* with a broad content area; social studies or health lessons may present an opportunity to connect science ideas. It is also taught on an *incidental* basis, as pupil interest or the occasion arises.

Since all three approaches contain potential contributions to learning, let us examine them more closely. We shall consider each in terms of *scope*—the range or breadth of study, and *sequence*—the order in which learnings are taken up.

Science as a basic program. The *scope* of a modern science curriculum is likely to be almost as broad as science itself. Consider the range found in the Los Angeles, California course of study:[4]

Living Things
   Relationships Among Living Things (In grades K,1,2)
   Plant Life (K,1,2)
   Animal Life (K,1,2)

[4] *Course of Study for Elementary Schools*, Los Angeles City Schools, Division of Instructional Services, Publication No. 375, 1964 Revision, pp. 215–238.

Animal and Plant Diversity (3,5,6)
Growth and Development (3,4,5,6)
Structures and Functions (3,4,5,6)

Matter and Energy
Nature of Matter and Energy (K,1,2,3,4,5,6)
Physical and Chemical Change (2,3,5,6)
Electrical and Magnetic Energy (K,1,2,3,4,5,6)
Sound Energy (3,4,6)
Solar Energy (6)
Nuclear Energy (6)
Light and Heat Energy (K,2,3,5)
Mechanical Energy (K,1,2,4,5)

Earth
Atmosphere and Weather (K,1,2,4,5,6)
Seasons and Climate (1,2,4,5,6)
Oceanography (3,5,6)
Structure and Change (K,1,3,5)

The Universe
Earth-Moon-Sun Relationships (K,1,2,3,4,5,6)
Solar System (4,6)
Inter-Stellar Space (2,5,6)

Under the "expanding generalization" or "spiral" plan in the foregoing materials, large generalizations are taught at least several times through the elementary grades. For example, "Heat is a form of energy that is transferred in several ways" may be studied in the primary grades as simple heat conduction from the source through solid materials, such as metal, plastic, wood, and so on. In the intermediate grades radiation and convection might be introduced, in addition to a more refined treatment of conduction. Upper-grade pupils may learn about heat transfer as molecular energy. Each of the experiences and smaller ideas studied contribute to understanding the overall idea of heat transfer. At the same time, progress is made toward understanding the very broad concept of "energy."

Many curriculum guides today contain generalizations and activities developed by blocks of grades—K–2, 3–4, 5–6—for instance. Others develop many of the larger ideas in every grade. Some guides list broad topics assigned to each grade level. Regardless of the organization of guides, at least two general

practices seem clear. Most contain some consideration for the study of larger ideas of science; and such study is usually developmental. That is, some attempt is made for the child to study broad ideas more than once in the several grades. Because of this, you can see that it is highly important for representatives from all school levels—elementary, junior high, and senior high—to plan together in curriculum construction.

It is general practice to organize convenient teaching segments of the entire curriculum into *units*. Although not everyone would agree with this definition, for our purposes *a unit is a sequence of related ideas and activities organized around a theme or topic*. Examples of units appear in Part II of this book. The trend at present is to teach fewer, but more intensive, units during the school year. Leading the trend are several elementary-school science textbook series.

In the Holt, Rinehart and Winston series,[5] for example, after introductory exploration activities in kindergarten and grade 1, four units are studied in depth within each grade:

Grade 2
Animal Life
Water and Air
Sound and Light
Heat Energy

Grade 3
Plant Life
Simple Machines
Rocks and Minerals
States of Matter

Grade 4
Living Things and Their Surroundings
The Solar System
The Earth's Changing Surface

Grade 5
Forms and Functions of Living Things
Electricity and Magnetism
The Atmosphere, Oceans, and Space
Weather and Climate

[5] Abraham S. Fischler, Sam S. Blanc, and Lawrence Lowery, *Science—A Modern Approach* (Elementary Science Series), New York: Holt, Rinehart and Winston, 1966.

Grade 6
Microorganisms and Man
Atoms and Molecules
Optics and Sound
Force and Motion

An interesting aspect of such depth study is that concepts from several subject areas within science can be thoroughly related to one another. So in a study of the atmosphere, let us say, behavior of molecules, change of energy forms, properties of water, and the like are seen together in an understandable context.

The trend to fewer units is a reaction to needless repetition of topics and superficiality of study that characterized elementary science programs some time ago. In many curricula today, similar topics are scheduled in two- or three-year cycles, rather than every year. Such planning still insures a developmental approach and a broad scope of study, but lessens such occasions where children say, "What, weather again?"

Sequence of learnings in a basic program is decided by the complexity of the ideas involved, ways they can be logically arranged in order, and how children tend to perceive the ideas. (We shall go into more detail in later chapters.) Often certain principles are "placed" at designated grade levels, after some trials have been conducted to see if they can be efficiently taught. It is not unusual to see the same principle placed at varying levels in different curriculum guides and text series, and in somewhat different sequences. Ordinarily, these differences are unimportant. The vital question is: Do children efficiently learn the principle? The fact is, we have yet much to discover about sequence in learning before we can be more precise in curriculum development.

It should be clear that we have used knowledge or "product" objectives as the foundation for both scope and sequence in the spiral approach just described. But how about thinking or "process" skills? How is the accomplishment of these important objectives planned for in this organization? This is hard to answer specifically because again we

find many different practices. Perhaps the commonest method of handling this provision is to insure that at least several generalizations within each unit are developed by the children in a problem-solving manner.

Specific process skills used within this method often are similar to those listed in the Los Angeles Course of Study:[6]

Questioning	Observing	Drawing Conclusions
Defining the Problem	Discovering	
	Recording	Generalizing
Hypothesizing	Discussing	Applying
Researching	Organizing	Knowledge
Planning the Solution	Verifying	Understanding Relationships

Is it possible to reverse the usual practice and have *process* methods as the basis for scope and sequence, with subject matter selected only as it furthers process? It is possible, and indeed some newer curriculum experiments are using this organization. For instance, let us examine the American Association for the Advancement of Science experimental program.[7] The following process abilities have been identified for kindergarten through grade 3:

1. Recognizing and using space/time relations
2. Recognizing and using numbers and number relations
3. Observing
4. Classifying
5. Measuring
6. Communicating
7. Inferring
8. Predicting

For grades 4 through 6, more complex abilities are stated which are an extension and an elaboration of the abilities developed in the primary grades:

1. Formulating hypotheses
2. Making operational definitions
3. Controlling and manipulating variables

[6] Los Angeles City Schools Course of Study, page 216.

[7] AAAS, *Science—A Process Approach, Commentary for Teachers*, Second Experimental Edition, Washington, D.C.: The Association, 1964, pages 9, 18. By permission.

4. Experimenting
5. Formulating models
6. Interpreting data

A sequence of specific developmental activities is followed throughout the several grades to develop pupil competency in each stated skill. The subject matter within which skills are developed is taken as needed from four broad areas:

The universe. Its galaxies, our solar system, the earth, and (the child's) immediate environment; the range of measurements used to describe astronomical and geological phenomena.

The structure and properties of matter. Elements and compounds; chemical reactions and changes in properties; atoms and molecules; electrons, protons, and neutrons.

The conservation and transformation of energy. The electro-magnetic spectrum, energy of motion and potential energy, electrical energy, and chemical energy; force and work, gravitational and magnetic fields.

The interaction between living things and their environment. Animal and human behavior, the relation between biological structure and function, reproduction, development, genetics, evolution, and the biological units—cell, organism, and population.

A program whose scope is based on process is most attractive. What can be more important than developing the ability to think? But there are serious difficulties in the approach that we should keep in mind. Process skills are not yet as well defined as subject-matter generalizations, and their sequential development is not so well understood. It is also questionable whether children can learn enough subject matter. However, experimental programs such as the foregoing are guided by highly competent persons who are taking great pains to overcome these troublesome considerations. Such programs may yield results that we must not overlook.

Correlated teaching. It is only commonsensical to realize that learning in any subject area requires skills and knowledge from other segments of the curriculum. When one of your pupils looks up information in an encyclopedia, he is reading. He uses arithmetic when he determines differences in weight of a moist and dry food sample in a nutrition experiment. He employs language skills to make a well-organized report on theories of why dinosaurs became extinct. When several children draw a large panel picture to illustrate several conservation practices, this is art. Such integration of "subjects" is not only desirable, but unavoidable when you use a variety of activities to bring about learning.

There are occasions, however, when an entire subject, or an important part of a subject, is correlated with science. Social studies, and health and safety are usually the most likely areas of the curriculum to be treated in this fashion. The advantages of teaching health and safety with science are clear—there is less likely to be finger-wagging admonition and prescriptive rule-making. There is likelier to be clear understanding of cause and effect relationships, especially when real problems are studied: Why do most dentists recommend fluoridated water? Why should we play quietly after a large meal? Many educators now make no distinction between health and science. As far as they are concerned, good health teaching is good science teaching. It becomes an important emphasis within the overall science program.

Advantages also occur when carefully selected social studies ideas are joined with science ideas. It is hardly likely that conservation practices and laws can be profitably studied in the absence of scientific information. And such questions as, How do we get our water? and, Why did they build Megalopolis City in that location? are also examples of times where social studies and science ideas intertwine. Such correlation makes it easier for cohesive, whole understandings to form in pupils' minds than when we teach similar ideas in isolation.

Many relationships between science and social studies may be profitably planned. But there is a tendency for some persons to seek such relationships beyond the bounds of effective learning. Consider the study of technological applications of science in a communications unit. The children may learn the

FIGURE 1 When studying about weather, it is natural to want to draw pictures about it.

names and biographies of several famous inventors, their inventions, and resulting influences on cultural change. This is important and useful in social studies. Yet such an approach is likely to neglect the science principles themselves, unless specific provision is made for their study. It may become difficult to build a structure of basic knowledge in science. The first choice for selecting subject matter in this case is social studies, and the tendency is to look for cohesiveness and completeness in it, rather than in science.

Even if adequate time is provided for the exploration of science principles, both scope and sequence of science are likely to be impaired if first consideration for subject matter selection is given to social studies. Many important areas of science can be neglected, as they may not fit conveniently in the scope planned for in social studies. Also, attempts to develop an acceptable sequence in two areas at one time typically lead to the neglect of one subject or the other. It is just too hard to juggle both sequences at one time.

Sometimes correlation of subject matter is seized upon as a solution to the crowded time problem. The thinking goes, "Since there is not enough time for science, let's just correlate it with something else." An examination of the number of principles taught usually discloses the now-you-see-it, now-you-don't quality of this approach. If there are ten science and ten social studies principles to explore, this makes a total of twenty principles. About the same length of time is needed to teach all of them whether taught together or separately. If anything, needed correlation should take somewhat longer if relationships among the two areas are made clear.

Despite the long history of science teaching in some elementary schools, only in recent years have large numbers of schools elevated its status to a basic, rather than supplementary, study. It is only natural to see a real problem about time for teaching emerge as the importance of science education grows with our changing culture. But to meet the time problem we must establish a policy of priorities, rather than "lose" one subject in another.

Incidental teaching. Children exhibit a great deal of curiosity about the world around them. It is clear that some of the questions with which we began this chapter could have been asked because of discoveries made outside of the classroom, while others may have been stimulated through in-school work. When questions are raised during study of a generalization and are pertinent, the teacher may wish to handle them within the context of the study. But sometimes children's questions have little relation to what is currently being investigated. Or, they may come up at a time when no science unit is in progress. In these cases, questions may need to be handled on a separate, incidental basis. As important and interesting events occur in and out of the classroom, sincere questions cannot be ignored if the children's need to know is respected.

Incidental teaching is valuable in maintaining spontaneity, currency, and some provision for individual curiosity and interest. Yet it cannot replace the need for an organized, basic program. Children's interests may flicker out quickly; perhaps only a few may be deeply interested in a topic at one time. Scope of study can be so narrow ("Let's study about rockets again!") that little is done in other vital areas of science. Sequence of learnings is likely to be so haphazard only little assurance is gained that children are ready for increasingly complex experiences in later years.

To summarize, all three provisions for teaching—basic program, correlated, and incidental—are useful. The basic program organization provides a teaching structure of big ideas within which children can develop important skills of inquiry. The correlated approach permits social and other relationships to be vitally joined with science phenomena. Provision for incidental teaching lends extra assurance that children's interests will be considered.

Thus far, we have been concerned with the overall setting and organization of science in the elementary school. Among other things, we have seen that modern programs are committed to the teaching of both process and product objectives. The next several chapters show how these two basic intentions may be accomplished. Chapter 2 mainly considers the broad strategy that underlies much of modern science teaching. Chapter 3 presents specific tactics we can use.

Strategy in Science Teaching

Our present concern with the teaching of both product and process makes it important to organize activities that can best develop each objective. Accordingly, most of the experiences that children have in elementary science can be divided into two broad types: *background-centered* and *solution-centered*. Sometimes we are interested mostly in helping children become aware of certain factual information; the facts give a background of knowledge to draw upon when needed. Other times we are concerned more with their ability to think with facts; the thinking is pointed toward working out solutions to problem situations. But often we help establish purposes for either kind of activity by raising questions, or by capitalizing on questions children ask. Because of this, it will be helpful to know about the specific purposes behind each kind of activity.

BACKGROUND-CENTERED QUESTIONS

There are several reasons for using background-centered questions; the following four tend to complement and overlap one another:

1. To establish some background of knowledge before introducing a problem.

Example: "What sounds can be made with this instrument?" leads to the solution-centered problem, "What causes the differences between high and low sounds?"

Clearly the "what" of a subject usually precedes the "why." In other subject areas, children must be aware that food may spoil before the reasons are explored. They will be unable to guess (hypothesize) intelligently about the causes of night and day if unaware that the earth is in space and receives light from the sun. In short, a certain amount of informational background is necessary before children can work meaningfully with a problem.

2. To fill in gaps or omissions to form a more complete understanding after a problem has been studied.

Example: "We have discovered through experimenting that saliva changes starch to sugar as we chew. But how are other foods broken down and digested? Let's read and find out."

By establishing a context within which problem findings are related, the pupil is helped to see the big picture. Also, it would be impossible through problem solving alone to study more than just a fraction of the present curriculum. Many discoveries are beyond the abilities of children, and time for teaching is limited. While we should avoid superficially sailing over a sea of subject matter, a substantial portion of human knowledge must be sampled by pupils if they are to become liberally educated.

3. To satisfy children's curiosity about things or ideas encountered before or during the unit which are not problems as such.

Examples: "What are shooting stars?"
"What do you have to know to be a jet pilot?"
"Who invented the Diesel engine?"

Often the reasons that cause children to ask such questions are similar to those in item 2. Sometimes personal interests are reflected in questions of this type.

4. To cope with special procedures that may have to be learned as the class studies science.

Examples: "How do we use and take care of a microscope?"
"How can this insect be mounted?"
"Can the yardstick help us measure how much taller this plant has grown?"

These needs are usually best handled as they come along rather than being pretaught. Then the pupil can develop a functional awareness and skill with regard to a procedure, rather than just acquiring easily forgettable knowledge about it. A desirable way to handle such needs is through demonstrations.

Questions within the above categories sometimes may be quite narrow and specific:

"How many legs does an insect have?"
"What are the main parts of a plant?"
"What are the highest clouds called?"

Or, they may be very broad and general:

"How does the weather bureau help us?"
"What objects are in space?"
"What are some of the ways in which animals take care of their young?"

Some background-centered questions lead to involved but narrowly prescribed answers:

"How is a photograph developed?"
"How is steel made?"
"How does blood circulate in the body?"

Practically all background-centered questions have several factors in common:

1. Their answers usually feature a basic reliance for explanation upon some *authority*, whether it is the teacher, book, specialist, film, or other reference.

2. Answers are often immediately available, or available within a short period of time.

3. While children may make guesses or hypotheses as to possible answers, these are not really needed.

We must emphasize that the foregoing comments refer to elementary-school children, as contrasted with scientists. Obviously, scientists are still trying experimentally to answer in detail, "How does blood circulate in the body?" as well as other questions that appear here.

Background-centered questions are helpful in establishing purposes for many activities. But they should not be presented as "problems." The elements that make up an interesting problem are not present. What these elements are, we shall consider next.

SOLUTION-CENTERED QUESTIONS

Many times we see statements of a "scientific method" supposedly useful in solving a problem. Usually, the method includes five steps: (1) defining the problem; (2) making a hypothesis or guess as to the solution; (3) testing the hypothesis; (4) assessing the findings; and (5) drawing a conclusion. Criticism of this method has become widespread. Scientists and educators rightly point out that problem solving cannot be so neatly described. But does this mean that it is useless to categorize problem-solving behavior? Not at all. As we shall see in Chapter 4, a similar classification will be helpful in determining the kinds of process behaviors we should teach. However, it does mean that we must recognize the proper uses and limitations of a classified process.

Perhaps the commonest objection to the five-step "method" stems from the fact that many teachers present the steps as almost a guaranteed way to solve a problem. Of course, mindlessly following a ritual is likely to be unproductive in any endeavor. Consider for a moment the novice stock-market investor about to purchase some common stock. For financial success, all he needs to do is follow a two-step method: (1) buy at low prices, and (2) sell at high prices. But he soon discovers from his broker and other sources that there are numerous relative factors to consider, assumptions to be examined, and all-important judgments to be made *within* the two steps. Under proper conditions, these things can be learned to a considerable degree; but the investor hardly has a guarantee of success.

Productive thinking in science education also is based on the examination of relative factors, assumptions, judgments, and more. Actual problem solving seldom proceeds in an orderly, sequential way. There is much deviation and backtracking. However, the process does have elements within it that can be taught. As with the stock-market example, such teaching would involve helping the child learn how to ask questions, how to get the best information possible, and how to reason and make intelligent judgments with this information. But here, too, there is no guarantee of success.

Solution-centered questions are probably the best means we have to foster such a wide range of thinking procedures. Let us consider now some criteria we can use in developing these questions.

Almost everyone can agree that the school must be selective in the learning experiences provided for children. The purpose of the school is not to take up any or all things that may come up. It is instead to get children to reflect upon important ideas and thinking processes that will enable them to learn more efficiently than they would without schooling. When an important science generalization is selected and then set up in a problem-solving way, this purpose is likely to be realized.

Once a worthwhile generalization has been selected, it is helpful to think of cause and effect in attempting to develop a problem. A problem can generally be stated in terms of an effect or real-life application. Pupil hypotheses should be stated in terms of probable causes. Consider the following:

Generalization (actual cause). The greater the density of a liquid, the more buoyancy it provides.

Problem (effect or application). Why can a ship carry a heavier cargo on the ocean than on the Great Lakes?

Hypothesis (pupil's proposed cause). Things float more easily in salt water than in fresh water.

Notice that a more complete or better hypothesis would bear more resemblance to the actual generalization, which offers the best cause. However, seldom does a child's hypothesis match a science principle in preciseness and completeness. We strive toward this, and progress does occur as the experiences and abilities of children increase through the years.

The answer to a worthwhile problem should not be obvious immediately. When possible, there should be some discrepancy or paradox present, apparently caused by a reason which demands some thought. This stimulates the children to develop several or more hypotheses which can be critically screened and tested.

Sometimes teachers state a problem in such a way that the venturing of a hypothesis is needless. There is a big difference between a real problem and a generalization merely cast in question form. A generalization turned into a question often has that fatal (to pupil interest), "teacherish" aura about it. Look at these contrasts:

Does air have weight?
What makes the liquid go up a straw when you drink pop?

Does warm air hold more moisture than cold air?
Why do our lips and skin seem so dry today?

Does sunlight cause a chemical change in colors?
Why do the sides of books have brighter colors than ends, if they are stored on a shelf for a while?

The factor that makes a real problem intriguing is that at least several plausible explanations are possible. It is interesting to have potential disagreement; pupils tend to become committed to testing what seems to be the most plausible hypothesis. In the first example of each pair above, even the alternatives of "yes" and "no" are not truly present. The children know full well that if the answer were "no" the question would not have been raised in the first place.

Notice that the more desirable questions are formed from *applications* of the generalizations. Since an excellent measure of the understanding of a generalization is the ability to recognize its real-life applications, this is a fruitful way to begin teaching for such understanding. In addition, such an approach has the advantage of going from an observation to a proposed description or explanation (hypothesis). This enhances the possibilities for thoughtful inquiry. Such problems need not always be practical. But usually they tend to be more interesting and immediately understandable to children when rooted in their lives. Since forming effective problems from applications is important for developing worthwhile experiments, we shall consider it in more detail in the next chapter.

Less desirable questions from an inquiry standpoint are the kind that not only make a hypothesis unnecessary, but also make the selection of a test a foregone conclusion. Consider the following:

Will snow melt when heated?
Does running water move soil from one place to another?
Does paint prevent iron from rusting?

However, when applications are hard to think of and emphasis is placed on the teaching of experimental procedures, the occasional use of questions of this type may be in order. This assumes, though, that the tests would not be quite so obvious as those above.

Sometimes well-intentioned persons say, "If a problem is presented by the children they are likelier to be motivated for study than if it comes from the teacher." What does this really mean? Perhaps the actual reasons for lack of motivation lie much more in the *form* in which the problem is cast, rather than in the source. It is true that personal interest in a particular problem arouses motivation, but

only occasionally will a child state problems that immediately stir the attention and interest of the entire class. When this happens, usually it is because the problems reflect personal experiences and interests; in other words, this happens when there is self-relating in the children. If these elements are present in the teacher's problems, the chances are good for the same high level of enthusiasm and personal involvement.

Yet seldom will we achieve complete commitment and interest with everyone. Each of us has a hierarchy of personal needs that makes us more or less sensitive to the stimuli we encounter each day. Although we may hope to influence what a child considers is important, we can hardly expect to completely rearrange each child's hierarchy of needs.

What is the difference between a solvable problem and an unsolvable one? Certainly we must be sure that the problem is not beyond the intellectual capacity of the children. But when a problem situation is pitched at their level, what else must be present to assist its solution? At least part of the answer seems to be the presence of pupil background or "input"—any information, skills, and attitudes previously acquired by the child that can be used in coping with the problem. Although the term "readiness" is sometimes used in this connection, somehow it seems less useful. Unless children already have or can develop with our help some process skills and information they can work with, the problem may be too difficult.

Sometimes analogies can provide input. (Notice the device used on page 258 to help prepare children for thinking about the relative distances of a windlass arm.) Other times, relatable information may be gotten through experiments or authoritative sources. But let us differentiate between consulting authority—a book, film, expert, etc.—for factual data *to use in the development of a solution,* and consulting authority *for the solution itself.*

Perhaps the important idea we must stress about input is this: What is needed to *solve* a real problem is not just related information, but data that the children can manipulate intellectually.

When we use background-centered questions along with problems needing solutions, we may face a real difficulty. The background source may reveal so much information in the form of connected facts and illustrative demonstrations that little material remains for the child's own reasoning. With care, a great deal of this difficulty can be avoided. Careful selection and use of materials, interwoven with some teacher-given information, can provide much background or input for pupils without destroying the chances for thinking.

When the child lacks sufficient input, exposing him to a careful sequence of learning activities is probably the best means for developing it. By having enough input, we are saved later on from continually "feeding in" clues, so that all the child does is respond to our questions. Since the idea of input is important but elusive, this may be a good time to skim through several units in the latter part of this book to note how it is developed in various activity sequences.

Let us extract now, in summary form, the important factors within a useful solution-centered problem. Keep in mind, however, that it is seldom possible to prepare or select problems that have *all* these characteristics:

1. The problem's solution leads toward the understanding of an important generalization.

2. Although authority may be used to acquire some needed data, solutions are developed through the children's own testing and reasoning.

3. At least several reasonable hypotheses may be offered toward the problem's solution.

4. It is reasonably interesting and challenging to the class.

5. The children have had enough input, or can acquire enough within time available, to cope successfully with the problem.

See if these criteria help you in distinguishing *probable* background-centered questions from solution-centered questions in the following list. (Answers appear in the next footnote.) Remember, there are no absolutely "right" answers.

1. How are magnets made?
2. What are things made of?
3. Why does the needle of a compass point north?
4. How far away is the sun?
5. Why do people wrap heater pipes with asbestos?
6. How does radar work?
7. Why does gas burn?
8. What makes a solar eclipse?
9. How does the engine in a car work?
10. How are fish classified?
11. What happens to a baby caterpillar as it gets older?
12. How can I make one light go on while the other goes off?
13. What makes the wind blow?
14. How do volcanoes get started?
15. Why is it daylight and then night?
16. What makes the fog come?
17. How do they know there is a neutron in an atom?
18. Why do they put oil in a car?
19. Why is the earth hot in the middle?
20. Where does salt come from? [1]

QUESTION AND PROBLEM SOURCES

It has been mentioned that questions and problems raised in class are usually pointed toward the learning of science principles and processes the teacher has in mind. We can find out what principles and processes to stress by referring to the course of study and textbook in use. But where will the problems or questions themselves come from?

Most district courses of study or teacher guides usually contain many excellent generalizations and activities. Unfortunately, only in rare instances do these aids indicate cause-effect type problems that pupils may explore in pursuing activities. Slightly more frequent in appearance are questions which you can use to help establish purposes for the activities.

[1] Items that tend to be solution-oriented: 3, 5, 8, 11, 12, 13, 15, 16, 18, 20.

Although often overlooked, or used inappropriately, modern science textbooks for pupils commonly contain many possible problem and question situations that you can use if you know where to look. There are several places in the text to search for such situations. Pictures, particularly introductory pictures, may contain an illustration or application of a principle. The children can be asked to describe what they see. They may then close their books and develop likely reasons why the event has happened. The same picture may be portrayed by you on the bulletin board, or in a chalkboard sketch, or just verbally. In these cases, the book is not used at all by the children at the beginning.

Another place to look for problems and questions in the text is just before a demonstration or experiment. Usually there will be some need aroused at this place by the author for such activities. There is little reason why you cannot use these problems yourself, provided you have the children keep their books closed until after the thinking and activity take place.

Do not neglect the accompanying teacher's guide for the textbook. It may contain direct statements of useful questions or problems you can raise. Often these may also be found in the topical headings or sentences in the text. It would be helpful at this time to examine several children's textbooks and search for useful questions and problems in the places suggested here. You may be pleasantly surprised at the range and excellence of some that can be extracted from children's text series.

A few science text series for children have accompanying workbooks or activity booklets that contain problems, in addition to projects and tests. Some worthwhile ideas may be gleaned by looking over ways that the authors have used to approach a topic.

Sometimes pictures may be found in magazines and elsewhere which can be developed into problems; an eroded hillside, a rusted bridge, a caterpillar, and a butterfly—all may serve as vehicles for conjecture. Or, questions may be raised about things observed on study trips. In many cases, motion pictures can be used to raise questions if shown with the sound turned off. Without sound, it often becomes possible to raise questions as one would on a study trip or with a still picture.

Thus far, we have included sources that permit a fairly firm measure of control by the teacher of problems and questions raised. Although children would no doubt make contributions as they moved along, it can be seen that the teacher would exercise primary responsibility.

There are times, however, when it is desirable to have more direct contributions from the children. In such cases, an "arranged environment" can be used successfully to raise questions at the beginning of unit study. Such an environment might include a bulletin board of pictures, with the addition of many accompanying materials that children can explore on nearby tables. In the act of exploring the materials, questions almost inevitably are raised by the children. For example:

In a primary-grade unit on magnets, a teacher gathers a dozen magnets of several kinds and places them on several tables next to the bulletin board. In addition, there are assortments of nails and paperclips, straight pins (brass[2] and steel), three bowls of water, a bar magnet suspended from a string, and several thin sheets of plastic, wood, and metal. The unit is introduced through a discussion of pictures on the new bulletin board. After desirable standards for conduct are reviewed, the children are invited to go to the materials and find out what they can about them. At the end of a prearranged time, the children return to their seats and are encouraged to tell first what they have found out and then to ask any questions they wish about their explorations. As expected, questions are posed by the class:

1. "How do they make a magnet?"
2. "Why can't the magnet pick up these pins [brass, but silver coated] when it picks up these [steel]?"

[2] Brass is not attracted by a magnet.

3. "Why does the [bar] magnet you spin stop in the one place all the time?"

4. "How can the magnet pull through water?"

5. "Why is this magnet weaker than this other one?" [They were otherwise identical.]

6. "Why does the magnet pull through the wood but not the tin [steel plate]?"

In the course of studying the unit, some of these questions are used by the teacher for establishing purposes for background activities (1, 4, 6); the others are used to motivate solution-centered activities.

Although desirable some of the time, raising questions and problems through an arranged environment is not always possible. When there are few materials, or few manipulative activities, it becomes difficult to set up a situation that incites much broad exploration. Then, too, it takes real skill to "build into" the materials latent problems which will be discovered by the children. For example, it was no accident that the teacher included identical-appearing steel and brass straight pins with the other materials. Although the pins looked the same, only some were attracted to the magnet. This was a real problem.

Because it is difficult to set up perfect situations which elicit problems, children's questions in the arranged-environment activity tend to be more the "what" kind than the "why" kind. In other words, we are far likelier to get from them incomplete, background-centered questions than solution-centered questions.[3] An arranged environment is often desirable to develop motivation and to indicate areas of individual needs. But we must realize the limitations of studying only questions or problems brought up by the children. Therefore, even when the method is used, informed teachers contribute additional ideas, problems, and questions when needed.

Unexpected results in demonstrations and experiments can also be used to advantage in arousing problems and questions. Sometimes the most interesting problems are the result of some difficulty that comes up in such situations. When intentional on the part of the teacher, it is not hard to guide the children to think through a satisfactory solution. But when it is unplanned, many teachers may not be able to assist children to develop a systematic and efficient search for the reasons why the "failure" occurred. Since this is a common area of concern, we shall explore this matter further in the next chapter.

Sometimes, children ask questions which arise from their experiences away from school. When they fall within the context of the generalizations you have planned, it is not hard to incorporate them into regular study. But when they fall outside of this context, and are unfamiliar to you, there may be some difficulty in handling them. Of course, it is always easy to say, "That's a good question. Why don't you look it up in the encyclopedia?" or something similar. Though desirable with some children, and on some occasions, this approach should be used sparingly.

There probably is no "best" way to handle all such questions. But if important enough to be considered for class or individual study, it is usually not too difficult to postpone the question's consideration until you have had time to consult some resource. Perhaps the best reason for this is not so much to find the proper answer, but to find out how the child can be assisted efficiently in thinking through the answer for himself. The reason for such postponement need not be disguised. It is safe to state that no one in the world can immediately assist any pupil to think through an answer to any question in science. To indicate gracefully the need for such postponement you might simply say, "I think I can find a book by tomorrow that can help us with this question."

QUESTION AND PROBLEM STATEMENTS

How well questions and problems are stated is quite important in determining how well

---

[3] As you can see on page 17, questions that feature the word "what" may not always be background-centered; however, there is a tendency toward this type when the word is used.

the rest of inquiry goes. This is why we see in most science books the reminder to make clearly defined problem statements before investigation begins. But children, like adults, tend to ask questions which make sense to them. In our haste to get children to define a problem "properly," we may introduce so many qualifiers and ramifications that the children become more puzzled than before.

One major reason why the teacher can break the problem down and define it well at the beginning is because he has previously acquired information about it, while the children have not. In order for children to break down a problem or introduce many qualifiers, they must study it first. In a true problem situation that involves many ramifications, stating precisely what we want to know is usually impossible until some work has been done toward the solution. This is one reason why there are objections to following "steps" in problem solving. Whereas stating the problem would be the first step in theory, in practice we often return at later times to redefine it in the light of further knowledge. Notice how this occurs in a problem about the breathing of a turtle, on this page.

Most children can profit from some assistance in stating their questions. Typically this is a matter of helping them use clear language. Garbled and incomplete sentences are as undesirable in science as elsewhere. Or, if someone uses a term that is vague, it should be made clear, and so on. But we must be careful not to become analytical beyond the limited capabilities of children. Increased capacity to analyze is a by-product of further experience and maturation. To sense when to stop analysis somewhere short of tedium is an art only developed with practice.

On raising problems and questions with pupils, there is some disagreement among educators. Should we take problems *verbatim* as given by children (with minor corrections in language), or help the children restate them in a broader, more organized manner? For example, the upper-grade child's question, "Is aluminum as strong as steel?" might become, "What are the properties of aluminum and steel?" Many teachers tend to feel that such immediate improvements in children's questions are premature. They contend that the broader questions should be asked after activities have been studied relative to the initial question. Thus, in their minds, the initial question becomes a springboard into a larger pool of experiences. This seems more consistent with the rationale expressed in this chapter.

CAUSE AND EFFECT THINKING

When an interesting problem is posed, immediately we begin casting about in our minds for possible explanations. In short, we hypothesize. The hypothesis is at once the germ of a generalization and a means by which we may avoid a chancy, trial-and-error attack on the problem's solution. But all hypotheses are not of equal value. How do we improve children's thinking? How do we help them hypothesize without doing it for them?

Sometimes pupils can be helped to improve their guesses by an indirect method, such as teaching them to identify and focus attention on key words in the problem.

Example: Why can't submarines go down to the *deeper parts* of the *ocean*?

In one class, by calling attention to the possible differences between shallow and deeper depths, a teacher elicited the hypothesis, "Water pressure gets greater the deeper you go."

Another indirect method to improve hypotheses is to teach children to question the inferences or assumptions that lead to the problem statement.

Example: How can a turtle breathe underwater?

The middle-grade girl who asked this question had observed a swimming turtle stay underwater "awhile." She inferred from this that it could *breathe* underwater. Her observation was accurate, but her inference was not. This caused her to pose a faulty question which surely would have led to faulty hypotheses. When this was called to her attention, she changed her problem statement to, "Can turtles breathe underwater?" Perhaps an even better problem statement would have been, "How do turtles breathe?"

Elementary-school pupils, particularly on the primary level, often pose problems that are based on hearsay. Frequently, they assume that their source of information was correct. When we focus attention on this and other assumptions without necessarily labeling them as such, they can be helped to cast better hypotheses by asking better questions.

The psychological climate of the classroom apparently can make a significant difference in children's behavior in forming and testing hypotheses. Atkin[4] selected eleven classrooms where the climate was judged "permissive," with regard to science instruction, and fourteen classrooms judged "less permissive." Criteria for "permissiveness" centered largely on the extent of pupil participation in learning activities. All classrooms were distributed among the first, third, and sixth grades in one school system. Although findings were similar in several respects, pupils in permissive classrooms made significantly more "original" hypotheses, in contrast with the other group's more frequent reference to authority, specific observation, or experience. The permissive group also relied less upon authority and more on their own means in testing these hypotheses, to a significant degree. If these behaviors seem desirable, the implications are clear.

At various times, observations are offered by the children in place of hypotheses. What is needed is to get at the assumptions behind the observations. These, then, become the hypotheses. For instance:

The main objective of a primary-grade lesson[5] is to teach that sea water provides

greater buoyancy than fresh water, because of its greater density. Two pictures are exhibited at the beginning of the lesson. Each shows a line drawing of a cargo ship that is apparently floating in water. The ships are identical in every respect save three: one ship is black, the other white; the black ship is low in the water, and the other is higher; cargo booms are down on the black ship, up on the white ship. The children are invited to note the similarities and differences in the pictures. It is established that the ships are identical in every way, except as noted, and that *they are carrying cargoes of equal weight*. Pupils are then invited to state the problem. After a brief discussion, this statement is considered satisfactory by the group: "Why is one ship floating higher than the other ship?" (Notice that "floating" is really an inference—at least one ship may be partially resting on the bottom.)

Now come the hypotheses, with the first several centered on the aspect of weight:

MIKE: "Well, one is black and one is white." (He means, "Black paint may be enough heavier than white paint to make it sink lower." By asking, "How would that make a difference?" the teacher helps Mike restate his observation as a hypothesis.)

LORIN: "The booms are down in one and up in the other." (This is the same kind of observation as the preceding, and the teacher clears it up in the same way. "The booms are heavier when they are down," becomes a hypothesis.)

NANCY: "The black ship has a leak and the other one doesn't." (This becomes "The black ship may have a leak, and the extra water inside is heavy.")

Now, let us examine these hypotheses from another perspective. The first two are based on comparative differences, of course, but these are not likely to be *critical* differences. By examining the three in terms of *cause* and *effect*, the children most probably will pick the last as the best explanation.

It is highly important to give children the task of screening out unlikely hypotheses before ways of finding out are planned. To accept and test every guess indiscriminately pre-

[4] J. Myron Atkin, "A Study of Formulating and Suggesting Tests for Hypotheses in Elementary School Science Learning Experiences," *Science Education*, December 1958, pp. 414–22.

[5] Adapted from a demonstration lesson taught by Mrs. Aileen J. Birch, Campus Laboratory School, San Diego State College.

vents the child from developing shrewdness in evaluating for the most probable reason. Children should develop a feeling for the "reasonableness" of a guess, whenever possible. Discussion as to what seems most promising for a solution enhances their critical thinking.

Interestingly, many of us do little "mental" experiments with the hypotheses at this time to discern the most reasonable one. This is why it is important to help children state their hypotheses in *testable terms*. However, this is not always possible immediately, particularly with younger children, or with older children who lack sufficient input.

Giving a few clues in question form to a child can cause him to re-evaluate his own hypothesis, and either amend or reject it in the new light of his thinking. For example, in the guess about the position of the booms ("The booms are heavier when they are down."), the teacher might say, "If you are weighing yourself and slowly put your arms up and then down, would it change your weight?" Where possible, for obvious reasons, we should give first opportunity for the evaluation of a hypothesis to the person who made it.

There is an issue as to *when* such evaluation should take place. Basically, we have two choices: accept all hypotheses and let the class evaluate later; or let the group evaluate each hypothesis at the time it is presented. More hypotheses are believed to be advanced by the first means and fewer but possibly higher-quality guesses generated by the second approach. However, each situation needs to be examined by itself.

Sometimes, hypotheses are few or irrelevant because the children fixate on the dominant feature of the scene or problem. In other words, there is a failure to consider all the elements that may be involved because of the overattention to one or just several elements. Around and around the children go, in futile, circular thinking. Here, a suggestion may be needed to consider other aspects. Thus in the lesson above the teacher says, "In all our guesses, we have been thinking about differences between the ships. Is there anything

else in the pictures besides the ships that might cause the difference?" Now more hypotheses are heard:

"The water is not so deep and the white boat is stuck on the bottom."
"Maybe one is on the ocean. Maybe ocean water is stronger [more buoyant] than lake water."

More clues through questions or information developed by the teacher could assist the pupils if the latter hypothesis did not materialize. Questions directed to past swimming experiences in fresh and salt water might help. Or, the teacher could say, "I've heard it's easier to swim in ocean water than in lake water, etc."

In this entire chapter, notice how important it is to give clues, especially somewhat indirect clues, to assist children in their thinking. This keeps them going, provided that sufficient input or background has already been developed. But is there any guide as to the number of clues we should extend to children? One teacher said, "I give my pupils the least number of clues I can for them to solve the problem within the time available." This may be the most satisfactory answer we have.

The child who "knows" the answer. You have picked out a fine experiment and a good problem. Much enthusiasm is expressed by the class when it is stated and discussed. Smilingly, you invite conjecture as to causes. Bill, your brightest pupil, sits with knitted brow. Suddenly it clears, and you have a sinking premonition of disaster. Bill quickly raises his hand and blurts out, "I know, it's because . . ." What does one do—within the law—when this happens?

One approach is just to treat the statement as you would any other hypothesis. Bill is reminded gently that he *thinks* he knows, which may be different from knowing. He is thanked for his contribution, additional hypotheses are invited, and evaluation takes place. If Bill's hand can be recognized after other children have had an opportunity to conjecture, this is better; there will be more hypotheses.

A variation of this technique is to ask Bill why he thinks he knows. In other words, he can be asked for proof. Chances are he will quote some reference or a casual personal observation, rather than an experiment. If he has no direct experimental evidence, he will be more willing to offer his knowledge as a hypothesis. In the unlikely case he does have a valid test, his statement should be treated as another hypothesis—something that may be worthwhile to try when there is time. This may be particularly valuable if you have another kind of experiment in mind; two valid experiments will be more useful than one.

Another approach is to explore Bill's level of ignorance. This can be done usually through the simple device of asking "why" just twice. Unfortunately, unless you know your subject matter, you inadvertently may disclose your own level of ignorance as well! Of course, this can happen to anyone, depending on the subject matter. Notice now how the two "whys" are employed here:

PROBLEM: "Why is one ship higher in the water?"
BILL'S HYPOTHESIS: "Because things float higher in salt water."
TEACHER: "Why is that?"
BILL: "I don't know."

What the situation now requires is to confirm first that things will float higher in salt water, and then to find out why. In other words, Bill's hypothesis has become the new problem, "Why do things float higher in salt water than in fresh water?"

There is another disadvantage to this approach, in addition to possible lack of teacher knowledge. Often it is unlikely that the second "why" can be tested through an experiment with children.[6] In all probability, au-

thority in some form would need to be consulted—a book, film, or whatever is available. In the hands of a knowledgeable teacher, however, and especially with gifted children, this approach may be excellent.

Actually, the individual differences of all the children need to be considered, if each is to learn as well as he can. Additional suggestions for coping with the individual differences of children are given in subsequent sections as the need occurs.

TWO SOURCES OF INFORMATION AND THINKING

Many of us have had the experience of wanting to buy some household product without knowing a great deal in advance about it. In the process of seeking the facts, good thinkers are likely to be more critical of this information than poor thinkers; therefore, they are likelier to emerge with a satisfactory product. Sometimes, we pick up criteria to use in the evaluation of such information without being too conscious of them, and at other times, we acquire criteria through having been "burned" by previous, unwise purchases.

Say someone wants to buy a new carpet. As usual, there are several conditions attached to its purchase: it has to be priced under so many dollars a square yard, not show excessive wear for at least five years around the heavily traveled areas, be stain-proof in case something gets spilled on it, and so forth. How does the prospective buyer know if the carpet will meet his conditions? First, he thinks of where he can find out: there are several carpet salesmen, a few friends, a consumer's magazine. Next, he mentally evaluates his sources: The salesmen recommend it highly. ("But they do have a vested interest.") *Consumer Reports* gives it a satisfactory rating. ("But will the carpet I buy be identical to the one tested?") A friend knows someone who seems satisfied with the same kind. ("But this is hearsay.") Another friend has found it to wear well. ("But he has only one child—not four.") We need to show

---

[6] In this case a partial test easily would be possible. Evaporating some sea water or salt water would reveal more mineral residue than in an equal volume of fresh water. A reference would then be consulted to verify and explain more fully the children's emerging concept of density.

children that getting information in science education is something like this. We have to know what sources are available, but we also need to know how to evaluate these sources.

In seeking information, there are only two main sources available to us: authority—in the form of printed materials, audio-visual materials, knowledgeable persons; and ourselves —in the form of personal experiments and observations. Through many years, elaborate safeguards have been developed by thinking persons to reduce the likelihood of error and unreliability in both sources. Criteria we use for appraising the information from each are both internal (Does it make sense?) and external (How does this compare with what is known?) in nature.

Do not be discouraged if it seems hard to develop in elementary-school children much immediate ability to appraise the merits of authority used in schools. There are several reasons for this difficulty. An obvious one is that elementary children just do not know enough yet. Also, they possess somewhat less logical ability than they will have later. Another is that materials used in the schools are likely to be reasonably accurate and reliable. After all, instructional materials must usually run the gamut of editorial supervision, numerous selection committees of educators, and other sources of appraisal; what survives is likely to be quite acceptable. If not, it is hardly likely that children will possess the intellectual skill and knowledge to detect error or otherwise evaluate critically. Certainly, they can be cautioned to watch for copyright dates, general conformity with what is known, to consult more than one source, to note the occasional conflict in fact, and the like. But the possibilities for critical appraisal of authority are relatively few, largely because of children's lack of background, limited logical capacity, and few appropriate materials. Therefore, we typically spend little time on critical analysis of materials. Instead, we help children learn the sources of authority that exist, ways to consult these sources efficiently, and how to comprehend what the sources say.

There are many more opportunities to teach critical thinking in the experiments and observations that children themselves make during the course of a unit. These activities are close to the raw, unadulterated facts—information minus the "thinking man's filter" already supplied when actual authority is consulted. Pupils must provide their own intellectual filter, with teacher guidance when needed, if the data are to be trustworthy. Gradually, they develop more understanding and skill in appraising their own methods of achieving information. In so doing, they also become abler to appraise critically, as well as appreciate, real sources of authority. Well before they complete high school, students with much experience of this kind do an amazing job in analyzing the assumptions, beliefs, and evidence behind the statements of authorities.

Anthropomorphism. Every child has read stories for entertainment in which animals talk, clouds cry, and steam locomotives suffer pitiably as they huff and puff up a steep mountainside. Giving such human characteristics to nonhuman things is called *anthropomorphism.*

Most of the time children have no trouble in deciding whether events like these are true or fictional. But sometimes they do make anthropomorphic inferences without realizing it, especially when dealing with living things. Do plant roots really "seek" water? Do squirrels gather nuts with the specific purpose of surviving a long winter? Why is a lion "braver" than a mouse? Why is a fox "sly"? Why is a wolf "nastier" than a dog? Because a chipmunk is beneath a bush, are we justified in saying that it is "hiding"?

Make children aware of faulty inferences wherever they are made. It will help them to become better thinkers.

Superstitious thinking. Most children have had some acquaintance with common superstitions, claims of magic, astrology, folk medicine, weather sayings, and the like. These conventions may offer excellent opportunities to teach the difference between genuine cause and effect, and mere correlation without causation. That is, because two events—breaking a mirror and then badly stubbing a toe, for instance—occur closely together, there is no logical reason to assume that one event caused the other.

Children enjoy exploring actual reasons that might have prompted superstitions. They become quickly adept at providing thoughtful explanations after a little practice. Interestingly, one upper-grade class actually offered a *psychological* reason for the toe-stubbing accident: The person got "unstrung" because he thought breaking a mirror would bring bad luck. This caused poor muscular coordination, with the result of a stubbed toe!

We should encourage pupils to analyze conventional beliefs and offer explanations as to how they got started and continue to be popular. A bright class can even be helped to differentiate between what is factual and what is merely plausible. One child offered these reasons for the popularity of the superstition that people who walk under ladders have worse "luck" than those who walk around them: Ladders are close to buildings. Things may fall off window ledges and strike people walking under a ladder, since they, too, would be close to the building. Also, workmen on ladders who drop objects would be likelier to drop things on persons walking beneath the ladder than around it. When the child was invited to show evidence that these things actually caused the superstition to develop or prevail, he began to see the difference between what is reasonable or plausible, and what has been factually determined.

FIGURE 2 It is easy to make anthropomorphic statements about some living things.

CHAPTER 3

Tactics in Science Teaching

Nearly all children are able to perform experiments in seeking solutions to problems. Although pupils can rarely gather all the data they need this way, an experiment does give the capable teacher an excellent chance to stimulate their thinking. But how is the teaching capability acquired? We could study many examples, but experiments differ greatly from field to field; and elementary-school children range so greatly in mental ability. Examples at one level may not be applicable to another.

What may be needed is study of some mediating devices—suggestions specific enough for us to begin thinking of specific techniques that may be applied, yet broad enough to include many examples that may arise. In keeping with this thought, we shall begin this chapter with five ways of stimulating thinking in experimental activities:

1. Bridging and applying
2. Use of controls
3. Use of analogies
4. Use of substitutions
5. Analysis of faulty procedure

These methods are a combination of older and newer ideas useful at any educational level, from kindergarten through college. Though far from representing all the techniques that might be applied, these suggestions can help you get off to a good start.

BRIDGING AND APPLYING

We have emphasized that applications of science generalizations are good to use be-cause they tend to improve the possibilities for thoughtful inquiry—children usually can relate their own experiences toward a solution. One method of stimulating thinking, *bridging* and *applying,* is a logical extension of this idea. Before children experiment, they must in some way be introduced to the problem, if they themselves have not raised it. Bridging is a process in which we first introduce the problem through a lifelike application, and then let children use their previous experience to think about it. Applying comes after the idea has been tested or otherwise verified. We go back to the lives of children and make other applications to their experiences.

Here is an example. The following generalization (or principle) has four common applications, shown on page 28. Many more could be included.

Generalization: The evaporation rate of water increases as its surface area increases.

At first glance, these applications do not seem to be closely related. Yet all are applications of the same scientific principle. Most primary children are unaware of this principle, *even though they probably have experienced at least several of its applications.* By bridging and applying, it is easy to teach the principle in a meaningful problem-solving way. Let us convert application 4 into a bridge:

Boys and girls, does anyone here own a dog? What does it need, especially on a hot day? Let me tell you about a girl who found out something very interesting. Each day, she used to fill her dog's bowl with water. At night, it was usually about half empty. One day, though, the bowl got lost and she had to use another one. It held the same amount of water as the old one, but it was shaped in a different way. Now, each night, she noticed that the water in this bowl was almost gone. Why was there always less water in this bowl than the other one?

In this case, the teacher praises such sound hypotheses as the bowl was cracked, the dog drank more water, etc., and then helps the children to focus on the shape of the bowl as the significant factor. Pictures of the two shapes are drawn on the board for additional assistance. A hypothesis emerges: "Maybe water evaporates faster from a wide bowl." The experiment is conducted with two bowls of different diameters. Children draw a tentative conclusion. Further applications (1, 2, 3, and others) are learned through additional experimenting, observing, discussing, reading, or other means.

This is bridging and applying. By beginning and ending experiments (and other lessons) with understandable applications, purposes for doing things are clear to children. In addition, they learn science principles in a way that means something in their lives.

Now let us digress for a moment. Teachers are often puzzled as to how they can guide children from the hypothesis to a test or experiment. We shall first explain the area of decision open, and then show it in context with additional examples of bridging. Ways of handling this operation should thus become clear.

Basically, your range of choices in helping the children make a test extends from no help

at all to furnishing the test yourself in the form of a demonstration. In the absence of much input, few children can make experimental tests without some assistance. Note the range of choice in these examples:

"How can we test this idea?"
"What can we use on the table which can help us find out?"
"How can this assembled setup help us find out?"

In the first example, the children are left to their own devices. If they are capable, this is best; they will do all the thinking. The second example is a useful compromise. It permits pupils to develop their own ideas, yet it avoids the confusion that may accompany too much choice. With an able class, it is almost always desirable to have unneeded materials on the table with the essential materials. This forces pupils to select materials thoughtfully as well as to assemble them. Sometimes teachers place before a slower class only the materials needed for the test. The difficulty in using the materials then depends largely on deciding the best way to assemble them. The last example offers maximum help short of an actual demonstration by the teacher. It features an already assembled setup. The children's task is to figure out how it can be worked, and what data may be gleaned from its use.

In getting children to think of an appropriate experiment for an hypothesis, there is another idea that will be helpful to remember. Whenever you provide materials for an activity, at least some should *relate to the bridge*. In the evaporation experiment, for example,

Application 1	Application 2	Application 3	Application 4
A spread-out, wet bathing suit dries faster than when it is crumpled into a ball.	Water in a rectangular aquarium dries up faster than a round one with a small opening at the top.*	Water puddles on a sidewalk dry faster when spread out with a broom over a wide surface area.	Water in an animal's water bowl dries up faster when the bowl is shallow and wide than deep and narrow.*

* Assuming both containers have equal volumes of water.

the teacher provided two bowls of different diameters because the bridge referred to bowls. Think of how confusing to the children it would have been if he had provided instead two wet bathing suits (application 1), or two aquaria (2), or a broom and a water puddle (3)! You realize that any of these materials could be used in an experiment to learn the same principle; but this is only because you understand the principle. Since the children do not, these materials—being unrelated to the bridge—would be confusing.

To return to more examples of bridging, observe how assistance with materials is provided in the following case. Assume appropriate responses after each question:

Have you ever noticed your shadow during the daytime? What causes the shadow? Does it always look the same? Why does the size of your shadow change? (Children offer hypotheses here.) How can we use this light to see if that can happen?

The bridge can be used to narrow the choices of hypotheses as well as materials:

Who would like to show us how to water this plant? Why did John water it that way? Well, do plants take in water through their roots or leaves? (A hypothesis is offered here.) How can this material help us find out?

The bridge may even furnish the hypothesis, in which case the test becomes the important factor in stimulating the children's thinking:

How many of you live in homes where a dairy-man leaves milk in the morning? When it gets cold enough for ice to form, do you notice anything strange that happens to the milk? What do you suppose makes the milk push out of the bottle like that? (Some opportunity for hypotheses is given here. If no one has a reasonable one, the teacher continues.) Some people think that the water mixed in with the milk gets bigger or expands when it freezes. Does this make sense? How could we use these materials to see if this is so?

It is also possible to pose several hypotheses in the bridge. The purpose would be to let the children select the most promising ones. Here, the teacher might say:

Some people think that the water in the milk expands when it freezes. Some think the milk bottle gets much smaller. Maybe air bubbles form on the bottom and push out the milk. What seems to be the best idea? (Choice here.) How can we use these materials to test this idea?

In the foregoing examples, the teacher extends the children's understanding of the generalizations by applying them in different ways. The sun's apparent movement in changing shadows is used to tell the time of day. Water absorption through roots becomes more significant as children realize that irrigation can help transform rainless deserts into green fields. Expansion of frozen water takes on additional meaning as children understand that this is one reason the car radiator is "winterized" against the cold. Of course, there are many additional applications.

Must we develop a special bridge and applications for *every* activity? The bridge is particularly important at the beginning of study of a generalization or a supporting idea. As a sequence of activities continues, each activity tends to lead to the next. Little or no formal bridging is necessary beyond relating the preceding lesson to the next one. Additional applications may be brought out or illustrated at the end of each sequence. The first unit of Part II contains specific examples of how this is done.

The limitations of this method—like any other—depend on how it is used as much as on the method itself. Do not restrict applications to the common daily experiences of children out-of-school. Bridging and applying may become a straitjacket. Our object is to broaden the outlook of pupils and to give them more opportunities for learning than they would have without school. Especially after the primary-grade period, we should include understandable experiences provided by the curriculum as well as by daily living.

USE OF CONTROLS

In doing an experiment, children need to be reasonably sure that the results flow from what they have planned. They must plan their experiments so that there is some way of singling out the factor or factors responsible for the results. If two different-sized inclined planes (ramps) are used to see whether the longer requires less force to push up an object, both must be placed at the same height. Also, both should be of equal smoothness, and the same amount of weight should be pushed up by each. By keeping all conditions the same except length, this factor is easily identified as the one responsible for any decrease in force. Notice that friction, weight, and height are all variables which need to be controlled. These factors would have to be identical in each paired example.

But children are seldom able to recognize all of the variables which can affect results of the experiment. Therefore, we must help them to learn to be cautious about connecting a particular effect to a particular cause. They should learn to do the experiment several times, and later check with a book or other authority source to sharpen the accuracy of their conclusions.

If a problem based on an application is used by the teacher, the children's hypothesis will usually contain the factor that needs to be tested and controlled.

TEACHER: Have you ever left your bike outside in the rain? What happens to the metal after a while? Where does it seem to rust first? Why is that? [1]

CHILDREN'S HYPOTHESIS: Paint prevents wet steel from rusting.

TEACHER: How can we test this guess?

The children now follow through by matching two pieces of steel, painting one and not the other, exposing each to the same moisture and temperature conditions, and allowing sufficient time. In addition, they could make a survey of some partly rusted toys, to see if there is a consistent relationship between no-paint and rust areas.

It is harder to use the idea of controls with

[1] Notice how much more natural it is to bring out a problem in this way than to say at the outset, "Will painted steel rust if it gets wet?" With this latter "problem" there is no real need for hypothesizing.

primary children, unless they are given help. Younger children as a rule have not yet acquired sufficient reasoning ability and background to see for themselves the several variables that might change the outcome of an experiment. When given some assistance, they often rise to the occasion very well.

One way to help younger children (and older ones, too) see the need for controls is to give them a limited, contrasting choice of action, and then to help them consider the consequences. In a kindergarten class, the teacher wants to teach the generalization, "Air slows down the speed of objects according to their shape." This is an introduction to streamlining. The first of a series of experiments features a miniature parachute made of a handkerchief, some string, and an empty wooden spool to represent the parachutist. The example begins at the bridge:

TEACHER: What does a jet pilot wear when he goes flying?

CHILDREN: Miscellaneous answers and: A parachute.

TEACHER: Why does he wear a parachute?

CHILDREN: In case something goes wrong and he has to bail out.

TEACHER: How will the 'chute help?

CHILDREN: He'll fall slower that way. (This is the hypothesis.)

TEACHER: Will a pilot fall more slowly with a parachute than without one? (This is the first contrast the teacher draws to point up the need for a control.) How can we find out? Can these materials help?

CHILDREN: Let's drop the handkerchief there. It will fall pretty slow.

TEACHER: Where is the pilot on this little 'chute?

CHILDREN: He is the spool underneath.

TEACHER: We want to find out if he will fall slower with the parachute than without a parachute. What can we do? I notice there is another spool on the table. How can that help?

CHILDREN: We could drop that one, too. (Nothing more is suggested.)

TEACHER: Should we drop it first and then the 'chute with attached spool; or should we drop them both at the same time? (Another contrast is poised.)

The teacher then gets them to think of what will probably happen. By releasing them at the same time, the children can notice any differences that take place as the 'chutes fall. The teacher can also inquire as to what difference it would make if the two were dropped at unequal heights, when released at the same time. The point to all this questioning, of course, is to make the children aware first that there are several variables present, and then to help them see the consequences of each. By beginning slowly in this or a similar way, children begin to grow sensitive to the need for controls. In some classes, perhaps only one of these controls could be brought meaningfully to the children's attention; in others, perhaps all three might be explored.

USE OF ANALOGIES

Many experiments and demonstrations in elementary-school science cannot deal directly with a real situation. Working with the real thing can involve danger, too much time, great difficulty, expense, and the like. However, there may be many opportunities to work with *analogies* of the real thing—in other words, materials and activities that bear a reasonable resemblance to the actual situation the teacher wishes to take up. Analogous experiments are often helpful in getting children to understand causes as well as "what happens." At the same time, children should be guided to see that an uncritical acceptance of an analogy may result in error. They should try to determine similarities and differences between the analogy and real thing whenever possible.

"Why can't a submarine go down to the deeper parts of the ocean?" is an illustration of an upper-grade problem that requires an analogous experiment. Here is an abbreviated account of how it might be conducted.

CHILDREN'S HYPOTHESIS: The water pressure gets greater the deeper you go in the ocean.
TEACHER: How can we test this idea? Is there anything here that might help?

CHILDREN: Punch some holes in the side of that can. Make them the same size for the control.
TEACHER: What should happen if our guess is right?
CHILDREN: The water will spurt farthest out of the lowest hole, if the pressure is greater there.

(The experiment is conducted, and results occur as predicted. It is done again to "make sure." The tentative conclusion is made that water pressure increases with depth.)

TEACHER: How does this help us with the original problem?
CHILDREN: Probably the sub can't go down too far because it would get crushed by the pressure.
TEACHER: But we found out about the water pressure in a can, not the ocean. How is that like the ocean? How is it different from the ocean? Do we actually know that this happens in the ocean?
CHILDREN: Answers are varied as they attempt to note similarities and differences.

This discussion leads to more reasoning from previous experiences and a careful check with authority, whereupon the hypothesis is confirmed. Clearly the use of an analogy presents a very real need to check further.

Analogies are used frequently in elementary science: the teakettle "cloud" for a real cloud; the globe and flashlight for causes of night and day; the string with attached weight that is whirled to simulate an orbiting satellite; the ping-pong ball "chain reaction" with mousetraps for nuclear fission; the piece of paper bent to simulate an aircraft wing; and many, many more. In the submarine example, the forces operating in the real situation are like those operating within the analogy. At other times the comparison is less complete. When using analogies, however, thoughtful teachers give opportunity for examination of assumptions, and for critical comparison of likenesses and differences to the extent children's capacities will permit. In this manner, the method can be used to produce much careful thinking.

USE OF SUBSTITUTIONS

Many times an experiment suggested by someone, or by some resource, includes materials that are unavailable or hard to get. When this is so, imaginative teachers and children are often able to substitute other materials that work almost as well or better than the original materials indicated. If a spring scale is suggested, perhaps a rubber band will do. A rubber comb (washed) may be an effective substitute for a rubber rod in a static electricity experience. A hot plate may be substituted for a Bunsen burner, and so on. Many examples of effective substitutions of materials are found in the units of Part II. The idea itself is a common one; for years, necessity has prompted teachers to devise substitutions of materials.

However, perhaps too much of the thinking about substitutions has been done by teachers rather than pupils. As most resourceful persons know, just any substitution may not do. There are criteria which must be met. These criteria boil down to the question: Will it work reasonably well? By letting children think through carefully the function of the material replaced and its probable effectiveness, they may become even more aware of what is taking place in the experiment than if substitution were not used. If very high temperatures are needed, for example, a hot plate won't do. Or if a permanent magnet is to be made, a steel object is preferable to one made of iron.

A visit to a large science fair for high-school students offers one of the best opportunities for observing the fantastic lengths to which effective substitutions may be carried. Of course, adequate essential equipment and materials should be a part of every school science program. But the potential resourcefulness and invention that can be stimulated by the need for substitution should be appreciated and exploited when possible.

So far, this discussion of substitution has been limited to materials that can be used in place of other materials. The experiment or demonstration remains essentially the same.

Sometimes, however, it may be possible to substitute the experiment itself. In other words, an entirely different experiment may be used in place of that originally indicated by the book, teacher, or someone else. Say we want to demonstrate that air takes up space. If a glass is inverted and carefully pushed down under the surface of a bowl of water, air in the glass will permit only a small amount of water to enter. If a small funnel is pressed into the vaseline-smeared opening of a small container, the air inside will prevent water poured down the funnel from entering. Both demonstrations show equally well that air takes up space. It is more effective to use both rather than one; there is reinforcement of learning and broadening of understanding as a result of seeing the generalization developed in more than one way.

Several things should be kept in mind if substitutions of experiments are used in teaching. These experiments can be analogous to the real thing; or they may directly involve the medium tested, as with air taking up space. Also, some topics—air and water, expansion-contraction of materials, and static electricity, for example—lend themselves more easily to substitutions than others. Lastly, as with analogies, the search for substitutions is a time when books and other resources can be employed in a specific, purposeful way.

ANALYSIS OF FAULTY PROCEDURE

Frequently, in high-school and college laboratory sessions, students run into experimental results which are contrary to expectations. Though some of this must be expected as the result of testing out a faulty hypothesis, often it is the procedure itself that is at fault. In the past, it was customary for the instructor to diagnose the difficulty and then point out what was wrong. The student would then correct his faulty procedure and continue. Fewer instructors at present are providing such direct assistance—with good reason. A situation that involves faulty procedure pro-

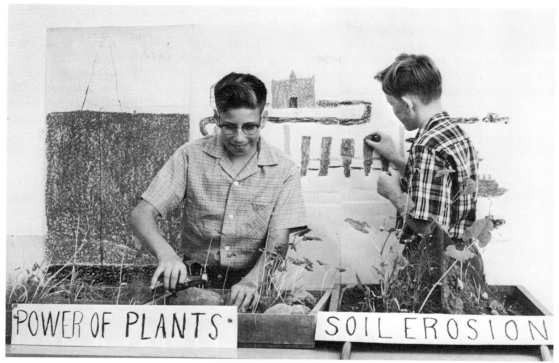

FIGURE 3 An experiment like this may bring out all five ways of stimulating thinking described in this chapter.

vides one of the best means for stimulating thinking. By teaching the student himself to cope successfully with the situations, the instructor allows him to become more self-sufficient. Similar opportunities exist to stimulate the thinking of elementary-school children, but in less complex ways, of course.

Many of the mistakes children make in experiments involve their assumptions about *materials*. A balloon is old and slightly porous; a dry cell is worn out; insulation has not been removed completely from a wire and proper electrical contact is prevented; substitute materials may lack the factor needed to make the experiment work.

Sometimes assumptions about *controls* are to blame. In an upper-grade experiment on causes of bread mold, two children bring in pieces of white bread. The "experimental" piece develops no mold but the control does! The children have assumed wrongly that the pieces are identical; in fact, one has been treated with a chemical to make it mold-re-

sistant. In all likelihood the commonest cause of faulty procedure involving controls is simply the lack of enough of them.

Occasionally, *time* is a factor in faulty procedure—too much or too little. It may take several days, rather than a few hours, of sunshine before a piece of colored cloth fades. Some seeds take much longer to germinate than others. Two hours may be too long to wait before measuring the possible temperature difference of hot water in differently insulated jars.

Beyond elementary school, measurements and computational errors in arithmetic are often likely to be the causes of faulty experiments, because of the degree of precision needed. Since much less precision is expected of (or received from) younger children, measurement and computation are less likely to cause difficulty in experimental findings.

From the preceding examples we can see that an experiment can be conducted and results obtained without any sign that an error has taken place. Therefore, faulty procedure can lead to faulty conclusions. This happens in science laboratories as well as in elementary-school classrooms. So it is important to examine carefully where things may go wrong when thinking through an experiment. By critically examining procedures and assumptions, fewer errors are made.

Sometimes children must be guided not to infer too much from the data at hand. When the familiar lighted candle under the inverted glass jar goes out, perhaps all we can say is that there no longer appears to be enough of something in the air needed by the candle flame. We cannot say from this experience that "Oxygen is required for burning" nor, "The air was all used up." Additional and different experiments may be needed before the inference can be made more specific. Yet, as indicated before, it may be difficult in some areas to find further experiments that can make the class more aware of the generalization in the teacher's mind. Rather than over-generalizing, what is needed at these times is reference to authority. This helps pupils to sharpen the generalization by supplementing the data received from the experiment.

OPEN-END EXPERIMENTS AND ACTIVITIES

Sometimes children study experiments containing several factors that can be changed in many ways. These are commonly called "open-end" experiments. For example, we can develop a bridge that leads into the problem, "What conditions must be present for bread to develop mold?" Conditions of temperature, light, length of exposure to the air, location of exposure, and moisture may be hypothesized and tried. Moreover, each of these factors may be varied almost endlessly in combination—"How much moisture with how much temperature?" for instance.

Additional examples of such problems are "What do plants need in order to grow?" and "How many ways can we make this light go out?" and "How many stimuli will make this earthworm move?"

There are also open-end activities in which only a *single factor* is investigated. These tend to be easier to explore because the search is mainly for additional examples. The same basic test is used. "What materials will a magnet attract?" and "What materials will absorb water?" and "What liquids are basic? acidic? neutral?" involve mainly the gathering and testing of further samples.

Sometimes the single factor is varied. "How does the temperature of water affect the amount of salt that will dissolve in it?" involves changing only the degree-of-temperature factor.

The open-end activity is good to use because it broadly extends children's knowledge. It enables many children to participate. It easily makes provisions for individual differences of children and may offer many opportunities for original thinking. But there are a few cautions needed in its use. For one thing, there may be a study of detail or examples to an unnecessary degree. Particularly where the single factor open-end procedure is used, the "what" aspect may overshadow the "why." Also, children's interest must be observed closely. If it begins to slacken noticeably, this may indicate that it is time to terminate the exploration. Nevertheless, for reasons given, the open-end activity is one of the most useful in the classroom and should be employed frequently.

DEMONSTRATIONS

We hear on every side that there is a distinct difference between an experiment and a demonstration. Indeed there is—if we adhere strictly to the classic definition of each. Strictly speaking, a demonstration is used to show something, to illustrate what is already stated as true or factual. An experiment, as we have tried to indicate, tends to be a quest into the unknown; it is an attempt to find one's own solution to a problem in a verifiable way. But in elementary science, there are many necessary and possible places to combine the two procedures. It sometimes becomes difficult to tell where one stops and the other begins. Perhaps this does not matter greatly in these cases, provided that children receive many excellent opportunities for doing independent thinking.

Sometimes demonstrations are needed to illustrate the use of materials or techniques, as when children are shown how to work with a microscope, make a measurement, construct a wind vane, properly store magnets, insert glass tubing into a stopper, and use vinegar to test for limestone. Although it is possible for these things to be "discovered" by the children, such discovery can be time-consuming and may imperil both children and materials needlessly. Demonstrations of this kind tend to be closest to the common definitions of the term.

At times, a demonstration may serve to introduce a problem in an interesting way:

1. A primary-grade teacher wants a class to learn some safety standards for bus travel. The children are asked to observe the demonstration, to tell what happened and why. A doll is placed in a standing position in a little wagon. The wagon is pushed and then suddenly stopped. The doll falls forward. Next, the doll is placed in a sitting position and again the wagon is pushed and quickly stopped. This time it stays about in the same position.

2. An intermediate-grade teacher slowly and deliberately wraps a wire around a nail and then touches the nail to some paper clips. Nothing happens. Next, the ends of the wires are connected to a dry cell, and the nail picks up several paper clips. One wire is disconnected and the paper clips fall. Now, a series of questions is posed by the teacher as to how and why this occurred.

3. An upper-grade teacher interested in teaching causes of winds has made a convection box. This consists of a topless cigar box placed on one side. Inside, at one end is a small candle, above which is a large hole. At the other end is another hole. The teacher lights the candle and then covers the open part of the box with a layer of Saran-Wrap. A piece of rope is set afire and then its flame

is blown out; smoke rises from it. Suddenly, the teacher thrusts the smoking end of the rope near the hole farthest from the candle. The smoke goes down into the box and then out the hole above the candle. The candle is blown out and now the smoke from the rope no longer enters the box. The class is asked to tell what happened and why.

Notice that these demonstrations have some of the characteristics of an experiment. Each is controlled. Only the position of the doll is changed in the first example; only the dry cell added in the second. The candle flame is extinguished in the last illustration. In other words, children see the manipulation of only one variable. Their proposed explanations are really hypotheses which may be checked through other activities or use of authority. Notice also that these situations contain some possibilities for comparison of an analogy (bus versus wagon, for example), substitution, faulty procedure, as well as controls. While the teacher manipulates the materials in these cases, there is no reason why children cannot participate.

When demonstrations are done in a "questing" manner, as contrasted with a "telling" manner, they are virtually the same as experiments. Several illustrations in which the two approaches are contrasted may help us to understand the differences. Assume appropriate responses after any questions. Assume further that each activity would be followed by others to clinch the objective involved. We shall begin each of our paired examples with a "telling" approach.

1. In a primary-grade class, the objective is to teach what causes night and day. There is a globe and an unshielded lamp on a large table; the room is darkened.

"Boys and girls, we want to find out why we have night and day. We have found out that the earth is in space and that it gets its light from the sun. Notice where I have put the little sticker; this is where we live. We are in daylight now. The sun is shining on us. Watch what happens as I turn the globe. Is it day or night now?" (This continues until the teacher is assured that the children understand. In many cases, the children might be asked to turn the globe or help in some other way.)

In another primary-grade class—same objective, same materials:

"Boys and girls, it's daytime now and we have plenty of light to help us see. But what will happen later on after we have dinner and must go to bed? How will it be in the morning? Why do we have night and day?" (They are uncertain.) "Well, we have already found out that the sunshine gives us our light and that the earth is in space. How could we use this globe and light to find out about night and day?" (The teacher helps the children locate their area on the globe. A white piece of tape is stuck to this spot. The children try rotating the globe. The tape moves into and out of the light consecutively. That seems to "make sense." The children begin to conclude that this is the cause. Here, the teacher cautions them to see if there is another way the globe could become light and dark. Several think so, and try taking the "sun"—the teacher helps with the cord—around the "earth." Now, there is a dilemma and more data are needed. So the teacher asks them where they can find out. And so on.)

2. In an intermediate-grade class, the objective is to teach that coloration is important to the survival of some living things. Materials are a small bag of confetti, and a green lawn outside the classroom.

"Class, today we are going to find out how color helps protect animals. Fewer animals are destroyed by their enemies when they are colored like their surroundings, because they can't be seen as well. You can find this out yourself with this confetti. Let's sort out the colors first and count how many pieces you have in each pile. Notice that we have **four** colors: blue, green, red, and white. Let's have four children each take 100 pieces of one color —Mary, Donna, Harry, Frank—and scatter them evenly inside the area marked by the four stones on the lawn. We will have three minutes to gather the confetti. Which colors

will be easiest to see? Of which colors will we gather the most pieces? Let's find out."

(The confetti is first distributed, then collected by the children. After returning to the classroom, children sort the colors and count them. There are 33 green, 48 blue, 65 red, and 70 white pieces of confetti. The teacher points out that this tends to verify his initial statement about color and its survival value.)

In another intermediate-grade class—same objective, same materials:

"Class, what are some of the conditions that help animals escape from their enemies? It does seem as though color might help. Let's say you are an insect that lives in or under a nice lawn, and you actually had a choice of green, blue, red, or white for your color. What would be the best color to have? Worst color? Why?" (Here, the teacher writes on the chalkboard choices of colors from best to worst: green, blue, white, red. Reasons for preference of rank are drawn out from the class.) "How could we use this confetti to find out if it is harder to locate colors which are like the background this insect lives in?" (The children themselves design the procedure. As they make mistakes or omissions in planning —not keeping track of the numbers of original colors, not planning for an even distribution of confetti, for example—the teacher asks pointed questions to help. After the search, pupils return to add and allot the data next to the four colors written on the board. The teacher asks the children what the data mean to them. Their conclusions are cautious, because the teacher brings out through questions the analogous nature of the activity. Animals may not perceive color as humans do. Besides, they reason, the sample is pretty small.)

The teacher also might have led the children to see the wisdom of having only confetti searchers who were ignorant of the hypothesis. This would eliminate the possibility of some persons trying to "prove" the point. Another class could have been used, or several children excluded from the initial discussion. And the teacher does not always need to guide the children to see possible mistakes before they make them. When the data seem wrong or contradictory, this furnishes an excellent need to examine why.

3. In an upper-grade class, the objective is to teach that light is deflected downward when it enters water. Materials include an aquarium half filled with water, a white button (resting on the bottom of the tank), a pointer stick, and a book.

"Today we are going to learn that light does not always travel in a straight line. Bill, you aim at that button with the pointer, but make sure the tip doesn't enter the water. I will hold the grooved edge of this book under the pointer when you have made your aim. That way, you can't change your aim. Now slide the pointer into the water. Class, notice how he goes over the target. This is because when light enters the water it is bent downward. Now that we realize this, all we have to do to hit the target is to aim a little above where the button seems to be. Let's try it, Bill. Notice that now he just about hits it." (Several more trials are made until the teacher believes the children understand.) "Why is this good to know if you are a spear fisherman?"

In another upper-grade class—same objective, same materials:

"Who likes to go fishing? What else do people fish with besides a rod and reel? Spear fishing is fun, but it helps if you know how light travels. Does anyone know where you have to aim at a fish to hit it when it is underwater and you are in a boat? Let's look at this setup. What could be the fish? The spear? What should we do? How shall we prevent the spear fisherman from changing the way he has aimed his spear? Would this book help?" (Two children are chosen to come up in front and "spear the fish." Neither is allowed to watch and profit from the mistakes of the other. The class observes silently that each aim passes over the target. The teacher now asks for hypotheses to explain what might be happening to the light as it goes from the button to the eye of the observer and *vice versa*. Since the stick looks "bent" in the water the class hypothesizes that the light bends

downward. The children are asked to reason in an "if-then" manner: If the light is bent downward, then what must the fisherman do? Proper advice is given the fisherman, and the target is struck. Now the class turns to its books to read the theory of why the light appeared to bend.)

The "telling" examples of these demonstrations may seem much more pallid than the "questing" illustrations and demonstrations in general may seem inferior to experiments. Yet there are many occasions when you will want to use simple, straightforward demonstrations. When there seems to be little in the activity that may further process objectives; when the materials or concepts are complex; when real-life examples are hard to find; when the activity is fitted into an involved, developmental sequence of activities—any of these may be reason enough to try the direct approach. It is easy to develop an exaggerated reverence for "discovery," because it is so highly motivational and thoughtful. But the approach you use must remain a matter of judgment. Remember you do have two kinds of objectives—process and product. When there is little to be gained toward process objectives, and meaning can become clear through a straightforward demonstration, this is often the best thing to do. Of course, even at these times, some participation of the children is usually both possible and desirable.

TEXTBOOK EXPERIMENTS

An easy way to place a textbook author on the defensive is to say that his experiments are of a "cookbook" variety. That is, because problem, materials, directions, and conclusions are furnished, there is little opportunity for children to think. All that needs to be done by them is follow the recipe. Some criticism of this kind does seem to be in order, in spite of greatly improved modern texts and guides. At the same time, it is hard to avoid the conclusion that many critics simply don't know how hard it is to prepare textbooks or activities for wide use.

It is difficult for an author to include an involved experimental problem that arouses several or more "original" hypotheses. Unlike the teacher, he cannot change his material to correspond with whatever emerges in the classroom. Should he have suggested courses of action for any reasonable hypothesis that might come up? Plainly, this is too cumbersome. It becomes more manageable to turn a fact into a question (Do seeds need water?) or to give a forced-choice comparison (Does alcohol evaporate faster than water?). These or similar techniques are used frequently.

Then there are objections because pictures of experiments are included and conclusions are drawn for the children. At least several reasons prompt authors to include this matter. Some children are poor readers. It would be unwise to restrict science instruction to good readers. Also, in many cases the experiment just will not be done. Perhaps there is insufficient time, materials, lack of confidence by the teacher, and so on. The textbook author must prepare for "those who won't" as well as for "those who will."

If used selectively and thoughtfully, a good textbook (even the "cookbook" type) can yield a surprising number of experiments and demonstrations for stimulating children's thinking. In examining a textbook experiment, especially note the way in which the author leads into the activity and his comments following it. Usually a purpose or question immediately precedes the experiment. Often it is based on an application of a principle ("Why does meat spoil?" "What makes airplanes fly?"). Or, the purpose may be in statement form ("Let's see how valleys are formed.") with extended applications written afterward.

If an application is available in the textbook experiment, or if you can think of one, this is a help in forming problems. With regard to materials, you have the options listed before: a range of choice from no materials at all to only those needed, depending on your judgment of what the children can do. Make provision—in moderation—for additional bridging and applying, or controls, or sub-

stitution, or analysis of faulty procedure and analogies. (Too much of this can be more confusing than helpful.) And perhaps most important, let the children draw their own conclusions.

The foregoing is much more thought-provoking when pupils' books are closed, rather than open. After the experiment is concluded, or at least planned, is the time to permit reading. The book, rather than the children, should serve as a source of verification. "It's fun to find out the book agrees with us," said one little girl, and she is right. It does not make sense to have pupils do the experiment to verify that the book is correct. The book is usually "right." However, when there is a particularly hard or involved procedure, perhaps it would be best to use the book as a guide for what to do. This can be done after the question is raised and the initial discussion has taken place.

Sometimes the book presents a straightforward demonstration of an idea. Instead of following the book you can introduce the idea and ask: How can it be demonstrated? In other words, after making the purpose clear, let the *children* figure out what to do with materials you provide or have them bring. The book can be opened and used for verification *after* the activity.

As an alternative procedure, the materials can be set up beforehand. The children then "work" the assembled setup and try to explain how or why it works, with the text consulted later. A variety of subtle applications and changes is possible in these procedures, depending on the subject matter and the children.

"WRITING-UP" EXPERIMENTAL ACTIVITIES

One of the most frequent questions beginning teachers ask about experiments is, "Should they be written up?" As with a great many other questions in methodology, the best answer is, "It depends." There appears to be little, if any, need in the elementary school for a formal experiment sheet with spaces for the problem, hypothesis, test, data, and conclusion. It takes some spontaneity away from the situation and is likely to be an unwelcome chore. It can make a ritual out of a process that should be flexible and largely focused on what is going on, rather than on what has gone on.

Yet there are times when it is helpful for the teacher or several pupils to write things down. For example, when planning, it is desirable for everyone to be certain about the purpose of the experiment. This is needed especially when the experiment takes some time. Or, if several hypotheses are presented, these should be written down in order to keep track of them. If much data are to be gathered, particularly over a period of time, it is necessary to have a way of recording the facts. The children can then consider the cumulative total of facts before they draw conclusions. These illustrations are typical:

1. In a primary class, there is a seed-growing experiment in a corner of the room. A small sign above two coffee cans of dirt reads:

"Can our bean seeds start growing without water?
　We will water one pan of beans every day.
　We will not water the other one.
　We will see where the beans grow."

2. In a middle-grade class, there are five groups at work with litmus paper. (This chemically treated paper changes color when dipped in acidic or basic liquids.) The children want to find out which of five "unknown" substances are acidic, basic, or neutral. Each group has a chairman, who records findings on his group's data sheet. The form of recording has been previously agreed upon in the planning phase:

1. acid　2. base　3. neutral　4. base　5. acid.

At the end of the work session, the teacher has a brief discussion as to how the results of all the groups are to be recorded on the chalkboard. The following emerges:

UNKNOWN LIQUIDS

Group	1	2	3	4	5	
Jane	A	B	N	B	A	
Bill	A	B	N	B	A	A = Acid
Kathy	A	A	N	A	A	B = Base
Robin	A	B	N	A	A	N = Neutral
Joe	B	B	N	B	A	

Notice that the form used for chalkboard recordings is consistent with the chairmen's recordings. By keeping the two somewhat alike, it is easier for the children to interpret the accumulated data. By having a code (A = Acid, etc.) written to one side, the teacher cuts down on the time needed to record the findings. The data are now compared, discrepancies noted, and possible reasons discussed. Careful retesting is planned. At no time has the teacher written down the purpose or procedure. There is no need in this case. The thorough discussions, recordings, and individual participation have made each clear.

3. Although an upper-grade class has already completed a weather unit, there is a chart in a corner entitled, "What pattern, if any, is there to cloud movements in fall over River City?" There are three columns for September, October, and November which feature consecutively listed numbers for days. Next to about half of the numbers are written United States Weather Bureau cloud-code symbols for the dominant cloud cover, if any, each day. Even though it is only partly completed, a pattern of sequence is becoming evident. After it has been completed, this sample will be compared with data gathered by the local weather bureau for similar periods in previous years.

OBSERVATION AND CLASSIFICATION

A child goes to a zoo and observes, among other things, a tiger, giraffe, hippopotamus, rhinoceros, baboon, sea otter, and rattlesnake. Ask him what he has encountered and chances are the immediate reply is, "Lots of animals!" By placing the zoo's inhabitants into a single group, animals, the child has done what scientists do when they classify things, processes, or phenomena. It is a natural tendency of the mind to group similarities or to form patterns among unordered data—in other words, to form concepts. The accuracy and completeness of our concepts help determine how well we think, whether they are about "democracy" or "density."

To classify things in science is to form concepts about them. Sometimes forgotten is the fact that a concept serves two functions. First of all, it identifies ideas or things belonging to a class or group, and thereby excludes dissimilar members. A concept also permits a chain of associations to be connected. When an informed person thinks of "wedge" many members of this class may spring to mind: ax head, tent stake, knife, teeth, even the bow of a boat. But he may also think of such associations as: narrowing the bow of a motorboat may increase speed with no increase in power; a sharp knife cuts more easily than a dull knife; it takes longer to get a sharp edge with a tempered steel blade than with ordinary steel, but it lasts longer; and a wedge is two inclined planes placed back to back, so it has the same decreased-force, increased-length relationship.

Let us use another example. Suppose a whale gets tangled in a strong fish net twenty feet below the ocean's surface. What will happen to the whale within a relatively short time? We might think: "Whale—that's a mammal. Mammals are lung breathers. A whale will drown." Notice how the concept of mammal as a classification inclusive of the whale brings up the associated understanding. This enables us to make a reasonably certain prediction.

It is in the associations linked to concepts that we get our best clues in choosing what to teach in observation and classification. Some time ago, a famous mountain climber was asked why he wanted to climb Mt. Everest. The reply was, "Because it's there." A more complete answer would have included the many associations that really motivated him.

Often the approach in science education has been to classify something just because "it's there." But this is not a satisfactory reason for many pupils. There is only one Mt. Everest. But there are over a million species of animals, and possibly half as many kinds of plants. In addition, there are the physical sciences to be heard from. Clearly, there must be some kind of selection to guide us.

One reason why some teachers get into difficulty with observation and classification is that they begin with the idea of teaching specific identifications—so many rocks, so many birds, and so on. It is much better to start with an important generalization which leads to the need to look at some examples. ("Now that we know how sedimentary rocks are formed, can you pick some out of this mixed collection?")

There is practically no end to identification as such. The identification of an animal species every day of an adult's life would cover little more than one per cent of those in existence. Given five thousand years to finish the animals, it would then be possible to begin studying each species of plant—assuming that there are no mutant forms in the meantime to reclassify!

Often specialists themselves find it hard to identify specimens at a specific level. It is by no means uncommon for an entomologist to consult an insect key, or a geologist to make a laboratory test, before even a local specimen can be identified. Therefore, it makes good sense to keep classifications as broad as possible within the posed objective. (Note how this is done in Unit 11, page 387.)

Sometimes it is useful to teach specific identifications of certain insects, rocks, or other materials. In these cases, we might consider three things: *what* it is, *how* we know, and what *significance* or application it has. For instance, we want to teach examples of parasitism—this is a cowbird (what it is); this is how it differs from other birds (how we know); the female lays its eggs in the nests of other birds, which take care of the eggs and hatched young (significance).

To teach these elements, notice how the reverse of this order may present a more interesting approach: Sometimes we see a young cowbird being fed and taken care of by a completely different kind of bird. How does this happen? (Significance is brought out.) Let us learn some ways to identify cowbirds. (How we know.) Can we pick out the three cowbirds in this collection of pictures? (What it is.)

Of course, it is not always necessary to use this technique. When children have initiated the search for identification, for example, the "what" aspect usually precedes the others. However, we should use the same selective purposes when guiding children to observe and classify as when selecting experiments and demonstrations. Observation is a means by which we can get children to use their senses—all their senses—to learn important ideas and processes.

Children are interested in many things about them. The sheer availability of a variety of colorful birds, rocks, insects, seashells, or other things will prompt them to observe, collect, and want to name many of the specimens. Here, a small shelf of identification books is helpful.

Most classification "keys" are unworkable with younger children and many older children. Therefore, the best procedure in finding the name of a specimen, once its broad classification is determined, is to match the specimen with the picture in the book. This children can do with astonishing skill and speed, given some practice. A list of suggested identification books may be found on page 72. Older children may find the identification keys in these books helpful in classifying some of the more difficult specimens. But with all children, the identification should be the introduction and not the end to inquiry.

The remains of such old-time approaches in elementary science as object study and nature-study-gone-formal are still reflected by some teachers. In object study, a meticulous study of detail brought out the maximum number of descriptive characteristics about a specimen. By first observing an object and then describing it in detail from memory, the "powers" of observation were supposedly strengthened. In the more superficial forms of nature study, a primary objective was to identify the variety of living things and other natural phenomena around the school and community. The "what" aspects usually overshadowed the "why."

The teacher down the hall, whose children spend most of the semester listening to bird calls and identifying birds with flash cards, is reflecting an approach that has been replaced by more efficient methods. There is now more place for studying the interesting physiology of birds and their relationships with other organisms, both plant and animal. As for powers of observation, we realize now that the most useful tools lie primarily in specific clues that make a difference. That is, *clues that enable us to control or predict or "explain" a situation or thing.*

An excellent approach to clue selection lies in the relationship of body structure to function, or the relation of cause to effect. The bill and feet of a bird are highly indicative of the food it may eat. Hollow bones and air sacs permit easier flight. Roundness of a stone found by a stream may indicate erosion through tumbling in a stream bed. Large crystals in a rock may indicate slow, below-surface cooling. Clues are tied to the subject studied, rather than the development of general "powers" of observation.

The use of scientific clues is helpful in observing noteworthy relationships. But we teach children who are inclined, as are adults, to observe only as carefully as their purposes motivate them to observe. So when introducing an activity that requires observation and classification, a teacher should try to begin with a bridge that either arouses or channels the children's interest. We have already shown how to begin with a "significant" application. Let us expand this idea somewhat.

If we wish to study igneous rock, it is interesting to begin with volcanoes, then volcanic rock, and then other forms of igneous rock.

Study of sedimentary rock in upper grades is begun interestingly through fossils and how they were formed. Or, in oil-producing localities, we might begin with oil and its origins. Metamorphic rock can be introduced through the odd appearance of sedimentary rock that is tilted or folded, where previous examples have been level. The identification of trees and shrubs might need to come about through the study of succession of plants in living communities. The usual succession is bare soil to grasses, grasses to shrubs, shrubs to softwood trees and then to hardwood trees. A survey can be made of the "stages" in local areas, with children's increased awareness of soil conditioning as an important factor in plant growth.

There are additional examples we can use: a small pond on the edge of town that will disappear before long because it is being filled by dying plants and growing plants invading the shoreline; the succession of clouds which indicates to some degree approaching weather conditions; the patterns of stars which give directional clues to navigators on earth and in space. All of these present reasons to observe, or to observe and classify, while each specific subject furnishes direction.

ESTIMATION AND MEASUREMENT

For a long time in our schools, particularly beyond the elementary level, many persons have thought of two kinds of science education—one for "serious" students, and another for everyone else. Students with an interest or aptitude in science often take a different type of course than other students. There is good reason for varying the difficulty of some course work. But provisions of this sort have tended to make one science program highly mathematical and the other completely nonmathematical. Consequently, some teachers in the later grades have felt that with one student they can "pour it on" while with another they must teach a superficial, descriptive science devoid of quantitative thinking.

Such extremes can work out badly for both kinds of students. An unnecessary degree of precision and tiresome detail may be pressed onto the highly capable. The complete absence of measurement in studies of other students can result in far less learning of both process and product than is potentially there. In addition, many students who take further course work are surprised to find that science has taken on a very different character.

Mathematics, through measurement and simple computation, can be included from the earliest grades to help all children learn science. Primary teachers find and encourage a natural tendency in children to seek understanding of such concepts as temperature (Is it warm, cool, cold?), weight (Is it heavy, light?), size (Is it big, little, tiny?), and many more. Seen in this way, measurement can be merely a gradual introduction of refinements to processes long begun.

However, experienced teachers note that children generally are not interested in measurements as such, any more than they are interested in other scientific processes as such. They tend to be more interested in the physical activity and its outcome than in the intellectual processes used. They are likely to become disinterested if too much emphasis is placed on measurement. For this reason, we should deal with measurement (and other processes, too) as a natural course of action in finding answers or seeking solutions. Children gradually can be helped to learn that the quality of the results they get in experiments usually depends upon the precision of processes they use.

There are other factors in the use of measurement we should keep in mind. For example, the mathematics curriculum must be considered. It is often easy to apply a process already learned in mathematics to science; but it may be more difficult to make a needed measurement not already introduced in the regular curriculum. Sometimes there will be no problem in introducing and teaching a new measurement or mathematical application in the science lesson. Other times, we may want pupils to skip an opportunity to measure something in science mainly because it is somewhat involved and can be studied later in the mathematics curriculum, perhaps in a more understandable way.

Learning in virtually any area of science is sharpened by the use of quantitative ideas. In electricity, the maximum load of a circuit is determined; cumulative voltages of dry cells are matched with the voltages of bulbs. Even the monthly electric bill can be calculated. In simple machines, an introduction to ratios is taught—distance to effort, speed to effort. Astronomy and navigation may demand some understanding of indirect measurement by triangulation. The mixing of soils may require some knowledge of fractions. The study of water and agriculture leads to the learning of such concepts as acre, acre-feet, and percentages of yield. Primary children measure lengths of shadows to help determine the time and relate the red line in a thermometer to feelings of warmth and coolness.

One way to improve the ability of children to estimate and measure accurately is to present specific *referents* (standards of measure) that can be borne in mind. If an acre-foot of water is the unit under discussion, it is helpful to measure off on the playground a square 208 feet on the sides to show an acre. A 1-foot ruler placed upright on the ground can help the class visualize the depth of water that would cover this area. If *g*-force is the unit, 2 *g*'s can be represented by a child holding "piggy back" another child of the same weight. The necessity of lying down during a rocket blast-off is readily seen when nine children are imagined to equal a force of 9 *g*'s.

Similar referents are needed for other concepts. Liquid volumes of ounces, pints, quarts, and gallons are easier to think about when there are appropriate containers in the room to which one can refer. With directions, north may be the front of the room. A mile may be a round trip to the local library from the school. Meanings associated with time and temperature can be developed by frequent references to the clock and thermometer.

Very early, children should learn that there is a need for standard units. "Stretchable" inches are not permitted, a pint is a pint, and a quart is a quart. Comparisons of different units can be made, as with the centigrade (Celsius) and Fahrenheit scales. If a balance is used to weigh things, and buttons are used for units, each one must be of equal weight.

By the time they enter junior high school, many youngsters have had some experience with a variety of measuring instruments: the ruler, yardstick, clock, thermometer, barometer, balance or scales, graduated container, wind gauge, galvanometer, and protractor. Children themselves should have the opportunity to select with guidance the right instrument for the activity underway. Sometimes they can even invent, construct, and calibrate an instrument when one is lacking. This may be the best way to teach them how some instruments work. But this should not be interpreted as meaning that accurate, commercial instruments are unnecessary or undesirable.

The invention and construction of a measuring instrument can be as challenging and interesting to children as any other activity. Consider the upper-grade problem of how to determine wind speed when constructing a weather station. A light, wooden flap is hinged to the side of a wind vane so that it swings freely. When the wind blows hard it pushes back the flap more than when there is a light breeze. But how can it be calibrated more accurately? Someone whose bicycle has a speedometer gets the idea to note the flap position while riding at various speeds. Another child points out that this had better be done on a windless day. Several others now suggest that it might lend additional accuracy to have the bicycle ridden in several directions and the flap positions averaged out. Even when this is done, there is some insistence that the procedure be done several more times "just to make sure."

Take a primary class working with simple machines. The teacher mentions that only the child who is pulling a toy wagon up several different inclined planes can feel how much force is required. How can everyone tell how hard it is? To make visible to all the varying

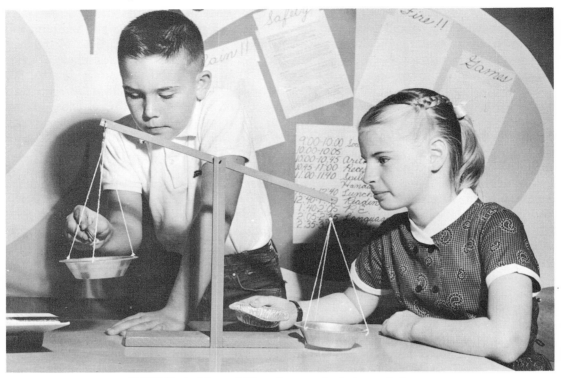

FIGURE 4   **These children have made their own balance.**

force required, the class suggests attaching a rubber band to the wagon handle. A ruler is placed next to the band to measure the amount it stretches.

When possible, bring out the approximate nature of measurement. It can be learned that even commercial products are somewhat inexact, as when several compasses give slightly different headings. When readings are hard to determine, as with a closely calibrated thermometer, it is instructive to have several children give their versions of the readings. This type of practice can illustrate the need for averaging and improving the instruments used.

The idea of sampling is also helpful here. A teacher working with a plant unit remarks to a class, "The seed box directions say that about 90 per cent of these seeds will grow under the proper conditions. How do we know that we won't pick out the 10 per cent that won't grow?" The time is ripe for discussion of assumptions and the need for random

selection. These concepts are not too hard for children to understand when they are approached in this fashion.

Occasionally, there is need for scaling in elementary science activities. A group prepares a large panel picture or mural depicting some ancient animals. Since the children want everything to be as authentic as possible, some reading is done to find the probable dimensions of these animals. It is agreed that the scale should be one inch to one foot. This is so noted on the lower left corner of the picture.

Another class wants to make a model solar system. After reading the sizes of the planets and the relative distances between them, it is realized that only one scale—either distance or size—can be shown in the classroom model. Because of the huge distances involved, for the model to fit within the classroom some planets would have to be made too small for easy viewing. The class, therefore, decides that size will be scaled in the model. Proper distances according to the scale will be indicated neatly in black ink under the model.

Scaling may also be necessary in the construction of graphs. In some cases, graphs are the best way to present comparative data. In a long-range experiment on how soils affect bean growth in sandy soil, rich topsoil, and clay soil, fifteen coffee cans—five for each soil type—are used. Growth is measured every day with each plant, averaged, and recorded in bar graph form. The graph scale is 2 inches to each inch of actual growth, since the recording takes place on a large bulletin board. The reverse would be the case if the recording were done on a small sheet of paper.

Another class wants to find out the warmest time of day. Readings are made on the hour for five consecutive days and then averaged. Each child makes a small line graph that shows the gradual rise, leveling off, and decline in outside temperature according to the time of day. The graph's vertical axis lists degrees in intervals of five degrees to an inch. The horizontal axis presents time at hourly intervals spaced 1 inch apart.

Most beginning opportunities for scaling come in map study. Many younger children are introduced to graphs through recording in various workbooks their scores in spelling or other subjects. Therefore, it is unlikely, at least after the primary grades, that children will think of these operations as unusual. But these skills are somewhat abstract. So do not expect much success in the primary grades. Note other experiences of the children. In most cases it is unwise to plan much work of this kind until they have a mental age of eight to nine years.

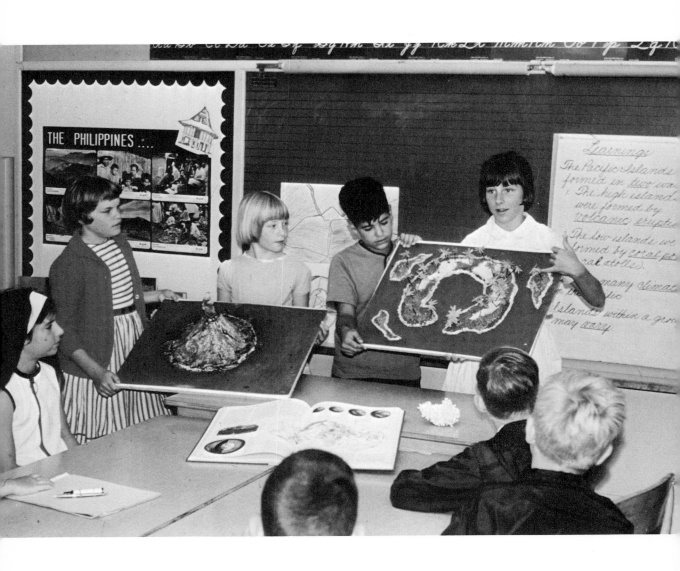

CHAPTER 4

Appraising Process and Product

How do we keep track of, let alone teach toward, the great number of objectives suggested for the elementary school? When objectives in science education are added to those in all other subject areas, it is no wonder that much confusion and uncertainty exist about ways to appraise their achievement in children.

When we evaluate the work of children we need to make judgments about how well they have achieved our objectives. But before we can do this properly, we must have our intentions clearly in mind. One way to ease the problem of coping with so many objectives is to reduce their number. This can be done with knowledge objectives by working toward generalizations rather than isolated facts.

The learning of a generalization or concept cuts down the number of details that must be remembered. Either includes or explains a great many things, and helps us to recall associated facts or ideas. That is, each becomes an intellectual peg on which to hang many facts or small ideas that might otherwise be forgotten after a short while.

The same idea can be applied to process or intellectual skill obectives in elementary science, as we shall see shortly. By using a relatively small number of broad classifications, each can help to recall a cluster of related subskills and techniques—provided these have been learned reasonably well. This is why a specific statement of objectives has been delayed until now.

PRODUCT OBJECTIVES

Chapters in children's science textbooks typically are developed around a structure of large ideas or generalizations. This is also true of units found in school district guides, as well as the units in the second part of this book. In textbooks, supporting ideas, specific facts, and vocabulary are developed to aid the child's understanding of the major generalizations. Activities and pictures of one kind or another supplement the written material. In units, such supporting ideas, facts, and vocabulary are also developed. But there is less dependence on reading and more on the outcomes of several other kinds of activities to bring about understanding of generalizations.

When teaching, it is wise to know the main generalizations which make up the whole structure of the text chapter or unit under study. This permits you to see things in perspective, and to help children connect or relate ideas. It assists you to make judgments about planning and sequencing activities, and is useful in numerous other ways. You will find that about a half-dozen generalizations seem to be ideal for a teaching unit framework. Fewer may make the outline too broad to be useful, and many more tend to become somewhat fragmentary and hard to remember. For illustrations of knowledge objectives as shown in organization, examine now a portion of the primary-grade unit on magnets in Part II of this book (page 193).

The method used in teaching the generalization, "Magnets attract things made of iron and steel," is to begin with experiences that involve a fairly large number of facts. The children learn that a magnet attracts nails and metal coat hangers, for example, and that these are made of iron. They find that scissors and pins are attractable, and that these are made of steel. In addition, nonattractable objects are tested and discovered, both metal and nonmetal.

In the course of learning these facts, vocabulary is introduced as needed. Such words as "steel," "iron," "rubber," and others are used to begin mentally combining similar materials. Gradually, awareness grows of what is attractable and what is not. Children begin to generalize about their experiences until a reasonable approximation of the generalization develops in their minds.

For assessing how well children have learned this material, it is convenient to think of several levels of knowledge. At the simplest level the children can state such facts as the magnet attracted a nail, it did not attract a comb, and so on. Or they may identify steel or rubber objects and use the words "rubber" or "steel" in an acceptable statement. A higher level of understanding may be revealed when children give the generalization, preferably in their own words, as a reason a certain material was not attracted. However, if the generalization is given for a specific example *which has not been taught or previously encountered*, this is even better. It furnishes some evidence that the child can apply his knowledge as well as recall it.

An applicable level of understanding is most valuable. It can be extended to untaught examples. It tends to stick in our minds after some of the specific facts have been forgotten. While recognizing this, many teachers have come to the false conclusion that the facts can be bypassed and the generalization taught directly. This is unfortunate. A child's knowledge of a generalization is strongly related to the quality and diversity of the facts he studies. This is so whether these facts are learned before (inductively) or after (deductively) the generalization's in-

troduction. It is largely because of this that we have continually stressed the idea of application.

In a more complex unit for older children, such as the one on electricity, the basic generalizations may be divided into subgeneralizations, or "contributing ideas," as we prefer to call them. It is typically convenient to assess understanding of a basic generalization through its contributing ideas, since they may more easily bring to mind examples of specific applications. This is illustrated later in the section on testing techniques.

PROCESS OBJECTIVES

Although it is important to possess knowledge one can apply, its attainment and use depend much upon the child's thinking abilities. But specifically what abilities must a child have to think clearly in science education? It is hard to find complete agreement among teachers and other concerned persons. (Recall the brief statements of process abilities in Chapter 1.) Yet there are some indications that a half-dozen or so broadly inclusive skills can be used as guidelines in setting up objectives for teaching. Many curricula, and several of the nationally used science tests, now base their process objectives on aspects of the problem method. As suggested previously, its categories can be most helpful if used correctly.

One of the clearest statements of process abilities is found in the teacher's manual for the Educational Testing Service achievement tests in science. It is used there to illustrate the kinds of abilities these tests are said to examine:

- **Ability to identify and *define* scientific *problems***

  Included in this category is the ability to isolate a problem from a mass of given material and to formulate the problem in a way which allows for systematic solution.

- **Ability to *suggest* or screen *hypotheses***

  Subabilities included here are the abilities to suspend judgment, recognize cause-and-effect relationships, recognize the logical consistency and plausibility of a hypothesis, and check it with relevant laws, facts, operations, or experiments, to select the principle applicable in a given situation.

- **Ability to *select* valid *procedures***

  This encompasses the design of experiments and the planning required for collection of appropriate data.

- **Ability to interpret given information and *draw conclusions***

  This includes the ability to formulate valid conclusions and to recognize or draw valid generalizations from data known or given.

- **Ability to *evaluate critically* claims or statements made by others**

  This encompasses the critical evaluation of advertisements, written materials, and audio-visual materials. Other abilities included are the abilities to detect superstition and fancy, recognize the pseudo-scientific, and avoid unwarranted extrapolations and generalizations; to distinguish fact, hypothesis, and opinion; and to distinguish the relevant from the irrelevant.

- **Ability to *reason quantitatively* and symbolically**

  Included under this heading are abilities to understand and use numerical operations, symbolic relations, and information presented in graphs, charts, maps, and tables.[1]

Notice the open-ended feature of each statement. Because the same statements are intended for science tests at three levels—elementary school, junior and senior high school—obviously the same degree of accomplishment cannot be expected for students at each level. Then, it is only fair to wonder, how far can we go in teaching process skills to children? Actually, no one knows in a specific sense. About the best we can do is to give them as much process as they seem able to take without giving up or losing interest. But this requires judgment and flexibility on the part of the teacher. It requires a sensitive

ability to "reprogram" ideas and questions as one teaches, in addition to the replanning usually done after the lesson.

Chapters 2 and 3 contain many suggestions concerned with teaching for process skills. Let us extract from these chapters pupil outcomes that might be expected to some degree after several or more years of purposeful teaching. We shall state these outcomes in terms of observable pupil behaviors, and classify them according to the six broad abilities of the Educational Testing Service. Accompanying page numbers indicate places where appropriate teaching suggestions are located in the two chapters.

The child identifies and defines science problems:
1. By questioning faulty assumptions that lead to a problem statement (p. 20).
2. By detecting an unstated problem in a situation and stating it as a question (p. 21).
3. By using clear English in stating the problem (p. 20).
4. By identifying key words in a problem statement (p. 20).
5. By returning when needed to a problem statement and restating it better (p. 20).

The child suggests or screens hypotheses:
1. By identifying the several things that may be involved before he makes a hypothesis (p. 22).
2. By stating a hypothesis in terms of a cause (p. 15).
3. By stating the hypothesis in a way that can be tested (p. 22).
4. By differentiating between an observation of a fact and a hypothesis about a fact (p. 21).
5. By selecting the most promising hypothesis from among several optional hypotheses (p. 21).

The child selects valid procedures:
1. By identifying the things that need to be controlled in simple experiments (p. 30).
2. By stating, after some study, the important similarities and differences between an analogy and the real situation (p. 31).

---

[1] Cooperative Test Division, *Sequential Tests of Educational Progress Teacher's Guide*, Princeton: Educational Testing Service, 1959, p. 72. By permission.

3. By suggesting effective substitutions for materials (p. 32).

4. By suggesting effective substitutions of experiments or demonstrations (p. 32).

5. By pointing out faulty procedures, such as incorrect assumptions about materials, controls, and errors in measurement (p. 33).

6. By stating, in his own words, the purpose for an experiment (p. 39).

7. By making observations where he notes the relationship of body structure to function, or where he relates a cause to an effect (p. 41).

The child interprets data and draws conclusions:

1. By recognizing when data need to be recorded and by correctly recording such data (p. 39).

2. By correctly applying the data to the stated problem, and in the form of a tentative conclusion (p. 34).

3. By limiting his conclusion to the thing tested until a broader conclusion is justified (p. 34).

The child evaluates critically claims or statements by others:

1. By questioning the relevancy and accuracy of information (p. 25).

2. By differentiating between cause and effect and correlation alone (p. 25).

3. By detecting and avoiding anthropomorphic statements (p. 25).

4. By consulting sources of information efficiently and accurately comprehending these sources (p. 25).

The child reasons quantitatively and symbolically:

1. By accurately pointing out or describing specific referents for units of measurement, such as inches, feet, yards, acres, etc. (p. 43).

2. By using correctly such common instruments as the foot rule, yardstick, clock, thermometer, barometer, balance, graduated container, galvanometer, and protractor (p. 43).

3. By suggesting the need for averaging measurements when appropriate (p. 43).

4. By performing correctly arithmetical computations when involved in science problems (p. 42).

5. By constructing and reading correctly simple graphs and charts (p. 45).

6. By constructing models and pictures according to proper scale as needed (p. 44).

Note that each of the specific subabilities under each broad ability is a referent or standard by which to evaluate pupil behavior. Each broad ability is only as developed as the competency to apply the specific referents in real situations. In other words, the more subabilities one can apply successfully, the better is each general ability.

While only several are listed, many referents could be written under each broad heading. The open-ended nature of each ability is such that no one, not even an Einstein, ever acquires full awareness of all the applicable referents possible. Therefore, a method devised for the purpose of teaching just one way to "evaluate critically," for instance, might be worse than no method at all. Pupils need to make flexible adjustments to the different situations they encounter, rather than rigid, set responses.[2]

We have presented a representative list of process outcomes that are possible for many children to exhibit reasonably well by the upper elementary grades. All are stated in a behavioral way. When objectives are expressed as observable behaviors rather than abstractions like, "To improve the mind," it becomes easier to judge how well they have been attained.

The idea behind behavioral statements is to increase the clarity of language. Most vague objectives are open to widely varying interpretations with different observers. Thus the more tangible and clear cut the definition of desired behavior, the easier it is to tell if the behavior is being expressed.

Much the same reason has prompted the use, wherever possible, of "operational defini-

---

[2] For mainly this reason, the six broad process abilities are identified wherever they are used throughout the units of Part II. Seeing the many ways these abilities can be specifically taught may help you to use them flexibly.

tions" in science. That is, a word or idea is defined in terms of a visible or measurable dimension, about which there is general agreement. For example, "work" is defined as the product of the distance a load is moved times the amount of force used, rather than the use of some energy.

Another important reason for clear referents is the need for pupils' intelligent self-appraisal. Teaching is worthless unless pupils themselves adopt useful behaviors. So we must make clear to children what the standards are, encourage them as they gradually develop these behaviors, and guide them when they need help.

Although these referents are put in behavioral terms, they do not tell how well or under what conditions the pupils must perform. For several reasons, *this must remain a matter of teacher judgment*. First of all, a standard of performance usually must be realistically attainable in the learner's mind before he will try to acquire it. So "Using clear English to state the problem" as a referent for a primary child might mean only that he is expected to state a complete sentence, or that his statement should make sense. An upper-grade teacher, on the other hand, also might be concerned with the expression of marginal grammar, redundant words, and shades of meaning. We clearly expect more from older children.

Moreover, as children advance in school, the material studied becomes more abstract. There are more things to relate. The material may be less connected to their present knowledge. Individual differences of children increasingly become obvious. What is easy for one child in the class may not be for another. This is true of whole classes as well.

Lastly, our notions are changing about what children can do, or want to do, intellectually. Many goals thought unreasonably difficult for children even as recently as ten or fifteen years ago are now exceeded easily by many classes. We do not really know what children can do until they try.

For the foregoing reasons, we must use our judgment in appraising children's progress. To write down how well, and under what conditions, each child should perform is to become bogged down by unmanageable and needless detail.

When confronted by the above list of some thirty specific objectives, one teacher remarked, "How on earth am I going to remember, *and* get my class to do, all of them?" It is natural to be concerned about this at first. But it is not as hard as it looks the first time around. For one thing, it must be recognized that these are long-range outcomes. No one properly expects immediate, dramatic changes in behavior from lesson to lesson. Gains are slow and cumulative.

It must also be recognized that these abilities are planned for in other content areas as well. We need not pose an entirely different set of general abilities in social studies, for example. Though some specific referents would change, as would the subject matter, "drawing valid conclusions" is as necessary in social studies as in science. However, this does not mean that abilities in science necessarily would be transferable to social studies. Practice in both areas is needed.

The ways of teaching for process abilities recommended throughout this book may further lessen the need to remember a long list of skills. Proceeding in a problem-solving way, for example, tends to set up many opportunities for process thinking in children. By asking such questions as, "What's the problem?" and "What's our best guess?" and "What do these findings mean?" children demonstrate their skill—and lack of skill. We do not set out to teach children formal methods of solving problems from A to Z. Instead, we place them in situations where they actually work with subject matter and materials through questions, problems, and other purposes. It is in the natural course of trying to fulfill their purposes that needs arise.

Therefore, your task is more to *recognize* when children need help than to recall everything in the way of process that is possible and then trying to cram it into lessons. This is not to deny that some intentional preplanning for process skills is important. We shall consider this in Chapter 6.

No educated person begins teaching with a

blank mind. Most of us already have a reasonable stock of criteria for good thinking. Occasional references to a list, such as the foregoing, may serve to add a few helpful criteria to what we already possess. Over the years, the ability to detect and correct errors in thinking continues to improve. As our usable inventory of specific referents grows within each of the half-dozen broad abilities, so does our capacity to help children. But this kind of growth never ends. When a student teacher asked a professor how many referents for each ability one should have, the reply was, "How capable a teacher do you want to be?"

Some persons rely heavily upon formal, written statements of objectives. Although these may be of some help, you are likely to get better results with process outcomes if your mind is organized than if the organization is only on paper. Teaching for process is often done best through the flexible, immediate tactics used in "teachable moments." These occasions arise continually if children are permitted to think for themselves. You need not be concerned if you know only a few usable referents at this time. They probably will serve better than long lists of written outcomes that are seldom translated into action.

Before we begin with specific examples of ways to appraise science achievement, a final point must be made: No child learns science in a vacuum. Progress in other academic areas, interests, aspirations, home background, intelligence, social skills, and psychological makeup all have an effect on achievement in science. Any appraisal of growth in science must be seen in the light of all the information that is available. Therefore, view the upcoming ways of appraising achievement as a contribution toward the evaluation of children's growth in science rather than as the entire operation.

TESTING FOR PRODUCT OBJECTIVES

As mentioned before, most of the product objectives appraised relate to vocabulary, specific facts, and generalizations or, if the generalizations are unusually broad, contributing ideas. Let us look at several ways of testing for this material. To be specific we shall use a generalization from the electricity unit of Part II (page 219): "Short circuits and overloaded circuits may create dangerously hot wires; fuses or circuit breakers are used to eliminate this danger."

Testing vocabulary (terms and concepts). A partial list of the vocabulary used in learning this generalization includes the following words and general definitions.

Fuse. A safety strip of metal that melts and breaks an electric circuit when the wires get too hot.

Circuit breaker. A safety device used to open a circuit in place of a fuse.

Ampere. A measure of the amount of electric current flowing through a wire.

Volt. A measure of the force or pressure behind the flow of electricity.

Watt. A measure that tells how fast electricity is being used.

Notice that these definitions may be less precise than perhaps some persons would like. In other words, what "forgiving" considerations or conditions, if any, must be extended to children? These words are concepts, and grow in meaning with pupils as additional experiences are acquired, particularly in the mathematics of high-school physics. So the acceptable degree of precision must be largely a matter of judgment.

Here, now, are several methods of checking knowledge of these words, expressed in terms of definite pupil behaviors:

1. Given the term, the child selects a correct definition.

A *fuse* is a:
a. tool that joins two wires together without heating them.
(b.) safety strip of metal that melts when a circuit gets too hot.
c. measuring instrument that tells how much electricity is used.

d. plug that increases the flow of electricity when two wires cross.

In this multiple-choice item, an attempt has been made to keep the incorrect options plausible so that the answer cannot be detected through common sense alone. Note further that the options are about the same length.

2. The child identifies an accurate or inaccurate definition.

(T)F A *fuse* is a strip of metal that melts when a circuit gets too hot.

Although a true-false item like this seems easy to write, take care to avoid the exact words given in the book or other source. This tends to reward memorization rather than understanding. You will also want to avoid the use of such words as *all, always, never, no,* and *none.* Brighter pupils know that these "specific determiners," as they are called by test writers, usually indicate a false item. *May, generally,* and *should* typically indicate a true item, and should be avoided, too. A main defect in use of a true-false item is the likely chance that pupils will mark the correct answer without really knowing it. Although this makes little or no difference in a person's class rank—the chances either way tend to even out—you never can be confident about a child's actual knowledge.

3. Given the term, the child supplies an acceptable definition in his own words.

What is a *fuse*?
A fuse is a thing used for safety. It melts when a wire gets too hot and breaks the circuit.

Although the short-answer method is excellent for revealing knowledge, a continual difficulty is the "originality" of the answers received. The answers are so varied their correctness is hard to judge. For this reason, restrict its use to situations that tend to have only one correct answer. Although this restriction often results in emphasis of simple, factual material, several short-answer items

demonstrated below show that it is also suited for reasoning items.

4. The child selects a proper synonym or analogy related to a given term.

A *fuse* is most like a bicycle:
a. horn   b. speedometer   (c.) brake   d. tire

An item of this kind is somewhat harder than the others already shown because the pupil must abstract a common relationship between two apparently different things. These items often are more difficult to write.

5. The child states the main likeness and difference between two given, functionally related terms:

A. How is an electric *fuse* like an electric *switch*?
B. How are these two things different?
(A.) A fuse and a switch can both open a circuit.
(B.) A fuse opens the circuit only when it gets too hot. A switch is used to open and close a circuit anytime.

This is another item that calls for somewhat more reasoning than some of the others listed previously. Being a short-answer type, expect the same difficulty of variation in answers as has been pointed out before.

6. Given the definition, the child supplies the name of the term.

A safety strip of metal that melts when a circuit gets too hot is called a(n)   fuse.

Observe the use of *n* with the article *a* to prevent it from becoming a context clue. The space allotted for the completion part may be another clue, and so should be of uniform length in other completion items. Although ordinarily it is less confusing to a child to respond to a question than to complete a statement, the meaning in this statement should be clear.

An interesting variation of this method for children is to use the form of a crossword puzzle. The number of spaces assigned each word provides an additional clue not present in the preceding example:

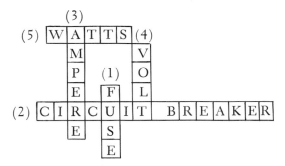

Down

1. A safety strip of metal that melts when a circuit gets too hot.
3. A measure of the amount of electric current flowing through a wire.
4. A measure of the force or pressure behind the flow of electricity.

Across

2. A safety device which shuts off a circuit that is too hot. (2 words)
5. A measure that tells how fast electricity is being used.

7. The child matches correctly given terms and definitions.

Watts   A measure of electric force or pressure.

          A measure that tells how fast electricity is used.

Ampere   A measure of the heat formed in a circuit.

Volt   A measure of the amount of electric current flowing.

In using a matching item, develop some degree of likeness among terms in the first column as well as responses in the second column. Otherwise, it is easy for pupils to reduce the number of options through common sense alone. Note that such common-sense elimination can also be offset by employing a larger number of responses than needed.

Testing factual knowledge. Some of the specific facts presented before or during the de-velopment of the generalization on short circuits are these:

1. A penny has a high melting temperature.
2. A fuse has a low melting temperature.
3. Insulation is used to prevent electricity from leaving a wire.
4. A house appliance cord contains two wires.
5. Electric current for houses usually is supplied at a steady 110–120 volts.
6. Nearly all houses use parallel circuits in electric wiring.

Testing for facts is accomplished much in the same way as vocabulary appraisal. Since this usually presents the least difficulty to teachers, only a few additional examples are presented. Numbers before the items refer to the facts listed above.

1.   A penny has a (high, low) melting tem-perature.
1–2. Which has a higher melting point, a penny or a fuse?
     A penny.
1–2. T(F) A penny has a lower melting point than a fuse.
3. Why is insulating material placed around an electric wire?
     Insulation keeps the electricity from leaving the wire.
4. Inside an ordinary electric appliance cord, there is (are):
     a. 1 wire (b.) 2 wires c. 3 wires d. 4 wires
5. Electric current for most houses is supplied steadily at about:
     a. 40 volts   b. 90 volts   (c.) 120 volts   d. 150 volts
6. Which one of these statements about house currents is correct?
     (a.) Nearly all houses are wired in parallel.
     b. Nearly all houses are wired in series.
     c. About half are in series, the other half in parallel.

It may be worthwhile to note that in the last example, the words "nearly all" and "about" appear. Ordinarily, these could be considered specific determiners. However, when they are balanced among all the options or within an option, their clue value disappears.

Testing applicable generalizations. Some persons assume that understanding of a broad generalization may be tested adequately through the use of only one item. This is most unlikely. A broad generalization contains at least several aspects that are usually difficult to examine unless items are designed especially for this purpose. Moreover, the application of a generalization involves a cumulative and integrative function in the mind. That is, when one uses a generalization, such use also involves previously acquired, lesser levels of knowledge—terms, facts, and contributing ideas.

To check for thorough understanding of a broad generalization, it is a good idea to use items based on its several contributing ideas. This allows you to probe for soft spots in the child's total understanding of the generalization. In other words, it is less likely that an important aspect will be omitted.

Another advantage in testing for contributing ideas is that most direct, factual testing, and to some extent vocabulary testing, can be eliminated. As we have pointed out, these tend to be included in the several broader items. And because the contributing ideas are more specific than the generalization itself, applications are easier to think of when writing items. This last point becomes clear when the present generalization and its contributing ideas are listed with possible applications:

Short circuits and overloaded circuits may create dangerously hot wires; fuses or circuit breakers are used to eliminate this danger.

1. A short circuit results when a resistor (light, appliance, etc.) is largely bypassed; the increased flow of electricity increases the heat of the wire. (Application: A lamp cord has been placed under a heavily traveled area of a rug. One night, the light goes out and part of the cord gets hot.)

2. Fuses are designed to open a circuit that is heating up before it becomes dangerous.

(Application: A man replaces a fuse with a penny and the house catches fire.)

3. Overloading a circuit with too many resistors also overheats the wires. (Application: A fuse melts when a housewife uses several heavy appliances at one time.)

4. Arithmetic may be used to find out the number of resistors that can be replaced safely in a circuit. (Application: A woman wants to know how many of her electrical appliances can be plugged in safely at one time.)

Items directed toward these applications tend to be of the "how" and "why" type. This is in contrast with the "what," "who," "when," and "where" kind usually found in items that test for a lesser level of knowledge. Another way of looking at it is to think of how and why questions as being solution-centered, while the others tend to be background-centered. The latter type of question is seldom stressed when knowledge of the *applications* of generalizations is considered more valuable.

Test specialists tend to prefer the multiple-choice item for testing reasoning. Such items have many benefits. Choices of options can be made as subtle or easy as needed. The kinds of errors can be analyzed through the options. Further, such items are easily and reliably scored. Their form lends itself to several formats. Scores tend to correlate highly with free-response questions that are carefully scored, and more. Because of this, emphasis in the examples below is on the multiple-choice type, although several other types also are included.

As before, each item is preceded by a short, behavioral statement. A further analysis of the child's expected intellectual behavior or the test strategy used occurs after each example.

1. Given an application, the child selects the cause.

A lamp cord is placed under a heavily traveled rug. One night, the light goes out and part of the cord gets hot. The trouble is probably caused by a:

a. burned-out bulb
b. disconnected wall plug

(c.) short circuit
d. worn, sepa-
rated cord

If proper reasoning takes place, it should be possible to select the proper answer in two ways: through a process of elimination—a, b, and d would all open the circuit—and by directly relating the "symptoms" to the cause.

2. Given several concepts, the child selects the one that does not belong and supplies the reason.

A. short circuit   C. hot circuit
B. overloaded circuit   D. broken circuit

D   does not belong because all the circuits would be hot but the broken one.

Although we might assume proper knowledge of the reason through the child's correct choice, the requiring of a written reason for the choice helps to confirm such knowledge. Of course, as with any free-response answer, we are faced with the problem of interpreting the correctness of "original" answers.

3. Given an application, the child selects a related fact.

It is unsatisfactory to replace a burned-out fuse with a penny because a penny:
(a.) has a high melting point
 b.   conducts electricity poorly
 c.   may cause a short circuit
 d.   blocks the flow of electricity

This item goes beyond the simple recognition of a fact by requiring the child to grasp the significance of the fact as part of a larger picture. If there is objection that the other options are not factual but are merely plausible distractors, the above could be written in a recall or short-answer form:

Why is a penny considered an unsatisfactory substitute for a fuse? A penny has a high melting point and will not melt and open a hot circuit as will a fuse. The house can catch fire.

4. Given an action, the child selects a future condition and reason.

A woman plugs in electric appliances that draw a total of 30 amperes. The house fuse is marked "25 amperes." Which one of these statements best describes the later condition of the fuse and the reason?
(a.) It has melted because the wires got too hot.
 b.   It has melted because there was a short circuit.
 c.   It is in good condition because a parallel circuit carries half the current.
 d.   It is in good condition because a parallel circuit carries only half the heat.

Note that without the additions of reasons this would be better cast in some alternate response form, such as a true-false or yes-no item.

5. Given some data, the child first selects a correct condition and then a correct prediction.

Your mother wants to use at one time—without harming the 30-ampere house fuse—a coffee maker (360 watts), waffle iron (960 watts), toaster (600 watts), and iron (1200 watts). How many amperes will these appliances draw all together?

$$(A = \frac{W}{V})$$

a. 22   (b.). 26   c. 30   d. 40

Which one of these statements would be correct?
(e.) The fuse will probably burn out.
 f.   The fuse will probably not burn out.
 g.   There is no way of telling what will probably happen.

Although the formula for calculating amperage is given, this problem requires knowledge of the amount of house voltage, how to apply the formula for the answer, and then the ability to think of the answer's significance. Were this item to be used, there would be little need for the preceding one. The problem's difficulty could be increased by omitting the formula. Note that an analysis by the teacher of the second answer would require knowledge of the child's first answer.

6. The child matches correctly given generalizations and applications.

Events	*Reasons*
<u>c</u> A light goes out and part of the light cord gets hot.	a. An electric current can be produced by changing heat energy into electrical energy.
<u>d</u> A door bell stops ringing.	
<u>e</u> A sound is heard in a telephone receiver.	b. Circuits may be hooked up in series.
<u>b</u> A five-cell flashlight is brighter than a two-cell flashlight.	c. A short circuit takes place when a resistor is by-passed.
	d. Current electricity flows only when there is a complete circuit.
	e. A magnetic field is formed around a wire that carries electricity.

When applications for several generalizations or contributing ideas are to be tested, the matching item form may be convenient to use. Much material can be covered in a short time in this way. But it must be remembered that getting some appearance of likeness among the phrases in each column is a continual difficulty in writing a matching item.

TESTING FOR PROCESS OBJECTIVES

It is convenient to think of the six broad categories of abilities identified on pages 49–50 as broad generalizations, and the specific referents within each ability as contributing ideas. Seen in this way, we can test for the broad ability from several angles, just as we did with contributing ideas. As before, the use of smaller, related ideas tends to make applications easier to think of than if the broad classification itself is used.

A main problem in evaluating process outcomes, as before, is to spell out clearly the criterion (referent) of the behavior we wish to examine. Once this is done, the task of writing an item is mainly to set up a situation in which the behavior may be expressed. The child then is expected to select or supply the appropriate behavior, which we in turn compare to the referent. Let us say we wish to test for the ability to identify and define a problem. The specific referent is "questioning or avoiding faulty inferences and assumptions that lead to a problem statement." Here is an item that can help:

John read about Mexican bullfights. A bull charged toward the bullfighter when he flashed a red cape before its eyes. If John asked a question about this, which one of these would be best?
   a.   Why does a bull get so angry when it sees red?
   b.   How did they learn that a red cape was best to use?
   (c.) What causes the bull to charge in the direction of the bullfighter?
   d.   Which causes the bull to get excited, the flashing cape or the color?

In the broad ability of selecting valid procedures, an important referent in simple experiments involves the identification of controls:

Larry wants to find out if a cut celery stalk placed in water will take up water. He plans to wait two days and then cut open the stalk. Which one of these procedures is best to do to be sure about the findings?
   a.   Slice the stalk the long way.
   b.   Slice the stalk crosswise.
   c.   Mix sugar in the water.
   (d.) Mix red ink in the water.

The broad ability to evaluate critically includes the referent of questioning the relevancy and accuracy of information:

Barbara heard from some friends that flying saucers from another planet had landed in the neighborhood one night. Which of these possible clues would be best to follow up?
   (a.) An airline pilot reports an unidentified flying object that night.

b. A local woman reports seeing a tiny, green-colored boy or man that night.

c. Purple-colored oil drops are found in several places nearby.

d. A plastic box is found nearby marked "Ig-3-Mars."

Although it is possible to write acceptable items for many process skills, many others are very difficult to put into a reasonably short test-item form. It is mainly for this reason that test writers do not produce more of these items. Consider an important behavioral referent we should like children to adopt in the identification of problems: "The child returns when needed to a problem statement and restates it better." There is nothing very difficult in checking out this behavior. It is clearly spelled out and quite noticeable. But what if we wish to write a test item that measures the behavior? It can be done, but only with more effort and time than it is probably worth, *especially considering that we can observe the same behavior with little difficulty.* (Note that places marked in margins of Part II show when these observations can occur.) This is but one limitation to conventional tests. Shortly, we shall take up other limitations and what we can do about them in a practical manner.

STANDARDIZED TESTS

Several published tests are available which have been prepared for distribution and use on a nationwide basis. Since items are prepared by qualified test specialists, technically they are well developed and edited. Incorrect options are plausible, specific determiners are rare, and vocabulary is well selected. "Grade norms" are developed by administering the test to a widely scattered sampling of school districts over the entire country. In other words, typical scores received in grades of the representative sampling are charted so that customary performance on the test at each grade level or thereabouts can be known.

Overall scores made on the standardized tests are usually highly *reliable*—that is,

scores received tend to be reasonably consistent from one administration of the test to another. But *curricular validity*—how relevant the test is to the goals of a specific school district—is often another matter. Before a standardized test is selected, it should be inspected closely for compatibility with local objectives. If items do not reasonably well sample the behaviors expected as a result of teaching, there can be little significance in scores obtained.

Although validity remains a problem, there are indications that newer standardized tests may be more widely usable than older versions. One reason for this is that emphasis on remembering specific facts is being shifted by teachers to understanding concepts and generalizations. Newer tests reflect the emphasis. In tests of this kind, therefore, it is less crucial to remember a specific, isolated fact to mark an item correctly. One group of facts may be as useful as another.

In addition, some tests include items designed to measure several process abilities. This innovation may be crude—a reliable measure of a broad ability cannot be determined from just one or two items. Besides, answers to such items may also depend on the recall of science generalizations. But there is hope for increased curricular validity in such tests as objectives in education change toward the broader, relatively permanent forms of learning.

Standardized tests in elementary-school science have a helpful but limited application in teaching. They are useful in indicating where a child stands in general science knowledge compared to his peers. Yet this indication is meaningful only in terms of what is measured in the test, and how closely it samples the behaviors taught in the district. With this in mind, these tests may also reveal the relation of a child's expectancy or aptitude scores to his science achievement.

Perhaps the best use for such tests is to give a partial indication of where the entire school district stands in relation to other districts, and how sizable segments of a large district compare with one another. When properly interpreted, this is useful knowledge. It can provide the spark for needed curricular or other changes.

But can standardized tests in science be used for evaluating a specific teacher's effectiveness? Or a child's success with several specific units? Or for diagnostic purposes? Most of the time we must say "no." The general nature of the science material sampled in the test prevents specific knowledge of where and how immediate teaching or curriculum is related to scores received. Such knowledge depends mostly on other means of assessment.

Typically, standardized tests in elementary-school science are included in overall achievement batteries, since most districts tend to test for several subjects at one time. However, separate science sections, from Grade 4 upward, usually are available upon request. Among the most widely used tests are these:

American School Achievement Tests, The Bobbs-Merrill Company, Inc., 4300 West 62nd St., Indianapolis, Indiana.

California Tests in Social and Related Sciences, California Test Bureau, Del Monte Research Park, Monterey, California.

Coordinated Scales of Attainment, Educational Test Bureau, Minneapolis, Minnesota.

Metropolitan Achievement Tests, Harcourt, Brace & World, Inc., 750 Third Ave., New York, New York.

Sequential Tests of Educational Progress, Cooperative Test Division, Educational Testing Service, 20 Nassau St., Princeton, New Jersey.

S R A Science Achievement Test, Science Research Associates, 57 W. Grand Ave., Chicago, Illinois.

Stanford Achievement Tests, Harcourt, Brace & World, Inc., 750 Third Ave., New York, New York.

Descriptions and critical reviews of these and other tests appear in the latest edition of *The Mental Measurement Yearbooks*, Oscar K. Buros, editor (New Brunswick, N.J.: Rutgers University Press).

LIMITATIONS OF WRITTEN TESTS

As we have seen, a main need in testing is to provide a situation that requires a behavioral decision by the child. But sometimes this is hard to do with all objectives, especially in the elementary school, if the means primarily used are paper-and-pencil tests. We have already indicated how a common process objective would be easy to observe but difficult to sample in written form. Also, children's ideas in science typically are further advanced than either their writing or reading ability, particularly in the primary grades.

Notice that thus far there has been no reference to essay questions. Besides the restricted sampling of learning that occurs with their use, and their unreliability when scored, writing itself may be difficult for pupils. Thus the essay test in science is an uncertain measure of what children can actually do, except perhaps with some children in the later elementary grades. This is why many teachers prefer to use a limited-answer item in its place, or essays whose answers are curtailed to a paragraph or two. Much the same problem is found with children's performance in reading. Items that are the most worthwhile, process and application-of-generalization types, are the lengthiest because a problem context first must be established before a behavior can be elicited. Although an item can be read by the teacher, it is better if the child is able to read the item for himself.

Few published paper-and-pencil tests exist for use below the fourth grade. In a study[3] with 350 fifth- and sixth-grade children, at least fourth-grade reading ability appeared to be necessary for achievement of average scores with the *Sequential Tests of Educational Progress* (Form 4A, 1957) and the *Stanford* (Form K, 1952) achievement tests in elementary science. Most readers at this level or lower achieved science scores far below the averages of their groups. Of course, these re-

[3] Peter C. Gega and Bjorn Karlsen, "Situational vs. Non-Situational Casting of Items in the STEP—Elementary Science," *California Journal of Educational Research*, May 1962, pp. 99–104.

sults may also indicate too much dependence on textbook teaching in science. But certainly there is reason for caution in interpretation of test results. This is not to say that adequate tests in science are impossible to construct below the fourth-grade level. Simpler vocabulary can be used, numerous picture items can be developed, including tape recordings, slides, and the like. But these usually involve a great deal of time and trouble, perhaps more than most primary teachers can afford without much assistance.

Writing excellent application and process items at any level takes time, and skill, too. Some help in providing tests is furnished in recent textbook series' teacher manuals and workbooks. Cooperative writing and exchanges by teachers of items is a worthwhile way to augment this help. More of this should be done among the faculties of schools and school systems that have similar objectives.

Certainly among the greatest limitations of typical tests is the unlikelihood that the results will materially affect the way in which the unit is taught. Tests are usually administered at the end of a unit. The immediate, corrective "feedback" often so necessary for highly effective teaching is thus absent. Since only limited time is available, it is difficult to go back and fully correct omissions and mistakes. While results may be helpful in presenting a future unit or in correcting certain general procedures, this benefit is limited at best.

Because the task of teaching is inexact, it is helpful to view it as a whole series of consecutively developed hypotheses. That is, each action, statement, or expression we make is a kind of hypothesis which we cannot be certain will be "accepted" (learned) by the children. If much teaching takes place before feedback indicates that learning has taken place, we may be making a whole series of unwarranted assumptions. Tests are helpful to find out what children already know, or to confirm and check in a uniform manner what has been learned. *But much more important for good teaching is a host of informal, in-context practices which provide the teacher with data for fast self-correction.* An important necessity in these practices is that they include practical techniques for teachers of primary, as well as older, children.

The need for self-correction is no less important with children. One of the overall ideals in education is to progressively make each child as self-sufficient as possible. Yet before a child can work toward this goal, he must first know what the desired behaviors are. Evaluative methods which enlist his cooperation in everyday activities gradually give him personal reference systems. These can be used for self-appraisal of process and product outcomes in science.

INFORMAL WAYS OF APPRAISAL

Observation. Daily observation of pupil behavior is the most frequently employed evaluation method of teachers. When done thoroughly, it probably furnishes the best classroom evidence of what pupils can do. It is also the most important procedure we have for the immediate, corrective feedback necessary for tactical changes in teaching procedure. Alert teachers have always been sensitive to the occasional blank stares, puzzled looks, frowns, faltering responses, or lack of upraised hands that signal the need to try another tack. But these are just a few of the general cues that changes may be necessary. What can we do to develop a more systematic basis for observation?

Perhaps nothing is more crucial to successful assessment through observation than a great deal of continual, active pupil involvement in learning experiences. In the absence of much pupil activity—intellectual and physical—there can be little evaluation. Corrective feedback comes from pupil responses. In the absence of responses, there is likewise an absence of feedback. To evaluate such responses, we again use our referents to make judgments, regularly and continually, as we teach.

For example, when a problem is to be identified and defined by children we note their faulty inferences or assumptions, or how well they pose an unstated problem as a question, or the use of clear English, and so on. If the children do not exhibit these behaviors at an acceptable level, the time to teach for improved behaviors is right at hand and ordinarily should not be postponed. The same is true when the time comes for the pupils to suggest hypotheses, select valid procedures, interpret data and draw conclusions, evaluate critically, and reason quantitatively. The important thing is *to provide the opportunity* for children to express the behavior, so that it can be assessed in the light of our criteria or referents. The purpose is not to "mark children down" for their mistakes, but to note what they do and do not need as we teach. (For specific opportunities to assess process skills note again the places marked in the margins of units in Part II.)

Similar in-context observations can take place when dealing with knowledge objectives. Some vocabulary referents might be: Do they use old and new terms correctly? Can they define the words? Can they give a synonym for the word? Factual referents can be: Do they answer satisfactorily when asked about important *what, who, when, where* facts? Do they use correct facts in discussions? Generalization referents might include: Can they give specific examples of applications? Can they restate the generalization in their own words? Can they supply the cause of a given application? Can they predict what will happen and tell why? *These last four referents are possibly the most useful to assess product objectives,* either orally or on written tests.

To reveal such evidence, it is an excellent idea as you teach to use *questions* often in place of statements. When done properly, this has the effect of stimulating the children to think through matters for themselves. At the same time it gives you an opportunity to evaluate their performance. Naturally, not all questions are of equal value. It takes a while to develop facility in posing questions that are likeliest to evince significant behaviors. We have seen material on questions in previous sections and chapters. But it is hoped that the activity sections of the units in Part II may be particularly helpful in furnishing examples.

This would be a good time to skim through some units to note where and how such questions occur as the units are taught. Many questions can be found by the marginal notations. In addition, a few quotes from the primary unit on machines (pp. 243–263) may help you know what to look for:

Ask them what the findings seem to mean. (p. 247)
Ask why animals seem to choose a longer, zig-zagged route rather than a shorter, straight-up route. (p. 247)
Invite them to hypothesize as to which would be the easier to drive into the ground. (p. 252)
. . . try to bring out a reason why it works when both the figures and the board are moved. (p. 254)
Ask the children to design a demonstration to show that increasing the length of the force-arm permits work to be done with less force. (p. 254)

Observation of the work that children do in everyday activities and discussion compares favorably with tests as a valid way to learn about what they can do. Yet this technique usually lacks the reliability and broad sampling—of children as well as subject material—possible in a well-prepared test. Fortunately, there are several things we can do to reduce these deficiencies. Let us take the idea of sampling first.

One method to learn what all the children, rather than just several, think about a problem statement, or hypothesis, or conclusion, and so on, is occasionally to ask everyone to write it down on a slip of paper and turn it in. Since the context has already been established by the activity itself, only a short, quickly written statement is needed. Statements are analyzed rapidly with the appropriate referent in mind; then appropriate actions are considered. A broad sampling of the material comes about by doing something like this with sufficiently different situations over a period of time.

Much the same thing is done with drawings. An experiment, demonstration, or picture is drawn to depict a test, illustration, or application, as the case may be. These need not even be turned in, but can be used as "flash cards," held under the chin so that you can observe the whole group at once. This also works well when there are measurement problems. When answers are written large and held up for teacher observation, you can note quickly if more help is needed. Of course, getting the right answer does not always mean it was arrived at properly.

But what if the children do not write or draw well enough, even though the problem has been made less complicated? In this case, seeking a representative sample may help. For instance, you can go around to a half-dozen or so children and ask them to whisper the needed control, conclusion, definition, application, or whatever. While not everyone may be heard from, some indication of class understanding can be received if children of varied competencies are checked.

In addition to this procedure, some teachers ask their children to respond frequently to choices. Instead of asking for hands to show agreement with a hypothesis or a conclusion, thereby permitting anyone to go along mindlessly with the majority, children are asked to hold up one finger for agreement, two for disagreement. When done somewhat in the manner of flash cards, close to the body and under the chin, it is difficult to observe the choices of neighbors. Reasons for agreement or disagreement are then explored.

This technique works very well with screening hypotheses. If several or more are to be evaluated for the best choice, numbers are assigned to each. A survey of choices is made rapidly just by observing the number of fingers children show corresponding to the hypothesis numbers. Once the children are conditioned to responding in this manner—and the teacher conditioned to posing questions that involve alternate choices—a great deal of feedback is possible. This is especially likely to happen if reasons for choices are also followed through on a selective basis. However, this does not mean that alternate-choice questions are always best to use. The technique is suggested as just another useful evaluation method.

We mentioned early in this section that much pupil involvement is necessary for successful assessment. If children participate continually in learning activities over some length of time, an alert teacher receives many indications of their progress. Such indications present an easier and more reliable pattern to interpret when viewed cumulatively rather than separately. Also, we sometimes unknowingly neglect some children and overconcentrate on others in evaluating performance. For these reasons, it is worthwhile to make sure that all the children have had a reasonable opportunity to provide information about what they need to learn, and how well they are doing. Some teachers seem to remember unaided the needs of children and their progress. But many more find that taking occasional, brief notes is helpful in recalling information for this purpose.

Standard setting. Experienced teachers realize the value of enlisting children's cooperation in setting standards for everyday activities. Besides the desirable side effects of higher interest and improved room control, this process gradually provides the child with the personal reference systems necessary for self-appraisal. It seems natural, also, to teach standards as an internal part of the activity itself. Typically children are interested in the activity and its outcomes rather than direct attempts to teach the "great truths" of science, whether they be process or product.

Some time should be set aside for group discussion of standards when working with activities. Brief discussion sessions just before and after the main activity of the lesson help to clarify purposes, develop or review needed standards, and evaluate performance. For example:

1. A primary class going on a study trip plans specifically what to look for and the kind of conduct appropriate for the site. A discussion after the trip helps the class to evaluate whether all went according to plan, and the reasons.

2. A middle-grade group working on several large panel pictures of ancient animals

and plants decides that the animals must be drawn to scale and in relation to one another, that only animals of one epoch should be shown together, and that the plants must be as authentic as possible.

3. A competent, upper-grade group writing imaginative stories on space exploration decides that a realistic accounting of a trip would include the proper use of such previously studied terms as acceleration, re-entry, zero gravity, and micrometeorites.

Sometimes brief charts are helpful to keep standards of various activities in mind, although this can easily be overdone. In some cases, a chart may serve for several subject-matter areas:

> A good reporter—
> uses his own words;
> uses the right vocabulary;
> can answer some questions;
> shows pictures or sketches when needed.

In other cases, a chart may be more specifically suited for science alone:

> A good demonstrator—
> tells what the purpose is;
> uses controls if needed;
> handles materials properly;
> can answer some questions.

An excellent example of how standards are used to help children evaluate the designs of animal experiments is furnished by Educational Services, Incorporated.[4] While the criteria are given to the class in this case, it is clear that they may also be worked out cooperatively by teacher and pupils:[5]

How to Experiment with Animals

Before proceeding with more investigations of mealworm behavior, thought might be given

[4] Educational Services, Inc. (Elementary Science Study), *Behavior of Mealworms*. Published by Educational Services, Inc., 108 Water St., Watertown, Mass. (n.d.), pp. 7–9. By permission.

[5] These criteria are worked out cooperatively by teacher and pupils in a revised edition.

to some of the errors commonly made when experimenting with animals. To help accomplish this, a list of six criteria for good experimentation is given to the students.

1. In order to know if the animal is doing something different, one must first know its usual behavior.
2. An animal must given a choice if it is to show a preference for one thing over something else.
3. What is done to an animal must be described in detail.
4. The description of what the animal does in the experiment must be complete.
5. The same experiment should be done more than once.
6. The conditions should be controlled so that the animal responds only to what is being tested.

Descriptions of ten hypothetical experiments are distributed and students decide which of the six criteria are violated in each example. There is no single right answer. In many cases, two, three, or even more responses may be considered correct. The purpose of having the children write an answer is to force them to consider the experiments carefully. Discussion of the "answers" in class should elicit a lively debate.

1. I wanted to see if mealworms liked high places. I put my mealworms on a book and raised it five feet above the floor. This was done about 25 times with several different worms. Every time except once the mealworm crawled around the book until he fell off onto the floor. It took from 8 seconds to 6 minutes and 15 seconds for this to happen. The one mealworm which didn't fall off just sat on the book and didn't move. I don't think mealworms like heights.
2. I tested my dog to see his reaction to music. So every night after his dinner, for two weeks, I put him in the playroom and turned on some music. On almost every night he was asleep within 10 minutes. It seems that music makes my dog go to sleep. . . .
8. Does temperature affect the number of times a cricket cricks? To answer this question I performed the following experiment. I used 17 adult male crickets in separate outdoor screened cages. Between 2:00 and 3:00 in the afternoon of March 12th, I counted the number of times each cricket made a noise

in a minute. The average was 38 times. The temperature was 67 degrees F. On the same night from 8:00 to 9:00, when the temperature was only 42 degrees F., the average of cricks was 21. I have concluded from this experiment that temperature does affect the cricking of crickets.

In sum, we can say that our main functions in helping children set standards is to know some usable referents for process and product, recognize when they need to be applied, and be able to translate each referent into terms that children can grasp. Eventually, the children will acquire their own standards, patterned largely after those learned from a succession of teachers and other competent sources. Hopefully, our pupils will then no longer need us.

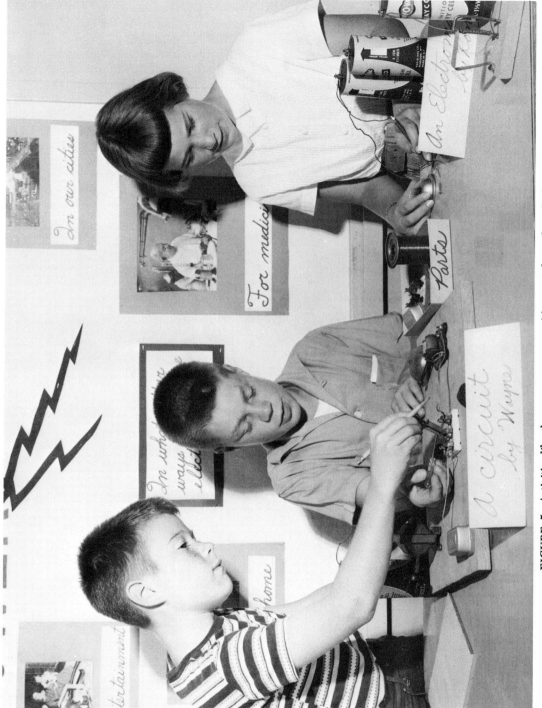

FIGURE 5 Activities like these present opportunities to evaluate through observation.

CHAPTER 5

Providing and Using Materials

Are educators today *really* taking elementary school science seriously? One of the most convincing indications is the increasing attention paid in school districts to the problems of providing adequate instructional materials. It is true that in far too many cases teachers are still given little more than a set of science texts with which to conduct a program. But in some situations science materials go unclaimed because teachers do not know how to acquire them, or gather dust because teachers are uncertain of their uses. This chapter should help you learn many sources of materials commonly available, along with some considerations in using materials.

GETTING EQUIPMENT AND SUPPLIES

Most of the materials used in elementary science are simple and readily accessible; the kind found around the home, in local stores, or other convenient places. Frequently the children themselves bring in a share of the items needed for experiments, demonstrations, and other activities. This is a good practice, for several reasons. When common things are used, pupils can do many school-inspired activities at home as well as in class. Participation in getting materials usually includes some participation in planning for their use. This can increase pupil understanding and responsibility. Materials are usually brought in by children as a result of previously

stated purposes. Unfortunately, prestated purposes may not always be present when supplies and equipment are purchased by the school district. Purchases may be made solely on the basis of recommended lists appearing in various publications, with little relevance to the local science program itself.

It is desirable for children to participate in gathering materials from time to time. But it is plainly unreliable and inadequate to base a complete program on the materials they contribute, however cooperative they may be. Commercial sources must be consulted—science supply houses, hardware stores, drug stores, and department stores, for example. All science supply houses provide catalogues that describe available materials and methods for obtaining them. A usual practice among several school districts is to circulate periodically to teachers and administrators an equipment and supply list that is at least partly based upon the items found in supply-house catalogues. The district representative then orders for everyone at one time, benefiting all from the usual price discount that accompanies large orders.

Some general supply companies have developed special elementary-school catalogues. These reduce the difficulty of selecting materials suitable for children from the innumerable items intended for research or education at more advanced levels. In spite of this, commercial materials available for younger pupils can be disappointingly inappropriate. It is still difficult to find large thermometers with

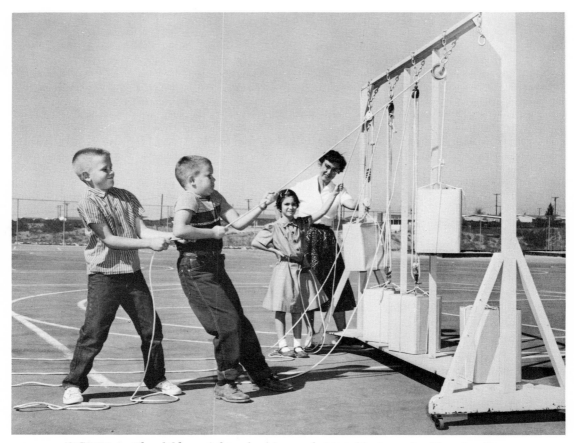

FIGURE 6   **The children of this school know what it is like to work with *real* pulleys.**

thick, red-colored columns, and large numbers for use in the primary grades, for instance; or easily handled and durable electric switches, lamp sockets, large pulleys, and the like. Instead of materials of this kind, most supply houses may offer only items that are too tiny or fragile for small, uncoordinated hands and fingers. Since much attention is being given to this problem, desirable changes for the better are sure to increase.

Special catalogues for elementary-school science may be requested from:

Cambosco Scientific Company, Inc., 37 Antwerp Street, Brighton Station, Boston, Massachusetts;

Central Scientific Company, 1700 Irving Park Road, Chicago, Illinois;

Central Scientific Company of California,

6446 Telegraph Road, Los Angeles, California:

Nasco Science Materials, Fort Atkinson, Wisconsin;

Ward's Natural Science Establishment, Inc., P.O. Box 1712, Rochester, New York;

The Welch Scientific Company, 1515 Sedgwick Street, Chicago, Illinois.

It is important to consider quality when ordering instructional supplies and equipment. Passage of the National Defense Education Act of 1958, Title III, made available large sums of money to local school districts for programs in science, mathematics, and foreign languages. This resulted in the sudden formation or expansion of hundreds of supply companies, some selling products of marginal quality. It became increasingly important for educators to learn desirable specifications and performance standards for materials and equipment. To meet this need the Council of Chief State School Officers developed a purchase guide for programs in the three fields. The guide was revised in 1965,[1] with foreign-language materials deleted and placed in a separate publication. The 1965 guide is intended for all science and mathematics programs, NDEA-sponsored, or otherwise. The following excerpt from page 172 illustrates the kind of assistance it provides:

2450
MAGNIFIER, READING GLASS

- **Biology** · Basic, one for each student
- **Earth Science** · Basic, one for each student
- **Elementary Science** · Basic, one classroom set for each school
- **Physics** · Basic, 4 for each classroom

For magnification in elementary biological and other laboratory work, including reading topographic maps.

  • *Specifications:* The reading glass shall consist of a lens, approximately 2 in. to 4 in. in diameter, mounted in a durable rim and ferrule, and set in a durable plastic handle.

It shall be available with focal lengths ranging from 4 in. to 10 in. and corresponding magnifications ranging from 2X to 1X. Purchaser shall specify focal length and magnifications desired.

Besides descriptions of "hardware," the guide contains lists of annotated professional books and trade books, descriptions of new curriculum studies, and ways to use materials. Every school should have one of these useful guides, and, of course, every purchasing agent.

Another concern of importance is the quantity of materials that should be used. In a program where children are to be active participants, ten magnets, for example, are more appropriate for a class than one. The expense may prevent each teacher from receiving this number of magnets. However, a policy of cooperation and different time scheduling for teaching the same units in the school may make sufficient supplies available. This assumes that an adequate total number of items has been ordered in the first place.

Despite elaborate order lists provided by numerous schools, it is difficult to anticipate everything that will be needed in teaching. Sometimes articles are needed between order periods. In these cases a petty cash fund, administered through the principal's office, is most useful. Besides being convenient, such a fund lends encouragement to the teacher willing to depart from routine.

Many elementary schools possess self-contained *science kits*. Consisting of a durable box or chest with a teacher's manual and numerous materials stored inside, the science kit provides for many activities without most of the storage and distribution problems that accompany the ordering of individual supplies.

But the gain in convenience is offset by several important disadvantages. The kit is likely to be much more expensive than items gathered separately. Also, there is the natural tendency to want to use fully what has been purchased. The materials tend to dictate the program, rather than the other way around. Yet it would be unjustified to disapprove of kits in all school situations. Their availability has without doubt assisted greatly in the improvement or development of science programs where little or nothing existed prior to their use.

It is becoming more common for elementary schools to have a special *science-supply room* for supplementing and replenishing materials used in the classroom. Replacements may be stored for such consumable supplies as dry cells, miniature light bulbs, balloons, simple chemicals, candles, and so forth. Other items may include those that are used by various classes only some of the time, or that are too expensive to buy in quantity. Typical examples are cages of various types and sizes for animals, microscopes, commercial weather instruments and models, hot plates, and telephone sets.

[1] Council of Chief State School Officers, *Purchase Guide for Programs in Science and Mathematics,* 1965. Boston: Ginn and Company. By permission. (Neither the Council nor any State Department of Education officially endorses any specific product described in the guide.)

KEEPING RECORDS...

FIGURE 7   Sometimes parent-teacher organizations volunteer to assemble improvised science kits.

A well-organized supply room reduces classroom storage problems. It saves the teacher from continually rushing out to purchase consumable items, and makes a wider range of instructional devices available to everyone in the school.[2]

READING MATERIALS

A great deal of reading matter exists for use in the classroom. Most common is the textbook, usually distributed on the basis of one per child. The modern textbook in elementary science is a great improvement over earlier editions. The range of subject matter is broader and more interesting; numerous

[2] For a comprehensive discussion of science kits, supplies, and science-supply rooms, see "Science Equipment and Materials: Science Kits," by Albert Piltz and William J. Gruver. (Office of Education Bulletin No. 30, 1963. Order from Supt. of Documents, U.S. Government Printing Office, Washingtin, D.C. 20402. 15¢.)

"doing" activities are included, along with attractive pictures and an appealing format. In spite of improvements, criticism of textbooks continues. Much of the criticism may be due to misuse of texts, or may be a result of unrealistic expectations. Even a good text cannot be a complete science program in itself.

We have previously indicated here and there some teaching techniques with the text. Let us now list in review, and in one place, some of the ways in which the basic text and its accompanying teacher's manual can be used:

1. *As a source of experiments, activities, bridges, problems, and basic generalizations.* When used for these purposes, the children's books are closed at first; the textbook author's ideas are used by the teacher.

2. *As a check-up source for experiments, analogies, and theories.* In these cases, the book serves as a check for the children to compare the completeness and accuracy of *their*

ideas and activities with those in the book. The book is opened for verification or comparison only after the initial thinking and doing have taken place.

3. *As a data and background source.* Now the book is consulted for details as needed to answer previously established questions or purposes. Note that these purposes may have developed through item one above. In a primary text consisting mostly of pictures, the pictures may be examined in detail.

4. *As a source of additional examples to reinforce a previous activity.* Study of open-end experiments, generalizations, or concepts can be enhanced by learning of additional examples. Frequently, such examples are either mentioned or illustrated in the text. The same is true of possible substitutions for previous experiments or demonstrations.

5. *As a summary of important ideas in the unit.* The clear, careful organization of subject matter typical in modern texts is ideal to summarize important segments of a unit, or even the entire unit itself. The additional filling in of detail, and seeing previously studied material in a new context through summary reading, provides reinforcement and more completeness in learning.

You may be aware that we have omitted using the text for the purpose of overviewing or exploring a unit. This practice is liable to be unsatisfactory in many, perhaps most, cases. Children are likely to get the idea that they already know well the material of the unit. While they may be urged to read quickly for a general overview, many will read for details. If you pose the author's problems, and so forth, the class will tend superficially to "know" the answers. Therefore, the author's ideas will not be as convenient to use, should you be fresh out of your own approaches.

Naturally, even the best of textbooks cannot always do an ideal job in each of the five uses mentioned. They would soon grow too heavy to carry and too expensive to buy. But there are other printed materials that can help out. Children's *trade books* are excellent for additional detail. Usually developed around one topic, such as simple machines, weather, soil, or electricity, they can provide the richness in depth difficult to put into a textbook unit. Less useful are those trade books of a survey type which deal with many topics. These tend to have the same deficiency in depth as many textbooks.

Some school districts prepare collections of books, or at least bibliographies, to accompany units. Local libraries may permit up to thirty or more trade books to be checked out to teachers for a limited period. Children can go to the local library, too, and find books which are helpful with the unit. An advantage in self-selection is that children usually choose books that they can read without much difficulty.

Trade books are probably the best means we have of providing for individual differences in reading. If a variety is available, it almost insures that excellent readers will have challenging materials. Slower readers, also, will usually have at their disposal books that are both interesting and within their more limited capabilities.

Many trade books and other books are printed every year. It is a continual problem just to keep up with what is published, much less to pick out quality material. Fortunately, we have several places to which we can turn for help. Among the more useful sources is an organization called "Books on Exhibit, Incorporated." This concern publishes yearly annotated listings of new elementary and secondary science trade books of most leading publishers. In addition, a free exhibition of these books may be provided to school districts upon request. A free catalogue and more information may be obtained by writing to:

Books on Exhibit, Incorporated
North Bedford Road
Mount Kisco, New York 10549

In 1963, the American Association for the Advancement of Science published a comprehensive (1219 titles), annotated list of trade books called, "The AAAS Science Book List for Children." This careful selection serves well as a basic acquisition guide for a district science library. In addition, the association publishes a quarterly review of newly printed books in science and mathematics at the elementary through junior-college levels. Unlike many review guides, this one has "bite." The four ratings given range from "highly recommended" to "not recommended." Here is a sample excerpt from a low-rated book: ". . . this book deals with the topic in a highly superficial manner, and the text is filled with scientific inaccuracies, poor grammar, and vague explanations." Specific references of both publications are:

Science Book List for Children, Second Edition, 1963 ($1.25 paper, $2.50 cloth), Hilary J. Deason, editor.

SCIENCE BOOKS: A *Quarterly Review*, Hilary J. Deason, editor. Subscription: $4.50 per year; $3.00 for additional copies to the same address.

The address for both references is: Association for the Advancement of Science, 1515 Massachusetts Avenue, Washington, D.C. 20005.

Encyclopedias are also useful in providing additional information to children. But most of them are difficult for younger children to read without some help. Above all, discourage the usual practice of simply copying information out of the encyclopedia. When this happens comprehension may reach the vanishing point. On the other hand, you should help the children interpret information when necessary. It may even be advisable occasionally for you to read short segments aloud, so that individual pupils can jot down in their own words facts they wish to report or know.

Care should be taken not to rush into reading activities. Our ability to comprehend the printed word relates directly to our experiences. The child should be permitted to engage in some exploration of environment and problems before he reads. In this way, he begins to acquire ideas and a vocabulary needed to understand the verbal material.

To make many reference books available, and provide for differences in reading ability, many schools buy a half-dozen or more series

of textbooks instead of one. In these cases a third-grade teacher with thirty-six children, let us say, may have six copies from each of six different series of books. Often some of the books are one grade below regular level, some at grade level, and at least several above grade level.

There appears to be no good reason for this practice. Some series may contain nothing at all on the unit being studied. And developmental sequences of concepts in each series rarely are fully exploited. Perhaps the major objection is that textbooks are not intended for reference use in the first place. They lack the detail of a good trade book and the comprehensive, logical organization of an encyclopedia.

On the other hand, a worthwhile textbook series with teachers' manuals can offer a useful base for a science program. It can provide security for the teacher unfamiliar in science. It can enable the pupil to refresh and reinforce his knowledge of generalizations at several grade levels and in several different contexts. Yet even an excellent text series needs to be supplemented with other reading materials and used with local emphases in mind. Merely buying several sets of texts does little to help in these respects.

From time to time we need to use *identification books* in the classroom. These are references whose major value is to group or order natural things in a logical way, so that they can be classified or named. As brought out in Chapter 3, it is important to have books that are well illustrated. Most pupils rely more on matching pictures than on use of keys for identification. An excellent and inexpensive shelf of books with colored illustrations is the *Golden Nature Guides* series. It is available in inexpensive paperback or cloth editions from Simon and Shuster, Inc., Rockefeller Center, New York, New York. Titles include *Birds, Flowers, Trees, Insects, Stars, Reptiles and Amphibians, Rocks and Minerals, Fishes,* and *Seashores.*

Besides reference, trade, and text reading materials, many teachers discover that magazines, newspapers, charts, workbooks, catalogues, almanacs, bulletins, and the like are worthwhile for seeking information. Not surprisingly, it is found that the use of a variety of reading matter often has double benefits. Not only do children become more proficient in locating science information, but they may also increase their ability to locate information in other curriculum areas.

A less familiar reading resource is the *programed text* or *self-instructional program*. These materials differ from the conventional textbook. The pupil is required to respond continually to questions concerning the material learned as he proceeds through the program. After each response is made, it is compared with the correct answer. Subject matter encountered later presumes mastery of previous material. Therefore, the child cannot continue properly unless he comprehends what he has read. Such mastery is not too difficult. Programs are typically presented in small steps learnable by most children for whom they are intended. When the program is used in a machine, there may be an automatic recording of errors. Errors may also be noted by requesting pupils to write their responses before comparing them with the correct answers.

A great many programs in elementary school science are becoming available.[3] While not all are verbal in nature, most can be used in somewhat the same manner as other supplementary reading matter. The primary advantages of programs are in the greater comprehension that may come about, and the self-pacing in speed of learning. There is little question that this form of instruction represents a promising step forward in providing for individual differences of learners.

NONREADING MATERIALS

We come now to the many nonreading materials broadly available in the classroom, often called *audio-visual aids*. These include still pictures, films and filmstrips, construc-

tions and models, microscopes and microprojectors, television and radio, and records or tapes. (Strictly speaking, even these materials may involve some reading—captions in films, descriptions of pictures, and the like.) As with books, a valid purpose should always precede their selection and use.

It is wise to vary the ways in which these materials are applied. For instance, using a film solely to begin science units or lesson series can eventually dampen pupil interest and enthusiasm. Such use unnecessarily restricts an instructional aid that is helpful in at least several other ways. Since there are excellent books[4] available devoted entirely to instructional materials, there is no need here to make a comprehensive analysis of these aids. However, a brief section about their specific applications in elementary science can result in more awareness of their possible contributions to teaching.

Pictorial materials. Let us begin with *pictures, filmstrips,* and *films.* Each of these familiar materials may be used in at least four general ways:

1. As a means of introducing or overviewing lessons and raising problems.
2. As an information source to help answer questions.
3. As a way to review or summarize what has been studied.
4. As a means of furnishing applications or additional examples of what has been studied.

Pictures or illustrations probably are the most common aids used in elementary science, perhaps because their sources are so accessible. Among the many magazines where useful illustrations may be found are *Life,*

---

[3] For further information, write to The Center for Programed Instruction, 365 West End Avenue, New York, New York 10024.

[4] For example, see: Walter A. Wittich and Charles F. Schuller, *Audio-Visual Materials: Their Nature and Use,* Third Edition, New York: Harper and Row, 1962; R. Murray Thomas and Sherwin G. Swarthout, *Integrated Teaching Materials,* Second Edition, New York: Longmans, Green and Co., Inc., 1963; James S. Kinder, *Audio-Visual Materials and Techniques,* Second Edition, New York: American Book Co., 1959.

National Geographic, Holiday, Look, and *Arizona Highways*. Books also may contain numerous, helpful photographs or drawings. Sometimes valuable pictures can be obtained from old or discarded books. District and local libraries frequently furnish collections of pictures to interested teachers. A large supply is also obtainable from free and inexpensive commercial sources. These will be listed later.

For most purposes the best kinds of illustrations are large and easily seen, with a single, central emphasis, and minimum of detail. This is especially important in the primary grades. An occasional difficulty with such pictures may be the absence of clues to indicate relative size, as with some animal pictures, for example. The *opaque projector* may be used to project and enlarge an image of a small picture, as well as any other illustrations that one may wish to trace with pen or crayon.

Pictures furnish an excellent means of introducing lessons and raising problems. There are also times when you may want to develop your own sketches. It is somewhat awkward and difficult to place children in a situation where they sense and define a problem by themselves without using language that gives it away. But when confronted with an illustration that contains a visual paradox or application, the job of describing what they see and defining the apparent problem is the children's own. Notice how the sketch on page 109 can help to introduce a problem.

All of us have had the experience of hearing someone describe a scene, person, or thing, and of then being surprised to see a picture of what was described. This is why pictures furnish an excellent way of clarifying ideas and procedures. Because one scene may contain a great deal of information, it can be used to advantage where there is need for review or summary of ideas.

The Part II unit on machines (page 243) contains numerous places where pictures may provide additional applications and illustrations of science principles. Notice especially the extending activities. When children find pictures of applications, this extends and broadens meaning.

After only a short time of collecting pictures or illustrations, the need for a handy way to file them becomes obvious. You can solve this problem by first mounting the pictures on tagboard or stiff-paper backing of uniform size, then filing the pictures upright in an orange crate or a cardboard box of the right dimensions. Almost any careful system of cataloguing should assist in retrieving desired illustrations. A system that seems to work well is to file illustrations first by units and then according to specific generalizations within units. Be sure to use cross-filing notations on any pictures that can be used with more than one topic.

Carefully chosen *filmstrips* have most of the advantages of pictures and can be used in as many different ways. A helpful feature of the filmstrip is its sequential ordering of frames. At the same time this is a potential inconvenience. When a process involving details needs to be shown—as with the steps to develop photographs, manufacture steel, propagate plants, and so on—a good filmstrip develops the several aspects involved in a logical, carefully ordered way. Static details are brought out clearly. The captions supplied with each frame help clarify the pictures. But in many cases there is little need to present all the frames of a filmstrip. The class may already be familiar with part of the process or some of the events. Part of the filmstrip may not apply to the specific idea being investigated.

A partial solution to the problem is to select and show just the specific sequence of frames needed. Since the frames are numbered, a rapid skimming through unneeded frames should lead to the section wanted. Yet sometimes this is not too useful, because the sequence itself may not be in the order desired. There may also be some pupil dissatisfaction with being "short changed"—children like to view all the frames. These are the reasons why some teachers prefer individual slides in place of filmstrips.

When *motion pictures* are well constructed and properly used, they make available in the classroom vicarious experiences that are other-

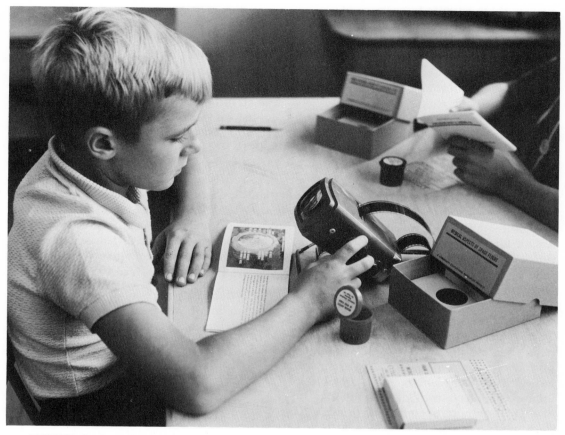

FIGURE 8 An individual filmstrip viewer may help provide for individual differences of children.

wise difficult, hazardous, or impossible to realize. Through the technique of animation, molecular theory is seen and understood better in dynamic form. Microphotography enables children to see cell division, rare and active microscopic life, and body defenses reacting to invading germs. Time-lapse sequences enable the movements of developing plants to be recorded. Slow motion permits the leisurely analysis of swift and complex movements. Photography also makes possible the repeatable, safe viewing of solar eclipses, volcanoes, and other natural events. These are just a few examples of techniques and applications available in educational films.

While they possess a variety of useful and entertaining characteristics, many films contain shortcomings of some concern. Perhaps the most noticeable defect of many motion pictures prepared specifically for elementary science is that they illustrate experiences children could engage in directly, rather than view on a screen. Besides, many films encompass far too broad a scope for the short time of presentation. This forces us to use films of this kind almost exclusively for introductions or superficial reviews.

Part of the difficulty lies in the economics involved. No commercial producer wants to prepare films for which there is only a very small and unprofitable market. But perhaps a more important reason is simply lack of insight into what this medium can contribute.

In recent years such educational organizations as the American Institute of Biological Sciences and Educational Services, Incorporated have developed or otherwise encouraged the making of "single-concept" films—motion pictures that concentrate on a specific point or principle. Also increasing in use are *film loops*—short, silent motion pictures sealed into plastic cartridges. The film cartridge is easily and quickly inserted into a simple projector without threading. The film runs continuously without end, since both ends are joined. The specific idea shown in the film can be viewed over and over as needed.

As more interest is expressed in films such as these, and market activity is stepped up, it seems likely that the present tendency for comprehensive or broad-scope films will be lessened.

Another difficulty with some elementary science films is the vocabulary of the accompanying vocal commentary. Some of this may come from choosing a film that is too advanced for the class involved. But even films that contain easy-to-learn concepts become hard to understand when adult terms are used. There is no reason why we must "utilize" instead of use water hoses, see a "holocaust" instead of a large fire, and view "extensive" rather than much damage. It is desirable to improve children's vocabularies. But the use of a large number of unfamiliar words in a short time can make an otherwise understandable film somewhat vague. It becomes hard to introduce important words to the children before showing the film. Instead of concentrating on just a few vital terms, we must decide and note what will cloud meaning in the entire commentary. Frequently, the list grows too long for effective presentation.

A subtler defect in too many motion pictures for elementary science is the authority-centered context in which the action takes place. Children are typically seen to seek adults to define their problems, provide materials, explain things, or otherwise provide counsel. Less frequently are children seen to think things through for themselves or to plan for ways of tracking down information. While the latter can be overdone, it is strange that educators have stressed for so long the need for children's growing independence in learning without this emphasis being reflected in our educational films.

Let us look now at some points in ordering and using films for teaching. "I ordered a film but it came too late." "The A-V department returned my order with a note saying the film was not available." These comments are heard all too frequently. What can we do when this happens?

In a large conference for instructional-materials specialists some years ago, there was an informal discussion of such comments. The twelve discussants involved represented different-sized districts in several parts of the United States. Each of these persons had obtained much experience with the problems of supplying materials. Each had made a careful study of the criticisms of teachers in his district. The consensus of these specialists, and our own observations, lead to these points:

1. Much of the time films or other aids that are late in arrival are not ordered with an eye on recommended time deadlines. Occasionally it is possible to fulfill the request in spite of this. At other times it is impossible.

2. Audio-visual aids are often not obtainable because nearly everyone teaches the same thing at the same time. The obvious remedy is to stagger unit times throughout the semester. This may have to be arranged in the school or on the district level.

3. Many teachers organize their lessons around topics and facts rather than generalizations. If a generalization involves animal homes or ways of caring for young, for instance, it may be possible to order alternate films or other aids. In these cases, it may make little difference if our first choice fails to arrive. On the other hand, if a specific subject is considered, such as frogs, beavers, or white mice, then only a film directed toward the exact animal will do.

Keeping these ideas in mind can help reduce the problems of ordering films or other instructional materials. Naturally, when too few materials or inefficient distribution systems exist, such inadequacies must be corrected at the source.

When possible, a film should be carefully previewed before it is shown. A previewing reveals how the film might be used. If the scope is broad and somewhat superficial, perhaps the best use is as an introduction or review. If some detail or depth is presented, the film may be useful for background or solution-centered information. It is worthwhile to reshow detailed treatments to the class, just as it is desirable to reread a text that develops much detail. A previewing also tends to disclose if the level of presentation is suitable for the class. Sometimes a film is unrealistically recommended for six or more grade levels in the accompanying producer's guide or descriptive brochure.

During the previewing it is worthwhile to make a brief outline of the film, and note significant or important scenes and details. If there are other useful ideas or processes given besides those that originally prompted placing the order, it may be desirable to bring these out with the pupils before the film is shown. Difficult vocabulary, obscure sequences, and unusual photographic techniques may need to be explained to the class. An accompanying producer's guide can be helpful in providing information about all the points mentioned here.

Just before the film is viewed by the children, be sure to clearly state the purpose for its presentation. You may also wish to give a brief outline of its content. In addition, it is important to write some of the more difficult terms on the chalkboard and to use them in several understandable contexts.

Sometimes it is desirable to leave off the sound while viewing a film. This might be done in a review lesson, with children supplying the commentary. Or the children might be asked during viewing what they see to discover their present level of knowledge. When the commentary contains many difficult terms, you may wish to turn off the sound and substitute your own commentary.

A final comment on films. It is easy to cut down the effectiveness of a good film through overanalysis of a few ideas or exposure of too many ideas at one time. If a great deal of material is presented perhaps it would be wise to show only part of the film, or to reshow

the film on a later occasion. Covering too much material at one time may result in less learning than if only a few important points are taken up. This comment is especially pertinent for younger children.

Microscopes and microprojectors. When we need to work with real objects or specimens that are too small to observe in detail, the microscope is an asset. It used to be difficult to find a microscope in elementary schools. The situation now is often very different. Although some elementary schools still lack this aid, others may have several microscopes for each classroom above the primary-grade level. In addition, some children have microscopes at home which occasionally are brought to school.

Children typically desire to see the highest possible magnification of a specimen. The result is usually unsatisfactory. It may be difficult to focus the instrument properly. The field of observation may be too narrow to locate the desired area on the specimen; any minor movement or shifting of the slide is greatly exaggerated when viewed through an eyepiece. Moreover, it is possible that children will not understand what they are observing. For these reasons, well-built microscopes of lower power—and somewhat lower cost—are satisfactory for elementary schools.

A useful instrument for children is the "wide-field" type. In this case a magnified view of a whole insect or other small object is possible. Necessity for focusing and slide-making is held to a minimum. In a primary grade, it may be best to avoid entirely the use of microscopes. A dozen or more good quality hand lenses can be purchased at the same price. The portability of hand lenses, their greater total use, and relative unimportance of high magnification at this level, commonly indicate this choice.

Since we can seldom be sure of what children are viewing, and since it is likely that only one or a few microscopes can be available for use at one time, many teachers prefer the *microprojector*. With this instrument it is possible to project an enlarged image of the

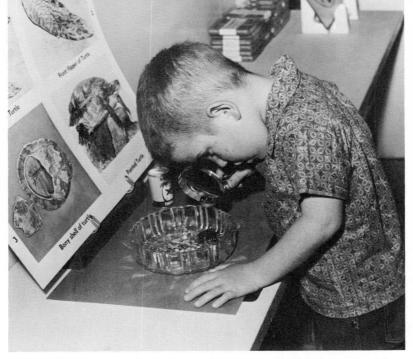

FIGURE 9 There are times when nothing is more useful than a hand lens.

specimen onto a screen, much in the manner of other visual projectors. It is convenient when instructing a whole class because everyone can view together what is taking place. When both kinds of instruments are available, some teachers find microscopes convenient for individual viewing or projects.

"We know that microscopes and microprojectors are useful in secondary-school activities, but are they really of any importance in elementary-school science?" This question is asked frequently in both preservice and inservice science education classes. Perhaps the best way of finding out is to investigate some sample uses of these aids in modern textbooks. A superficial examination of almost any text series might reveal such opportunities as these for viewing on a microscopic level:

Compound eyes of the housefly, various insect eyes. Fiber structure of wool, cotton, and other materials. Penetration of inks and dyes into several materials. Newly laid insect, frog, and snail eggs. Anatomy of the mosquito and bee. Pores and creases in human skin. Composition of human hair, several kinds of body cells, blood cells. Crystals of salt, sugar, other common substances. Algae, fresh-water protozoa. Effects of disinfectants on protozoa.

Composition of mold growth, bacterial colonies. Parts of a flower, leaf, seed. Onion, root, stem, leaf cells. Root hairs, capillary action with colored water. Circulation of blood in the tail of a goldfish. Heartbeat of a water flea. Mouthparts of harmful insects. Fiber structures of various kinds of paper.

Additional activities described in detail, with numerous suggestions for making or purchasing slides, may be found in the following publications:

The Microprojector and World of Microbes, Norfolk County Public Schools, Norfolk, Virginia.

Working with Animals, by J. Myron Atkin and R. Will Burnett. New York: Holt, Rinehart and Winston, Inc., 1959.

Working with Plants, by J. Myron Atkin and R. Will Burnett. New York: Holt, Rinehart and Winston, Inc., 1959.

Microscope Instruction Manual, Testa Manufacturing Co., 10126 East Rush Street, El Monte, California.

Elementary Explanation of Microscopic Slides and Classroom Experiments, Ken-A-Vision Manufacturing Co., Inc., Raytown, Missouri.

Teacher's Manual for the Bioscope, Model 60, Bioscope Manufacturing Co., Box 1492, Tulsa, Oklahoma.

Television and radio. One reason why the scientific literacy of children is increasing is found in the numerous television and radio programs devoted to science topics. Almost any weekly schedule of programs for the general public contains several or more titles of interest. Encourage your pupils to view or listen to a regularly scheduled series and then discuss or demonstrate ideas learned with other class members. Notify them in advance when a particularly pertinent telecast or broadcast will take place. Encourage pupils to be on the lookout themselves for notices of future programs of unusual value.

Special educational programs for school systems or regions, notably in television, are increasing in number. Often these programs are important parts of large-scale experiments to determine the usefulness of television instruction. Some large school systems—New York City is a typical example—have found that television is a useful medium for inservice instruction of teachers in elementary science, as well as in other aspects of the curriculum. Some school districts have regularly scheduled televised programs for science instruction of children. The classroom teacher acts as a resource person, discussion leader, or in some other related capacity, after the telecast has been completed.

Many programs our oustanding. Eminent scientists may appear and speak or demonstrate. Excellent demonstrations are conducted. Clearly illustrated instructional aids are shown, usually in a well-organized context and interesting format. However, it is probably too soon to judge in an overall sense how effectively television can be used for elementary science instruction.

Certain problems have already been identi-

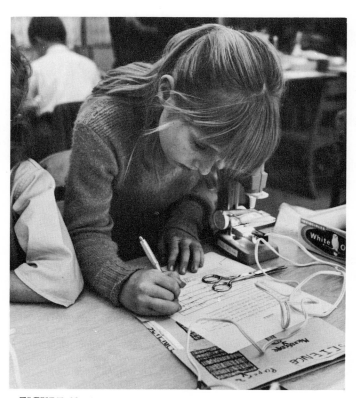

FIGURE 10 Microscopes are best used for individual projects.

fied which should be considered when plans are made for such instruction. A common problem is the overly ambitious attempt to cover too many grade levels at one time. Some children inevitably are bored. Others may struggle with ideas for which they are not ready. Another drawback is the customary discontinuity of the presentations. Numerous, unrelated topics are less useful to an individual teacher than a more sustained approach. Perhaps the most important objections are the lack of feedback from pupils to the television teacher, and the all-too-frequent passive role of children in the lesson. Of course, letters can be written to the studio teacher. This is some help. And activities can be planned *after* a televised lesson. But frequently these methods are less desirable than working directly with the class. Specialists in television instruction are well aware of the difficulties which attend this form of teaching. Expect this important medium to be more effective as measures are taken to cope with such problems.

Recordings. Although usually given more limited use than some of the materials mentioned above, recordings, especially tape recordings, can be employed in at least several functional ways. Excellent radio programs broadcast after school hours can be recorded and played back at more convenient times. Interviews with science authorities, or sounds heard during a field trip, can also be recorded.

If a "listening post" or multiple plug-in device is attached to the recorder, and several sets of earphones are available, it is possible to provide assistance to either fast or slow learners without disturbing the rest of the class. It is much easier to prepare a simplified version of a difficult passage from a book through reading it aloud in a simplified way and taping it, than it is to rewrite it. It is likewise possible to tape more difficult material for children whose reading vocabularies have not yet caught up with their ability to think. Doing these things frees you for other possibilities. Also, evaluation sessions with children are helped by analysis of their taped oral discussions or reports that may accompany science activities.

Constructions and models. A great deal of time is given in some classrooms for constructing apparatus and making models. When attention is focused on the intellectual part of the activities—in learning the ideas involved—such experiences are usually worthwhile. But unless the construction involves some useful science knowledge, the time taken may merely result in less opportunity for thoughtful learning.

How much time should be spent in model making and other constructions? There are few definite answers, but perhaps the following observations may furnish some guidance in thinking of desirable practices. The best kinds of constructions are *functional*; that is, they work by teaching an idea, a process, or helping to gather data. Such working constructions as telegraphs, weather instruments, electric circuit boards, and so forth, usually involve thoughtful planning on the part of the class. Less useful are constructions that might be called *props*—materials that are more decorative and atmosphere-lending than functional: a "spaceship" made out of cardboard, a paper "glacier," a chicken wire and papier-mâché "dinosaur," etc. This is not to say that such materials are useless. They often have a worthwhile purpose in dramatic play, or art-centered activities, for example. But time for science should not be largely used up in this way.

Perhaps in the past we have tended to overstress the possibilities for home and improvised materials. When constructions are too intricate for pupils or too time-consuming to assemble, try to get commercial items. There are many true-to-life scale models and other constructions available through local hobby shops and supply houses. These may bring about more actual understanding and interest than inadequate constructions developed during the neglect of more important learning activities.

Free and inexpensive materials. You can borrow or permanently acquire a host of instructional aids from commercial and institutional sources through request only, or at nominal cost. Films, filmstrips, charts, pictures, booklets, samples of raw or processed materials, models, posters, recordings—all these and more are available. But before making requests for their acquisition, check the policy of your school district with regard to such materials. Many commercial, institutional, and other donors in the past have used free and inexpensive materials as an advertising or propaganda medium. Educators have been forced to develop restrictions regarding their use. However, in recent years the supply of obviously objectional materials has decreased significantly.

Distributors of free and inexpensive materials usually have a large inventory of items available, so be very specific when requesting things. If a stock number appears in the catalogue consulted, be sure to include it in your request along with a specific description of

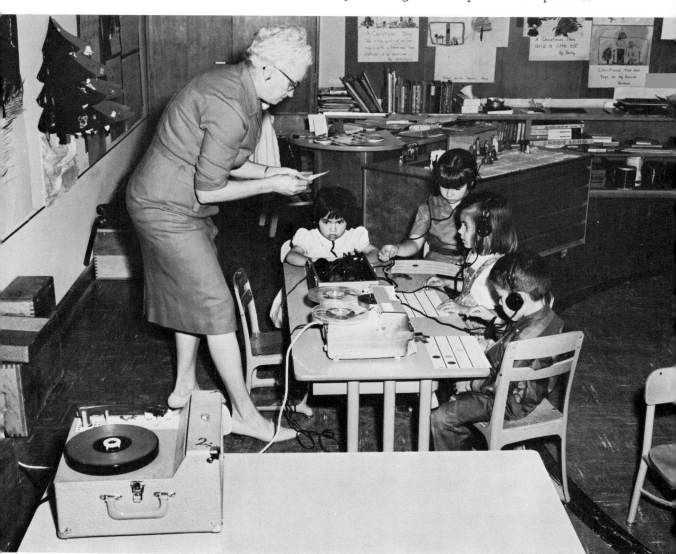

FIGURE 11 A listening post provides for individual differences while freeing the teacher for other possibilities.

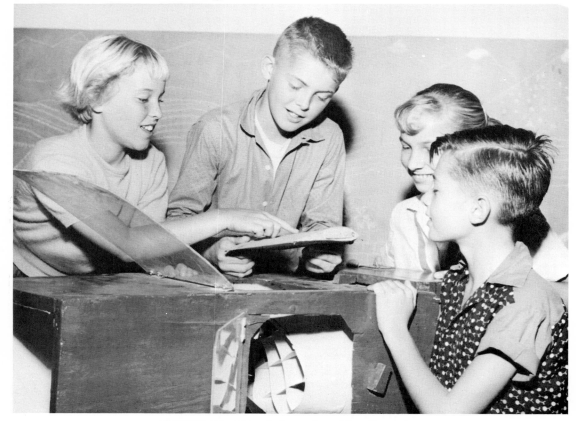

FIGURE 12   This wind-tunnel model really works.

what you want. As there are usually many requests for material, allow at least four to six weeks for its receipt. Processing takes time, and requests of this type typically are given low priority. Most free and inexpensive materials are two-dimensional. When received, they can be stored in the same manner previously recommended for pictorial materials.

The supply of donated and low-cost materials is notoriously unreliable. It is wise to use current and reliable listings in making requests. The following compilations of sources are revised each year. Efforts are made to edit out those sources that either have misrepresented their materials or have otherwise proved unsatisfactory:

Educators Guide to Free Science Materials
Educators Guide to Curriculum Materials
Educators Guide to Tapes, Scripts and Transcriptions

Educators Guide to Films
Educators Guide to Filmstrips

All of the *Educators Guides* are available from Educators Progress Service, Randolph, Wisconsin 53956.

CLASSROOM FACILITIES

No one in an elementary school needs a shiny laboratory to have interesting and worthwhile activities take place. But science teaching is greatly facilitated by a few conveniences or special arrangements easily provided in most self-contained classrooms. At least one electric outlet is desirable, so that a hot plate or other electrical device can be plugged in. However, it may be possible to substitute a propane tank burner, an alcohol lamp, or "solid alcohol" (Sterno) as a source of heat. A sink with running water is also handy in many experiments and demonstrations. Yet it is possible to get by with a bucket and pan. If you have constructions in mind, several hand tools and materials are indispensable—hammer, saw, pliers, screwdriver, lumber scraps, nails, and so on. A few of these items may be borrowed occasionally for brief periods from children's homes.

Seating arrangements. "My children complain that they can't see when we do experiments in front of the room." "What do you do when attention seems to drift away after the first few minutes in a demonstration?" Teacher remarks of this type usually indicate the need for a more satisfactory furniture or seating arrangement.

A sturdy table and movable chairs are helpful when planning for demonstrations or experiments for an entire class, notably with smaller children. If there is a reading "circle," the same chairs can be arranged into a U-shaped pattern or semicircle around the table. Girls sit on the chairs. Boys sit on the floor, Indian-fashion, one in front of each chair. Everyone is close to the table. No one's view is obstructed. There is ready access to the table as individual children are called upon to participate. With some reminding, participating pupils will remember to stand *in back of* the table, so that everyone can see what is happening. An arrangement of this kind is especially needed with younger children. It is easy for them to lose interest or become distracted when seated some distance away from the activity source. A nearby chart holder or chalkboard in back of the table can serve for any needed recording.

When enough materials are available for everyone to participate at the same time, the semicircular pattern is convenient in several other ways. You can set standards with pupils for small-group activities, and assign areas of the room for working. After the several groups or committees have completed their work, having them reassemble into the initial seating pattern makes for easier reporting or discussion.

With older children there is less need for this type of seating arrangement. Short attention spans and distractions are less of a problem. An initial, functional grouping of desks and chairs may serve for most occasions. But the materials table should be reasonably close to all the children when experiments and demonstrations are done before the entire class. There is usually no difficulty with class control when everyone can see what is happening. In cases where class desks are permanently fixed to the floor, it is desirable to use a higher-than-usual table for adequate viewing. It may be necessary sometimes to let some children change seats or move to a more satisfactory location.

A science area. The self-contained classroom in elementary schools often contains several *center-of-interest areas.* These are places in the room where several pupils at one time may go to work independently on art, language, science, or other activities. A desirable science center may contain a work bench, a display table for specimens, several collections, a microscope or several hand lenses, an aquarium, one or more small animal cages, and a collection of science books. An attractive bulletin board nearby may be set up to provide additional interest, or for use in a unit under study. In the science center a child can observe more closely the results of an experiment performed before the whole class. He can repeat a demonstration if materials are provided. He can work on unfinished projects, or look up information on a special science interest. Here, he may also wish to display his favorite collection of rocks, or proudly exhibit his latest lizard.

A worthwhile science center takes some care. Materials should be changed reasonably often. When it lapses into an isolated table for display of a few uninteresting and dust-covered objects, opportunities for worthwhile learnings may disappear entirely.

Setting up an aquarium.[5] An *aquarium* is an excellent source for observing firsthand ex-

[5] For a free set of detailed leaflets on keeping animals and plants in the classroom, see page 388.

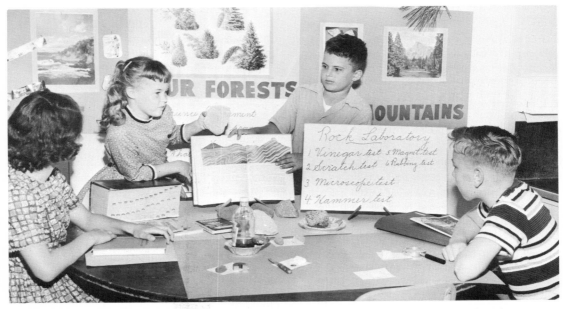

FIGURE 13 This science area encourages pupils to perform many individual, open-end explorations.

amples of important biological principles. In this watery community, plants and animals adapt to their environment, and reproduction takes place in several ways. It is likewise possible to see a balance of nature through interdependence, and the consequences when there is an imbalance.

The basic materials needed are a tank, some sand (not the seashore variety), a few aquatic snails and plants, and several small fish. A rectangular tank of at least 5- or 6-gallon capacity serves best for a classroom aquarium. The rectangular shape has less distortion in viewing than a bowl. It also permits more oxygen from the air to dissolve in the water, because of the relatively greater surface area exposed at the top. Although it is possible to construct a tank with properly-cut glass, tape, and cement, the very high probability of leakage makes this venture impractical for most beginners.

The tank must be clean. Dirt, grease, or caked lime can be removed by scrubbing thoroughly with salt and water. The salt is abrasive enough to have a scouring effect. Should detergent or soaps be needed, repeated rinsing of the tank is essential. Any

residue may be harmful to future inhabitants. About two inches of clean sand may then be placed and spread evenly on the bottom of the tank.

A pet store can supply several varieties of inexpensive plants, any of which will serve well. *Sagittaria* and *vallisneria* will produce more oxygen than others, and are rooted plants. Anchor the plants firmly in the sand. If needed, several clean stones can supply support. Placing the plants toward the back of the tank will permit easier viewing of the fish.

Put a large piece of paper or cardboard over the plants before pouring or siphoning water into the tank. This prevents the plants from becoming dislodged and helps to keep the sand in place. The paper should be removed immediately thereafter. Should tap water be used, it must stand for at least 48 hours to permit the chlorine to escape and the water to acquire room temperature. The water level should be about an inch lower than the tank top. Moving the tank after it is filled may warp the tank seams and start a leak.

Goldfish and guppies are among the best fish to use, as they can withstand a broad temperature change. Small catfish, sunfish, and perch are also easy to keep and interesting to observe. If several water snails are purchased at the pet store along with the plants and fish, they will provide added interest and value. Snails keep the aquarium clean by scavenging refuse and by eating the green slime (algae) that may form on the glass. Only a few are needed, as they multiply rapidly. Children delight in examining snails' eggs, laid on the glass sides, and in seeing the snails scrape off and eat the algae. A few hand lenses placed around the aquarium make the viewing easier.

A properly balanced aquarium needs little attention. Plants give off oxygen needed by the animals, and the animals provide carbon dioxide needed by the plants to photosynthesize. What if there is an imbalance? Here we can look for clues that may indicate improper light, temperature, oxygen, feeding, or cleanliness.

If algae grow rapidly on the sides, there is too much light. A northeast corner location or other place of good but indirect light should work best. Adding more snails and wrapping black paper around the tank for a while can retard growth of algae. However, it may also be necessary to clean the tank. While algae will not hurt the fish, visibility is hampered.

If the temperature is too low reproduction will slow down noticeably, or stop. Some fish may die. When most kinds of tropical fish are used, a heater is a necessity. This can be in the form of a light bulb placed in the cover of the tank.

Insufficient oxygen is indicated when fish stay very close to the surface of the water. This is where the greatest amount of oxygen dissolved directly from the air is located. Occasionally, some fish might be seen to break the surface and gulp air directly. Overcrowding can cause this condition. About an inch of goldfish per gallon is proper. If guppies are used, about six per gallon are satisfactory. Having too many snails will also contribute to an oxygen-poor condition. Planting more *sagittaria* and *vallisneria* might result in enough extra production of oxygen to take care of this condition. A motor-driven aerator, purchasable at pet stores, is another way to increase the oxygen supply.

A dirty tank can result from excessive waste material and overfeeding the fish. Bacterial action on uneaten food poisons the water and contributes to the growth of other microorganisms. A few more snails are then needed for scavenging. A small sprinkling of packaged fish food once a day—enough to be completely eaten in about five minutes—is sufficient for feeding. Tiny bits of chopped beef and earthworm can also be used. No provision need be taken for weekends, but some means for feeding during vacations is necessary.

In spite of reasonable care, it may be necessary to clean the tank more frequently than is convenient unless the aquarium has an automatic water filter. This consists of a combination charcoal and spun-glass filter through which water is pumped by a small electric motor. Purchasable for about five dollars and up at pet stores, an automatic filter can reduce cleaning periods to once a year. A filterless aquarium needs to be cleaned once a month or oftener. Although the filter needs to be washed occasionally, this is a simple and quickly performed task. A filter also takes the place of an aerator, should one be needed.

A glass top or piece of Saran-Wrap may be used to cover the aquarium. This helps to maintain clean water and cuts down on loss of water through evaporation. It also serves to illustrate condensation and precipitation, since water droplets form on the bottom surface and fall back into the tank.

Setting up a terrarium. A terrarium is a container in which a miniature land environment may be set up to feature several small plants and animals. Almost any large glass receptacle will do for the basic structure—a large pickle jar turned on its side, a leaky aquarium tank, or other sizable glass container. After the tank or jar has been cleaned, about an inch of small pebbles and bits of charcoal may be placed on the bottom. The pebbles provide drainage, and the charcoal helps to prevent the soil from turning sour. Equal parts of peat moss, soil, and sand mixed together with a little additional charcoal should be spread evenly over the base to a height of roughly 3 inches. Dwarf ivy, ferns, liverworts, and lichens are ideal plants. Partridge berry and mosses provide satisfactory ground cover, if desired.

A small, shallow dish pressed partly into the soil can serve as a source of water for the animals. Although the ground should be sprinkled until moist, it must not be left wet as molds and fungi may develop. In about a week, the plants should take hold and the animals can be introduced. A land snail, earthworm, small land turtle, salamander, or small frog are quite suitable for this kind of environment. A little lettuce will feed the snail and turtles; earthworms receive nutrition from the soil. Satisfactory food for frogs and salamanders include small live insects, such as flies, sow bugs, ants, and the like.

A glass sheet placed over the top of the terrarium, loosely fitted to permit air circulation, will help keep the humidity high and reduce the need to water the soil. Water will evaporate from the soil, condense on the underside of the glass cover, and fall as "rain," in a miniature water cycle.

SCHOOL AND COMMUNITY RESOURCES

It is possible for us to get so engrossed in acquiring books, films, and other materials for classroom use that we forget there is an out-of-class environment for science exploration. The school building itself is a good place to start. Why are there cracks in the masonry and plaster? How do the fire extinguishers work? Why are the stairs worn in the middle and not at the sides? What's causing some of the paint outside to peel? How is the school heated? How many simple machines does the custodian use?

Things are happening on the schoolgrounds, too: Why are they planting ground cover on the hill? Why is the hot asphalt on the playground "steaming" after the cloudburst? How does the seesaw work? What are the names of the birds around the schoolyard, and where do they nest? Why are the shrubs planted on the north side growing more slowly than those on the south side? Why is snow still on the roof of the main building when it has melted on the other roofs? Why are shadows longer in the afternoon?

The surrounding community may contain many places to visit for direct observations: a zoo, wooded area, garden, nursery and greenhouse, pond or brook, pet store, bird refuge, observatory, natural history museum, road cut, stone quarry, "vacant" lot, construction site, waterworks, sewage-treatment plant, dairy, airport, and weather bureau. All these and more are rewarding places for elementary-school pupils to visit. Specific suggestions for study trips to some of these locations are made in several units of Part II.

Before a study trip is taken, some preparation is needed to help make it worthwhile. A school district catalogue may be available of suggested places to visit in the community. This can assist in giving most of the necessary details for educational trips. In general, however, you will want to keep the following points in mind:

1. Be clear about the purpose for leaving the classroom. A common reason is to stimulate interest and problems at the beginning of a unit. Sometimes a study trip is helpful to give additional topical information or to see applications of generalizations.

2. Check with the principal for school policies. Chances are several procedures will need to be followed—notification and permission of parents, a phone call to the site-of-visit, transportation request made, and so forth.

3. Visit the site yourself, if possible. It is much easier to make plans when you actually know what conditions are like.

4. Plan with the children what to look for. A list of questions or purposes may be needed, and some background, to enable them to observe intelligently.

5. Develop with the class some behavior and safety standards to be remembered. A "buddy" system can be used—each child helps keep track of another. Less reliable children can be placed at the head of the line. Several parents or monitors at the end of the line can prevent straggling.

6. At the site, make sure everyone can see and hear adequately, and can ask questions if desired. If the class is large it may be necessary to divide it into smaller groups.

7. After returning to the classroom, help pupils evaluate the trip. Did they achieve their purposes? Were safety and behavior standards observed?

When it is impossible to arrange visits away from the school, resource persons from the community may be able to visit the classroom.

Numerous districts compile lists of informed persons who are willing to donate some of their time and talent for the education of children. As with study trips, maximum benefits from a classroom visit are likelier to happen if there has been some preplanning.

The class should decide what questions it wants to ask the visitor. The person's name and some background—occupation, qualifications, experience, and such other relevant information—are useful to the children. In some classes it may be worthwhile to have a brief rehearsal of how the class will participate before the guest arrives, just to make sure that things will go according to plan.

Inform your guest beforehand of the grade level, interests, and general characteristics of the children. Provide him with a list of questions the class wants to ask. These prepara-

FIGURE 14 **A study trip to the seashore provides many interesting specimens for examination.**

tions will insure a more effective experience. If the speaker can respond informally to questions rather than give a formal speech, the chances are better for a more understandable and pertinent lesson. Should your guest have a tendency to drift from the subject or use difficult vocabulary, you may want to ask tactful, clarifying questions as needed. Above all, make sure the length of time for the presentation is well understood in advance. Most primary children grow restless after a half-hour. The maximum length of time for older pupils is usually about an hour.

Marshaling community resources. Many communities, especially the larger ones, have an enormous wealth of scientific and other resources potentially available for instruction. But identification and organization of such resources are needed before they can be used. Typically, some of this is done in school district study trip guides and the like, but seldom is full value obtained from what is there.

A shining example of what can be done to marshal local resources for school use is found in the Community Educational Resources Project of the San Diego County (California) Department of Education. In 1960, several task groups were formed of volunteers from local industrial, technological, scientific, educational, and military complexes. These persons thoroughly surveyed the Greater San Diego area for possible educational resources in their respective fields. The search turned up a gold mine of potential materials—films, charts, maps, models, photographs, sites for study trips, and more.

Since the project's beginning, hundreds of instructional materials have been rapidly and expertly processed from primary resources in such areas as oceanography, space exploration, nuclear energy, botany, marine geology, zoology, and mathematics. These materials often contain the latest contributions of persons on the cutting edge of scientific research and technological innovation. This has drastically reduced in many instances the lengthy time lag which normally occurs between actual discovery and classroom study of the discovered.

Perhaps in the future we shall see regional or even nation-wide networks composed of similar educational resource groups, each sharing the unique features of its community resources with communities elsewhere.

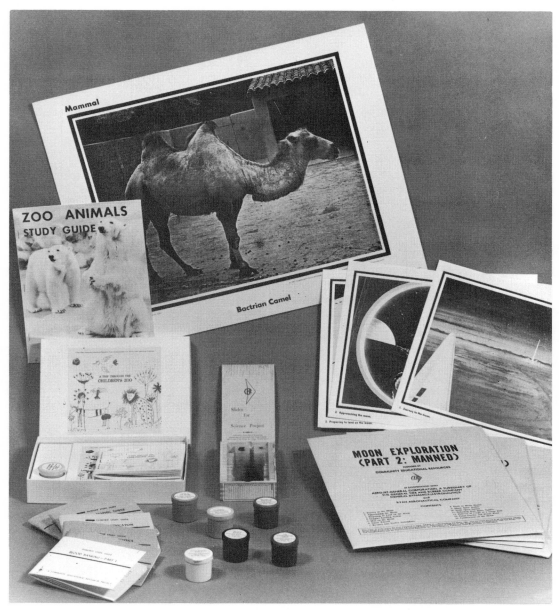

FIGURE 15 Some materials developed from local resources by the Community Educational Resources Section, Department of Education, San Diego County, California.

CHAPTER 6

Planning for Teaching

In every school there are some teachers who are more effective than others in teaching science. If we try to find a specific reason for their effectiveness it is often hard to pin down. There are so many differences in their teaching behavior. But at least one of their general characteristics stands out clearly: they are likely to be well organized. You will want to know some of the ways that successful teachers use to plan learning experiences for children.

THE THREE BASES OF PLANNING

Three questions reveal the gist of planning: *What* do we teach? *How* do we teach it? *How well* are we teaching it? This is what we have been discussing in the first five chapters. We shall now apply in one place many of the preceding ideas.

The "what" of planning. The *what* consists of process and product objectives. You remember that the many ways of investigating can be categorized conveniently into six broad processes: (1) identifying and defining problems, (2) suggesting or screening hypotheses, (3) selecting valid procedures, (4) interpreting information and drawing conclusions, (5) evaluating critically, and (6) reasoning quantitatively. Each of these classifications can help to recall some subskills which can be used as specific referents to guide teaching.

(For a review of some thirty subskills, see page 49.)

Do these specific referents need to be written down each time we make plans? Only if we are vague as to what they are. At first, it is probably a good idea when planning to jot down several which seem hard to remember. Later there will be no need. They become a permanent part of our teaching behavior when used often enough. As for the broad categories, these are potentially part of most lessons we teach, not just in science, but in social studies and some other areas as well. Having different process objectives for every subject area is confusing to both teaching and learning.

Product objectives should also be small in number. Six subject-matter generalizations or so are adequate for most units. Most textbook chapters feature no more, and many have fewer. These specific generalizations usually change from one topic to the next. But *the four behavioral referents we use to evaluate a child's knowledge of generalizations stay the same, just as referents for process behaviors stay the same.*

For example, we have said there is reasonable assurance a child knows a generalization when he (1) gives specific examples of applications, (2) restates the generalization in his own words, (3) supplies the cause of a given application, and (4) predicts what will happen and tells why. This kind of mastery, then, is the classroom goal. *These behavioral refer-*

ents can be used with any properly stated generalization, and in any subject.

In Chapter 4 we also supplied referents for concepts and facts. But, as explained there, in many cases you may not want to use these directly, since the generalization referents usually include the correct use of concepts and facts. As with process behaviors, there is no need to always put in writing the broad or specific knowledge behaviors we wish to bring about unless we are vague about what they are. With continual application, they become a permanent part of your teaching behavior.

The foregoing ideas emphasize the pervasive nature of both process and product objectives, when they are well-constructed. So, *the only objectives that typically need to be written down in planning are the specific generalizations that point toward the subject matter of the lessons to be taught.*

Do we need to think of specific behavioral objectives in process and product for each child? Some educators would firmly—and unrealistically, perhaps—say "yes!" What are the implications of such a view? An important process referent when a child selects procedures in an experiment is his ability to identify the need for controls. But how many controls? How subtle should they be? How difficult is the experiment? What are the limitations imposed by the materials involved?

An important product referent with generalizations, as we have seen, is the child's power to state specific examples of applications. But how many applications? How subtle should they be?

It is physically impossible in classroom teaching to develop specific behavioral goals for each child. There are too many individual differences, too many children, too many subjects. "Granted," some teachers say, "but shouldn't we at least state the minimal behaviors we expect to develop?" Ironically, this can become a way of ignoring individual differences. *The best teaching rapidly and continually widens individual differences.* In fact, it is one of the best indications we have of determining how successful we are in meeting the needs of our pupils. Goals in teaching

should be clearly stated. The best way to make them clear is to state them as observable behaviors. However, statements of these behaviors must be *open-ended*, because we can never be sure how far children can go. We can and should develop *general* expectancies for individual children and help them grow toward increased performance through the referents. To go much beyond this is not only impractical but also undesirable.

Another way of saying this is: The specificity with which we state behavioral objectives can reach a point of diminishing returns. Some specificity is needed for clearness. Yet to go too far gets us tangled in a web of unmanageable details, and may set unnecessary limits on children's performance. We need referents to make *judgments* about our teaching and the children's learning. This we cannot avoid any more than the courts can rigidly state once and for all what is "due process," or "a clear and present danger."

Perhaps needless to say, the foregoing statements are directed toward conventional teaching with a group of thirty or more pupils. This contrasts with programed instruction directed toward individual learners in a tightly controlled learning sequence.

The "how" of planning. Basically, our task in planning *how* to teach science is to expose children to activities where they can gradually learn generalizations in an understandable, process-rich context. This develops both kinds of objectives. When generalizations are not so broad as to be vague, and not so specific as to be minor details, a great many teaching-learning activities become available. (How to quickly locate these activities we shall consider shortly.)

Emphasis on *activities* as the data source, rather than the teacher, has advantages. Data are likelier to be complete and accurate. The children have chances to develop their own abilities to locate and interpret data. There is no need to attempt the impossible task of becoming an "expert" in every area of the curriculum. This is not to slight the great importance of being a well-informed person, but rather to stress the importance of wisely using the many resources at hand.

The more activities we can find to choose from the better, but they should be relevant to the generalizations. A common fault of learning activities found in many curriculum guides is that they pertain only loosely to the generalizations involved. Note the variety of learning experiences we can employ:

experiments	discussions
demonstrations	lectures
reading	interviews
audio-visual materials	reports
study trips	observations
constructions	written work
collections	art work
exhibits	

Having a variety of experiences gives the children opportunities to explore from many perspectives facts and ideas leading to generalizations. In addition, it gives us the chance to suggest assignments of varying difficulty to accommodate individual differences.

A valid purpose should precede each activity, otherwise the likelihood of aimless busy-work increases. Sometimes purposes are background-centered. Our role here is to make available books or other materials that can directly give the class awareness of facts and ideas. We may also want to explain directly some ideas or teach some skills. Sometimes purposes are solution-centered. In these cases, we are more inclined to guide children's discovery of ideas, which involves a greater degree of process methods than before. In other words, activities are arranged to provide input and opportunity to work in a problem-solving way.

The "how" of teaching process and product requires more on our part than just collecting a group of activities that correspond to generalizations and then turning the children loose. We need to select and arrange available activities in a teaching order that yields the most learning for the time and energy expended. Ordinarily, learning increases when the sequence goes from the simple to the complex, the familiar to the

unfamiliar, the present to the past, the more interesting to the less interesting, and the specific to the general. Occasionally, these and other criteria mentioned conflict. The unfamiliar may be more interesting than the familiar, the general more teachable than the specific. These are the times for us to exercise judgment about what should come first.

The "how well" in planning. Evaluation is probably the most neglected of the three bases of planning. But it need not be. Once we have some behavioral referents in mind, pupil involvement in activities and discussions provides much feedback for corrective action. The work the children do, the things they say, how they respond to our questions—all take on significance. Much of the time referents are mental criteria by which we observe and judge progress. But we have also seen how they can be built into tests. The "how well" aspect is largely an internal part of planning what to teach and how to teach it. If we have done a thorough job with the first two aspects, the last is greatly facilitated. Evaluation, then, is a process that begins with the first lesson, rather than a single paper-and-pencil test given when our teaching ends.

RESOURCE AND TEACHING UNITS

One of the best means of turning our three bases of planning into a teachable and interesting framework is the *unit of work*. We have already said that a unit "is a sequence of related ideas and activities organized around a theme or topic." Units found in curriculum guides supplied by school districts are likely to be *resource units*. That is, each of these contains many more suggestions for study than is possible with any one class. The idea is to select from the resource unit only those objectives and activities that seem best to fit the needs of a specific class within the time available for study. When organized into a teachable sequence of learning experiences, the resource unit becomes a *teaching unit.* A well-done resource unit has sections that contain suggestions for nearly everything needed in teaching, from start to finish:

Objectives
Initiation suggestions
Learning activities
Local references and resources
Evaluation suggestions
Culminating activities

Let us briefly examine each of these.

1. *Objectives.* Long lists of such mind-numbing statements as "To learn the nature of the skies" thankfully are disappearing. There is a trend toward a small number of objectives, clearly written in terms of intended behaviors (but open-ended) toward which to teach. These reflect both process and product goals. Generalizations are listed for product goals, and reflect the more important ideas of the topic, instead of facts or minor ideas.

2. *Initiation suggestions.* Ways for initiating study of the unit may involve one activity or a combination of activities. For example, the room environment may be arranged to include a stimulating bulletin board with accompanying materials on a nearby table; pictures, various trade books, and other printed materials may be spread out on the library table; a film may be shown with the sound turned off, while the teacher asks the children questions about what they see, and so forth.

These activities tend to differ from the usual in that they encompass a broader scope of study and are designed to raise more questions than they answer. Thus, in addition to getting the unit started, the initiation serves several other functions. It helps to arouse interest. It gives the teacher some opportunity to learn what the group already knows, and what it wants to know. It provides the class with at least a partial overview of what it will be studying.

Sensible though it may seem, whether a specific initiation phase is *always* the best means to exercise these functions is an arguable point with experienced teachers. There-fore, we shall consider initiations again later in this chapter.

3. *Learning activities.* The best units contain a large number of varied activities. As previously mentioned, this helps teachers to cope with individual differences among pupils. Local environment and facilities are emphasized when applicable. The surrounding terrain, nearby museum of natural history, and district-sponsored study trips give an immediacy and vitality to learnings that are difficult to achieve in other ways. Activities in such units are usually placed under or next to pertinent generalizations. Often there are accompanying questions or problems that can provide purposes for the activities. Unfortunately, when such questions do appear, they are seldom more than restatements of generalizations or facts, and are mostly background-centered.

4. *Local references and resources.* Local materials and resources not already included under specific activities are placed in a special section for convenient reference. All the instructional materials available in the district which pertain to the unit may be found listed here: trade books, grouped according to difficulty levels; teacher references; audio-visual aids; free and inexpensive materials; special equipment, and so on. Although the same information might be scattered among a half-dozen or so catalogues, curriculum specialists find that placing it in the unit itself insures greater use of available resources.

5. *Evaluation suggestions.* Sometimes tests are provided, in addition to suggestions for teacher observation of significant behaviors. As with activities, the teacher is selective. Items are chosen which closely correspond to what is done in the teaching unit itself. Other aids might include pupil work standards which can be developed with the class, self-rating checklists for pupils, and other evaluation ideas.

6. *Culminating activities.* To reinforce learning, it is desirable to summarize and review important parts of the unit. Culminating experiences are primarily designed to bring this about at the unit's close. Typical activ-

ities suggested may be a "quiz" on the ideas studied, a small science fair that features constructions made during the unit, pupil reports, or a large mural which reflects important ideas studied, planned and painted by the entire class.

The modern trend is to play down or eliminate specific closing activities. Many teachers like to summarize learnings regularly throughout the unit, and prefer a smooth transition from one unit to another. Perhaps partly accountable for the trend are educators' adverse reactions to the extravagant preparation and near-theatrical atmosphere which accompany some culminations.

As might be expected, the quality of district-supplied units varies enormously. It is clear that an excellent resource unit takes care of a great many instructional problems. But what do we do when the unit-at-hand consists of little more than a declaration of good intentions? Or when there are no units at all? In these cases, the best course of action may be to develop a unit based on the organization of the pupils' textbook.

TEXTBOOK-BASED UNITS

A chapter in a well-written textbook is more than just a logical exposition of subject matter, supported by a few supplementary activities. It is a psychological presentation of ideas and activities that can be used for highly effective teaching. Two of its most serious defects are likely to be lack of depth —although this is fast improving—and absence of local resources. When we know how to overcome these handicaps, what often emerges is a unit not just comparable to one that is wholly developed in the local district, but one that can be greatly superior. We cannot present here a detailed accounting of why textbook-based units are often desirable to construct. But as some justification for this recommendation might be expected, here are a few reasons.

Only a minority of school districts can provide the money, personnel time, and expert study needed to develop a curriculum "from scratch" in any one field. When they can, we see excellent results. Districts that attempt ambitious programs of curriculum construction in science without fulfilling the necessary conditions develop curricula that are disappointingly ineffectual. In addition, such disappointment may provoke contempt for theory and skepticism toward the usefulness of cooperative practices. That this is wholly unreasonable and unwarranted scarcely needs to be stated.

Fortunately, other educators take a more sensible approach to the problem. They realize that a soundly conceived textbook series in science contains the nucleus of an entire curriculum. They know that much attention has been given to principles of child development; that activities are carefully tested; that the teaching order in each chapter helps to indicate a learnable sequence, and so on. But it is also known that teaching the text itself usually results in page-to-page following, with more opportunities for background learning than for thoughtful inquiry; that additional activities are needed, especially those which take advantage of local resources.

These reasons, and more than we can mention here, explain why many school districts of restricted means base their science units upon the adopted text or texts. Chapter organizations are expanded or deepened, and "localized" with an abundance of resources. Suggestions for additional approaches and improvements are contributed. In effect, much of the same desirable cooperation and trying-out of ideas takes place as before, except that a better product emerges, and in far less time, than when attempts are made to start from no structure at all.

The main things we need to know in developing a textbook-based unit are how to determine the generalizations which may be taught, and how to compile activities which may be used to teach the generalizations.

Determining generalizations. The chapters of virtually all textbook series are organized around large generalizations. These may range in number from three to ten. Rarely are there fewer or more than this, and the average seems to be about six. The teacher manuals of some series contain outlines with the large generalizations clearly labeled. When this is the case, all that is needed, if the scope seems satisfactory, is to begin locating activities. In other series, generalizations are lumped together with facts, concepts, contributing ideas, and so forth, into "learnings," "understandings," or other broadly inclusive categories. Your job here is simply to determine what the basic generalizations are. The following procedure may be helpful:

1. Read the entire chapter quickly. This enables you to sense what it includes. Topical headings may reveal at least some of the large ideas involved. The pictures may illustrate them.

2. Check the accompanying teacher's manual. It probably contains at least a general outline of the chapter, or a list of "learnings." Either can help point up generalizations and aid in checking others.

3. If the chapter is long and thorough, the generalizations you compose may each contain several factors that should be emphasized individually. These can become contributing ideas and should be placed under each appropriate generalization. Your outline may then consist of, say, five or six generalizations, with several contributing ideas under most of them. Do not be concerned if there are no contributing ideas under some generalizations if you have checked the outline carefully for completeness. This probably only reflects the present structure of the chapter. Later, when gathering activities, or teaching the unit, you may decide to add some contributing ideas of your own.

4. To check the accuracy and completeness of the outline, go through the text chapter again. Notice how the outline corresponds to the topical headings and sentences and also the amount of material allotted to each topic. When there is a long list of learnings in the teacher's manual, another check can show how well the generalizations encompass them.

If all of the learnings can be placed under appropriate generalizations, the outline is probably satisfactory.

It is easy to get the impression from looking at these suggestions that a long time is needed to determine the large ideas. This is unlikely. Pick out a chapter in a child's text and carefully read it. With average ability in outlining, you can probably synthesize its main generalizations in ten to thirty minutes.

Whether you use the text chapter as a base for a unit or as the entire program, *it is extremely important to think through its basic organization.* When making a unit, you need to know the generalizations in order to compile activities, but the importance of analysis goes beyond this. It contributes to your confidence by providing a sense of direction. It leads to the feeling that, if needed, you can make a few changes, and add some children's ideas. It helps to focus on what is important and what is not. In contrast, when merely following the book, you go where it leads.

Determining activities. One advantage in using the book as a base is the assurance that at least some activities are "automatically" available and pertinent to each generalization. The text contains reading matter, pictures to examine, and other things to do. It is our job, then, to expand its present inventory of activities. The more the activities, the easier it is to select exactly what is most fitting at the time of planning specific lessons.

Many school districts provide for this purpose books and catalogues that contain collections of activities. The following titles collectively contain several thousand experiments, demonstrations, and other things to do:

David E. Hennessy, *Elementary Teacher's Classroom Science Demonstrations and Activities,* Englewood Cliffs, N.J.: Prentice-Hall, Inc., 1964.

Elizabeth B. Hone, Alexander Joseph, and Edward Victor, *A Sourcebook for Elementary Science,* New York: Harcourt, Brace and World, Inc., 1962.

National Science Teachers Association, *Space; Matter and Energy; Earth Sciences; Motion; Living Things; Waves* (Each is a separate publication.) Darien, Conn.: Teachers Publishing Corporation, 1964.

UNESCO, *700 Science Experiments for Everyone,* Second Edition (originally published as *UNESCO Source Book for Science Teaching*). Garden City, New York: Doubleday and Company, Inc., 1964.

Having access to a sourcebook that contains many activities is beneficial. We can usually find additional activities without wasting a great deal of time, if the generalizations selected in the first place are truly fundamental.

In addition to a good sourcebook, consult your local audio-visual and other catalogues. Write down under each generalization what experiences will assist you to teach it. Also record recommended study trips.

Do not neglect other local facilities, such as the school building and grounds, and local resource persons. It may be worthwhile to check a free and inexpensive materials catalogue for other possibilities. Trade books may be available on the subject, either at the school district library or the local public library. After the primary grades, encyclopedias are worthwhile for additional information and reports. Further, children can check newspapers and magazines for stories and pictures.

A convenient way to keep track of the generalizations and activities is to use 5- by 8-inch cards. Write one generalization at the top of each card, then put the corresponding activities under each generalization. (If there are contributing ideas, the activities will be placed under these, of course.) The use of cards has advantages. They can be shuffled in any desired sequence. It is easy to add and take away generalizations and activities. Special sections can be fitted in and items filed: outstanding bulletin board ideas, news clippings, evaluation suggestions, or whatever else is desired to help make the unit easier to teach.

A fine unit does not spring full-blown from the first organization. The more it is taught, the more you will want to modify it. Activities may be strengthened, the teaching order changed, scope added to, and so on. With much experience, you can often detect from inspection alone where your organization will falter with your classes. In the meantime, you learn largely from teaching it and noting what happens.

PLANNING BEFORE UNIT TEACHING

Just prior to teaching a unit, you need to make decisions about some practical problems. These decisions involve the choice of unit, your subject-matter background, the making of a general plan for teaching, and how to begin.

Choosing a unit. Some school districts leave the choice of units entirely to the teacher. Others prescribe that thus and so shall be taught. Many districts have both required and optional units. This arrangement seems to work well. The required units are planned so that there is some continuity in ideas among the several grade levels, and a reasonably wide scope is represented. At the same time, some provision is allowed for the desires of children and teachers. When there is a choice, these are some considerations that should enter into your decision:

1. What has the class studied previously? This can be learned to some extent by looking at the cumulative records, talking to its previous teachers, and informally asking representative children.

2. Is a balance of topics being maintained? Children should experience science instruction in at least several different areas each term. If the class has studied living things all year, perhaps it is time to take up a physical science.

3. What are the children interested in? If motivation is present and strong in most of the children, it would be unwise to ignore it. On the other hand, there are few topics in

elementary science which fail to arouse interest if they are well planned.

4. What is the possibility of correlation with other curriculum areas? Should the material correlate well with whatever else is being studied, this offers a chance to reinforce and extend learnings by showing them in another context.

5. How much time is available? The best answer to this question is stated in *hours*, unless the definitions of other terms used—"weeks," "days," "lessons"—are clear.

6. Is the unit seasonal? In most places, a class garden is a better activity in spring than fall. Observation of certain animals may be inconvenient or impossible in winter, and so on.

7. How many others will teach the unit at this time? If many teachers in the district plan to teach the unit at the same time, it is probable that district materials will be few and unpredictable in arrival.

Developing a subject-matter background. Once the decision is made as to what unit will be taught, it is wise to assess your own subject-matter background. Of course, if you have no background at all in the unit topic, this might be a factor to consider when choosing the unit. Most of the time, gaps in background can be overcome without too much effort. The activities planned will provide most of the needed subject matter, and you can learn along with the class. However, it is important to do some background reading if you feel insecure about the basic generalizations to be studied.

When using a text-based unit, read the children's text chapter and correlated section in the teacher's guide. More guides now contain subject matter for quick reference along with suggestions for teaching. A child's trade book on the topic, or a teacher's reference book available from the school or district, may also be worthwhile to examine. The purpose for reading should be to get acquainted with some facts and ideas *related to the generalizations in the unit*, rather than to acquire an encyclopedic background on the topic from which to draw. You need to know something about the generalizations to teach them satisfactorily. But there is no need to know "everything." That is what reference books are for. Besides reading, you will find it helpful to try your hand with unfamiliar demonstrations or experiments that seem appropriate for class study.

Making a block plan. With some background, you are ready to go on. Select the generalizations and activities from the resource unit (or text unit, or text) which seem most appropriate for the class. Lay out a tentative block plan for study. It is better to plan *large blocks of time for daily study* than to schedule science for twenty minutes or so a day, two or three days a week. It takes too much time to set up and distribute materials—and otherwise institute a program where children actively do things—for short periods to work well. Forty minutes or more may be satisfactory with most primary children, and about an hour is desirable with older pupils. The day-to-day contact with ideas and activities of the unit is important for continuity and reinforcement in learning. It also contributes to a continuing sense of participation and interest. Daily teaching of science may mean that part of the year science will not be formally scheduled in the school day. This is far better than having brief, discontinuous sessions during the whole year where little can be done except textbook reading.

Observe the block plan in Chart 1, drawn up by a student teacher for Unit 6 of this book (page 243). (Although the units in this book are not truly of the resource type, the form of laying out a block plan is much the same.) The school district involved recommends that social studies or science units be taught during the first hour of the day, after opening exercises and current-events reports. This leaves from forty minutes to almost an hour for unit teaching, depending on how much time is taken up at the start of day and the amount of time judged desirable by the teacher. Three "weeks" have been allotted

Chart 1

A BLOCK PLAN FOR A PRIMARY UNIT ON SIMPLE MACHINES, SCHEDULED FORTY-FIVE MINUTES DAILY FOR FIFTEEN DAYS

	April 6–10	April 13–17	April 20–24
MONDAY	*1. Inclined plane; force changes with its tilt.* Introduce with pictures. Do experiments 1, 2, 3.	*3. Wedge; force changes with sharpness.* Do experiments 1, 2. Remind class for extending activity.	*5. Windlass; force changes with size of wheel.* Do experiments 1, 2. Remind class for extending activity.
TUESDAY	Do experiments 3, 4, 5. Remind class for extending activity.	Do extending activity.	Do extending activity.
WEDNESDAY	Do extending activities 1, 2. Make bulletin board.	*4. Lever; force changes with force-arm length.* Do experiments 1, 2.	*6. Pulley; force changes with number of supporting lines.* Do experiments 1, 2, 3.
THURSDAY	*2. Screw; force changes with pitch.* Do experiments 1, 2. Remind class for extending activity.	Do experiments 3, 4. Remind class for extending activity.	Do experiments 4, 5, 6.
FRIDAY	Do experiment 3, and extending activity. Order film 370. 15 for April 24.	Do extending activity.	Show film 370. 15 "How Simple Machines Help Us" (20 min.) Discuss and evaluate whole unit.

for a science unit in this case; that is, fifteen sessions of about forty-five minutes each are available.

Note that only the broad aspects of planning are considered: shortened statements of the generalizations to keep purposes in focus; probable days when experiments will be taken up; reminders to inform the class about materials needed on different days; a notation to order a film, and so forth.

The student teacher may find that her judgment is not completely accurate. For example, it may take more than two sessions to clinch understandings with the pulley, and fewer sessions with the inclined plane. For the last day, she has scheduled a film that reviews all six simple machines, rather than the trip suggested in the unit. If it is a good film, it may reveal more than the study trip site available to the class. At the same time it can help culminate the unit.

It should be understood that the planning represented in Chart 1 does not mean rigid restrictions have been placed on the time, activities, or sequence in question. Flexibility is encouraged in virtually all school districts.

Although a certain amount of time has been set aside, it can be expanded or cut down, depending on what happens in the classroom. So the block plan is what we *start* with. It may be changed, and frequently is, when we see how our lessons go from day to day.

Should everyone put into block plans what appears in this one? Planning is a highly individual matter. When thirty experienced teachers in a college summer-session course were asked to make a block plan for another unit, wide differences appeared in the notations they felt were necessary for their own guidance. Nearly all these teachers strongly endorsed the making of a block plan, but few agreed as to precisely what it should contain.

The opening activity. Usually the last aspect of preplanning is to decide what opening lesson or lessons to use. Should you begin right off with a "regular" lesson? Or should there be a specifically planned initiation phase in which you attempt to (1) find out what the children know and want to know, (2) heighten interest, and (3) give the children an overview of what they will be studying?

There seems little point in having a formal initiation if the children are enthusiastic at the outset about the unit topic, and you have a reasonable idea of what they know. You will find out much more about their knowledge when they engage in specific activities. If you encourage them to ask questions during the entire unit, they will be far likelier to ask significant "why" questions instead of "what" questions. What about the overview? This is useful, but a complete overview at the very beginning of study is questionable. It may be much more understandable, especially with primary children, to give several smaller previews of future study at different points throughout the unit.

Teachers frequently ask, "Should pupils take part in long-range planning?" What we have been discussing requires much more knowledge than pupils have of the teaching-learning process, subject matter, and activities of the unit. It is desirable to involve pupils in planning, but this should be in specific, short-range situations, within an overall framework developed by the teacher. Some of these situations are pointed out in the next section.

LESSON PLANNING

Students of public speaking quickly catch on to the Big Secret of Success: "Tell 'em what you're going to say, say it, and then tell 'em what you've said." Or, translated: "Briefly establish the purpose of your talk, give the talk, and then briefly summarize it."

We do much the same thing in lesson planning:

1. A background or solution-centered purpose is established.
2. The children engage in background or solution-centered activities.
3. They summarize and apply what they have learned.

Let us examine our role in each of these three phases.

Purpose setting. When we teach a lesson, we start out with a certain amount of "good will" from the children. Whether it grows or dissipates much depends on the interest worked into the lesson. When we start a lesson with a "bridge" or application that poses a question, it provokes interest, and naturally leads to the need to find out and apply what has been learned. If the question is background-centered, we help the children determine what to look for when they consult authority. If the question is solution-centered, we help the children plan the ways in which they will test their hypotheses about the question—the materials needed, what they will do, and the controls they will need. In the course of finding answers to the questions raised, the children begin to learn the generalization we have in mind. At the same time, they learn process methods which are developed in an understandable, purposeful context.

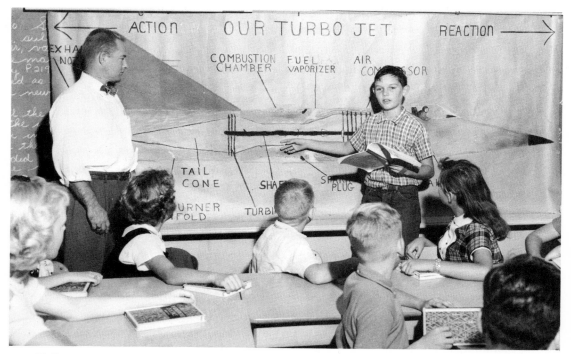

FIGURE 16 The best reports and projects relate to generalizations studied by the entire class.

The beginning of the lesson, then, is when we motivate, pose questions, and plan how to find out. We need to know the activities we are going to use, the materials needed, and the bridge.

Activity phase. The next part of the lesson is where the children pursue the purpose raised. They view films, read books, perform experiments, see demonstrations, and engage in any of the other possibilities for activity. When there are enough materials to go around, the children work in small groups, or individually. We circulate around the room to iron out problems, assist slow readers, and so on. If we work directly with the children, as with a demonstration or an experiment, we now ask questions and give clues to help children think about what they are doing.

This is also the time when individuals work on reports or construction. Or, if they have prepared them already, they give their reports or show to the class what they have made. The best reports and projects are those that relate to generalizations studied by the entire class. It is hard for all pupils to benefit from these activities unless they have some background for understanding.

Summary and applying phase. The last part of the lesson is when, through discussion, we help the children grasp the meaning of what they have done. Through our questions, based on process and product referents, we discover how much they have learned. We guide them to evaluate their successes and failures, and to make generalizations.

Sometimes it seems hard for a class to generalize. More activities may be needed. But even when substantial time is taken for finding out, generalizing may be difficult with many primary children. They may be at an intuitive, preverbal level—a condition in which they seem to understand, but cannot put it into words. In this case, you might let them "improve" a generalization you write. Or let them complete a partial statement of a generalization that you have begun for them. But never press the matter if the going seems very hard.

Some teachers record the important ideas discussed on a "We Found Out" chart. When placed next to a chart of related questions, it provides a record of progress, and a means for reviewing learning.

The end of the lesson is also the time when you do some planning with the children for the next lesson. Are materials needed? Perhaps the children can bring some from home. But you remember that children, especially the younger ones, are unreliable. So you ask several pupils rather than one to bring in an item. Have some children asked questions during the lesson? Perhaps these can be studied within the generalizations you have planned. If not, you must decide whether they should be studied individually, or by the entire class. Was process thinking satisfactory? Perhaps some particular referent requires stressing in future lessons. How much of this planning is done with the children depends, of course, on their maturity and ability.

When the children seem to understand the essentials of a generalization, many teachers use the last part of a lesson for applying and extending what they have learned. Numerous examples of applications are brought up. The class may be encouraged to find other examples out of school. Activities of varying difficulty may be assigned to provide for individual differences.

Although we have analyzed the lesson as to phases, in practice the transition from one phase to another is almost unnoticeable. And not always will all of these phases be completed in one class session. For example, there may be occasional need to spend several sessions on the activity part alone.

Summary of planning (the GAB-BAG approach). Because many details are presented in this chapter, it is easy to lose sight of the overall strategy of planning for thoughtful teaching and learning. The following device should help make this strategy clear.

In *planning* a unit, you select
G eneralizations, then find
A ctivities, then develop
B ridges, for the first activity of
each sequence.
In *teaching* a unit, you begin with a
B ridge, which leads the children to
A ctivities, which cause them to form a
G eneralization.

By planning your teaching in this way, process opportunities develop naturally, one after the other. To help bring out these opportunities in the units of Part II, notations have been placed in the margins of each unit.

Some of the same shortcomings exist in setting down steps in planning as were found in our two-step method for beating the stock market (page 15). Good planning or teaching is not a routinized, rule-of-thumb activity. It calls for imagination, personal innovation, and adaptability. It requires knowledge of when to "break the rules," and to adjust to the press of things that come up unexpectedly. In previous chapters we have taken pains to present many of the considerations involved in making decisions. But thus far, there has been very little opportunity to study teaching in situations that put together these previous ideas. Part II will provide such situations.

HOW PART II OF THIS BOOK CAN HELP YOU

The units found on the following pages are designed to reflect the typical kinds of subject matter, activities, and materials encountered in teaching elementary-school science. They depart from the usual resource units in that they illustrate specific lessons arranged in teaching sequences. The lessons are instructional models which together contain applications of all the ideas of process and product development brought out in the previous chapters.

Few instructional models can be developed which will work perfectly for everyone and in every situation. As you work with children or try out these instructional sequences in your methods class, you will begin to see where changes are desirable. But first you need something concrete with which to work. In the course of thoughtfully going through the units, the ways of teaching that have been emphasized will become increasingly familiar. The second part of this book, then, is an attempt to teach deeply what is introduced in the first part.

There are twelve units in Part II, selected from the three representative, broad-field areas used in elementary teaching: physical science, earth science, and life science. There are four units each for the primary, intermediate, and upper-grade levels. The grade levels are only suggestive, as considerable overlapping has been purposely planned for. Each unit is constructed around a framework of important generalizations. Every generalization is preceded by a subject-matter section to help provide you with ample background. Following each generalization are the important aspects needed for teaching: materials, an interesting bridge, basic activities, vocabulary, and extending activities.

The sequence in each model unit generally goes from simpler ideas and activities to those more involved. When working with children you will want to start where they are. If they have little or no background in the topic, begin with the first activity. With children who have some background, begin teaching at the place in the sequence for which they seem prepared. When insufficient time is a problem, cut down on the number of *generalizations* you teach in a unit. This will bring better results than lightly touching on all the suggested activities.

Part II

Applications of
Science Teaching Methods

Molecules and Heat Energy

(Intermediate)

One significant difference between modern science education and some former approaches is in the emphasis now given to fundamental understandings. Perhaps nowhere is this attention to fundamentals better seen than in units on energy. In the present one on heat, intended for children of the middle grades, a serious effort is made to acquaint them with molecular theory. Too hard? Not if approached on an intuitive plane that stresses concrete experiences, in contrast with verbal learning. Children will explore such concepts as heat and temperature, expansion-contraction, heat transfer, and changes of state. As is typical at this level, we shall be concerned mostly with physical, rather than chemical, changes.

BASIC GENERALIZATIONS

I. Most materials expand when heated and contract when cooled.

II. Adding or taking away heat can cause materials to change state; different materials change state at different temperatures.

III. There is a difference between the temperature of a material and the heat it contains.

IV. Heat energy may come from many sources; it travels by conduction, convection, and radiation.

QUESTION: How tall is the Empire State Building?
ANSWER: I don't know; it keeps changing.

Although answers like this seldom win prizes on television quiz shows, it is a valid one. The height of a tall structure may vary a half-foot or more, depending on temperature differences in effect when the measurements are taken. Similarly, a steel bridge may change more than a foot in length, and a ship captain may stride a slightly longer deck in southern, in contrast with northern, waters.

The molecular theory of matter offers an interesting explanation for these and many other events. To understand molecules, let us look for a moment at a drop of water. If we could subdivide it with an imaginary eye-dropper for years on end, eventually we would get to a point where one more subdivision would produce two atoms of hydrogen and one of oxygen. Both are gases, and of course look nothing like water. From this we can say that a molecule is the smallest particle of a substance which can exist by itself and have the properties of that substance.

Strictly speaking, only gases are exclusively made up of molecules. Some liquids and many solids are composed of electrically charged atoms or groups of atoms called *ions*. A typical example is table salt, which is revealed through X-ray pictures to contain a boxlike, crystalline structure of sodium and chloride ions. However, since virtually all ionic particles possess physical characteristics very similar to molecules, it will be convenient to treat them as such at the elementary science level.

Is there any direct proof that molecules exist? Recently, yes. Pictures of some larger molecules have been taken through use of powerful electron microscopes. But for the most part scientists have had to rely on indirect evidence. It is a remarkable tribute to the intellectual ability of earlier scientists that they were able to forge so powerful a theory from their secondhand observations.

Many early experiments were so simple they may be duplicated today by children. An ounce of volume of alcohol added to an ounce of water results in slightly less than two ounces of liquid. When gold and lead bars are clamped together for a long period there is a slight intermingling of these elements. Solid sugar crystals disappear when stirred into a hot liquid. Fine powder sprinkled into a water drop may be observed through a microscope of good quality to jiggle and move erratically.

From these and scores of other experiments and observations, the following ideas have been advanced:

Matter is composed of tiny particles that have an attractive force (cohesion) between them.

There is space between molecules. In a solid material, molecules are very close together, and are relatively "fixed" in place because their cohesion is greater than that of gases or liquids. Molecules of most liquids are farther apart; their weaker cohesion permits them to slide about and take the shape of a container. Gas molecules are widest apart and have almost no cohesive attraction. Therefore, they can conform to a container's shape, or escape from an uncovered container.

Molecules are always in motion except at absolute zero ($-460°F$). Those of solids vibrate in place, while liquid and gas molecules move faster and more freely. With increased heat energy motion increases and the mole-cules move farther apart. The reverse happens when heat energy is decreased. This is why most matter expands when heated and contracts when cooled.

Although this theory states that liquids contract when cooled, we note an interesting exception when water temperature drops toward freezing. Water does contract in volume with decreased temperature, until about $39°F$. Then its molecules begin to assemble into a crystalline form which takes on a solid appearance as ice at $32°F$. The latticelike arrangement of these crystals takes up more space than an equal amount of free-moving water molecules. This is why water pipes and water-cooled automobile engine blocks may burst in winter, and why frozen milk may push up and out of the bottle. Milk is largely water.

It also explains why a lake freezes from the top down, rather than the reverse. At $39°F$ water is densest and sinks to the lake bottom. Colder water, being less dense, floats to the surface. It freezes into surface ice, and traps the heat energy possessed by the slightly warmer water below. Unless the air temperature is extremely cold, this energy is sufficient to keep the pond from freezing completely.

The importance of this phenomenon to living things can hardly be overestimated. Though it is clear that aquatic life is saved, consider what would happen to the world's climate if bodies of water froze from the bottom up. Since the heat now trapped by ice would escape, ice formation would increase. Gradually, the earth's climate would become increasingly cold, and eventually fatal to most life forms.

Different materials vary in their rates of expansion and contraction, because their cohesive forces vary. It is easier to tear a paper sheet apart than a thin steel sheet because steel molecules attract one another with much greater force. A cohesive disparity is likewise true of alcohol and water. Notice the difference in surface tension of water and alcohol in Figure 1-1. The cohesive force of water molecules is greater than that of alcohol. This helps explain why equal amounts of heat energy cause alcohol to expand more than water. It is easier to overcome the weaker cohesive force. It also indicates why alcohol evaporates faster than water.

Expansion-contraction, and as we shall see later, changes of state from solids to liquids and gases, are the results of a relentless tug-of-war between heat energy and cohesive force. Which "side" wins depends upon which force is the more powerful.

Before you begin the activity section, a note about materials may be useful. As with all of the following units, this one can be taught with supplies usually found about the school or home. However, there are several items which should be bought or borrowed to gain the greatest benefit from several forthcoming activities. Especially useful will be some glass tubing, a one-hole rubber stopper, flask, and a test tube. All the glassware heated in this unit should be of the Pyrex type. Ordinary glass expands more, and more unevenly with heat, and may crack. For the quickest heating source, a propane gas burner is best. However, an alcohol lamp or even a candle will serve in many experiments. It will also be useful to have an electric hot plate.

Some experiences will require use of fire. Supervise these occasions closely. Always use a metal tray or other fireproof material to contain a burning substance. Develop standards about not touching a hot plate or other materials at random. No activity in this unit is even remotely dangerous, provided common-sense precautions are taken.

BASIC GENERALIZATION I: Most materials expand when heated and contract when cooled

Contributing idea A. Solids expand when heated and contract when cooled.

1. *Materials:* 3-foot copper bellwire, with insulation removed; two candles; matches; small object to use as a weight; two chairs; bulletin board or chalkboard sketch of Figure 1-2.

Call attention to your sketch of Figure 1-2

FIGURE 1-1 Surface tension in alcohol and water.

and tell the class, "These sketches show how some telephone wires looked at two different times of the year. Do you notice anything odd? What seems to be the problem?" Guide the children toward a simple, clearly worded statement, such as, "Why are the wires sagging in June and not in December?" *define problems[1]*

Encourage hypotheses. Acknowledge such reasonable guesses as, "The wires stretched after a while because they are heavy, etc." Give clues as needed: "When it is December again, the wires will look as they do in the top picture. What time of year is it in the second picture? How does the weather differ in most parts of the United States at these two periods of the year?" Help them to include heat as a possible cause. *suggest hypotheses*

Lead an evaluative discussion of each hypothesis. Invite the children to test their most reasonable guesses. A hypothesis that heat will lengthen wire can be tested with the

December

Six months later

FIGURE 1-2

[1] For complete statements of marginal notations, and specific subabilities, see pages 49–50.

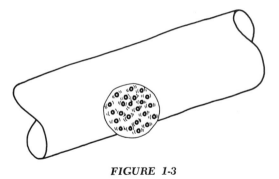

FIGURE 1-3

select procedures

above materials. Let pupils suggest how to set up the experiment. Bring out the analogous nature of the materials, if needed: bell-wire for telephone wire; legs or sides of two chairs for telephone poles, between which the wire may be stretched and fastened; for the sun's heat, two candle flames passed up and down the wire will do. But if the wire only sags slightly, how will they tell? A small weight or object may be suspended from the center of the wire by a string or paperclip, so that it just misses the floor when slightly swinging. If the wire sags when heated, the weight should touch.

draw conclusions

select procedures

Permit several trials. In each case emphasize that the wire *expands* when heated and *contracts* when the candle flames are taken away. Capitalize on possible faulty procedures. For example, only one candle may not produce enough heat for expansion to be noticeable.

2. *Materials*: sketch of Figure 1-3.

To explain what happens on a molecular level, you might use this approach: "Scientists think they know why a solid material like our wire expands and contracts. Any material is made up of very tiny bits called *molecules*. Molecules of different materials are of different sizes. But all are so small that only a few of the very largest have been seen by scientists with special microscopes. The molecules which make up our wire are too small to be seen. But if we could see them, they might look like this." (Show your sketch of Figure 1-3.)

Develop the following ideas slowly and carefully:

a. In a hard, solid material like wire, molecules are very close together. But there is a small space between each molecule and the next one.

b. Each molecule stays in a fixed place because it is attracted to others next to it. The molecules are like tiny magnets which attract one another.

c. Molecules in a solid material are always vibrating or jiggling in place because they contain heat energy. When extra heat is applied to a solid the vibrating motion becomes faster, and wider in range. Therefore, spaces between the molecules get larger. This is why a solid expands.

d. When a solid loses some heat energy, the opposite happens. Vibrations are slower and smaller in range. The solid contracts.

3. *Materials*: glass Mason jar and metal screw lid; transparent bowl of very hot water; bimetallic strip (Get from a scientific supply house or borrow from a junior high-school science teacher.); two ice cubes; candle; matches.

To help children learn that different materials expand and contract at different rates, try the following activities.

select proced

Tighten the screw top on a Mason jar until it cannot be unscrewed by a child. Show the capped jar to the pupils. Tell them the cap is stuck and ask for advice on how to unscrew it. After several children have tried and failed, ask how their knowledge of molecules might help. Indicate the bowl of hot water, if a clue is needed.

define proble

If the jar top is inverted and placed into the water for a moment, it should be possible to easily unscrew the lid. Guide an explanation of what happened on a molecular level. But point to a flaw. Glass is made of molecules, too. (Don't the glass molecules expand along with the metal molecules?)

sugges hypot

Lead to a tentative hypothesis: Maybe the metal expands more than the glass. Will one material expand more than another? Exhibit your bimetallic strip. Explain that it is made of two different metals fastened together. If one part expands more than the other, what should happen? (The strip should bend.)

suggest hypotheses

Let someone hold the strip sideways and slightly above a candle flame. The strip will bend. Now invite conjecture as to whether ice will produce an opposite effect. Will one metal contract more than the other? Hold the strip sideways between two ice cubes for a brief period. It will bend the opposite way.

draw conclusions

Help the class understand that different materials will expand at different rates.

Explain that bimetallic strips have many uses. For example, they may turn house heaters off and on automatically when connected to an electric circuit.

Contributing idea B. Liquids expand when heated and contract when cooled.

1. *Materials:* Pyrex baby bottle or flask filled with water; one-hole rubber stopper to fit the bottle opening; 12-inch glass tube (Insert about one-third of the tube into stopper. Always use a twisting motion when inserting glass tubing into a stopper. A paper towel wrapped around the tube will protect hands should the glass break. Wetting either the stopper or glass reduces friction.); red ink or food coloring; glass bowl, partly filled with a mixture of ice cubes and water; small rubber band; hot plate or substitute. (A cafeteria tray or shallow pan will contain any spilled water in this or subsequent experiments with water.)

Bridge into the next experiment with these comments:

One summer day, the driver of a tank truck was asked to deliver a tankful of water to a distant road-building project high up in the mountains. At noon, he had the tank filled to the top; it held exactly 1000 gallons. (A gallon referent would be useful here.) He then started up the mountain and arrived at the project location in the evening. When he unloaded the water, he was puzzled to find that only 990 gallons came out of the tank. How many gallons less is that? What do you suppose happened?

suggest hypotheses

Acknowledge but counter the idea of evaporation. Say that the tank was so designed that only a gallon or two might have been lost this way. If needed, provide clues as to possible temperature differences of the start-

ing and ending places of travel. Remind the children of their previous experiment, and that water—a liquid—is made of molecules, too.

select procedures

When contraction through cooling is suggested, ask for a test with the provided materials. The flask can be filled with water at room temperature. A few drops of red ink or food coloring will improve visibility. Cap with a one-hole stopper through which a tube is inserted and press down firmly. This will seal the liquid in the flask and cause it to rise slightly in the tube. When the flask is placed in a bowl of ice and water, the colored water will contract and go down the tube. Draw out the need for a *control*. A rubber band placed around the tube will indicate the previous level. If available, an identical flask setup can be put alongside the first, but not placed in the water. Its water level should remain constant.

suggest hypotheses

Invite your pupils to predict what would have happened if the driver had started with a tankful of water at a cold location and had driven to a very warm one. (The tank would have overflowed.) This may be tested with

select procedures

the same setup; but now the flask should contain chilled water, and be placed on a hot plate. As the water warms, some will flow up

draw conclusions

and out of the tube.

2. *Materials:* sketch of Figure 1-4. (It will be helpful for comparisons to place this sketch next to that of Figure 1-3.)

To acquaint the class with what happened on a molecular level, exhibit the sketch of Figure 1-4. Explain that it shows a small puddle of water, and the behavior of its mole-

FIGURE 1-4

cules. Develop the following ideas slowly and carefully:

a. In most liquids, molecules are farther apart than in a solid.

b. Although the molecules are attracted to one another, this attraction is weaker than in a solid. Therefore, the molecules can slide and move around from one place to another. This is why a liquid takes the shape of its container.

c. When liquid molecules gain heat energy they move around faster, bump one another oftener, and spread wider apart. This is why a liquid expands.

d. When they lose heat energy, the molecules move around more slowly and come closer together. This is why a liquid contracts.

3. *Materials:* two small, identical Pyrex flasks with one-hole stoppers and glass tubes, one filled with red-colored alcohol, the other with red-colored water; two rubber bands (to mark the water level in each tube); a rectangular baking dish filled with very hot water, and another containing ice and water; thermometer (optional).

A previous activity demonstrated that different solids expand and contract unequally. The next experiment will teach that this is also true of liquids.

suggest hypotheses   Invite pupils to give a molecular explanation of how thermometers work. If an ordinary wood-backed thermometer is available, warm the bulb slightly over a hot plate. Let them see that the liquid column does expand, and then contract when taken away. Should the children be unable to read a thermometer accurately, draw a simplified scale on the chalkboard and help them to learn. Discuss various uses of thermometers, such as taking one's temperature, recording meat temperatures in cooking, in making candy, and so on.

Now confront your group with an apparent paradox. You have two homemade thermometers. The liquid in each is of the same temperature, and the tubes and flasks are identical. But they are acting strangely. If the class *define problems* observes closely, perhaps it can tell what is odd about the behavior of these liquids.

Place both flasks in the baking dish that contains the very hot water. (*Never put a container of flammable fluid such as alcohol over an open flame or glowing hot plate.*) Within a short period the liquid in each tube will rise. The rate of rise in one (alcohol) will exceed the other (water). Remove the flasks before they become too warm and overflow.

After several moments for discussion—this will also give time for each liquid to cool—put both flasks in the baking dish of ice water. The alcohol rate of contraction will exceed that of the water. How can this be explained? *sugges hypot* (The previous input with solids should help their thinking.)

Gradually help the class to focus on the liquid itself. Probably most of the children *define proble* assumed—"took for granted," is an understandable way to express it with children—that the liquids were identical because they appeared that way to the eye. Identify the fast-acting liquid as alcohol, if pupils' noses have not already told them.

Remind them that different solids may expand and contract unequally; the same is true of liquids. If alcohol and mercury thermometers are available, compare them. Be sure to bring out that a thermometer's size of bore would also play a role in the expansion-con- *draw* traction rate. Or, if glass tubes of different *conclu* sizes are available, let the children discover this.

Contributing idea C. Gases expand when heated and contract when cooled.

1. *Materials:* 24-inch string; toy balloon; warm, sunny window area or hot plate.

Have your class try to help a mythical little child who is in trouble with his mother. John got a new balloon one morning. His mother warned him not to break it. When he was called to lunch, he carefully placed it on a window ledge. After lunch, he found that his balloon had burst. His mother was angry and reminded him of her warning not to blow up the balloon too hard. When John said he hadn't blown it up very much his mother replied, "How can a soft balloon break by it- *evalu* self?" *critic*

Encourage conjecture as to what probably

happened. If necessary, provide clues. If the window ledge was sunny, maybe warmth played a role. What will happen to a soft
balloon when heated? What test can the children set up?

If there is no sunshiny ledge on which to leave it, a balloon can be warmed over a hot plate. If slowly rotated while warmed, the balloon and its air will heat up quicker and
more uniformly. Guide the use of some string for before and after measurements. Let pupils feel and compare the increased firmness of the balloon after it has been heated. How does this show that it is not just the balloon that
has expanded? (Although larger, the balloon would be softer than before.) Allow it to cool and contract for the opposite effect.

Assist the children in a brief summary. They know that air is made up of different gases. It seems that gases expand and also contract. (Before going on to the next activity, however, perhaps someone can provide a pleasant ending to John's sad story.)

2. *Materials:* large sketch of Figure 1-5. (It will be helpful for comparisons to place it next to your sketches of Figures 1-3 and 1-4.)

Reveal the sketch of Figure 1-5. Indicate that it is a balloon and that they have an imaginary microscope so powerful it can detect the gas molecules which make up the air inside. With their previous knowledge about molecules, can the children explain why the
balloon expands and contracts? Be sure to bring these ideas out carefully in the discussion:

a. In a gaseous material like air, molecules are even farther apart than in a liquid.

b. Although the molecules still have some attraction for one another, it is very slight. Therefore, they move about freely, and take the shape of their container.

c. When gas molecules gain heat energy they move around faster, bump one another oftener, and so spread wider apart. When heat energy is lost, the opposite happens.

d. A balloon becomes firm in two ways. We can blow more and more air molecules into it until the molecules become "crowded." Or through heat, we can make the fewer mole-

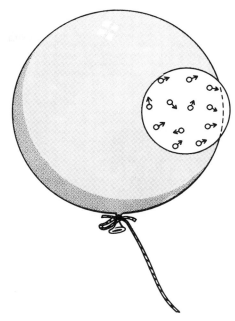

FIGURE 1-5

cules inside a soft balloon move around faster. This causes them to bump oftener against the inside skin of the balloon and with one another.

3. *Materials:* balloon; small Pyrex flask or bottle (with a neck small enough for the balloon's open end to be stretched over it); hot plate; a container of cool water (optional).

It would be useful at this point in assessing understanding to see if the class can set up and explain a substitute experiment. Exhibit the above materials. Challenge pupils to devise an experiment which shows that air expands and contracts.

Stretch the balloon's opening over the bottle's open end, and set the bottle briefly on a hot plate. In several moments, expanded air will enter the balloon and inflate it. When the bottle is cooled (by placing it in or under some water, or simply waiting) the balloon will deflate.

Encourage a molecular explanation of what
happened.

Extending activities

1. Press for a molecular explanation of this

draw conclusions — event: A partly filled milk bottle is taken out of a refrigerator and placed on a table. About ten minutes later, the top suddenly pops off. How can this happen "all by itself"?

2. Encourage children to locate many different kinds of thermometers or pictures of them. All will operate on the expansion-contraction principle, whether air, liquid, or a solid is used. Have children explain how they operate.

draw conclusions

3. Let several able children calibrate a homemade water or alcohol thermometer by comparing it with a commercial instrument. A white card taped in back of the tube will serve for recording marks. After several weeks, a wide temperature range will be established. A drop of oil placed on top of the liquid column will reduce evaporation.

reason quantitatively

4. Motivate a home and neighborhood search or magazine picture search for expansion-contraction effects and devices. Fathers can show the radiator overflow valve on the family automobile. Sidewalks have cracks, bridges expansion joints and rollers at one end. Railroad tracks have small openings between individual rail lengths. Concrete roads include tar separators between sections, which are squeezed up or pulled apart. Rivets in steel girders and beams are hammered in while hot; when cooled, they contract and form a tightly binding connection. Tank trucks and railroad tank cars often have several domelike expansion chambers visible on top. Let pupils report, show, and discuss what they have found.

evaluate critically

Sometimes we get so accustomed to our environment it is hard to think of the things about us in new ways. Most everyone knows that air is a mixture of gases. Yet a favorite stunt of science demonstrators at high-school assemblies is to pour liquid air grandly from one container to another. Many persons know that carbon dioxide is a gas. Yet it is possible to trip over some, or drop it on your toe when it is in the form of dry ice. Steel is certainly a most durable solid. But high-temperature tests for possible spaceship uses turn it into vapor.

The state of matter at any given moment depends on the temperature. Temperature is a measure of the speed of molecular movements. When increased heat energy is applied to a solid, its molecules vibrate faster. If the motion is powerful enough to overcome the molecules' cohesive forces, the molecules move farther away, and the solid becomes a liquid. If further energy is applied, the molecules move even faster and farther apart to become a liquid. With loss of heat energy the opposite occurs. The decreased speed of molecules enables cohesive force to be reasserted, thus forming a liquid, then a solid, should sufficient heat be lost.

Does a solid become a liquid before it becomes a gas? Or a gas a liquid before it becomes a solid? Usually, yes. But a moth ball changes to a gas directly; so does dry ice. Frost is an example of vapor freezing directly into a solid state. This phenomenon is called *sublimation*.

Different substances change state at different temperatures. Adding salt to fresh water lowers its freezing point. Sea water, for example, freezes at 28.5°F, instead of 32°F. Unless the temperature is very low, sprinkling rock salt on an icy sidewalk melts the ice. We add an antifreeze liquid (ethylene glycol) to our automobile radiators to prevent freezing. A heavy salt solution would be even more effective, except for its unfortunate tendency to corrode metal.

Pressure also has an interesting effect upon changes of state. As a liquid warms, some of its molecules move so fast they bounce off into the air. We recognize this as evaporation. The same thing occurs with boiling, except the process is faster. To leave the surface of a liquid, however, molecules must overcome not only the cohesive pull of nearby molecules, but also the pressure of air molecules immediately above. At sea level, a square-inch column of air extending to outer space weighs 14.7 pounds. At the top of a tall mountain there is much less air—and thus weight—pressing down. With less pressure it is easier for liquid molecules to escape into vapor form. So, at 90,000 feet, water boils at room temperature. Astronauts or pilots of high-altitude airplanes wear pressure suits, or are enclosed in a pressurized cabin, to avoid the possibility of their blood boiling.

Since we normally associate boiling with a temperature of about 212°F, it is important to realize another practical effect of decreased pressure. Boiling point temperature decreases about 1°F for each 550-foot increase in altitude. At a high location it is difficult to cook foods satisfactorily in an open container, because of the low temperature at which boiling occurs. A pressure cooker is almost a necessity.

The effect of a different kind of pressure is readily observable with ice. Why is it possible to skate on ice, when we cannot on other smooth surfaces? The answer is that we do not skate directly on the ice. Our body weight exerts enough pressure through the ice skate blades to melt the ice. This furnishes a water-lubricated surface on which we slide. As the temperature drops, however, it takes increasing pressure to melt the ice. It may be difficult to skate at all.

A change of state always results in the absorption or release of heat energy. It requires energy for the fixed jiggling molecules of a solid to acquire a more freely moving liquid state. Additional energy is required for liquid molecules to move fast enough and far enough apart to become a gas. Heat is absorbed from whatever accessible substance is warmer than the changing material. Therefore, if you hold an ice cube in your hand, it removes heat from your body. More heat is required as the liquid evaporates. This is why evaporation has a cooling effect. As the speed of evaporation increases, so does cooling. Ethyl chloride, for example, evaporates so quickly it is used by physicians to numb flesh for painless surgery.

Conversely, heat energy is released when a gas condenses to a liquid or a liquid freezes to a solid state, since molecular motion continually decreases. It used to be common in rural homes to place tubs of water near cellar vegetable bins. As the water freezes, enough heat is given off to prevent the vegetables (which have a slightly lower freezing point) from freezing.

The knowledge that heat is absorbed in evaporation and released through condensation is applied in modern electric refrigerators. A liquid refrigerant is released at low pressure into the freezing unit. As it flashes into a vaporous state, it cools rapidly and absorbs heat. As the now slightly warmed vapor leaves the unit, a motor-driven pump continually compresses the vapor until it has changed to a hot liquid under high pressure. The liquid next circulates in a condenser and releases its heat to the air. The cycle then begins again.

BASIC GENERALIZATION II: Adding or taking away heat can cause materials to change state; different materials change state at different temperatures

Contributing idea A. Solids melt into liquids when heated; liquids freeze into solids when cooled.

1. *Materials:* hot plate; several similar-sized solid materials for melting, such as candle wax, solder, lead (an old fishline sinker will do), and bare copper wire; a clean, identical tinned can for each item to be melted; pair of pliers or tongs.

Ask the class what happens to a tray of ice cubes after it is removed from a refrigerator and left standing in a warm room. Elicit that it melts, changing from a solid *state* (condition) to a liquid state. Bring out that the water would refreeze, or go from a liquid to *draw conclusions* solid state, if placed back in the freezer compartment of a refrigerator.

Hold up a candle. Mention that it is a solid, although it has never been in a refrigerator. Ask, "Why doesn't it melt? (Not warm enough.) Will all solids melt at different temperatures?" (Answers will vary.)

Indicate the several solids—for example, wax, solder, lead, and copper—that might be tested. Have pupils try to predict the correct

suggest hypotheses

order of melting. Put each item in a separate can. It should be possible, if small cans are used, to place all on the hot plate at one time.

evaluate critically

While waiting for the materials to heat sufficiently for melting, invite everyone to detect solid materials in the classroom that might once have been in a liquid state. Encourage discussion and speculation about these suggestions, but avoid any definite conclusions at this time.

draw conclusions

In a short while, all but the copper will be in liquid form. Remove the cans carefully from the hot plate with tongs or pliers and set them on a metal tray for cooling. Soon, the materials will resolidify. If copper is used, bring out the probable reason why it does not melt. (A temperature of about 2000°F is needed.)

2. The next problem and experiment will help pupils understand that different liquids may solidify at different temperatures. Because refrigeration is needed, it is convenient for children to do this experiment at home. Begin with a bridge that contains an unstated problem, such as this:

One cold winter day an airplane pilot was flying over a small ocean harbor. He saw several small boats speeding around in the harbor. Just half a mile away he saw a very large lake on which some children were ice skating. This puzzled him. What do you suppose there was in this scene that didn't seem right?

define problems

Draw out a concise statement of the problem. Why was the lake frozen and not the harbor? Guide the discussion eventually to the composition of the two liquids; one is salt water, the other fresh. Hypotheses that will probably emerge are salt water will not freeze, and salt water will freeze at a lower temperature than fresh water.

suggest hypotheses

select procedures

Have pupils plan specifically how they might perform an experiment at home. Paper cups are adequate containers. Different concentrations of salt, measured in teaspoonfuls, may be dissolved in the water and then compared with equal volumes of fresh water. A check of the freezer every hour—mothers may become impatient with more frequent inspec-

tions, and the freezer inefficient—will help determine which solutions freeze first, if at all.

On the following day let children report their findings. Although precise data cannot be expected, of course, it will be obvious that adding salt does lower the freezing point of fresh water. Bring out through reading or another authoritative source that even the ocean freezes in cold climates. Perhaps some pupils can find pictures showing the earth's polar regions.

draw conclus...

Speculate about the addition of other substances to water to lower its freezing point. Mention that alcohol is sometimes added to automobile radiators in winter. If the children seem interested (and their mothers still patient), an open-ended experiment can be tried to determine the effect of adding rubbing alcohol to water in various proportions.

select proced...

draw conclu...

3. Bring out an explanation of melting and freezing on a molecular level:

a. When molecules of a solid are heated, they vibrate faster and faster. If enough heat energy is present, the molecules break away from their places and slip around every which way. We say the material has *melted*.

b. When molecules of a liquid lose heat energy, they slow down and then settle into specific positions. They continue to vibrate as long as some heat is present, but they do not move around. In some cases we say the material has *frozen*.

Be sure pupils understand that any hard substance formerly in a liquid state is "frozen." Since this word is usually associated with cold temperatures, however, make clear it is more typical to use such other expressions as "become hard," "cooled to a solid state," etc.

draw conclu...

Contributing idea B. Liquids evaporate into gases when heated; gases condense into liquids when cooled.

1. *Materials:* hot plate; two identical pans, each containing the same amount of water; empty ice cube tray or metal pie plate.

Draw out of the class that spilled water, rain puddles, and so on, dry after a while. Most children will know that this water disappears into the air, or *evaporates*. Let them see the word "vapor" in the larger word. Clarify it as a gaseous state of matter. The water has changed from a liquid to a gas.

Exhibit one pan of water. Elicit that after a while the water will evaporate. Inquire as to how this evaporation might be speeded up. The hot plate probably will be suggested. *select* *cedures* Establish the necessity for controls: one pan can be left off and another placed on this heating unit. After some boiling, it will be obvious that the evaporation rate in the control pan is far slower.

Now hold the empty ice tray or pie plate about a foot above the water. Some of the escaping water vapor will condense back to a liquid on the tray bottom and fall back into the pan.

Guide a molecular explanation of these events:

a. Heat energy causes the moving molecules in the water to move faster. Some molecules move fast enough to escape from the others, and go off into the air. Adding extra heat to one pan of water speeds up the movement of molecules. That is why the water evaporates faster.

b. The tray is cooler than the escaping molecules. This slows down the molecules and makes them more attracted to one another. Some molecules slow down enough to come together again and change back into a liquid state.

Explain that when spread out gas molecules come together again, they *condense*. This means that they now take up less space. This process, which is the opposite of evaporation, is called *condensation*.

2. *Materials:* hot plate; pan of boiling water; ice cubes; two metal pie plates or ice trays; paper towels.

Tell the class, "We found out that adding heat energy to water molecules made them evaporate faster than usual. Can we do the opposite thing? Can we make evaporated water molecules condense faster than usual?"

Discuss this briefly. Now show the children the boiling water, two pie plates (both should be at room temperature), and ice cubes. Have

them do some reasoning. A surface cooler than the vapor slows down molecules. Will a still cooler surface slow them down even more? Challenge them to predict which tray —one cooled by ice cubes or another at room temperature—will cause the most condensation. Some children may predict no difference. *suggest hypotheses*

Develop needed controls. Each pan will be held in turn about the same distance and time over the water. The falling drops will be counted, if possible. Try the untreated tray first. While this is being done, place some ice cubes on the second tray. If this is accomplished too soon, some moisture may condense out of the surrounding air, and spoil the experiment. Placing the cubes in the tray about a minute before the trial should produce satisfactory results. Much more condensation from the evaporated water will appear on the cooler plate. Discuss.

Wipe off whatever moisture is underneath the two plates. Hold each up high. Have children observe them closely. They will notice condensation occurring on the colder metal. Bring out that this moisture is coming from the air itself. A surface that is sufficiently cool causes *dew* to form when the air contains sufficient moisture. Let them recall common experiences with dew formation. *draw conclusions* *evaluate critically*

Extending activities

1. Encourage pupils to develop a list of specific objects around the home and school which have been in liquid form but are now "frozen." Help them classify the specific objects into broader categories, such as candy, plastics, glass, dairy products, wax, and metal. *evaluate critically*

2. Most children know from personal experience that evaporation is a cooling process. For example, let them recall how cool wet skin and a wet bathing suit feel after emerging from water.

Now ask, "Why are hospital patients who have very high temperatures sometimes given an alcohol rubdown? Why don't they just use water?" When someone suggests greater cooling, challenge the group to develop a comparative test of alcohol and water as cooling agents. *suggest hypotheses* *select procedures*

An easy method is to wrap the bulbs of two identical thermometers with small pieces of cotton, one saturated with alcohol, the other with water. Fan rapidly with cardboard. After a moment or so, the alcohol-treated thermometer will show a significantly lower temperature.

Spill identical, small amounts of alcohol and water on a surface. Have everyone note how much more rapidly the alcohol dries. *draw conclusions* Bring out that the faster a substance evaporates the faster heat energy is removed from the surface on which it rests.

3. Get a porous ceramic pot or canvas water bag and fill with water. Fill another similar-sized, but nonporous container with an equal volume of water. Have pupils note the temperatures of both containers periodically throughout a school day. The porous container will be consistently cooler through evaporation. A good bridge for this activity is *suggest hypotheses* to inquire why porous materials are often used to store water in hot climates. Isn't some water wasted that way? Then conduct it as an experiment.

We have stated that the temperature of a material is simply a measure of the speed of its molecules. Molecules of a cold substance move less rapidly than those of a hotter substance. The beginning activity of this section offers pupils a test of this statement through observation of colored water drops as they diffuse through water of unequal temperatures.

Although the concept of temperature is understood by many intermediate children, quantity of heat is a subtler idea. Consider a white-hot horseshoe just removed from a blacksmith's forge, and a large bathtub of hot water. Which contains the most heat? Very probably the water. The amount of heat a material contains depends on how many molecules it has, as well as how fast they are moving. This is why the owner of a large house pays much more for his winter fuel (heat energy) bill than someone who owns

a small house, although the same air temperature may be maintained. It also explains why it takes about twice as long to bring a quart than a pint of water to a boil. There are twice as many molecules to heat.

Different materials have different capacities for heat energy. For example, it takes more heat for iron to reach a given temperature than equal weights of glass or lead. More energy is required to heat water to a given temperature than any other common material, liquid or solid, and water retains this heat longer. The most important effect of water's high heat capacity is found in weather and climate. Since the earth's oceans and lakes gain and lose heat more slowly than the land, they moderate changes in air temperature throughout the world. The most noticeable effects are found in coastal regions. Summers are cooler and winters warmer here than they are inland.

Two measures are commonly used to determine heat capacity: the calorie and British Thermal Unit (BTU). A calorie is the quantity of heat needed to raise the temperatures of a gram (about 1/28 ounce) of water 1° centigrade. The caloric value of a food is found simply by burning a dry sample of known weight in a special chamber of a carefully insulated container of water. The temperature rise is multiplied by the weight of water in the container. For example, assume 50 grams of water rises 20°C. $50 \times 20 = 1000$ calories. To make calculations less cumbersome, a "large" calorie is used in finding heat value of foods. Equivalent to 1000 small calories, the large calorie is what you see published in diet lists and nutrition recommendations.

The British Thermal Unit is used widely by engineers. Defined as the quantity of heat needed to raise 1 pound of water 1° Fahrenheit, it is also found by multiplying the mass of water by the temperature increase. Thus, to raise the temperature of 5 pounds of water 30°F requires 150 BTU.

Of course, this information is intended more for your use than for the pupils' at this level. However, it is not too early for many children to grasp the general idea of heat quantity. It is for this reason we have included several appropriate activities in the following material.

BASIC GENERALIZATION III: There is a difference between the temperature of a material and the heat it contains

Contributing idea A. Temperature is the measure of how fast molecules are moving.

1. *Materials:* two eye-droppers; two large, identical drinking glasses; blue ink or food coloring; water. (Fill one glass with hot water, and the other with water at room temperature. Let each stand for at least three minutes to settle the water. Do not move after settling.)

Review that heat energy speeds up the motion of molecules. The higher the temperature, the faster molecules move. Indicate the two glasses of water. Inform the children that one—do not specify which—contains hot, and the other cooler, water. Draw out that a drop of ink will spread (diffuse) throughout water when placed in it.

Develop the problem: If the hot water molecules are moving around faster than the cold water molecules, how will this affect a drop of ink placed in each? Let pupils discuss and defend their predictions through reasoning about molecules. (The more rapidly moving molecules should scatter the ink molecules faster.)

Hold each eye-dropper over a filled glass and release one ink drop from each at the same time. Request everyone to observe carefully. A white piece of background paper will assist observation. After several minutes, it will be interesting to check quickly the accuracy of the pupils' inferences. Label one glass "1" with a small card, and the other "2." Ask everyone to hold up guardedly one or two fingers to indicate which container holds hot water.

Have several children report what they saw. Guide a related discussion. This will help their reasoning, and also give additional time for more complete diffusion to take place. A

[margin: ggest heses]

[margin: draw sions]

pupil might now check the two water temperatures with his hand for verification. Should one or two thermometers be available, they will be preferable to use.

If your group is able, it may be more challenging to use three water temperatures, rather than two—cool, warm, and hot. Avoid extreme temperatures, however. Water vapor condenses on a cold glass. Very hot water may "steam" somewhat and also provide a clue.

2. Try faulty procedure on retrials. For example, stir the cooler water on some pretext ("This water is cloudy; let's clear it up a bit first.") before dropping in the ink. This will bring an indignant chorus of protest from an alert, thinking class. If the faulty procedure goes undetected, help them analyze the conflicting data.

[margin: reason quantitatively]

[margin: select procedures]

[margin: draw conclusions]

Contributing idea B. The amount of heat a material contains depends on how many molecules it has, as well as how fast they are moving.

1. *Materials:* large pan of water; hot plate; two Pyrex transparent bowls, one large, one small; two ice cubes. (To save time, heat water before this experiment.)

Ask everyone who likes to swim in a pool to raise his hand. Tell these pupils they seem to be just the ones to figure out a very puzzling problem. A large swimming pool may have to be heated for several days before it is warm enough to swim in, yet a small pool can be heated to the same temperature in perhaps half the time. Why is this so? Ask for a molecular explanation. Develop these ideas:

a. A large pool has more water molecules than a small pool.

b. Heat energy is used to speed up molecules to the desired temperature.

c. The more molecules there are, the more heat energy it takes to reach a desired temperature.

Pour some hot water into the small bowl, much more into the larger one. Explain that the bowls are like the two swimming pools, one smaller and one larger. Elicit that water temperature is the same in both cases; the molecules are moving at about the same

suggest hypotheses

speed. But which bowl should contain the most heat energy? (Large.) How can the guess be tested? If ice cubes are visible, someone will probably suggest dropping an equal-sized cube into each bowl. Have someone stir

select procedures

each bowl an equal number of times to speed the melting process. Help develop a tentative conclusion that more heat energy is present in the larger volume of water.

2. *Materials:* hot plate; one small and one large nail; two small, identical tinned cans, containing equal volumes of water at about room temperature; two thermometers; pliers.

Just before starting this lesson, place the two nails on the hot plate, and heat them for about five minutes. If the hot plate lacks a metal cover, the nails should be placed on a clean, tinned-can lid or other sturdy metal surface as they are heated.

Call attention to the two heated nails. State that they have been heated for some time, and now both are at the same temperature. But one nail is larger than the other; it is made up of more molecules. Now ask,

suggest hypotheses

"Which nail contains more heat energy?" (Large.)

select procedures

Refer to your materials. How can they be used to find out which nail contains the more heat energy? Guide pupils toward putting a nail in each can to heat the water. (Be sure to use pliers or tongs in transferring the nails from hot plate to cans.) If there is more heat energy in one nail, it should raise the water temperature higher than the other.

But first the water temperatures will need checking to see if they are the same. After the nails are immersed, the thermometers can be used for stirring the water in each glass to an even temperature. When the temperature rise in each can stabilizes, degree readings should be recorded. Of course, it is wise to get as many procedural ideas as possible from the class itself.

Data might be recorded like this:

	Before	After	Difference
reason quantitatively Large nail can	70°	74°	4°
Small nail can	70°	71°	1°

Assist class reasoning toward a conclusion

of more heat energy in the larger nail. Point *draw concl* out that the amount of heat energy in a fuel or food is determined similarly by scientists. A fuel or food is burned to see how hot it can make a certain volume of water. The measure used is a *calorie.* Another is the *British Thermal Unit,* or *BTU.* Tell pupils they will find out more about these measures of heat energy in later grades.

Extending activities

1. Pupils will enjoy and profit from the following experience. It should help them understand the unreliability of determining temperature by touch. Fill three pans with water —one very cold, one hot, and one at room temperature. Label the pans "cold," "hot," and "room temperature" for easy reference. Keep the room temperature pan out of sight while choosing a volunteer. Have a blindfolded volunteer place one hand in hot, and his other hand in cold, water for at least two minutes. Let him withdraw the "cold" hand and put it into the room temperature water. He will say it is "warm." Pretend to remove this third pan, and replace it with another. Now have the volunteer withdraw the "hot" hand and put it into the same room temperature pan. He will say it is "cold."

2. Invite pupils to give a molecular explanation for this situation. Two persons in a restaurant order tea—one iced, the other hot. Both use one lump of sugar for sweetening. Which one will stir his tea longer, and *draw concl* why?

3. Challenge the class to develop bulletin-board ideas to illustrate the difference between temperature and the amount of heat energy present in a substance.

Until the nineteenth century it was generally thought that heat was a fluidlike substance ("Caloric") which could be poured from one material to another. Scientists now realize that heat is a form of energy—energy being defined as the capacity to do work.

Many experiments have shown that energy can be transformed from one form to another.

Our practical experience also indicates that this is so. Electrical energy changes to heat in toasters and hot plates; chemical energy yields heat through fires and explosives; mechanical energy (motion) provides the force necessary to overcome friction, and in the process heat is released.

Heat, in turn, changes to other forms of energy. Hot fuel turns a generator to produce electricity; gasoline is burned in automobile engines to produce mechanical energy, and so on. The initial activities of the present section are intended to help children achieve some understanding of this important idea.

If you put a pan of hot water in a cool room, after a while the water cools to room temperature. But place a pan of cool water in a hot oven and the water warms to oven temperature. Heat energy always travels from a place of higher temperature to one of lower temperature. In moving from one location to another, heat energy may travel in one or more of three ways—by *conduction, convection*, and *radiation*. Let us consider these ways one at a time.

If you grasp the metal handle of a hot frying pan you quickly let go. How is it possible for the heat energy to go from the hot stove grid to the handle? Molecular conduction is responsible. As heat energy enters the pan bottom, its molecules begin to vibrate faster. This motion is passed along, molecule by molecule, up the pan's sides to its handle. Eventually all the particles are vibrating faster, and you feel the heat.

Of all solids, metals are the best conductors. Their molecules are very close together and transmit the heat energy quickly. But each type of metal varies somewhat in conductivity. Copper is the best common conductor, followed by aluminum, steel, and iron. Other solids are comparatively poor conductors, including ceramic materials. This is one reason we use a ceramic cup to hold hot coffee. As any army veteran knows, drinking hot coffee from a metal cup can be a painful experience.

Since molecules of liquids are farther apart than solids, it is reasonable to expect that their conduction of heat is less efficient than in solids. Ordinary experiences with bathwater help confirm this thought. When hot water is added to cooler water, it takes a long time for the heat to reach all portions of the tub. For this reason, most persons stir the water a bit to hasten the process.

Gases are the poorest conductors of all. Their molecules are spread so far apart they do not collide often and regularly enough to pass on increased energy to any appreciable extent. This is why it is possible for frozen-food sections in supermarkets to have open counters. Very little heat energy is conducted downward from the warmer air above the counter.

Although liquids and gases conduct poorly, it is easy to heat a pan of water quickly to boiling temperature, or quickly roast a frankfurter in the hot air over a fire. There must be another, more efficient method of heat transfer in liquids and gases than conduction. Let us examine first what happens when air is warmed.

Watch the smoke from a burning cigarette. Why does it rise? Is it unaffected by gravity? A clue to its behavior is found when a burning cigarette is placed in a vacuum chamber. The smoke particles fall like lead weights. Therefore, smoke does not just "rise"; something must push it up.

When the glowing tip of a cigarette warms the adjacent air, the increased energy agitates air molecules to increased speeds and they spread farther apart. Since now fewer molecules take up a given volume of space, they are lighter than an equal volume of the surrounding air. The lighter air is pushed up with the smoke particles as it is replaced by heavier, colder air. As the mass of lighter air rises, it carries increased energy with it. This is why air near the ceiling is warmer than air near the floor.

When there is an opening for warm air to escape and cool air to flow into a room, a *convection current* is set up. This is a principal method by which our homes are heated. It is also the primary cause of winds in the atmosphere.

Similar convection currents are set up in

heated liquids. Warmed, expanded water in a pan rises as it is continually replaced by cooler, heavier water until the same temperature is reached in the entire container. Because of the way convective currents move, a heating unit is usually located at the bottom of a hot-water tank and a cooling unit at the top of a refrigerator.

Convection also helps to set up ocean currents. Warm water at the equator is continually being replaced by cold water flowing from the polar regions. Air convection currents form winds which contribute to the distribution of these giant water currents. A third important factor is the earth's rotation. Because water has a high heat capacity, ocean currents are responsible for altering the climates of many countries.

A common example of the third method of heat transfer is found in the fireplace of a home. This is especially noticeable when the air temperature is low. As you warm yourself in front of the fire, only the portion of your body that faces the fire feels warm. Conduction is poor, since air is the conducting medium. Convection is negligible, since most of the hot air escapes up the chimney. Heat reaches you by radiation.

All vibrating molecules release a certain amount of energy through invisible heat rays, called *infrared waves*. These waves largely pass through transparent materials like air and glass, but are absorbed by opaque objects, which become warmer as a result. We are conscious of radiant energy only when the emitting source is warmer than body temperature. The sun is by far our most important source of radiant energy. In its rays are found visible light, invisible infrared waves, and other forms of radiant energy. We shall go into more detail in the unit on light energy (page 157).

Knowledge of how heat travels permits us to control it. We use *insulation* to prevent or retard heat energy transfer. For example, to retard conduction, we use poor conductors. Since air is a poor conductor, materials with air spaces, such as wood and wool, make excellent insulators.

In homes, convection and conduction are reduced by using hollow walls designed to trap the air. Since some convection takes place anyway, some homeowners fill the walls with a light, fluffy material, such as rock wool.

An excellent way to insulate for radiation is to reflect it away, since it behaves like light as it travels. This is why insulating materials in the home may use a shiny foil exterior, particularly in the attic. It explains, too, why silver-colored paint is used on large gasoline storage tanks.

One of the concluding activities of this section presents an opportunity for children to discover, in an open-ended way, the efficiency of many insulating materials.

BASIC GENERALIZATION IV: Heat energy may come from many sources; it travels by conduction, convection, and radiation

Contributing idea A. Many sources of energy can be changed to heat energy.

Materials: magnifying glass; sandpaper and block of wood; toaster; small can of plaster of Paris, water, and stick for stirring; match and candle; hammer, large nail, and block of wood.

Bring out that, although the class has learned much about the effects of heat energy, not much has been said thus far about its origins. In how many different ways can molecules be made to move faster? Invite a discussion of how the materials might be employed to produce heat energy. Permit groups of pupils to explore their ideas. Help organize on the chalkboard activities which convert some other energy forms to heat energy. For example:

Electrical energy—a plugged-in toaster; heat from a light bulb.
Chemical energy—a burning match; burning candle; mixing water and plaster of Paris.
Mechanical energy (energy of motion)—friction produced when rubbing hands together, and rubbing sandpaper on wood; a hammered nailhead gets warm.

Light energy—a magnifying glass focuses the sun's rays.

Add several forms which the children cannot easily investigate:

Sound energy—absorbed sounds speed up molecules in the sound absorbers.

Nuclear energy—heat is released in atomic reactions.

Emphasize that, regardless of its origin, heat travels in only several ways. Now the children will have an opportunity to explore these ways.

Contributing idea B. Sometimes heat travels by conduction.

1. *Materials:* candle and match; 10-inch piece of heavy, solid copper wire with insulation removed; four wax balls. (About pea size. Make from warm candle drippings.)

Have everyone recall experiences of taking hold of a hot metal pan handle, or spoon immersed in a hot liquid. Draw a large spoon on the chalkboard. Bring out that its molecules are vibrating but relatively fixed—that is, moving only within a small space—since it is a solid. When the spoon's oval end is immersed in hot liquid, its molecules must vibrate more rapidly. But what about the handle? How does it become hot? Elicit that only three ways seem possible:

a. the whole handle becomes hot at once;

b. the handle tip gets hot and heat energy moves toward the immersed part;

c. the heat gradually travels from the immersed end through the spoon's entire length.

Guide a discussion as to which of these ideas seems most reasonable. Encourage molecular explanations.

select dures

Invite a test of the children's ideas with the materials. (An old spoon may be used instead of the wire.) Several wax balls may be fixed to the wire at 1-inch intervals. When the wire end is held in a flame, the order in which the melted wax balls drop off should indicate which idea is best.

draw sions

The order of dropping will be from flame to the wire's opposite end. Encourage a molecular interpretation. As molecules in the heated end begin jiggling faster, they agitate others. Finally, increased motion is passed along the wire's entire length. Write *conduction* on the chalkboard. Emphasize that heat energy travels by conduction when one molecule passes on its increased energy by striking another molecule.

If additional clarification seems necessary, set up on end a row of closely spaced dominoes. When one domino is pushed, all the others will fall in turn.

2. *Materials:* candle and match; small steel kitchen pan with copper-coated bottom; six small balls of wax; 10-inch piece of heavy, solid copper wire with insulation removed; 10-inch piece of heavy iron wire from a wire clothes hanger.

Exhibit the kitchen pan. Draw out that heat from the stove is conducted through the pan metal to heat food. Inquire as to why the bottom part is coated with copper. Guide toward an hypothesis of better conductivity with copper than steel. Mention that you have iron wire, which is similar to steel, and copper wire on hand. (If steel wire is available, of course it would be better.) Encourage a test with these materials.

suggest hypotheses

select procedures

Three wax balls can be attached to each wire, about 1 inch apart. As ends of the two wires are held at the same time in a candle flame, conductive efficiency will be revealed as the wax pellets drop off.

Bring out that copper is a better conductor than iron. Also, the order of conductive efficiency among common metals is copper, aluminum, brass, and iron. (If identical rods of these materials are available, it would be worthwhile for pupils to discover this through a similar experiment.)

draw conclusions

3. *Materials:* metal pie plate or substitute; brick; piece of wood; piece of cloth; folded newspaper page.

The following experience will help children group some common solids in descending order of efficiency in conducting heat energy. It will also lead to an understanding of why one material may feel colder than another, although both are at an equal temperature.

Say, "Let's learn more about how well

solids conduct heat energy. How many of you like to walk barefooted outdoors?" Develop that some surfaces seem colder to the touch than others. Elicit the most obvious reason: some are in shade and some are in the sun. But now the children are going to discover something very odd.

Point out your materials. Emphasize that all have been standing in the room for some time, and all are about the same temperature. Will they all feel equally warm or cool to the touch? You will need two barefooted volunteers.

Have each person stand on two different materials at one time for comparisons. Let each independently indicate his ranking of the materials, from cooler to warmer. The pupils' opinions will tend to agree. Metal will feel the coolest, then the brick, wood, newspaper, and cloth, in that order.

suggest hypotheses

But how can this be? They were all about equal in temperature. If adequate references are available, they might be consulted. Lead toward an explanation that features conduction of heat. Some materials conduct heat well and some poorly. Good conductors conduct heat energy away rapidly from our warm skin at the point of contact. This makes them seem cool. Poor conductors pass along heat slowly. This makes them feel warmer, since less heat is lost from our skin.

select procedures

draw conclusions

4. *Materials*: large, Pyrex test tube; ice cube; small piece of steel wool; candle and match; pliers or tongs; water.

State that thus far the class has considered solids as conductors. Now there will be opportunities to investigate liquids, then gases. Review briefly what conduction means. Is conduction likely to be as good in most liquids as in solids? Entertain discussion. (Since the molecules are farther apart, it would seem less likely.)

suggest hypotheses

Place an ice cube fragment in the test tube. The ice cube may be broken up by placing it in a handkerchief and tapping it with a hammer or substitute. Use a bit of steel wool to wedge the ice firmly at the bottom of the test tube. Fill with tap water. Place the tube's top end diagonally in a candle flame while holding the opposite or bottom end in your fingers. Have everyone observe closely that water boils on top while the ice fragment remains largely unaffected. Elicit that water is a poor conductor of heat. Draw out that glass also appears to be a poor conductor—otherwise the tube would have been too hot to hold. Avoid touching the heated end of the tube.

draw concl

Empty the test tube. Place inside another ice fragment of similar size, and water. Hold the tube vertically with pliers and place it directly over a candle flame. In a short while, the floating ice will melt. Can any pupils explain this odd event? (The water has been heated by convection, not conduction.) Mention that shortly they will learn about another way in which heat travels. They will then understand more clearly what happened.

draw concl

5. *Materials*: candle; matches; pliers.

Remind everyone that air molecules are even farther apart than water molecules. Is air likely to be a good conductor? (No.) Ask for keen observation of the next demonstration.

draw conc

Use pliers to hold an unlit match. Position the match head at one side of a candle flame, about one-half inch or less away. Have someone count slowly to 10. No ignition should occur. If it does, increase the distance slightly. Bring out that air seems to be a poor conductor.

Now place the match head above the flame at a similar distance. In several seconds, it should burst into flame. How can this be explained? Mention that this and the preceding demonstration will be cleared up now as the children learn about the second way in which heat energy travels.

sugg hyp

Contributing idea C. Sometimes heat travels by convection.

1. *Materials*: small, capped ink bottle containing hot ink or hot colored water; aquarium tank or deep glass bowl two-thirds filled with tap water.

Review briefly that a liquid expands when heated. Show the ink bottle of hot water. Bring out that it weighs slightly less than an equal-sized container of cold water because of expansion. Place the ink bottle inside the container. Ask pupils what they think will happen to the ink when you unscrew the cap. (It will rise.) Now take off the cap and withdraw your hand from the water. Do this gently to avoid disturbing the water excessively. Entertain an explanation of what happened. (The hot expanded water was lighter than the surrounding water. It was pushed up while being replaced by the colder, heavier water.)

2. *Materials:* two identical milk bottles, one filled with hot, red-colored water, the other with uncolored, cool tap water; 3- by 5-inch card.

Put the card over the hot-water bottle opening. Invert the bottle, and place it gently on top of the second bottle. Explain that the top bottle contains hot, and the bottom bottle cold, water. Invite predictions and reasons as to what will happen when you remove the card. (There should be almost no mixture, as the cold water is heavier.)

Now take hold of each bottle carefully, and reverse positions. The heavier cold water will quickly displace the hot water. The hotter water will rise into the other container as the colder water empties.

Discuss to insure understanding. Identify this means of heat transfer as *convection*. The lighter mass of fast-moving molecules conveys or carries heat energy along with it as it moves from one place to another. Draw out how, in a previous demonstration, the floating ice cube melted rapidly when the test tube was heated at the bottom.

Some children may recall personal experiences with unevenly heated swiming pools and lakes. Sometimes a distinct current of warmer or colder water is noticeable. Help them to understand also that one cause of ocean currents is convection set up in unevenly heated water.

3. *Materials:* 6-inch piece of clothesline; matches; yardstick; cellophane tape; string; two identical paper bags; lamp or substitute. (Set up materials as in Figure 1-6. Slide an opened paperclip along the yardstick to

achieve a perfect balance. Leave the bulb unlit for the present.)

Light a rope end and blow out the flame. A clearly visible stream of smoke should result. Ask why it rises, rather than falls. Aren't smoke molecules affected by gravity? Lead toward a reasonable explanation. Maybe the air is also heated by convection. How can we see if warm air rises? Invite a test with the assembled materials.

The warmed air rising from the bulb will cause the bag above to rise. Help pupils to reason that wind is probably moving air caused by cooler air replacing warmed, expanded air. To check this idea further, they will want to do the next activity.

4. *Materials:* schoolroom with a top and bottom window opening; two thin, tissue paper streamers, about 10 inches long; cellophane tape; thermometer; stick or window pole. (This demonstration works well when the outside temperature is much lower than that of the schoolroom.)

Guide this activity one step at a time to develop maximum understanding:

a. Is the warmed air in the room rising? (If so, air at the ceiling should be warmer than air at floor level. Encourage thermometer readings. Air temperature near the ceiling may

FIGURE 1-6

be measured by strapping a thermometer to a long stick or window pole.)

b. Is there a place for warm air to move out of the classroom? (An open top window is needed. Since air is invisible, taping a streamer at the opening should reveal air movements as they occur.)

c. Is there a place for cooler, heavier air to enter the room? (An open bottom window is needed. Another streamer taped at the bottom should also reveal air movements.)

draw conclusions   Emphasize through reading and discussion that all winds basically are caused by convection resulting from the unequal heating and cooling of the earth's surface. Help pupils realize that many heating systems use convective currents in heating homes, schools, and factories. Have someone point out hot-air registers in the room or other places where warmed air sets up air currents in the room.

draw conclusions   Pupils should now understand why the match held above the flame in a previous demonstration ignited quickly. Most of the heat energy traveled upward through convection.

Contributing idea D. Sometimes heat travels by radiation.

1. *Materials:* electric iron; magnifying glass.

Plug in the electric iron and let it get moderately hot. Hold the iron parallel to the floor. Have a pupil place his hand 6 inches or so under the iron. He will sense the heat immediately. Ask why he feels the heat. Is it traveling from the iron by conduction? (No. Air is a very poor conductor. Also, he feels the heat immediately. Conduction takes more time.) Is it traveling by convection? (No. Any warmed air currents would rise.)

draw conclusions

Through purposeful reading or your exposition, inform the class that the heat energy travels through *radiation*. Bring out that heat rays are like light rays from the sun, except that we can only feel them and not see them. Elicit that the iron itself would glow and be visible in the dark if made hot enough.

Emphasize that when heat travels by radiation, there need not be any molecules to pass along (transfer) the energy as in conduction and convection. Let someone focus the sun's

rays with a magnifying glass on a piece of paper. Help pupils to understand that the sun's energy is radiating through largely empty space to the earth. Only when the radiant energy causes the paper's molecules to move faster is the heat noticed.

Develop that nearly all objects give off some radiant energy, but this is not noticeable to us until they are fairly warm. Have children recall the warmth that exudes from a fireplace for some time after the fire is out, or the warmth radiated from sidewalks and stone buildings shortly after sunset.

2. *Materials:* two thermometers; two identical tinned cans (one painted black inside and out); cardboard lids; hot water.

Inform the class that we use radiators to give off as much heat energy as possible. Examples are radiant heating in homes, steam or hot-water heating employing room radiators, and automobile radiators. Describe, or have pupils read about these cases.

Now introduce a related problem. Most room radiators are painted silver, or some other light color. Most automobile radiators are painted black. Yet in both cases we want these objects to lose (radiate) as much heat energy as possible. Why aren't both painted the same color? Develop speculation, and a possible test with the available materials.   *sugge hypo*

To determine which radiates heat faster, pour hot water into each can and cover with a cardboard lid. For continual temperature readings, a hole may be cut in each lid just large enough to accommodate a thermometer. Have children record temperatures within both cans, and times taken on the chalkboard. If no thermometers are available, temperature differences will be noticeable by touch after a short while.   *selec proce*

Help pupils conclude that the darker color apparently helps to increase the radiation, since the water temperature drop is greatest in the dark-colored container. Encourage duplicate experiments at home or school for verification.   *draw conc.*

Request a pupil survey of parents and friends who have painted home radiators a light color. Assist in concluding that this is done for appearance, rather than efficiency.

Contributing idea E. Knowing how heat travels allows us to control it through insulation.

1. *Materials:* large sketch of Figure 1-7; Thermos bottle. (Borrow one from a child who brings his lunch to school.)

Hold up a Thermos bottle, and establish its dual purpose of keeping liquids cold or hot for an extended time period. Point out that to do this, the bottle designer must have developed ways of controlling conduction, convection, and radiation. Invite the class to speculate how this was done by looking at a cross section of a vacuum bottle (your sketch of Figure 1-7). Use a series of questions to assist reasoning:

draw
clusions

Why is a glass container used instead of metal? (Glass is a poor conductor. Heat from a warm liquid will not pass easily to the outside; the reverse is also true if the liquid is to stay cool.)

Why is air removed from the hollow glass walls of the container? (No air conduction can take place. No convection can take place.) Develop that the removal of air leaves a *vacuum*—a space in which no molecules are present. Mention, however, that it is at present impossible to remove all the air. Therefore, it is not a perfect vacuum.

Why are the two inside surfaces of the glass walls given a silver coating? (Probably most of the children will only be able to speculate that it might have something to do with radiation. This will help lead into the next experiment.)

2. *Materials:* two identical tinned cans, one with a shiny metal exterior, the other painted black; tap water; silver foil lids, one painted black; two thermometers (optional); sunshine.

Should a picture be available of large, silver-painted gasoline storage tanks, show it. If not, it is likely that enough children have seen these tanks to have a discussion. Bring out that gasoline is highly flammable, and it is wise to keep the storage tanks as cool as possible. But why are they painted bright sil-

—Plastic or cork top

Glass with double wall

No air

Silver coating

FIGURE 1-7

ver? Why not black? Both paints would protect the steel tanks from rusting.

Guide toward a reasonable hypothesis. The sun's radiant energy may be largely reflected from a silvered surface, which would keep the gasoline cooler than if black paint were used. Help pupils develop an appropriate controlled experiment.

suggest hypotheses

Two tinned cans, one painted black, may be filled with water, capped with foil, and left in the sun. About an hour's exposure to strong sunlight should be more than adequate to notice the difference of water temperature in the two cans, even if thermometers are not used.

select procedures

Help pupils conclude that a shiny, silver surface is useful to reflect radiant heat. In the case of a vacuum bottle, two such surfaces help to keep heat from entering or leaving the container.

draw conclusions

Call attention to the shiny, foil bags used to transport ice cream home from a market, or the foil wrapper on a popsicle. These, too, are used to block radiant energy.

3. *Materials:* a piece of wool and piece of cotton cloth; scissors; glass of water.

Have the class discuss the need for clothing to conserve body heat, particularly in winter.

FIGURE 1-8

suggest hypotheses

Bring out that woolens are worn oftener in winter than in summer. Develop speculation as to why woolens are warmer. Let some children closely inspect the weaves of cotton and wool cloth. Comment about the wool's looseness of weave. They have found out that air is a poor conductor of heat. Does wool contain more trapped air than cotton?

select procedures

Encourage a test. Equal-sized pieces of cotton and wool can be pushed under water, one at a time. The cloth releasing the most bubbles probably holds the most air. Develop the need for retrials and careful observation.

draw conclusions

Comment that the children have been discovering about *insulation*, the ways of slowing down or preventing the movement of heat energy from one place to another. Draw out how animals use insulation for warmth. A polar bear has heavy, fluffy fur that traps air. This is such a good insulator that zoo bears in summer sometimes are supplied with large cakes of ice and chilled water to maintain good health. Birds fluff their feathers often in chilly weather. This traps more air, which provides more insulation. Through reading or reporting, let pupils find out that many Eskimos wear animal fur inside out. The skin deflects wind, while the trapped still air inside the fur offers excellent insulation.

4. *Materials:* two small, identical tinned cans; two other larger identical cans, large enough to hold the smaller ones; cotton; two cardboard lids for the larger cans; two thermometers (optional).

Bring out that one reason a house is constructed with double walls is to take advantage of the still air trapped between. Develop that, in spite of this, many homeowners have this space filled with fluffy, cottonlike material. How helpful is this practice in conserving heat?

select proce

Assist pupils in setting up some materials to find out. Place the two smaller cans in the larger ones. Pack loose, fluffy cotton around one smaller can. Fill both with hot water. If thermometers are available, have someone record the initial temperatures. Cap both large containers with cardboard lids. Have periodic readings taken. Should the group be able, the use of a simple graph, such as in Figure 1-8, will be profitable. This can be made an open-end activity by children experimenting with many insulating materials at home or school and exhibiting their graphs with subsequent reports.

reaso quant

draw concl

Help the children to understand that wall and ceiling insulation reduces heat passage through convection and conduction. When a shiny, reflecting foil is used to sandwich the soft, fibrous material, this gives additional insulation against radiation.

Extending activities

1. Invite an explanation of why a freezing unit is usually located in the top section of a refrigerator and a heating unit beneath a hot-water tank or hot-water heating system.

draw concl

2. Lower a small piece of metal window screen (or wire gauze) over the tip of a candle flame. No flame will appear above it, although most of the gas continues upward. Encourage able pupils to find out why. (The metal screen conducts heat energy away so fast the gas is no longer hot enough to burn.)

evalu critic

3. Show a film or filmstrip on heat transfer by conduction, convection, and radiation.

4. Have a committee report on how homes

are heated by the three ways of heat transfer.

valuate
ritically 5. Encourage the children to conduct a hunt for insulators in the kitchen and elsewhere in their houses and list them. Some items that may be recorded are: hot pads, cloth pot holders, wooden and plastic handles on cooking utensils, oven and refrigerator insulation, insulation in ceilings, walls, and floors, weather stripping around doors and windows, double-pane glass windows and sliding doors, storm windows, and asbestos coverings on hot-water or steam pipes.

6. Conduct a study trip to a nearby home construction site to observe heating and insulation provisions. Also visit and inspect the school heating plant. Ask the custodian to explain how it operates.

7. Contact a local building insulation contractor or dealer for possible display of some materials available for home insulation.

Sound Energy

(Intermediate)

Play a radio loudly, and the windows rattle. Watch a parade at a distance and the marchers seem to be out-of-time with the music. Sing in the shower and suddenly your voice takes on new dimensions.

There are few topics that present so many available materials and interesting "whys" to explore as sound energy. In this unit, children learn what sounds are and how they are made. They measure distances at which echoes appear, experiment with changes in pitch, and manipulate molecular models. This is a "doing" unit virtually all the way through.

BASIC GENERALIZATIONS

I. Sounds are caused by vibrations that travel in waves.

II. Sound waves travel in air, water, and solids—at different speeds.

III. Sound waves can be reflected and absorbed; echoes are reflections at a distance.

IV. Pitch changes as the speed of vibrations change.

V. Sound waves can cause forced and sympathetic vibrations.

VI. Many sound waves can be heard by us, but many cannot be heard.

Every so often in science fiction a sinister scientist invents a machine capable of collecting and playing back all the sounds that have ever been made. Though at first he uses the machine to help historians determine what King John *really* said at Runnymede, shortly he is offering the enemy military secrets discussed at the Pentagon.

Of course, all indications are that such a machine could never be invented. Sounds are simply waves of compressed molecules pulsating outward in all directions from a vibrating source. Consider the air about you. It is composed of tiny, individual molecules of different gases mixed with relative uniformity throughout the lower atmosphere. These molecules are rapidly and randomly moving about. A fast vibrating source—hummingbird's wings, bell, guitar string, a "twanged" ruler held on the edge of a desk—squeezes billions of these molecules with each back-and-forth movement, because the molecules are in the way. Since air molecules are apparently quite elastic, they quickly assume their original shape after moving out of the vibrating object's path. But before this happens, they transfer energy to other molecules over a distance.

Let us emphasize that it is the *wave of energy* that may travel a great distance, rather than the molecules. Each molecule may move less than a billionth of an inch; but this is enough to bump the next randomly moving molecule and so pass on the outward movement. Figure 2-1 shows a wave motion resulting from a compression and rarefaction effect on the molecules started by the vibrating source.

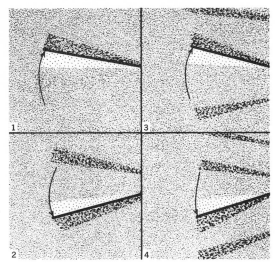

In (1) the ruler is squeezing the air molecules together (compression). Notice the thinned out space below it (rarefaction). Picture (2) shows the opposite happening, with the first part of the sound wave now moving away. (3) and (4) show another sound wave being produced. The wave moves outward as the squeezed molecules push others in the way, which in turn squeeze other molecules.

FIGURE 2-1 A vibrating ruler producing sound waves.

A sound fades away when energy behind the original vibrations is used up in the transmitting process. As one molecule bumps another it uses a tiny amount of energy. As more molecules are bumped, there is less energy available. The sound stops when energy of the randomly moving molecules exceeds the wave's energy. The molecules simply resume their normal helter-skelter movements.

How is loudness explained? First of all, let us call it *intensity*. "Loudness" is what we actually hear. If our ears are functioning poorly, a very intense sound may be barely discernible. So loudness is a matter of individual perception. On the other hand, intensity can be consistently and accurately recorded by a sensitive sound detector in terms of the *decibel*, a unit of measurement in sound. The distinction between loudness and intensity may be too subtle to be worth teaching at the intermediate-grade level.

Shouting requires more energy than whispering. Expenditure of more energy forces any vibrating medium to vibrate to-and-fro more widely than usual, but in the same amount of time. This squeezes molecules more forcefully, and the greater energy is able to move more molecules.

Of course, distance is also a factor in sound intensity. The farther away we are from the source, the weaker the sound. Molecules are pushed less because there is progressively less energy available. Interestingly, the same mathematical relationship is found in sound loss as exists with such other forms of energy as light, gravity, magnetism, and electricity. Intensity diminishes as the square of the distance between any sound source and perceiver. At 20 feet a sound has only one-fourth the intensity it exhibits at 10 feet from the source. With a distance of 30 feet intensity drops to one-ninth of the original sound. At 40 feet only one-sixteenth of the original intensity remains.

Sometimes the analogy of a water wave is used to teach how sound travels. A pebble is dropped into water and a circular series of ripples spreads out on the water's surface. This may be useful to show to your class. However, this example contains two main defects. Water waves are up-and-down motions which travel at right angles to the line of the waves. These are called *transverse* waves. Sound waves come from back-and-forth motions that result in *longitudinal* waves. Also, water waves move only horizontally, whereas sound waves travel outward in all planes. Many science teachers ask students to imagine sound waves as they would a series of rapidly blown soap bubbles, each enveloped within another that is slightly larger, all quickly expanding outward in all directions.

The wave idea is useful to distinguish between *sounds* and *noises*. A sound consists of regularly pulsating vibrations—the time interval between each compression and rarefaction is the same. Noise is heard when irregular vibrations are transmitted.

BASIC GENERALIZATION I: Sounds are caused by vibrations that travel in waves

Contributing idea A. Sounds are caused by vibrations.

Tell your pupils that they are going to see and participate in a number of demonstrations with sound makers. (Five are suggested.) You have decided to be completely silent except to give occasional directions. Each demonstration will feature something that makes a sound. Everyone is independently to develop a satisfactory answer to this question: How are the sound makers alike?

1. *Materials:* desk or table; a thin 1-foot ruler or flat stick or hacksaw blade).

Hold down firmly about one-third of a ruler with the heel of one hand on a table edge; the remaining two-thirds should stick out over the edge. Press down the projecting end with the other hand and quickly let go. Repeat several times. The humming sound made will be loud and prolonged if about an inch of ruler is left between your hand and table edge.

2. *Materials:* tuning fork; one grain of puffed rice suspended from a foot-long thread. (Thread it with a needle and knot the end, or glue it.) Any small, light object can be substituted—puffed wheat, bit of cork, bit of balled tissue paper, pith ball, and so on.

Sharply strike the tuning fork against a rubber heel. Draw the suspended object closer to the vibrating fork until it touches and bounces away. Repeat several times.

3. *Materials:* tuning fork or triangle (the kindergarten usually has one); small, shallow dish or small, transparent bowl; a few ounces of water.

Sharply strike a fork or triangle to make it vibrate. Hold it loosely against an empty dish. A loud ringing noise will be heard. Now pour some water into the dish. Strike the fork again, and thrust the vibrating ends into the water. It will splatter slightly.

4. *Materials:* toy drum (One can be made from a coffee can or cylindrical oatmeal container by covering the open end with a piece of balloon or inner tube. Fasten down with string, tape, or staples.); a tablespoon of sand (or some bits of anything light—cork, salt, sugar, puffed rice, and so on).

Sprinkle sand or substitute material over the drum head. Strike the drum. Particles will bounce up and down as the head vibrates, thus making vibrations easier to see.

5. *Materials:* rubber bands. (One for each child is ideal. Children will bring them from home if reminded a day in advance.)

Ask the children to clench one end of a band in their teeth, and to stretch the other end slightly with their thumb. (A brief word here about standards will prevent some from stretching the rubber bands to the breaking point.) Have them pluck the strands with their fingers. Ask them to stop the sound before it stops by itself. Most will find out they can do this by pressing a finger against the vibrating bands. Inquire if sound starts again when they take their fingers off the band. (It does not.)

Elicit from your class the thing common to all the demonstrations: a to-and-fro movement called *vibrations*. Without vibrations there is no sound. It might be worthwhile to have children briefly demonstrate the sound makers again to clinch this idea. Or it may be useful to divide the class into small groups. Each group can manipulate one set of materials for a short time and then move on to another set. *draw conclusions*

6. *Materials:* a rubber band for each pupil; chalkboard or chart sketch of human vocal cords (see Figure 2-2).

The children should be ready now for learning how they make sounds with their vibrating vocal cords. Inform them that shortly they will be asked to explain how they make sounds with their voices. Have each child stretch his rubber band slightly, with the two strands close together. Tell them to hold the band very close to their lips, and gently blow out air. Vibrations will be heard. Many children will feel a ticklish sensation as the moving strands touch their lips.

Now tell them to take a breath and hum

FIGURE 2-2 Voice box (larynx) seen from above.

softly with mouths closed, while touching their "Adam's apples" gently with their fingers. Direct them to pinch their noses gently with thumb and forefinger of the free hand, and to notice what happens. (Sound stops.) The sound can be interrupted and started again by alternately closing and opening the fingers.

Now ask the children to open their mouths, expel all the air they can, and then try to make a sound. (They will be unable to do so, unless they breathe in.)

draw conclusions Get them to reason how they make sounds with their voices: Air is forced from the lungs, up the throat, and through something in the Adam's apple that seems to vibrate. When the air is stopped or there is no air, vibrations are not possible. Show them a sketch of the *vocal cords*. Develop that their vocal cords are two elastic-like membranes located inside the Adam's apple. These membranes vibrate when air rushes past. It would be advisable to avoid an explanation at this time of how changes of pitch are accomplished. This will become more understandable after later experiences.

The class will be interested in learning that such animals as cats and cows, for instance, are easily able to make sounds with their vocal cords as they *breathe in*. Let the class practice for a moment saying, "Are you there?" in this way. It can be done, but it is awkward and unsatisfactory.

Contributing idea B. Sound travels in waves that spread out in all directions.

1. *Materials:* a bell, or any other sound maker; several chairs.

Point out to your pupils that they have discovered there is no sound without a vibrating object. But how does sound travel outward from a vibrating object? Does it travel only in one direction? Does it go high and low? Develop conjecture. The children may hypothesize that sound travels in all directions from the source. Whatever their guess, get them to set up a way of testing it by positioning themselves in various places in the room and using their sound detectors (ears). Some may use chairs to stand on; some may crouch low. Others may form circles of increasing size and distance from the sound source. When they reach the tentative conclusion that sound travels outward in all directions from the source, it will be interesting and challenging to them if you give another explanation. *suggest hypothe* *select procedu*

You might say, "What *real* proof do we have that sound travels through air in all directions? In every case we were connected in some way to the floor. Maybe the sound is just traveling through the floor and up our bodies. How could we find out if sound can travel through the air?" For proof, someone may offer that airplane noises can be heard; that skyrocket explosions can be heard on the Fourth of July, or that thunder can be heard. All these indicate that sound can travel through air. But invite pupils to develop their own test. If clues are needed, tell them that two jumpers might be able to find out. (Both children can jump up high simultaneously while one calls to the other.) *select procedu*

2. *Materials:* ten marbles; two yardsticks; ruler or stick.

Tell pupils they are going to see several more demonstrations which will help them understand how sound travels. Explain that everything is made up of *molecules*. A molecule is a very tiny bit of anything—gas, liquid, or solid. Most are too small to be seen even under powerful microscopes. Atoms are even tinier, and join together to form molecules.

FIGURE 2-3

FIGURE 2-5

Develop that gas molecules which make up the air move about every which way, bumping against one another. A sound starts when a vibrating object pushes against some molecules, which push other molecules, which in turn push others. Tell the class it will be able to understand this better by seeing the following demonstration.

Arrange two groups of five marbles each about one-fourth inch apart in a groove formed by two yardsticks. (See Figure 2-3.) Ask the class to pretend that the marbles are molecules. Wave a ruler to and fro from the wrist a few times to remind the pupils it is now pushing air molecules. Place the ruler between the two groups of marbles. With a slow vibratory motion knock one end marble into the rest on one side, then repeat on the *draw* other side. Establish that each "molecule" *clusions* travels only a short distance, while the wave motion itself continues. Repeat several times.

3. *Materials:* "Slinky" toy spring (available at toy stores or borrow from a child); table.

FIGURE 2-4   A slinky toy.

A "Slinky" toy will better convey the idea of wave motion. Lay it on a table, and have someone hold one end. Stretch it slightly, holding onto it with one hand. Pinch together several coils at one end with your free hand and release them quickly. A wave motion will travel from one end to the other. Have someone mark the movement of an individual coil by placing a small strip of folded paper on top of the coil. It will move only slightly. Elicit that one coil pushes the next, and so on. Bring out that when the energy wave reaches our ears, we hear sound.

4. *Materials:* small rubber ball; set of dominoes.

Arrange a set of dominoes as shown in Figure 2-5. Drop a ball into the center. A wave motion will travel outward.

Children should criticize the models used in the three preceding demonstrations. Their *evaluate* chief criticism should be that the models *critically* showed only horizontal movement, while sound appeared to travel outward from the source in all directions (planes). Mention again that air molecules are in constant random movement.

Contributing idea C. Loudness of a sound depends upon its energy and distance traveled.

1. *Materials:* drum or substitute; tablespoon of sand or substitute; pencil.

Ask, "Who knows how to make a soft sound with this drum?" Before the drum is struck with a pencil sprinkle sand on top so that vibrations can be seen. The sand will move up and down slightly. Now inquire how a loud sound can be made. Everyone should note greater sand movement as the drumhead is struck with greater force. Bring out that more *energy* is used to strike the drum the second time. Explain that energy is the ability to move things. Movement in this case is a vibrating drumhead and the arm used for striking the drum. Develop that the children would get more tired from pounding a drum loudly for an hour than from striking it gently for an hour, because they would use more energy when pounding.

2. *Materials:* thin 1-foot ruler; table or desk.

Permit a few children to make loud and soft noises by vibrating a ruler on a table edge with varying degrees of force. Call attention to the greater force (and so greater energy) needed to make the sounds louder.

3. *Materials:* ten to fifteen marbles, one-fourth inch apart; two yardsticks; cellophane tape. Arrange as in Figure 2-6.

Announce that you will demonstrate two "sounds" with an air molecule model. The pupils are to distinguish between a soft and loud sound. Gently push the end marble into the next so wave motion stops after a distance of several marbles. (A little practice will make this easy.) Also, if a stretched cloth or desk blotter is placed under the yardsticks, marbles will be prevented from rolling too freely. Rearrange the marbles. This time give a slightly harder push, so that wave motion *draw conclusions* continues past the previous point. Bring out that the second "sound" wave travels farther because it has more energy and can push more molecules.

Emphasize that the class has been working with a model (analogy), and that one way to test how well a model explains things is to see *evaluate critically* how it matches actual experience. *Does a soft sound travel as far as a loud sound? Is it easier to hear a sound when close to or far

away from it?* Answers should be related to the model. Help the children conclude that loudness of sounds depends on both the energy of a sound wave and the distance it has *draw conclusi* traveled. Even a loud sound ceases when it has used up its energy to move molecules.

Extending activities

1. Divide class members into several discussion groups to evaluate the following statement: An inventor claims that he has developed a sound-gathering machine. He says it *evaluate critically* can collect all the sounds from the air that have ever been made—the voices of George Washington, and so on. Is this possible if our understanding of sound waves is correct? Why or why not?

2. Encourage children to bring in as many sound makers as possible. Each contributor explains how sound is produced in his material. A display table and bulletin board may be arranged.

3. Pupils can read and consult authorities to learn how animals of many kinds make sounds—insects, fishes, mammals, reptiles, amphibians, birds, etc.

4. Ask an able child to make a report on the loudest sound ever recorded—a volcanic explosion on what was once the island of Krakatoa, in Indonesia. The sound wave was so powerful it traveled thousands of miles.

FIGURE 2-6

Watch a parade from afar and band members appear to be out-of-step with the music they are playing. Observe a carpenter hammering a nail on a distant roof top, and you hear the sound as he lifts the hammer instead of when he strikes the nail. Note the increasing speed of aircraft, and be assured that protests to the Federal Aviation Agency over sonic booms continue to mount!

The speeds at which sound waves travel lie behind each of these events. Light travels so fast—about 186,000 miles per second—it seems instantaneous to our eyes. But sound is another matter. At sea level and 42°F., sound waves move about 1100 feet per second in the air—as fast as a rifle bullet. (This number is rounded off to 1000 in the unit to make computation easier.) Sound also travels in liquids and solids. It moves about five times faster in water than in air; in steel, sound may travel fifteen times faster than in air.

Three conditions determine the speed of sound: temperature, density, and the elasticity or "springiness" of the molecules conducting the sound.

Density by itself does not increase the speed of sound. In fact, the speed of sound decreases with density. But often associated with density is greatly increased elasticity of molecules. When highly elastic, close-together molecules of a solid transmit sound, it travels much more rapidly than in either air or water. In the following section, construction of a simple molecular model (see page 139) is suggested to demonstrate speeds of sound in three mediums. A principal defect of this model is that comparative elasticity of molecules is not shown.

A temperature increase results in increasing the speed of sound about 1 foot per second for every 1 degree Fahrenheit. Have you ever wondered why sounds carry such large distances on certain days? On a cold winter day with snow on the ground, for example, air next to the ground is often colder than higher air. Instead of a sound wave spreading out uniformly and rapidly dying out, the temperature difference causes parts of the wave to travel at different speeds. The upper part begins to travel faster than the lower part and bends back down toward the ground some distance away.

Given the same medium and temperature, all sounds travel at the same speed. If this were not so, it would be difficult, if not impossible, to conduct concerts in large auditoriums. The reedy sound of an oboe and brassy timbre of a trombone always reach your ears at the same time, if they are begun at the same time.

If they live in a community where sonic booms occur with some frequency, it is likely that children will ask what happens when an airplane "breaks the sound barrier." We know that a sound-producing object sends out sound waves in all directions. When the object is set in motion it continues to send out waves in all directions. But let us continue to increase this object's velocity. As it goes faster it is more difficult for waves to travel outward in front of it. When an airplane reaches a certain speed (about 750 miles per hour; but it varies greatly with altitude and temperature) air compressions of these sound waves pile up into a dense wall of squeezed air. This can subject the airplane to severe stresses.

A powerful engine and proper design enable an airplane to slip through the barrier of squeezed air. Sound is largely left behind to anyone riding in the airplane. But what happens to the wall of squeezed air? The tremendous energy is passed on—molecule to molecule—until it hits the earth as a booming shock wave. The shock wave continues on the ground several or more miles wide and traces the airplane's flight path. It stops only when the pilot slows down his aircraft below the speed of sound. Sonic booms that cause the least damage start at very high altitudes. By the time energy in the original wall of compressed air is transmitted to the ground, much of it has been dissipated.

Similar shock waves are formed by an explosion, except that they move out equidistantly in all directions. Very rapid expansion of gases in an exploding bomb compresses the surrounding air. As the shock wave of compressed air moves outward, it flattens virtually anything in its path until such pressure finally dissipates over a distance.

Since energy in a sound wave is always transmitted onward molecule by molecule, it is impossible to have sound waves in a vacuum. The moon appears to be virtually airless. These two facts often lead persons to observe, "There can be no sounds on the moon." The present section closes with a problem based on this idea. Your class should be able to see how a solid might be used as the transmitting medium.

BASIC GENERALIZATION II: Sound waves travel in air, water, and solids—at different speeds

Contributing idea A. Sound waves travel much more slowly than light.

1. *Materials:* small piece of scrap wood; hammer; playground.

Point out to your pupils that if they watch a parading band from some distance, the band members will appear to be out-of-step *suggest hypotheses* with their music. Entertain hypotheses that would account for this. When travel time for *select procedures* sound is suggested, invite them to test this guess with a block of wood and hammer. They will need to do this outdoors, of course. A distance of 100 yards or more will provide a dramatic and obvious difference between when they see the block struck and when *draw conclusions* they hear the resulting sound. It is interesting to shorten this distance gradually to note decreases in the time lag.

Back in the room, help the children to recall other experiences they may have had of this kind: hearing the crack of a baseball bat after a ball has been struck; seeing the puff of "steam" (condensed water vapor) from a steam whistle before they hear the sound; hearing thunder after a flash of lightning. Explain that light travels so fast it reaches us almost instantly; light can travel a distance equal to seven and one-half times around the world in just one second! In comparison, sound travels through the air about 1000 feet a second.

2. Introduce the idea that by knowing how fast sound travels we can tell how far away some sounds are, if we can see the sound maker in action. You might say, "Since there are about 5000 feet in a mile, how many seconds will sound take to go a mile? Remember sound travels about 1000 feet a second." The simplicity of your approach, of course, will need to vary with the mathematical ability of your class. An easy method might feature a column of 1000's to add, with a corresponding column of seconds. After each five 1000's, mark off one mile. By using the chalkboard and round numbers or combina-

tions of fives, it should be possible to do such *reason quantit.* problems as these:

a. You see lightning; 10 seconds later you hear thunder. How far away was the lightning?

b. You see a tug boat blow its steam whistle far up river; 15 seconds later you hear it. How far away is it?

With practice, some children will develop the ability to estimate a second's duration. Repeating the words, "a thousand in one" in time to a clock's second sweep will aid in developing this ability.

Contributing idea B. Sound waves travel faster in water than in air, and fastest in most solids.

1. *Materials:* aquarium tank, about half-filled with water (Or a water bucket. Even the room wastebasket will do, with a cafeteria tray underneath to catch leakage.); a small bell (or two hard objects that can be knocked together to make a sound).

Tell the class you have learned that some swimming pool owners are interested in radio speakers that will play music underwater. Can sounds be sent through water? Would they be louder or softer than if made through the air? Encourage pupils to think of a test for the two problems by using an aquarium *select procedu* tank and bell (or substitutions). Although no one can—or should—put his head underwater, an ear can be pressed against the outside of the tank under the waterline while a bell is rung underwater. To test for the second question, a bell can be rung slightly above the waterline with a child's ear also above the waterline, and again pressed against the tank. For controls, ear and bell are the same distance away in both cases. The bell is rung with equal force. Many children will be surprised to find that sound does travel underwater, and that it is louder.

2. *Materials:* broomstick (or window pole or yardstick).

Mention that sometimes an automobile mechanic will put an end of a broomstick to his ear and touch various parts of a running

motor with the other end. Press for reasons. If someone suggests that the mechanic can hear motor noises that way, inquire why he does not just lean close to the motor and listen without a stick. Someone will immediately guess that sounds are heard better
through the handle. Ask how this guess can be tested. A child can scratch one end of a broomstick lightly with his fingernail while another listens at the other end. For a control, the listener raises his ear from the handle but stays at the same distance. (Be sure he does not touch the broomstick as he might sense some vibrations with his fingers.) The scratcher continues but now these noises will
be inaudible to the listener. Pupils should be able to design this or a similar experiment by themselves, with needed controls.

In discussion, bring out the old practice of Indians putting their ears to the ground to listen for hoofbeats. Also, how a railroad maintenance worker may place his ear on a rail to listen for an approaching train. Tell your pupils to place an ear against one end of their desks, and to scratch the top softly with a fingernail at the other end. Then have them raise their heads slightly while continuing the scratching motion.

3. *Materials:* an old spoon or fork; 2-foot string. (These materials for everyone, if possible.)

Have each child tie a string to his spoon. Each child should now gently swing his spoon against his desk. A musical sound will be heard. Now have each pupil put the end of his string against his ear. Sounds will seem much louder. Encourage the children to experiment to see what they can discover. Some may stop the vibrating string with their fingers and then release it. Some may shorten
or lengthen the string. Help them to tentatively conclude that sound appears to travel better through a string than through the air.

4. *Materials:* four yardsticks (or four strips of heavy tagboard); a ruler; twenty-two marbles. Arrange materials as in Figure 2-7.

Call attention to results from the children's several preceding experiences: Sound appears to travel "better" (with less energy loss) in

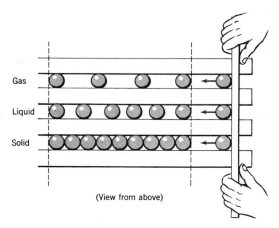

Gas

Liquid

Solid

(View from above)

FIGURE 2-7

water than air, and in a solid substance better than water. Entertain theories that will explain why. Few will be forthcoming. Suggest that a model can help them to understand what happens to a sound wave in a gas, liquid, and solid substance.

Explain that liquid and solid materials are also made up of jiggling molecules, but that they are closer together than in a gas. Help pupils to identify which rows of marbles represent a gas, liquid, and solid. Tell them you are going to start a "sound wave." But first invite them to predict which wave will travel
most quickly. Push the three "molecules" resting against the ruler into the three groups. (Be sure to stop the ruler's forward motion *before* the marbles collide.) The wave will be fastest in the solid, slower in the liquid, and slowest in the gas model. In addition, the last "molecule" in each model will be knocked away to varying distances, with the solid molecule going farthest and the gas molecule going least far. Help the children observe that not only does the solid molecule wave travel fastest, but it also seems to have the
most energy at the end. This, because of the distances each end molecule travels. Guide them to understand that the sound wave with the most energy will be loudest, as they have noted before.

5. Continue by emphasizing that they have observed a model, and it would be wise to check its accuracy. Have someone look up

speeds of sound in air, water, and steel, for example. Or, provide these speeds:

Air—about 1000 feet in one second (more than three football fields).

Water—about 5000 feet in one second (a little less than a mile).

Steel—about 15,000 feet in one second (a little less than 3 miles).

Once again local referents for these distances would be helpful.

reason quantitatively Establish that for every foot sound travels in air it would travel about 5 feet in water and about 15 feet in steel. This may be drawn to scale on a chalkboard or bulletin board and labeled. The easiest scale will be 1 foot for each 1000 feet.

Contributing idea C. Sound cannot travel in a vacuum.

Reveal through reading, a report, or telling that scientists believe there is no air or water on the moon. Suggest that this may raise a problem when people get to the moon and want to chat with their companions, especially if they have no radio. Ask the children *define problems* to define the problem in terms of sound. Help them to state it clearly and concisely. "In what ways, if any, will sound travel on the moon?" might be one such statement. Through reasoning, they should tentatively conclude that sound might be transmitted *draw conclusions* through the ground, or by talking with space helmets touching. Bring up possibilities of communication other than sound: wig-wag, flashlight signals, etc. Introduce the word *vacuum*—a space where there are no molecules of any kind. Let pupils read to confirm that sound cannot travel unless there is a substance to transmit the wave.

Extending activities

1. Let someone consult an encyclopedia for information on how a hydrophone is used to detect many different sounds in water. Although children at this level will be unable to understand exactly how this water microphone works, it is interesting for them to note the various kinds of sounds that have been detected with it.

2. Try to get a film which demonstrates that sound cannot travel in a vacuum. A usual setup features a glass jar containing a suspended electric bell. As the bell is rung, air is quickly pumped out of the jar. By the time a near vacuum exists, sound can no longer be heard. Then, as air is introduced again, the sound gets louder and louder.

3. Challenge very able pupils to draw the speeds of sound in air, water, and steel to *reason quantita[tively]* these scales: 1000 feet to 1 inch, one-half inch, 3 inches, and 6 inches, respectively.

4. Encourage the children to make tin-can "telephones." Each pair of pupils will need two clean metal cans (or cereal boxes), open at one end and free of jagged edges, and a string. Punch a hole with a nail in the closed end of the cans. Thread the string through both cans and knot each end to prevent it from pulling out. When in use the string is stretched tightly while one child talks into one container and another holds the second container to his ear. Sound waves coming from the mouth set the diaphragm (end of container) in motion. This, in turn, transmits vibrations to the string. These vibrations travel the string's length and set the other diaphragm in motion. Air is set in motion by the second diaphragm and sound enters the ear.

This apparatus works *unlike* a real telephone. In a real telephone sound energy is changed to electrical energy and back to sound energy again. (An explanation of how the telephone operates may be found on pages 228–229.)

Children will gain much information and enjoyment if this activity is treated in an "open-ended" fashion. A question such as "How far away can you talk before it stops *select procedu[re]* working well?" yields many facts. Among other things, it depends on (1) loudness of the voice; (2) can size; (3) elasticity of the diaphragms; (4) type of string—a "hard" *draw conclus[ions]* string or a waxed string works better than a soft one; and (5) tautness of the string. No matter how hard the children try, eventually the sound waves will die out. There will not be enough energy to push molecules in the

*select
procedures*

string or move the diaphragm in and out.

In addition, note if pupils can detect such faulty procedures as a slack line interfering with free vibration of the line, or dampening diaphragm vibrations by holding the can at its closed end.

One reason why singing in the shower or bathroom is so popular comes from the nature of sound reflections. As a sound hits the smooth walls, it bounces back and forth, increasing in loudness and prolonging the notes a little. This is pleasing to the ear. The smoother the reflecting surface, the better sound reflects. On a very smooth wall, sound reflections bounce off similarly to light reflections from a mirror. The angle of reflection equals the angle of incidence.

Notice how different sounds seem in a room before and after furnishings are installed? Rugs, drapes, and cloth-covered furniture absorb more sound waves than we may realize. However, even a furnished room may have a "hollow" sound if the walls and ceilings are hard and smooth. The use of porous acoustical tile on ceilings aids in cutting down sound reflections. So does the use of rough, porous plaster blown on with a compressed-air applicator. Besides absorbing some sound waves, a rough surface interferes with the wave reflection, somewhat in the manner in which light is diffused when it hits an irregular surface.

Sometimes children ask, "What happens to the molecules when they enter a porous material?" It appears that sound energy is changed to heat energy. The regular pulsating movements of a wave are broken up into the normal, irregular motions of individual molecules. As this happens, any energy passed into the porous substance is transmitted to other air molecules, thus very slightly raising the temperature. (Temperature is determined by the speed of molecular movements. The faster they jiggle about, the higher the temperature.)

Because sound can be reflected, we can direct or channel it in certain directions by using different devices. Open-air theaters often have a large shell-like structure surrounding the stage. This enables sounds to be directed toward an audience with reduced energy loss. The same principle is used with cheerleaders' megaphones.

An even more efficient way to conserve sound energy is to enclose it in a tube. Since the sound is kept from spreading out by continual reflections within the encircling wall, such concentrated sound loses energy slowly and may travel a long way. Physicians' stethoscopes and speaking tubes in apartment houses and ships are familiar applications.

A reverse application of this reflection principle is found in the old-fashioned ear trumpet, and in the ears of such animals as rabbits and donkeys. In these cases sounds are "gathered," or reflected inward. Besides large ears, many animals have the additional advantage of being able to cock them separately in different directions.

Since sound takes time to travel and can be reflected, it stands to reason that at a certain distance you should be able to hear a distinctly separate reflection of an original sound —an echo. Most persons need an interval of at least one-tenth of a second to distinguish between two sounds. If the interval is shorter than this, you hear one sound, much in the same manner your brain interprets separate frames of a motion picture as continuous motion.

Assuming a speed of 1100 feet per second, in one-tenth of a second sound travels 110 feet. To hear an echo—a distinguishable, separate sound—we must stand far enough away from a reflecting surface for the sound wave to travel a total distance of 110 feet. Since the sound travels *to* the reflecting surface and *back* to our ears, a distance of 55 feet from the surface is adequate to hear an echo. Remember, this distance varies a bit with temperature variations.

Sometimes the combination of a loud sound and many distant reflecting surfaces produces multiple echoes, or *reverberations*. A common example is thunder, which may reverberate

FIGURE 2-8 **A bat's ears are well suited for echo-ranging.**

are inaudible to humans. How was their "secret" detected? The answer lies in the ability of scientists to cast shrewd hypotheses and make careful tests. In the last activity of this section, children are challenged to do similar thinking.

There is a related point which you may find intriguing. In addition to ultrahigh sounds inaudible to humans, bats not in flight make squeaky sounds which are clearly audible. Scientists have discovered that ultrahigh sounds are reflected more strongly from small surfaces (such as an insect in flight) than sounds of lower frequency. Since bats can make lower or higher sounds, why do they make the higher sounds in flight? Are they "choosing" to do so because better echo-ranging occurs?

back and forth from cloud to earth and between clouds.

A few ship captains still use echoes from fog horns to gauge the distance from icebergs or a mountainous coastline. However, the use of radio waves (radar) for this purpose is much commoner, since it is more convenient, accurate, and reliable. A variation in temperature at different air levels could result in misleading calculations with sound echoes.

An interesting application of echo detection is found in a U.S. Navy device called *Sonar*. (The term is coined from the words, "SOund NAvigation and Ranging.") This apparatus sends a sound wave through the water and detects reflections from any direction. The time between an initial sound and its received echo enables a Sonar operator to know the distance of a reflector, whether it is a submarine or an underwater obstruction. Similar devices are used on fishing vessels to detect schools of fish.

A strange use of sound reflections is found in the bat. By listening to reflections of its cries, a bat flying in total darkness avoids collisions and may even catch insects in mid-air. An interesting aspect of this odd form of echo-ranging is that these sounds are so high they

BASIC GENERALIZATION III: Sound waves can be reflected and absorbed; echoes are reflections heard at a distance

Contributing idea A. Sound waves can be reflected and absorbed.

1. *Materials:* metal wastebasket (empty).

Begin by inquiring, "Have you ever noticed how your voice sounds in an empty house or room, before the furniture and curtains are put in? Or when singing in the shower?" Most children will be aware that their voices seem louder than usual in these places. Someone may venture that sound is reflected off the walls. Withhold verification until after the next experiment.

suggest hypothe

Give someone a wastebasket. Have him hold it up sideways, with the open end close to his face. His back should be toward the class. Instruct him to count slowly and loudly into the open end. Next, have him try it without the wastebasket. (He should be at least 10 feet from a wall, to avoid a strong reflection from it.) A difference in loudness will be even more noticeable if one note is sung for 10 or more seconds without interruption, while the container is alternately raised to his face and then lowered. Elicit that sound waves were apparently reflected off the container's sides and bottom and sent out the open end, past the child, and toward the class. Draw out similarities between this demonstration and sound reflections in an empty room.

draw clusions

2. *Materials:* two metal wastebaskets; several old rags; small bell. (A ringing sound can also be made by hitting a spoon against an empty glass.)

Let a few children recall how sounds change after carpeting, drapes, and furniture are put into an empty room. When decreased loudness is brought up, invite some pupils to devise an experiment with the materials to verify their common experiences. A bell can be rung with equal force near the bottom of two containers, one empty and the other lined with rags. A noticeable difference in loudness of the two sounds will be heard. Clarify that sound is largely *absorbed* by soft or porous materials.

select cedures

draw clusions

3. *Materials:* large megaphone (make from tagboard, fasten with tape or staples).

Call attention to the common practice of cupping hands to the mouth when shouting at a distance. Have the children recall experiences of observing megaphones in use. Lead to a possible explanation of these practices: sound waves cannot spread out as easily; sounds are reflected from the cupped hands or megaphones, and are thus sent toward a specific direction.

suggest otheses

Tell your pupils they can demonstrate to see if their explanation well fits the known facts. This should be performed outdoors, preferably on a windless day. If there is some wind, have the demonstrator face it and the class. Position him about 20 feet from the other children, who should be bunched closely together. The demonstrating child sings and holds a single note with uniform loudness for about 10 seconds. During this time he slowly turns in place at least one full circle. Let him repeat this procedure with the megaphone. There will be a noticeable difference in variation of loudness, with the megaphone's variation dramatically obvious. Repeat both procedures with different children. Back in the classroom, help them to discuss the demon-

stration and how it tends to verify their previous explanation. Encourage them to think of other ways in which sound can be directed through reflection. (For example, see extending activity 4.)

draw conclusions

4. *Materials:* megaphone; wrist watch.

Remind pupils that occasionally they see a person cup his hand to an ear while listening. Develop conjecture as to why. When increased loudness is suggested, let them cup one or both hands to their ears while someone sings or talks in front of the room. Establish that once again sounds seem to be reflected, but this time into the ear. Contrast with directed sound sent outward, as in the last activity. Point to a megaphone and watch. Ask how a controlled experiment could be set up to learn if sounds are "gathered" with a megaphone and are therefore easier to hear. Their directions might be similar to the following:

suggest hypotheses

select procedures

Place the megaphone over the ticking watch. Put an ear to the smaller opening. Gradually raise the megaphone. The ticking sound can barely be heard. Remove the megaphone. The ticking should be inaudible.

Object (if no one else does) that the group has no visible proof that sound is or is not being heard. Since there is not enough time to have everyone try it, what could be done to show everyone that sound is heard with the megaphone? If no one can suggest a way, provide the clue that a listener may have to keep his eyes closed or be blindfolded during this experiment.

select procedures

Let the class try the experiment again. But once distance is established for barely hearing a ticking sound with the megaphone, the watch can be stealthily removed or replaced, as the listener uses his megaphone. He can be asked at random if he hears the watch. This gives proof of whether it is heard or not, provided he cannot see. It now would be interesting to have the blindfolded listener move beyond the point of audibility and guess as to when the watch is in place. Any discrepancy between these guesses and the experiment should become quickly apparent.

draw conclusions

Clinch class understanding of the sound-gathering efficiency of large reflectors by discussing such examples as donkey and rabbit ears, and the old-fashioned ear trumpet.

Contributing idea B. Echoes are caused by sound reflections over a distance.

1. *Materials:* hammer; block of wood; 10-foot string; chalk; suitable outdoor location.

draw conclusions

Have everyone recall the nature of sounds in an empty corridor, bathroom, or other place where sounds reflect well. Bring out that in addition to loudness the sound seems to be slightly prolonged. Establish that as an empty room or other reflecting place gets larger, the sound is increasingly prolonged. Help the children reason why this is so: sound takes time to travel. When it reflects back we hear it in addition to the original sound. Thus, it lasts a little longer, and is louder.

Let the class guess what would occur if distance were gradually increased between a sound reflector and listener. *Echoes* will probably be mentioned. If not, ask pupils if an *echo* seems likely. Explore their understanding of this concept for a moment. Recall with them the physical conditions present in their previous experiences with echoes. Establish that three factors appear necessary: a reasonably large sound reflector, such as a wall; a sound maker; and some distance between the reflector and listener. Inform them that the school building wall (or some other appropriate reflector) might serve to reflect sound. Invite them to discover the distance, if any, that an echo should appear.

select procedures

Together, design an experiment. A string of known length (10 feet is a handy size for both addition and rapid measurement) can be used to mark the distance from a reflecting wall. At each 10-foot interval the wood block can be struck with a hammer to give a sharp sound, while everyone listens for a possible echo. The first discernible echo should appear at some point between 50 and 60 feet. If sounds are made at increasingly far distances, the echoes will appear at later time intervals. Have pupils reason why this offers proof that sound does take

reason quantitatively

draw conclusions

time to travel. Dramatically compare the pupils' measurement of when the echo first appears with the 55-foot distance calculated by scientists. Everyone will be delighted with the close "agreement." You might mention, however, that the speed of sound varies with air temperature.

2. It may be useful and interesting at this time to inform the children of how echoes enable bats to fly safely in total darkness. This information can lead to a "thought" experiment. You might say, "Does anyone know what a bat is? (Discuss for a moment.) Scientists now know that a bat can fly safely and catch insects in the air even if it is blindfolded and there is complete darkness. It does this with echoes. The bat makes very high sounds that bounce back from anything in the way, even from tiny flying insects. When it hears the echoes it can tell in what direction an insect or object is, and how far away. It wasn't easy for scientists to find this out, though, because the sounds bats make are so squeaky-high that human ears can't hear them."

"Let's say that we are scientists who want to find out how bats can fly in the dark without bumping into things. We think that maybe a bat makes high sounds, and then listens for echoes. But we aren't sure. Say we have several bats. We also have a large room with posts sticking up into the air and wires strung from floor to ceiling. How could we test to see if echoes are used by the bats to fly safely?"

select procedu[...]

Suggestions may vary. An obvious method would be to blindfold the bats or otherwise eliminate vision. The sound factor could be taken care of in either of two ways or both: plugging both ears, and taping the mouth shut. If the class is alert, inquire as to which of these two latter measures would be better, if only one could be employed. (Plugging the ears. It might be possible for the bat to "hum" through its nose, someone could surmise! In which case the nose could also be covered for a short time.)

If designing the test seems too difficult

for the children without clues, you could merely ask, "What could we do with its ears? Mouth?" and so on.

draw
clusions

After the children have designed and reasoned through their experiment, inform them of what scientists actually did, so the children

evaluate
critically

can check their reasoning. They will be pleased to learn that:

(1) Bats were blindfolded and flew just as well as before; this showed that sight was unnecessary.

(2) The noses and mouths of some bats were covered and they flew into objects; this showed that the bats probably needed to make sounds.

(3) The ears of bats were plugged, and they again flew into objects in their way; this showed that the bats probably needed to hear the sound reflections.

Extending activities

evaluate
ritically

1. Have the class evaluate this statement: "A man shouted loudly at a far-away mountain. Several days later he heard the echo." Is this possible? Why or why not? (It is impossible. No one possesses enough power to shout the thousands of miles the sound would need to travel for such a long-delayed echo.)

2. Ask a capable pupil to report on *Sonar* and its uses.

3. Visit places in the school building that feature sound insulation. Point out such provisions as porous plaster, soft wallboard, heavy drapes and curtains in the auditorium, and acoustical tile.

4. Encourage several pupils to bring garden hoses to use for speaking tubes. Point out the similarity between these "tubes" and those still used in many apartment buildings and ships. Because the sound waves cannot spread out, sound energy may travel as far as several thousand feet in properly designed tubes.

5. Let the children check their heartbeats with a homemade "stethoscope"—a funnel fitted into the end of a short hose or rubber tube. The funnel is placed over the heart while a listener holds the tube's free end to

his ear. Have pupils listen to heartbeats before and after moderate exercise, such as deep knee bends. They will be surprised at the more powerful sound vibrations produced by a rapidly beating heart.

Many pilots of certain crop-dusting airplanes actually rely on sound to gauge the safeness of their air speed. It is difficult while skimming low to watch both an air-speed indicator in the cockpit and ground obstructions. Flying speed is estimated by listening to the pitch of sound produced by the vibration of the airplane's struts and wires as the relative wind rushes past. Some seasoned pilots can judge their margin of safety to within 5 miles per hour by this method.

Sometimes children fasten small cards against the spokes of their bicycle wheels to simulate a motor sound while riding. As the spokes go around and hit the card, it vibrates and makes a sound. The pitch rises with increased speed of vibrations, and lowers with decreased speed.

In a stringed instrument pitch is determined by the length, tightness, and thickness of the strings. Shortening a string causes the frequency of vibrations to increase, raising pitch. Lengthening it has an opposite effect. Tightening a string also increases pitch, whereas lessening tension decreases it. A thick string vibrates more slowly than a thin one, and thus produces a lower sound.

You know that different instruments—a violin and a cello, for instance—may play a note at the same pitch and yet sound different. This is because of the *quality* of tone produced by these instruments. Most vibrations include more than just simple back-and-forth movements along a string's entire length. Although there is a fundamental vibration which governs the basic pitch, other parts of the string vibrate at faster frequencies. The combinations of vibrations are different with each string and with various stringed instruments. Together they produce tones of distinctly recognizable qualities.

In wind instruments, sound is produced by a vibrating column of air. The vibrations may be started by a player's lips, as with trumpets and tubas, or by blowing past a reed, as with the saxophone and clarinet.

Pitch is regulated by changing the length of the air column vibrating within the instrument. This is easily shown with several identical soda bottles filled with varying amounts of water. When someone blows across the bottle tops to produce a sound, the bottle with the least amount of water produces the lowest sound.

In a wind instrument such as the saxophone, air-column length is changed by opening and closing valves with the fingers. In a trombone, air-column length is regulated by pulling or pushing a long, closed, double tube, called the slide.

The characteristic of quality is also present in wind instruments. In this case it is caused by the combinations of additional air vibrations set up within each instrument. Quality of voices is produced in much the same way. This is regulated by the size and shape of air cavities in the mouth and nose.

BASIC GENERALIZATION IV: Pitch changes as the speed of vibrations change

Contributing idea A. Pitch increases with the speed of vibrations.

1. *Materials:* bicycle (upside down, resting on the handlebars and seat); small card.

Ask the class to listen carefully for how sounds of a vibrating card change in this demonstration. Hold a card against the rear wheel spokes of a bicycle, near the rim, while someone slowly turns the sprocket by cranking around a pedal arm. The cranking speed should be gradually increased, then decreased. As the wheel spins faster, the pitch of the vibrating card rises. As it slows, the pitch decreases.

Discuss what happened. Introduce *pitch* as the word for highness and lowness of sounds. Draw out that pitch seems to increase as the card vibrations increase in number; that pitch

decreases as vibrations decrease in number.

2. *Materials:* two- or three-speed record player; record; piece of tape.

Inform everyone that this demonstration will be best done without comment. The children are to keep their eyes and ears open. Review standards briefly, as what they hear will seem funny. Place a record on the player and stick some white tape on the record's rim. (This will make it easy to see the varying speeds at which the machine is run.) Start the record at slow speed, and gradually increase it at intervals of 15 seconds or so. Then reverse this process.

Inquire as to what the children notice. *draw* Gradually bring out the relationship between *conclus.* turntable speed and pitch.

Contributing idea B. Length, tension, and thickness affect the pitch of a vibrating string.

1. *Materials:* two rubber bands, thin and thick (for every child, if possible).

Tell your pupils that although it is fun to know how the pitch of a vibrating card can be changed with a bicycle wheel, it is not too useful. If they want to play a musical instrument, for example, they must learn more about how to change the pitch of sounds. After all, who has ever heard of a bicycle player in an orchestra! Raise conjecture as to *suggest* how pitch is controlled on a stringed instru- *hypoth.* ment, such as a ukulele or violin. Hint that there are three "secrets." Announce that some exploration with plucking two rubber bands in different ways will reveal important clues about the secrets for changing pitch in a stringed instrument. Set a specific time limit— *select* say, 5 minutes—for such exploration. Rubber *proced.* bands can be clenched in the pupils' teeth, stretched with one hand, and strummed with the other. (Discuss standards again to prevent excessive stretching, noise, etc.)

Upon reaching the time limit, press for three means by which pitch might be con- *suggest* trolled in a stringed instrument: tightness, *hypoth.* length, and thickness of the string. Agree that these seem to be reasonable guesses; but before the children can be sure, careful experiments should be done.

2. *Materials:* two rubber bands, thin and thick; two pencils; cellophane tape; book. Set up as in Figure 2-9.

select cedures

Let the class express what must be done to test for length if it affects pitch. Pupils will probably suggest what they seem to have discovered: By holding one end of a band between the teeth and stretching it to varying degrees, pitch changes. Develop that this procedure also increases tightness.

Ask how length alone can be tested. If ideas are not forthcoming, show the setup as found in Figure 2 9. Challenge the children to use it for length. By placing a finger at various points between the two pencils while plucking, pitch is raised and lowered. Tightness remains the same. This happens with bands of either size.

Question how tightness can be tested using the same setup. Bring out that this time length must remain constant. Someone can tighten the band while keeping the same vibrating length between the two pencils.

3. *Materials:* same as in preceding activity; also four paper clips; two identical weights (two scissors or two small books will do). Set up as in Figure 2-10. Cut the two rubber bands. Fasten a paper clip to each end of both bands. Imbed two paper clips deeply into the top of a book—about 40 or 50 pages should be clipped to provide a firm anchor. Fashion two other clips into hooks at the opposite ends. Any identical weights may be suspended. For the time being, leave off the weights. When using this setup, hold the book at its open side to prevent it from opening. Put the book on a table edge so that the weights hang freely.

Point out that the children have tested satisfactorily for tightness and length, but a test for thickness remains. To do so, they

select edures

must think of a way to set up properly a thick rubber band and a thin one. Both must be pulled with equal force. Length of the vibrating strings must also be equal. Encourage

aluate tically

conjecture and criticism of the various methods suggested. If ideas bog down, reveal the Figure 2-10 apparatus. Draw out from the children what is needed. Two identical

FIGURE 2-9

weights which pull with equal force should be attached. Equal vibrating lengths can be taken care of by placing a finger on top of each band at the bottom pencil while strumming. If controls are observed, the thick band will make a noticeably lower sound.

4. *Materials:* any stringed instruments available—violin, guitar, ukulele, autoharp, etc.

Review briefly the three "secrets" of pitch control. Let the children examine various instruments. Have any classroom players of stringed instruments demonstrate how they vary pitch when tuning up and when playing.

FIGURE 2-10

5. Materials: two rubber bands, thick and thin (for every child, if possible).

suggest hypotheses

Call attention to differences in pitch between adults' and children's voices. Pursue hypotheses about vocal cords that might account for this. A reasonable guess is that adult vocal cords are thicker and longer. Have each child blow between the strands of a stretched rubber band. The children will notice that lengthening the vibrating portion results in a lower sound, and shortening it results in a higher sound. A thick band always produces a lower sound than a thinner band when tightness and vibrating length are identical.

draw conclusions

By stretching the bands tighter as they blow, pitch is raised. Point out that this is like tightening their vocal cords with their throat muscles.

Contributing idea C. Length of the vibrating air column affects pitch in wind instruments.

1. Materials: three identical soft-drink bottles, one one-fourth full of water, one half-full, and one three-fourths full.

suggest hypotheses

State that perhaps everyone thus far has neglected the musicians who play wind instruments: saxophone, clarinet, tuba, trumpet, etc. Tubas can't be strummed in a ukulelelike fashion. Nor are there strings on a trumpet. Then how does a wind instrument work? How is pitch controlled?

select procedures

After brief discussion, indicate the three bottles. Invite the children to use them to find out more about pitch in wind instruments. Let someone blow across the tops of each. The lowest note will come from the bottle with the least water. Ask them to account for the differences in notes. Emphasize the varying distances from bottle top to water. Remind them that increased length in string instruments also resulted in lower tones. Have them reason through how they could give the same pitch to all three bottles. Hint that there are two ways. (Redistributing the water equally; emptying the bottles.)

After the experiment is concluded, explain that wind instruments contain a vibrating column of air. Air vibrations can be started in several ways: a horn player's lips vibrate; in reed instruments, a thin, wooden reed on the mouthpiece vibrates. (Pictures of instruments would be helpful.) Tell them that shortly they will be able to make their own "clarinets."

2. Materials: scissors; straws; straight pins. (Materials for everyone would be ideal.)

Carefully demonstrate the procedure to produce a soda-straw clarinet. Flatten one end of a straw for about three-fourths of an inch. Cut off the corners, but hold the scissors almost parallel to the straw as you cut. This will insure a long enough "reed" to vibrate.

Put about an inch of the straw into your mouth. Keep lips closed but somewhat loose. Blow hard and then gradually slacken force. You will quickly learn the right force to produce a sound. Have another prepared straw at hand in case you have some difficulty. While holding a note, quickly snip off parts of the straw. The note will get higher and higher with each shortened length. Point out how impractical it is to raise the pitch this way: One can only do it while the instrument lasts!

select procedures

Ask the children to think of a way to change pitch without snipping away the instrument. If necessary, hint that a pin might help. When putting holes in the straw is suggested, make three holes 1 inch apart.

3. Materials: several straws, glass of water; picture of a slide trombone or the actual instrument.

Discuss how pitch is changed by adjusting slide length on a trombone. An actual demonstration would be excellent. Demonstrate a "slide trombone" made from a straw and a glass of water. Hold one-third of a straw down in some water. Blow over the top, as with a soda bottle. With your other hand holding the glass of water, move it up and down so that length of the air column changes in the straw. Pitch will vary accordingly. Remind the class that pitch in a trombone and other horns, such as a trumpet, bugle, tuba, etc., is also regulated by tightening or loosening the lips.

4. Materials: any wind instruments available, reed and horn variety.

Let the children examine several wind instruments. Have any classroom players of these instruments demonstrate how they control pitch through closing or opening air valves and adjusting lip vibrations.

Extending activities

1. Invite the group to make chimes from five or six tinned cans of varying sizes. Punch holes in the bottoms, thread through and knot strings. Individually suspend each inverted can from a yardstick placed between the backs of two chairs. When struck with a spoon or stick, sounds of different pitch are emitted—the larger the can, the lower the pitch. Flower pots may be used in similar fashion.

draw lusions

2. Show how to make a pin "harp" from eight straight pins. With a hammer, tap the pins into the side of an open cheesebox or 8-inch block of wood. Gradually increase pin height from low at one end to high at the opposite end. By tapping gently here and there, it is possible to approximate a musical scale. To play the harp, pluck it sharply under the pinheads with another pin or small nail.

3. Let everyone count to 10 by alternately saying a number aloud, then whispering the next. If fingers are held to throats, vocal cord vibrations will be noticed only when numbers are spoken aloud. Explain that we speak by using the air cavities in our mouths and noses in addition to our vocal cords. Have pupils whisper o-o-o-h, ah-h-h-h. Each will notice a slight change in pitch caused by the changing air cavity in his mouth, although his vocal cords are unused. Have each child pinch his nose a few times while speaking some words aloud. A distinct difference in voice quality will be noticed.

If you place a vibrating tuning fork handle against a table top, the sound suddenly gets louder. The vibrating fork forces the table top to vibrate with equal speed. This sets in motion many more air molecules than would the fork alone. Try putting a vibrating tuning fork against other objects. Almost any hard object can be forced to vibrate at the fork's natural frequency.

A peculiar example of forced vibrations can occur when a group of soldiers marches over a bridge. If there are enough persons marching in step, the entire structure can be forced to vibrate in time to the step. The bridge may weaken or collapse. For this reason, a standing military order is, "Break step when crossing a bridge."

Thomas Edison used his knowledge of forced vibrations when inventing the phonograph. He attached a sharp needle to a thin diaphragm which vibrated when sound waves struck it. The needle was placed against a cylinder wrapped with soft tin foil. As he spoke, he slowly cranked the cylinder around and around. The vibrating needle cut a series of impressions into the metal. To play back his sounds, he placed the needle in the impression first scratched and cranked the cylinder. As it followed the impressions, the needle was forced to vibrate, thus causing the diaphragm to vibrate. Edison could hear his recorded voice!

A similar basic principle of recording and playing back sound vibrations is followed today. But now electricity is used to assist in the initial cutting of a wax record and for playing back recorded vibrations. Sounds sung or spoken into a microphone are changed to spurts of electricity. The variable electric current causes an attached needle to vibrate as it cuts a wavy groove in a wax disk. Duplicate records are pressed from forms of the initial master disk. When playing a record, the moving wavy groove forces the needle to vibrate. This motion is changed into variable electrical impulses which vibrate the phonograph speaker, and recorded sound is heard.

Have you ever heard windows vibrate in their frames as a low-flying airplane passes overhead? Or noticed dishes faintly rattle occasionally as a loud radio is played? To see why this happens, consider two identical tuning forks. If one vibrates and is held near the other, it also begins to vibrate. But with two tuning forks of different pitches, only the struck one vibrates.

When forks are of identical pitch, sound waves arrive at the proper time to set the still fork in motion. Each additional air compression pushes a prong as it starts to bend in from a previous one. Each rarefaction arrives as the prong starts to bend back out. The steady, timed, push-pause-push-pause sets the fork vibrating, in almost the same way as you would push someone on a swing.

When forks are of different pitch, the timing is wrong for this to happen. For example, a prong may bend in properly with a compression, but as it starts to bend back another air compression may strike it prematurely, and slow or stop it. The same thing would occur with a moving swing that is pushed while only part-way back on a downswing.

Every solid object has a natural frequency of vibration. If sound waves of that frequency push against an object, it may start *sympathetic vibrations*, as the phenomenon is called. Remember that objects vibrate sympathetically only when they possess the same natural pitch as the initial sound maker. On the other hand, objects *forced* to vibrate always do so at the frequency of the vibrating object placed against them, regardless of their own natural frequency.

You may have learned that a very loud note sung or played into a thin glass can shatter it through violent sympathetic vibrations, provided such vibrations represent the natural pitch of the glass. However, it is not true that "seashore sounds" may be detected in shell souvenirs, unless someone is listening at the beach. What is heard are only sympathetic reflections of nearby sounds. The section closes with an experiment designed to test this misconception.

BASIC GENERALIZATION V: Sound waves can cause forced and sympathetic vibrations

Contributing idea A. A vibrating object can force another object to vibrate.

1. *Materials:* string instrument, or picture of one; rubber bands; small boxes of different kinds—cigar, cheese, chalk, shoe boxes, quart or pint milk cartons with one side cut out; books; pencils.

Hold up a stringed instrument (or picture) and ask, "Why are the strings always attached to a large, empty box in string instruments?" After ideas are discussed say, "We have some boxes and rubber bands here. You have books and pencils in your desk. Let's make sounds first with the rubber bands on the books, then on the boxes. Shortly, you'll have a chance to tell about any differences you may notice when these boxes are used."

Distribute the materials. Some children may need assistance with fitting the rubber bands on their boxes. Others may have forgotten how to put two pencils under the rubber bands near each end of a book, so that the bands will vibrate freely.

After several moments discuss findings. Almost everyone will agree that the sounds are louder with boxes. Press for reasons. Inform the children that they will understand more about why the sounds are louder after their next activity.

draw concl

sugge hypo

2. *Materials:* tuning fork.

Sharply strike a tuning fork against a rubber heel to get it vibrating. As the sound begins to die away, place the fork base against a desk top or table. The sound will suddenly get louder. Try the same procedure with as many objects as possible: door (a thin plywood door makes an excellent sounding board); window; upturned drinking glass; various boxes; and so on.

Help the children reason about what happened. When the vibrating tuning fork was held against the object, it was forced to begin vibrating, too. Because the second object was much larger than the tuning fork in each case, it set many more air molecules in motion than before. This made the sound louder.

draw concl

3. *Materials:* tuning fork; a piece of clean paper; pencils; cotton (or hands over the ears).

Tell your group almost anything can be forced to vibrate. Even human teeth and bones! Ask someone to stuff cotton in his ears and then clench the base of a tuning fork between his teeth. Gently tap the fork with a pencil. The child will hear a clear sound. A similar procedure might be used solely with pencils. With hands over ears, one child clenches a pencil between his teeth while another taps the pencil gently.

Develop that although the child's ears were stopped up, vibrations traveled through the pencil into his teeth and through his jaw bones. From there they went into the place inside his head where hearing organs are located, and sound was heard.

4. *Materials:* record player; record; needle; three tagboard cards of different sizes, such as 2 by 2 inches, 3 by 3 inches, and 4 by 4 inches; small megaphone; magnifying lens.

Invite some children to examine a phonograph record with a magnifying lens. The grooves will appear wavy. Explain that record grooves are made by a sharp needle which has been forced to vibrate by electricity.

Now stick a needle into a corner of the smallest card and turn on the record player. Place the needle into a groove. A faint sound will be heard. Ask someone to explain what is happening. If no one can, provide this explanation: wavy grooves in the record are forcing the needle to vibrate. The needle is forcing the card to vibrate, and the vibrating card pushes air molecules into sound waves.

Hold up all three cards and ask which one would cause the most air molecules to begin moving in sound waves. Then ask which would cause the loudest sound. Try the remaining cards. The loudest sound, of course, will come from the largest card. Bring out that the children have heard *forced vibrations* —one object forcing another to vibrate at the same speed.

Now stick the needle into the small, folded end of a megaphone. Point the open end toward your class and lower the needle into a groove. An even louder sound will be heard than with the cards. Link this to the children's previous experiences with megaphones.

Close by saying, "Scientists have found they can make the best records if electricity is used to make vibration grooves in the records. Electricity is also used now to make sounds louder when we play records. But the ideas we have learned about forced vibrations are still needed."

Contributing idea B. Sympathetic vibrations occur when a vibrating object is in tune with another object.

1. *Materials:* piano. (An autoharp is a less satisfactory substitute.)

Say, "Have you ever noticed that dishes on shelves rattle slightly when the volume of a radio is turned up too loud? Have you ever heard windows vibrate when a large, noisy airplane flies low over your house? What causes this?" Anticipate some explanations based on forced vibrations. In this event, bring out that these vibrating sources of sound are *not* touching the dishes or window panes. You might then say, "Let's learn another way in which sound vibrations take place."

Take the class to a piano. If the instrument is in another classroom, do the following demonstration during a brief recess. Only several moments are needed.

Lift up the piano top—whether concert or upright. Have someone depress the "loud" pedal. This lifts felt dampers off the strings and permits them to vibrate longer. Sing a short, loud note into the strings. Several strings will begin vibrating. Let several children try singing short notes of different pitches. They should detect shortly that only those strings vibrate that are in tune (pitch) with their voices.

draw conclusions

2. *Materials:* three tuning forks (two identical, and one of different pitch).

Back in your room, encourage pupils to discuss what they found: only those strings that seem to be "in tune" with their voices made vibrations. Now strike the tuning forks one at a time and ask which two appear to be in tune. They will immediately pick the two identical forks.

Hold one of these in each hand. Strike a fork to get it vibrating and hold it a few inches away from the other. After a few seconds, stop the vibrating fork and listen to

ggest
neses

the other. It should now emit a faint sound, indicating that it is vibrating. Let several children hear and verify what is taking place.

Now try this procedure with one of the tuning forks and a *dissimilar* one. This time there will be no sound from the second fork.

draw conclusions Invite pupils to express what they have found out. Then provide the following summary: "We learned before that we could *force* almost anything to vibrate by holding a vibrating object against it. We have now found that we can get some things to vibrate without touching them. But before this can happen, both objects must have the same natural pitch, or vibrating speed. Otherwise, the sound waves cannot push at the right time to get the second object moving." Mention and write on the chalkboard the term *sympathetic vibrations*. Tell the class this term is used to describe the vibrations just experienced.

3. *Materials:* three soda bottles (two identical, and one of different size).

Remind everyone that air vibrates inside wind instruments. Have someone blow over the mouth of one of the identical soda bottles. It should emit a tone. Point out that this tone is the bottle's natural pitch. Comment as follows: "We have found that a string vibrates when in tune with a sound, and a tuning fork vibrates when in tune with another one. Will the same thing happen with a wind *suggest hypotheses* instrument, such as a bottle? In which of these two other bottles should air vibrations start when the first bottle is blown?"

Have one child sound short, forceful notes with one bottle while a second child stands close by and holds another bottle about a half-inch from his own ear. When identical bottles are used a clear sound should be heard in the second bottle as well as the first. If a half-dozen or more identical soda bottles can be obtained, more children will be able to listen at one time. Emphasize that vibrations in the "listening" bottles are sympathetic vibrations. Sound waves in these bottles move up and down at the same speed as in the first bottle and so make the same sound.

Let someone blow a note with the dissimilar bottle. Its pitch will be different from that of the other bottles. Invite someone to try sounding a note of the same pitch with two different bottles. He will be unable to do so. Point out that the natural pitch of an object cannot be changed unless the object is changed. Review how pitch was changed in previous activities by adding water.

4. *Materials:* several or more identical, empty milk bottles.

Hold up a milk bottle. Challenge pupils to find its natural pitch by singing into it. This can be done by holding the open end of one bottle about one-half inch from an ear while singing directly into the other bottle. Let them discover the natural pitch by singing a musical scale. When the right note is sung a loud sound will be heard from the "listening" bottle.

After the *key note* or natural pitch is found, let several or more children (depending on how many milk bottles are available) stand close to the singer. Have them listen as he sings the key note and then a note of another pitch. The key note will dramatically appear in each listening bottle as it is sung into the first bottle. For variation, take away the first bottle. Have the key note sung. Each listening bottle will continue to emit its key note.

5. *Materials:* a large sea shell; several small glass jars or drinking glasses.

Tell your group some persons believe that "sounds of the sea"—such as waves splashing—may be heard in a sea shell. Raise conjecture *evalu. critica* about the possibility of this belief being true. Develop how the class might explain sounds heard from a sea shell through sympathetic vibrations. Draw out that possibly some sounds nearby or in the room might cause air in the shell to vibrate sympathetically.

Invite children to test if someone can detect special "sounds of the sea" in a sea shell, as contrasted with sounds from other hollow containers. Someone can be blindfolded. Several glass containers and a shell might be held *select proce* near his ear by someone else. The listener can then attempt to tell when he hears "sounds of the sea."

Extending activities

1. If the class is very able, deliberately try "faulty procedure" with the sea shell experiment. Let someone knowingly listen to the shell first, so that he becomes familiar with its reflected sounds. Then, when he is blindfolded, do the experiment as usual. The child will probably be able to detect the sea shell, but only because he has had previous practice. Challenge the class to explain.

2. Encourage pupils to find the key notes of containers of many kinds. With cardboard boxes, the key note causes the most vibrations. They may detect this by lightly touching the containers.

3. Get a violin or other stringed instrument. Help children note that the strings force a bridge to vibrate, while the bridge forces a sound box to vibrate.

The ear must be ranked among the body's most remarkable organs. In our hearing, sound waves are channeled into the ear canal by the outer ear, which acts as a megaphone in reverse. As sound waves collide with the eardrum, this thin membrane of stretched skin begins vibrating at the same frequency. Just inside the eardrum are three tiny, connected bones: the hammer, anvil, and stirrup. A vibrating eardrum starts the attached hammer shaking and this movement is transmitted through the connected bones to the cochlea, or inner ear. This snail-shaped apparatus is filled with a watery fluid and lined with sensitive nerve endings that trail off to the auditory nerve and brain. The transmitted vibrations pass through the fluid and excite the nerve endings. These excitations are converted into electrical impulses which reach the brain. The Eustachian tube (Figure 2-11) is a narrow opening that leads from the back of the mouth to the middle ear. It equalizes air pressure on the eardrum.

Children should learn some reasonable rules for ear care and safety. A sharp object jabbed into the ear may cause a punctured eardrum. This greatly impairs or prevents ear-drum vibrations, and results in hearing loss in the affected ear. They should beware of a sharp blow against the outer ear. This compresses air within the ear canal, and may cause a ruptured eardrum. Blowing the nose forces air up through the Eustachian tube. If suffering from a cold, excessively hard blowing may force germs up the tube and infect the middle ear.

Elementary-school pupils find it interesting to learn how animals without visible outer ears detect sounds. Frogs, toads, and turtles have clearly noticeable eardrums of tough skin located slightly below and back of the eyes. Crickets and katydids hear through a tiny eardrum located on each foreleg, just below the "knee" joint. Look for an oval spot of slightly different color. Grasshoppers also have visible eardrums. These are located on each side of the abdomen's first section. Lift up the insect's wings and look for a disklike membrane just above where the rear legs are attached. Fishes hear with auditory capsules located deep within the head. In addition, many fishes have a lateral line of sensory scales which extend from head to tail. These are particularly sensitive to sounds of low pitch. Earthworms and snakes feel ground vibrations through the underneath portions of their bodies.

Although our ears are sensitive to a wide range of pitches, there are limits to what we can hear. Virtually no one can detect a sound that vibrates less than 16 times per second, or more than 20,000 times per second. As we grow older, this range is gradually narrowed.

Hearing ranges in animals often exceed those of man. A bat may detect sounds that vary between 10 vibrations to 100,000 vibra-

FIGURE 2-11

tions per second. A dog's hearing begins at only several vibrations and goes to 40,000 vibrations per second. This is why it is possible to use a "silent" whistle for calling a dog. The sound is simply too high for humans to hear. A cat can detect sounds up to 50,000 cycles. Sounds inaudible to man are called *infrasonic* when they vibrate too slowly, and *ultrasonic* when vibrations are too fast.

A forthcoming activity involves a dog trained to respond to an ultrasonic whistle. If no one has a trained dog, it is easy as a rule to train one in a short while. Children are delighted to participate in this process.

At meal times, the dog is called by voice, and the whistle blown immediately afterward. Several times a day, between meals, the child may repeat this procedure and reward the dog with a pat, or give it a tasty tidbit. After several days, only the whistle is sounded on every other occasion. After four days or so, the dog should react to the whistle alone.

Ultrasonic sound is presently employed in many ways. Surgical instruments immersed in a container of liquid are thoroughly cleansed and sterilized when ultrasound is passed through. Milk and paint are homogenized, and clothes in experimental washers made flawlessly clean. Delicate surgery in some instances may be performed with ultrasound focused on diseased tissue without cutting into skin or bone. In industry, metal castings are examined for invisible flaws through ultrasonic echoes recorded on a machine. These are but a few examples. Ultrasonic sounds seem certain to play a vital part in everyone's future.

BASIC GENERALIZATION VI: Many sound waves can be heard by us, but many cannot

Contributing idea A. We hear only those sounds that cause our eardrums to vibrate.

1. *Materials:* Borrow from the school nurse a large chart which shows a cross section of the ear. (Or project Figure 2-11 with an opaque projector.)

With chart or projected drawing, explain how the ears work. Air molecules of a sound wave enter the ear and push against the eardrum, which vibrates. These vibrations are passed onto three small, connected bones— the hammer, anvil, and stirrup. The stirrup causes tiny nerve endings in the inner ear (cochlea) to vibrate. These little nerves start tiny electric currents which flow up to the brain through a large, connected nerve. The brain tells us about the sound.

2. *Materials:* thin, wooden ruler or stick; "silent" dog whistle (This may be purchased for about 50 cents at pet shops, or obtained from dog owners in the class.); a dog (If this demonstration is done immediately in the morning, perhaps a parent can bring the family pet to school and take it home.)

Wave the ruler slowly up and down from the wrist. Ask the children what sound they hear. Express mock surprise when they say they are unable to hear the vibrations. Ask them to explain why. Help them understand that the air molecules were not pushed rapidly enough to vibrate their eardrums.

Hold down a ruler on the edge of a desk with most of its length sticking out over the edge. Press down the projecting part with your free hand and quickly let go. A low sound will be emitted. Shorten the length of the projecting ruler and again start it vibrating. Continue shortening the length and vibrating the projecting part.

Draw out facts from the children's observations: with very slow vibrations they heard nothing at all. Gradually, as the speed of vibrations increased, so did the pitch. Briefly review their previous experiences with pitch to confirm this. Now tell them that some sounds are pitched so high our eardrums cannot vibrate fast enough to send the sound into the middle ear.

Produce a dog whistle and blow it. No one will hear a sound. If a dog is available, ask the children to observe the dog's ears each time the whistle is blown. They will stiffen slightly in reaction to the "silent" sound. If a dog is not available, perhaps a child can try this demonstration at home and report what happened to the class.

3. *Materials:* trained dog; silent dog whistle; playground or other appropriate location.

An interesting experiment can be designed by the class if someone has a dog that has been trained to respond to a silent whistle. Have pupils set up an experiment to test if a dog responds to a silent whistle blown by its owner. Bring out that a dog usually has a keen sense of smell and good eyesight. A good design might involve a location where the wind is blowing at the dog's back. This will prevent it from using scents to find its owner. Perhaps the owner might be stationed just around a corner of a nearby building, so that he is out-of-sight. When he blows the whistle, his dog can be released. It should run immediately to the whistle source. This experiment can be tried again with the whistle blown by someone else.

Encourage the dog's owner to tell his classmates how he trained it to respond to a silent whistle.

Contributing idea B. Two ears are better than one ear for locating sources of sound.

Materials: eight pencils.

Say, "If you lost your hearing in one ear, would it really make any difference?" Guide the children to speculate if a hearing loss in one ear would make a difference first in loudness, then in being able to detect the location of sounds.

It will be easy for the class to think of a test for loudness. For example, someone might read aloud in front of the class while the children cover and uncover one ear. They will notice some loss. Point out that often hearing through the "good" ear becomes keener than it was before the hearing loss, although it cannot fully make up for the loss.

Now ask your pupils to design a test for their second problem: Can sounds be located as well with one ear as with two? A child might be placed in the center of the room, with other children in each corner. The center child should keep his eyes closed while he listens for sound locations with both ears. The corner children, in any order, may individually tap two pencils together. The listener should try to indicate the direction from which the sound came immediately after hearing it.

This procedure can be tried again, but now with the listener's hand held tightly over an ear. He should have great difficulty locating sound sources.

Ask the children to explain why it is more difficult to detect sound sources the second time. You may need to tell them that the explanation involves two facts learned before: sound takes time to travel; and loudness of a sound decreases with distance.

Draw out that with normal hearing one ear hears sound slightly before the other, if the head is at an angle. Also, one ear possibly hears a slightly louder sound than the other. The brain is then able to tell from which direction the sound comes. With one ear, there is no comparison of either speed or loudness. Thus locations are harder to judge.

Extending activities

1. Ask the school nurse to give an illustrated talk on ear care.

2. Have an able pupil report an interview with a local dentist or physician on how ultrasonic devices clean surgical instruments.

3. Let the children bring in a grasshopper, cricket, katydid, frog, toad, and turtle. Have them search for the external eardrums on these animals. Several hand lenses will be useful for this purpose.

select dures

luate ically

select dures

select procedures

draw conclusions

Light Energy

(Upper)

Why does something look larger under a magnifying glass? What makes a rainbow? Why do some people wear eyeglasses? Children want to know many things about the behavior of light. The broad range of ideas and activities developed in this unit will help pupils become aware of the very significant part light energy plays in their lives.

Several activities in this unit are best done in a darkened room. If the regular classroom cannot be darkened, perhaps an auditorium or substitute facility can be made available on these occasions.

BASIC GENERALIZATIONS

I. Light is a form of energy given off by a luminous source.

II. Light reflections are affected by the reflecting surface and slant at which light strikes the surface.

III. Absorbed light energy changes into heat energy and chemical energy.

IV. Slanted light rays are refracted when they pass from one medium to another of different density.

V. White light is composed of different colors; the color of objects depends on which colors are transmitted, reflected, and absorbed.

VI. The eye is a complicated organ that operates with the brain.

If you have ever stubbed a toe in a dark room, you have already discovered that some objects do not give off light, but only reflect it. Therefore, when it is dark, they cannot be seen. This is true of most things around us. But what about *luminous* objects—electric bulbs, candles, sun, and so on—those that give off their own light? How is this accomplished?

Let us look at the molecular level first. Imagine the slightly jiggling molecules of a thin wire filament in an unlit electric bulb. Now flip the switch. As electrical energy enters the filament the molecules begin moving faster and faster. At a certain point, tiny waves of radiant energy are given off in all directions. This radiant energy we feel as heat. In a split second, as more electrical energy is received by the filament, faster moving waves are emitted as well. We recognize these radiations as visible light.

There is a more complete explanation. Imagine a hydrogen atom. It has a single electron $(-)$ whirling about a proton $(+)$ nucleus. Ordinarily the electron moves in orbital motion a small distance from the nucleus. The mutual attraction of their charges keeps them fairly close together. But if additional energy is introduced into this atom in some way, perhaps through heat or chemical or electrical energy, the electron may jump to a higher orbit. When the electron is a greater than usual distance away from its nuclear partner, the atom is said to be in an "excited" state. But both particles continue to attract each other, as two magnets might attract. Finally, if the attraction is powerful enough, the electron hops back into regular orbit. The energy it loses in this process is released as a tiny particle of light, called a *photon*. A similar state of excitation can occur in the more complex atoms.

An interesting thing about the photon theory is that it envisions light as composed of separate particles moving in waterlike waves, rather than a stream of bullets. This apparent paradox is needed to account for many of the ways in which light behaves.

Light energy is so important that scarcely anything escapes its influence. It furnishes through sunlight the energy for photosynthesis in plants. The gasoline that fuels an automobile originally received its energy from the sun, through ancient plants and animals that died long ago. From them coal and petroleum were formed. Our changing weather is a result of the unequal distribution of sunlight (and therefore heat) in the atmosphere. There are countless other examples.

It is important to realize that light is *invisible* unless light waves enter our eyes directly from a luminous source, or are reflected into our eyes. Although this may seem obvious at first, let us look at some implications. Think of being in space, where there is virtually nothing to reflect light. Look away from the sun, and the space between it and any planet bathed in sunlight is totally black. Unless we look at the sun itself, it is impossible to see the energy waves in transit, because they strike nothing that can reflect these waves to our eyes. In contrast, we can see a distant searchlight probing a dark sky because the atmosphere is laden with water, dust, and gas molecules that reflect the light to our eyes.

A forthcoming activity presents these ideas. Since a weak light and short distance are employed, atmospheric reflections are minimized.

Does unreflected light always move in straight lines? Under "regular" conditions, it does. When we see something, we can reach out and touch it, and be confident it is there. Also, an unslanted shadow is a perfect outline of an opaque object.

But we can only be sure about these things when light is traveling in a medium of uniform density. Light waves slow down when going through water, glass, or colder air, for example. In these cases, light can "bend." (We shall go into this more extensively later.) Scientists now know that light passing through space is attracted and curved by the gravitational fields of massive objects in space. With these exceptions, light does travel in straight lines.

The speed of light is so incredibly fast that it took centuries before instruments could be developed to measure it. Only in the twentieth century, with the work of Albert Michelson and his colleagues, were reasonably consistent measurements first obtained. With the use of a rotating eight-sided mirror, these scientists timed light reflections between other mirrors placed on two widely separated mountain tops. Later, other experiments were conducted in a large, mile-long pipe from which air was removed to eliminate atmospheric interference. Many additional experiments using other methods have indicated a speed of 186,282 miles per second. For our purposes, we shall round off this figure.

Although accurate measurements of light velocity could not be made until refined instruments were developed, an ingenious method was devised by the Danish astronomer *Olaus Roemer* in 1675. It is included in this section as a teachable example of scientific reasoning at its best.

BASIC GENERALIZATION I: Light is a form of energy given off by a luminous source

Contributing idea A. Light is made up of tiny electrical particles that move in waves from a luminous or reflecting body.

1. *Materials:* a book; powerful flashlight with narrow beam; two cardboard boxes with

tops removed (About 12- by 12- by 13-inches or similar size. Line insides with stapled or pasted-on black construction paper, or paint black with tempera. Cut a flashlight-sized hole in the bottom of one box.); dark-colored ball or other object.

To arouse some initial motivation and conjecture about the importance of light, place an opened book in the bottom of a blackened box. Ask a child to read the book aloud. While he is reading draw down the shades, then suddenly turn out the lights. When the reader stops, ask him to continue. Of course, he will be unable to do so if the room is dark.

Guide the ensuing discussion into some questions to think about:

What exactly happens when there is no light to read by?

What is light?

What would life be like if there were no light?

The last question is particularly meaningful to discuss for several moments with pupils' eyes closed.

Bring out that light is a form of energy—something that can do work. For example, without it plants cannot grow, and so our food supply is dependent on light. Elicit other energy forms, such as atomic, heat, sound, and electrical energy. Mention that scientists believe light is composed of indescribably tiny electrical particles, called *photons*, that seem to move in tiny waves. Tell the children that light behaves in many interesting ways, and that they are going to find out about many of these ways.

2. To help the children realize that light comes from luminous and light-reflecting objects, perform the following demonstrations:

a. Put the box with flashlight hole on a table with the open top facing the class. Darken the room. Put the flashlight through the hole and turn it on. Ask if everyone can see the light. Turn off the light, and ask the same question. Turn on the flashlight again, and have each child put his hand between the light and his eyes. Can the children see the light now? Draw out that they could see the

light when it traveled from the flashlight to their eyes. When the light was off, or when it was prevented from entering their eyes, they could not see it.

b. Put the second box on a table with the open top facing the class. Place a ball or other object inside. Darken the room. Inquire if the ball can be seen. Now shine some light on the ball, and ask the same question. Have each person place his hand between the reflected light and his eyes. Can they see the light now? Draw out that they could see the ball only when the flashlight beam bounced off it and entered their eyes.

Elicit examples of *luminous* sources—objects that shine by their own light—such as the sun, electric lights, and fire. Bring out that heat energy accompanies light energy from these sources. Some children may mention fireflies, or even light-giving bacteria and deep-ocean fish. Explain that these organisms combine certain chemicals in their bodies which produce light with practically no heat. Perhaps an able child can report on *bioluminescence*, as this phenomenon is called.

Children will have little difficulty in thinking of things that *reflect* light. The moon, planets, and practically everything else in existence not totally black or luminous fall into this category. *evaluate critically*

Contributing idea B. Light energy is visible only when it strikes the eye.

1. *Materials:* two cardboard boxes, as in (a) above; narrow-beam flashlight; two dusty chalkboard erasers. Arrange the boxes on two tables about three feet apart, with open ends facing each other. The flashlight beam is to shine from one box into the other. Children should be able to see only the boxes' sides.

You might remark, "We found out light can be seen whether it comes directly from a luminous source or is reflected. But what happened when the light was blocked, so it could not enter our eyes?

"Can we say that light must enter our eyes to be seen?

"If we could shine a light beam from one place to another, without seeing the source or

FIGURE 3-1

having any reflection, would we be able to see the beam? Why or why not?"

suggest hypotheses

Raise conjecture. Encourage reasons for guesses based on what the children have learned. Invite them to plan a test of their ideas with the materials provided.

select procedures

For example, with room darkened, someone can put the flashlight part way into the hole of one box and shine it into the second box. Without informing the others, he might turn it on and off, while they try to guess when it is on. As proof to all that it is on or off, another child can clap the erasers together above the open area. Light reflecting from the chalk dust should make any beam easily visible.

(If reflections inside the boxes are noticeable, cut down light intensity by wrapping black paper around the flashlight head, and making a small circular or diamond-shaped opening in the center with a razor.)

draw conclusions

Help the class to conclude that light is *invisible* unless it strikes the eyes directly from a luminous source, or is reflected to the eyes. A powerful searchlight stabbing a dark sky is visible only because the dust, moisture, and gas molecules which make up the atmosphere reflect some light to the eyes. Although the same elements are present in classroom experiments, the light beam is too weak and distance too small for the same effect.

2. Let someone report or have the group read about why outer space appears dark although large luminous and light-reflecting bodies may be observed. (There is almost nothing in space to reflect light.)

Contributing idea C. Light ordinarily travels in straight lines and in all directions.

1. *Materials:* three felt, chalkboard erasers;

shallow dish; candle and match; three small cards; sharp pin.

Have the children recall that when the flashlight was beamed to their eyes, they could see it. When their hands were placed in front of their eyes, the light was not visible. Remind them that it appears to be impossible to see around corners with the unaided eye. Why is this so? A reasonable explanation can only involve the way light travels.

Bring out the three most likely possibilities of travel: a curved path, a zigzagged path, and a straight path. Let them reason through the implications of each. Invite them to think of a way to test their most reasonable hypothesis. If help is needed, provide the stated materials.

suggest hypoth

select proced

A hole can be punched in the same spot on each card, and cards arranged as in Figure 3-1. If erasers are unavailable, lumps of modeling clay will do for support. No matter how they are arranged, the candle flame will be visible through the holes only when they are perfectly aligned. Light travels in straight lines.

2. *Materials:* several straws; lighted candle.

Discuss how a straw might be used to test the same idea. The candle flame is visible when seen through a straw. But bend the straw, and it cannot be seen.

select proced

Establish now that light appears to travel in all directions from the flame. No matter from what position the flame is viewed through a straw, it is visible. (Except directly below, since the candle itself blocks the view.) Get the class to see that this is why the sun shines on the earth all year long, even though we move around it. Although we revolve about the sun in one permanent plane, children will realize that sunshine would reach the earth in any plane of rotation.

draw conclus

3. *Materials:* chalkboard sketch, as in Figure 3-2; candle on dish; match; pinhole "camera." (To make this, remove the top from a round cereal container. Center a pinhole in the bottom. Place thin tissue paper or waxed paper on the open end and fix in place with cellophane tape.)

Darken the room, and place the pinhole camera in front of the flame. Make sure the hole is in line with the flame. A book can prop up the container. Move the camera back and forth until a sharp, reversed image appears on the paper. (If an unsatisfactory image is obtained, the box may be too glary or the hole not sharp enough. Brush black tempera paint inside the box. Remove the bottom and replace with aluminum foil. A sharp hole is easier to make with foil.)

suggest
otheses Challenge the children to explain why the candle flame image appears reversed. Point out they already know enough facts to give a satisfactory explanation. If some clues are needed, point to the chalkboard sketch. Ask someone to supplement his verbal explanation by drawing dotted lines from the numbers, through the hole, to places on the right. Have the class note the reversed order of numbers when straight lines are drawn through the hole. Since light travels in straight lines, the candle flame image is similarly reversed in getting through the narrow hole.

suggest
otheses If you wish, change the foregoing sequence by showing and thinking through the sketch first, and trying the pinhole camera second. If light travels in straight lines, then what should a candle image look like if it goes through the tiny pinhole? A successful prediction based on their own thinking will be most interesting to pupils.

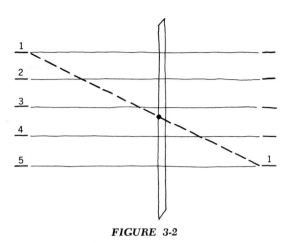

FIGURE 3-2

Contributing idea D. Light travels about 186,000 miles per second.

Materials: chalkboard sketch or opaque projection of Figure 3-3.

An opening comment might be, "Scientists have always been interested in how fast light travels. Many interesting ways have been developed to measure it. Perhaps we can measure the speed of light. How? Let's say we had a stopwatch and a flashlight. How could they be used?"

After a brief discussion, emphasize that light is so swift that such a crude measure

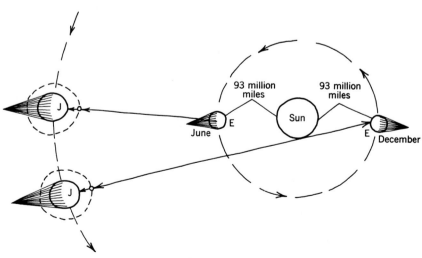

FIGURE 3-3

would never work. It can travel a distance equivalent to around the world in a wink of an eye. Instead, the children are going to see and think about some evidence scientists have used. Reveal a sketch of Figure 3-3.

Briefly review several easy facts: the earth revolves about the sun, as do all the nine planets of the solar system, including Jupiter. Jupiter has several moons which revolve about it, just as our moon revolves about the earth. But in the sketch, the class will consider only one of these moons.

Develop that when we observe Jupiter's moon in June (show the earth's position), it regularly casts a shadow on Jupiter every 42 hours. As the earth moves around in orbit we observe Jupiter's moon from different positions. Jupiter's moon seems to take a longer and longer amount of time to cast its shadow. *reason quantitatively* In December, it takes 1000 seconds longer than in June. Why?

Give clues as needed. We are nearest to Jupiter in June. In December, we are 186 million miles farther away. (Two radii.) The extra 1000 seconds represent the time it takes for the light to travel across our orbit. If light travels 186 million miles in 1000 seconds, how far does it go in one second? With regular division, or cancelling out zeroes, help pupils arrive at 186,000 miles per second. This is the speed of light.

But is this the only explanation possible? *evaluate critically* A sharp thinker might say Jupiter's moon could be changing its orbital speed. Establish that without additional facts the class can only take for granted that Jupiter's moon revolves at a constant speed. Bring out through reference or exposition that scientists do have these facts; the speed is reasonably constant.

Write *Olaus Roemer* on the chalkboard. Explain that he was a brilliant astronomer who worked out this method for calculating the speed of light almost 300 years ago. While he was unable to get the exact figure we know today—measuring instruments were very crude long ago—his method was the first useful one. Today, there are other ways of measuring the speed of light which are more accurate.

Extending activities

1. Let able children do some calculations *reason quant.* with the speed of light:

a. If the moon is about 250,000 miles away how long does its reflected light take to reach us? (About one and one-third seconds.)

b. If the sun is about 93 million miles away, how long does its light take to reach us? (About 8 minutes.)

c. The earth measures 25,000 miles around at the equator. If light could be bent around the equator, how many times around could it travel in one second? (About seven and one-half times.)

2. Let someone report on examples of *bioluminescence*—light radiations from biological sources.

3. Place a small lump of modeling clay on a globe. Insert a pencil perpendicular to the horizon. Darken the room. Shine a filmstrip projector directly on the pencil. Note the small shadow; this is noon. Challenge anyone to explain when it is afternoon, late afternoon, early morning, and mid-morning by *evalua. critica.* rotating the globe counterclockwise. Explanations should be related to increasing and decreasing shadow lengths.

Why does a woman powder her nose? Psychological reasons aside, she does it to scatter light reflections. You know that a ball thrown straight down on smooth, level pavement bounces back up. Try it on rough gravel, however, and its return path is unpredictable. A smooth, shiny surface reflects light rays with very little scattering. However, a rough or uneven surface may scatter the rays so thoroughly that reflections may be scarcely visible. What makes makeup powder so effective? Put some under a microscope. Greatly magnified, it resembles gravel!

Of course, even better reflections are possible with mirrors than noses. Sprinkle some powder over half of a mirror; leave the remainder clear. (Chalk dust will do for the conservation-minded.) Shine a flashlight on both sections of the mirror. Does the powder help to reduce glare? Scattered light rays are called *diffused* reflections. Light rays which are not scattered are *regular* reflections.

When you deal with flat or *plane* reflectors, a special kind of regular reflection becomes possible. If you stand by a mirror and can see the face of another person, that person can also see you. No matter from what position or angle you try it, the same results occur, provided both of you are close enough to the mirror to see a reflection. The angle at which light strikes a plane reflector always equals the angle at which it is reflected. In an experiment designed to help them understand this idea, children will use a white string to make obvious this equality of angles.

No attempt is made in this unit to develop an understanding of curved mirrors. The optical explanations of convex and concave mirrors are beyond most elementary school pupils. However, they can note that convex mirrors—those with a bulging center—reduce a wide field to a small area. This is why they are used for rear view mirrors on some automobiles, for example. Concave mirrors— those with a scooped-out center—magnify images. Thus they are useful for such purposes as cosmetic work or shaving.

If we could not look at our photographs, or double reflections in two mirrors, we would never know how we appear to others. A mirror always produces a reversed image of the observer.

To learn why this is so, study Figure 3-6. In a sense, a mirror image is an optical illusion. Note that the object's image appears to be just as far in back of the glass as the object is in front of it. An interesting demonstration in this section will help pupils verify this fact about mirrors for themselves.

It is customary to think of clear glass as completely transparent to light. Yet a small amount does reflect off the surface. Ordinarily, we do not see the reflected light, because it is only a fraction of the rest that passes through. But at night, when there is darkness in back of the glass, even dim light striking the surface results in noticeable reflections.

Mirrors have always held a fascination for man. In prescientific times, many superstitions were developed to explain what seemed to be a magical image. Even today, many persons cling to the belief that breaking a mirror brings "bad luck." We close this section with an experiment which children can use to test this notion.

BASIC GENERALIZATION II: Light reflections are affected by the reflecting surface and slant at which light strikes the surface

Contributing idea A. Rough, dull surfaces provide diffused reflections; smooth, shiny surfaces provide regular reflections.

Materials: filmstrip projector or flashlight; mirror; aluminum foil; one sheet each of black and white paper; book.

Have the children recall experiences when lighting conditions appeared too bright, glary, and hard on the eyes. Possibly they will mention reading a book with glossy paper under a bright light, or walking on a white, sandy beach, or in the snow on a sunny day. Briefly discuss conditions present in these experiences. Bring out that light *reflections* are responsible for the glare. *[draw conclusions]*

[evaluate critically]

Write on the chalkboard the following words and numbers: 1. white paper, 2. mirror, 3. shiny, crinkled foil, 4. dull, crinkled foil, 5. shiny, smooth foil, 6. black paper. Comment that each of these materials will reflect some light, but some more than others. Invite the children to renumber the materials listed in order of their probable ability to reflect light. Accuracy of this order can be tested with the materials provided. *[suggest hypotheses]*

With the room darkened, each material can be placed against a book and held vertically toward the class, while light is beamed on it from the flashlight or projector. Reflections will be more obvious if the book is turned from side to side as light shines on the material. Since most aluminum foil has a dull side as well as a shiny side, one piece should do for all three foil tests.

If you have several flashlights and enough

FIGURE 3-4

evaluate critically

materials, it will be worthwhile to use small groups in this activity. Each group can record its own data, then compare results with other groups for verification. Differences can be worked out through retesting.

Careful test results will show this order of decreasing brightness in reflections: 1. mirror, 2. shiny, smooth foil, 3. shiny, crinkled foil, 4. dull, crinkled foil, 5. white paper, 6. black paper.

Help the children think through why there was a difference in glare. The smooth, shiny objects gave *regular reflections*. Most of the light was reflected right back to their eyes. Rough, dull objects gave *diffused* or *scattered reflections*. Whereas some light was reflected back to their eyes, most of it bounced off the rough surfaces in many different directions.

draw conclusions

Remind them of their common experiences in bouncing a ball. When a ball is dropped straight down, on a smooth, level sidewalk, it bounces back straight up. But if tried on very rough ground, it bounces in any direction. Develop that light acts in a similar way.

FIGURE 3-5

Contributing idea B. When light travels to a smooth, flat reflector at a slant, it is reflected at the same slant, but in a new direction.

1. *Materials:* flashlight with narrow beam; mirror; about 20 feet of white string; tack; yardstick; chalk.

Inform pupils that they now know enough about light reflections to think about the following demonstration. Arrange materials as in Figure 3-4. Place a mirror on a low table or chair. Securely tack down the string, with equal lengths on either side. Have two children of equal height face each other an equal distance away from the mirror. Each should be able to see the other's face in the mirror. Let each child stretch his string tightly to his eye. Explain that the string will show the path of light. Give a flashlight to one child, and darken the room. Have the child beam his light onto the mirror at the angle indicated by the string. This light will be reflected into the other child's eyes.

Let the experimenters try various distances, still holding the string tightly to their eyes. As long as the flashlight holder can see his partner's eyes in the mirror, and the flashlight is beamed at the mirror, light will beam into his partner's eyes. From time to time ask the class what they notice about the slant of *draw conclus* each string. (Both slants are always equal.)

Move the table and mirror next to a wall. Shine the flashlight at various angles on the mirror so reflections are seen on the wall. Use the string to trace the slants of incidence and reflection.

Let pupils predict where the light will be *suggest hypoth* reflected from various angles before it is turned on. Have them use the string to trace the probable path. After sufficient practice, establish that light is reflected from a flat mir- *draw* ror at exactly the same slant at which it strikes *conclus* it, but in a new direction.

2. *Materials:* stack of books; two mirrors; empty wastebasket; ball; table. Set up these or substitute materials as in Figure 3-5, except for the mirrors.

You might remark, "We know light travels in straight lines and is reflected from a mirror at the same slant it strikes the mirror. Let's say someone's eyes are near level with this table top and he has two mirrors. How could he see over the pile of books to tell what is on the upturned wastebasket?"

If clues are necessary, gradually lead the class to understand that one mirror will be held above the books, while the lower one is left on the table. Encourage pupils to draw various angles of the mirrors on the chalkboard. When several drawings appear valid to the pupils, let them try the activity.

Emphasize the mirrors' similarity of slant. This is just another example of the reflection principle they have learned.

Some children will realize they have made a *periscope,* even though there is no tube into which the mirrors are fitted. Bring out that periscopes are useful in the armed forces, especially for submerged submarines. Since only the upper part of the tube need be out of water, chances of detection are reduced. Shorter periscopes are used in armored tanks. Terrain can be viewed from inside the tank, without risking exposure to enemy gunfire. A more pleasant use of periscopes is to see over crowds at a parade, or to see around corners at play. (Should some pupils wish to make their own periscopes, directions are provided in extending activity 1 of this section.)

Contributing idea C. A flat mirror produces a reversed image which appears to be the same size and distance away from the mirror as the reflected object.

1. *Materials:* one sheet of lined paper; black crayon; sketch or projection of Figure 3-6; mirror. (If pupils can bring small mirrors from home, all can participate in this activity.)

Print these words in a column on the paper; make heavy, black letters: JOHN, MOM, ƎHS. Use every third line to provide enough space. Hold up the paper and show it to the class. Now place the mirror perpendicular to the paper and show the images. Invite the children to tell what they notice.

Assist pupils in reasoning through why only "John" appeared reversed. Call attention to their own reversed images which appear whenever they look at a mirror. If another mirror is available, let someone hold it at an angle and re-reflect the letters. They will appear as originally drawn.

Reveal the sketch. Explain why reversals occur. Light rays bounce off the mirror and are reflected into the man's eyes. His eyes stare outward along the lines of the incoming light rays. To him, it appears as though his image is beyond the mirror's surface.

Bring out that the image distance and size appear to be identical to the original. Have the pupils observe again the block letters in the mirror. These images will also appear to be identical in size and distance. But are they? Inform the group there is an experiment which will help them to decide if mirror images accurately reflect these two factors.

2. *Materials:* small candle; small piece of transparent glass (a microscope slide will do); narrow drinking glass containing water; two small lumps of modeling clay. Arrange materials as in Figure 3-7, and darken the room.

Position a child in back of the candle. Have him direct another child to move the drinking glass until the candle image appears to be burning inside the glass. Let the class note

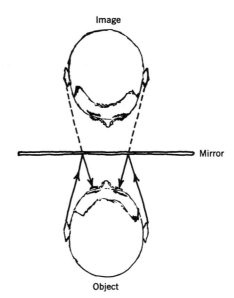

Image

Mirror

Object

FIGURE 3-6   **Why a mirror image is reversed.**

FIGURE 3-7

the identical distance of the candle and drinking glass from the improvised mirror. If two candles of equal size are available, these can be arranged so that only one candle appears in the glass mirror. Again distances will be the same. An image always appears to be the same distance and size as the reflected object.

evaluate
critically Draw out pupil experiences where window glass or water reflected images. Develop that this occurs when it is dark behind or below *draw* *conclusions* the normally transparent surface. While much light passes through, some is reflected back

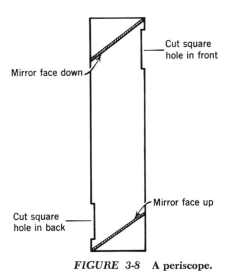

Cut square
hole in front

Mirror face down

Mirror face up

Cut square
hole in back

FIGURE 3-8 A periscope.

to the observer. Place a strip of black and white paper under a piece of flat glass to illustrate the point. Only the black background makes the glass a visible image reflector.

Extending activities

1. Constructing a periscope is instructive and interesting. Needed are a long narrow container, two mirrors, a razor, and cellophane tape. Since the mirrors are taped inside the container, select a container with a flap, as found on a waxed-paper or kitchen-foil carton. Construct as in Figure 3-8. Finish by wrapping several rubber bands around the box to prevent it from opening.

2. Challenge able pupils who can work with protractors to make up reflection experiments with a flashlight and mirrors held at various angles. They will soon discover complemen- *reason* *quantit* tary angles and some other geometric understandings. Ideas can first be worked out on paper and then tested.

3. Many preadolescents believe the superstition, "Breaking a mirror brings bad luck." An experiment may help dispel this belief. Several or more children can bring small, inexpensive mirrors from home. The experiment can be designed in two ways. The "luck" experienced by several mirror breakers can be compared with that of a matched group for,

say, three weeks. Or the mirror breakers' luck alone can be noted for a given period before *select* and after they break their mirrors. In either *ocedures* case, get pupils to set up the procedure, method for recording data, and ground rules. *define* What, for example, will be "bad luck?" An *problems* operational definition is needed. This experiment can be thought provoking and instructive in scientific procedures if some effort is put into it.

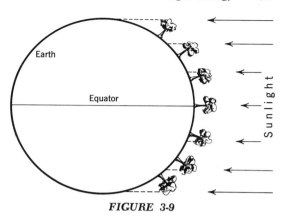

FIGURE 3-9

An air traveler who goes from a cold to a tropical climate in a matter of hours can scarcely fail to notice many differences in his new surroundings. Among the most impressive are house colors—largely light pastels and dazzling white. Similar differences can be noted in clothing colors. Although most adults know the basic reason—dark-colored materials absorb more sunlight than light-colored materials—the practical consequences of this fact are most impressive in a tropical climate.

Figure 3-9 reveals why persons in tropical countries find a greater need for lighter colors than those who live farther away from the equator. Light is most intense when it is received from directly overhead. If the same amount of light is spread out over a larger area, any given part of that area receives less light.

The transformation of light energy to heat energy is most noticeable when there is an effective way of preventing the heat from escaping. A common example is the temperature rise within a tightly closed automobile parked in sunlight. The rapidly vibrating short waves of sunlight can pass through the windows. When they strike the upholstery they are absorbed, then reradiated as longer, slower-vibrating heat waves. The longer waves are largely unable to penetrate glass, however, so most of the heat stays inside, building up in intensity as sunlight continues to stream in. Since the same thing occurs in greenhouses, this phenomenon is aptly called the *greenhouse effect*.

Our atmosphere also is warmed largely by reradiated heat waves. The atmosphere is like a giant glass cover that traps the longer, reradiated heat waves. However, this analogy is not perfect. Fortunately for us, the atmosphere is far less efficient than glass. A substantial amount of reradiated heat escapes into space. Were this not so, the earth would soon become intolerable to life.

Because of the greenhouse effect, air temperatures get warmest in the afternoon, rather than at mid-day. Although the sun is most nearly overhead at noon, the buildup of heat continues for several hours afterward.

This section ends with a brief study of *photochemical* reactions—the transformation of light energy to chemical energy when light is absorbed. Materials that react photochemically do not just change in physical appearance. A permanent change occurs in molecular structure. Although this can be annoying when a favorite sweater fades, the phenomenon makes possible many important events, from photography to photosynthesis.

BASIC GENERALIZATION III: Absorbed light energy changes into heat energy and chemical energy

Contributing idea A. Dark-colored materials absorb more light energy than light-colored materials.

1. *Materials:* two different-sized sheets of construction paper, one white and one black; scissors; two thermometers; sunshine.

Say, "When we did our experiments with light reflection we found light reflected least of all from black paper. Actually, with the right kind of black paper, there is practically no reflection at all. If so, where does the light energy go? What happens to it?"

suggest hypotheses

Provide clues as needed: "What colors seem more popular in summer than winter? Why is white worn so much in tropical countries? Why are light colors preferred for houses in the tropics?"

A reasonable guess is that light energy is changed to heat energy in materials of dark color. Pursue a hypothesis about the white paper. The children should reason that not as much heat energy would be produced because white paper largely reflects light. Press for a test of this thinking. If necessary, inquire as to how the materials might be used.

select procedures

An easy test is to place the black and white sheets over two thermometers in a sunny area. Leaving the upper-fourth of each thermometer sticking out at the top will provide advance notice of a temperature rise sufficient to break the thermometers. Someone should check temperatures every several minutes. Be prepared to bring out such needed controls as equal size of paper, recording identical thermometer temperatures before the test, and equal exposure time. When test results are in, guide toward a tentative conclusion: black paper seems to *absorb* light energy more efficiently than white paper. Therefore, it becomes warmer.

draw conclusions

2. If thermometers are unavailable, a similar test can be made with two small cans of water. Encircle one in black paper, the other in white. Place in strong sunlight for at least an hour. Pretest and post-test temperatures can be taken by dipping a finger into the water. This is less accurate, of course, but the difference should be noticeable. Children can also do this experiment at home and report their findings.

Contributing idea B. Vertical light rays striking a surface produce more heat energy than slanted rays.

1. *Materials:* two sheets black construction paper; two thermometers; stapler; sunshine.

Have pupils recall how warm it feels when sunlight shines on them. Develop that sometimes the sun's rays feel warmer than at other times. Establish the time of day when this occurs. The sun usually feels warmer in the early afternoon, as contrasted with morning or late afternoon sunlight. Ask for a reason. If clues are needed, let the class recall when shadows are longest. When light slant is suggested, challenge the children to set up an experiment. If needed, suggest use of the stated materials.

draw conclus

suggest hypoth

select proced

A pocket can be made for each thermometer by folding over the black paper once and stapling it at the bottom and side. Again it will be useful to leave the tops of each thermometer sticking out to receive advance warning of possible breakage. Both thermometers should be placed with tops pointing away from the sun. One thermometer should be level and the other propped up to receive vertical light. Again pretest temperatures must be identical.

Guide pupils in finding the correct angle for propping. A small stick or pencil can be placed upright on the covered thermometer. When there is no shadow, the light will be perfectly vertical. Prop with books or other handy material.

One pupil should check temperatures every several minutes. When the temperature difference is obvious, discuss findings and conclusions.

reason quanti

draw conclus

2. *Materials:* flashlight (narrow-beam or spotlight type); 6-foot string; chalk; chalkboard; piece of cellophane tape.

Inquire as to *why* vertical light results in more heat absorption than slanted light. If no satisfactory answer is given, ask your group to explain the following demonstration.

Fasten one end of the string to the flashlight; stick the other end to a spot on the chalkboard. Darken the room. Shine the flashlight on the chalkboard. Let someone carefully draw a line around the light received. Now move several steps to one side, and shine the light at a slant of 45 degrees or more on the same spot. (The string will insure a similar distance.) A line should be drawn around the second spot.

draw *usions* Draw out the idea behind this demonstration. An equal amount of light is distributed over a larger area the second time. This is like spreading out jam or butter over more bread; it has to be thinner. Each part of the larger area received less light. Therefore, there is less heat in each part.

aluate *tically* Elicit why the string was used. Show that light can also be spread out by increasing distance between the chalkboard and flashlight. Shine a beam on the chalkboard and have someone circle it. Gradually step back farther and farther. As the spot size increases, the intensity of light will decrease.

Contributing idea C. Light energy passes through glass, while reradiated heat energy is largely blocked by glass.

1. *Materials:* Mason jar with lid (A milk bottle may be substituted. Use Saran-Wrap and a rubber band for the lid.); piece of dark-colored cloth; two thermometers; scissors; sunshine.

Try this sequence of questions to develop need for an experiment:

"Have you ever opened the door of a car that has been tightly shut and standing in the sun for a long time? What did it feel like inside?" (The air and upholstery were hot.)

uggest *theses* "Where did the heat come from?" (The sunlight entered the closed windows and was changed into heat when absorbed by the upholstery.)

"Why didn't the heat go out through the closed windows?"

select *edures* "How can we do an experiment to find out if heat energy is blocked by glass?"

If necessary, exhibit the materials. A well-designed experiment might have the Mason jar or bottle in a horizontal position. A swatch of dark cloth placed inside will simulate upholstery. One thermometer can be placed inside, on the cloth. The other thermometer can be laid on an identical piece of cloth placed outside and next to the closed jar. *reason* *tively* When placed in sunshine for five or more

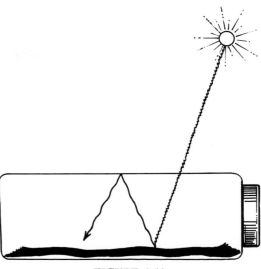

FIGURE 3-10

minutes, the inside thermometer should show *draw* *conclusions* a noticeable rise over the outside one.

2. *Materials:* chalkboard sketch of Figure 3-10.

Indicate that the sketch shows a path of a single ray of light out of many entering the jar. Invite an explanation of what is happening. Develop that the short light wave becomes a longer heat wave when reradiated. The longer wave is unable to get through the glass. (Explain that a certain percentage does get through under normal circumstances.)

Mention that this is called the *greenhouse effect*. Briefly discuss the functions of a greenhouse. If desired, develop the role of the greenhouse effect in heating our atmosphere.

Contributing idea D. Light energy may bring about chemical changes.

1. *Materials:* construction paper sheets of at least six different colors, and several white sheets; scissors; bulletin board space or window space for mounting the paper.

For an interesting bridge to this experiment, look for some common examples of color fading: faded dark paper on a bulletin board with darker outlines of letters; cloth garments with noticeable differences between inside or lined portions and outside parts; shelved books with faded cloth covers, espe-

draw conclusions

suggest hypotheses

select procedures

draw conclusions

cially on the part exposed to light; and so on. Examples are found in abundance with a little searching.

Confront the pupils with your examples. Ask them to name conditions which may have caused these materials to fade. Focus on the light factor. If possible, guide them to hypothesize about the relation of color type to rapidity of fading. Show them the construction paper. Will the darker colors fade more rapidly than the lighter colors? Children can record the probable order of fading, and then test it.

There should be little difficulty in setting up the design. Small, white squares can be pinned or taped to each colored sheet. These can be placed on a bulletin board facing the windows. A week's exposure to light should produce some changes. But portions under the white squares will remain unfaded. Quicker results will be obtained by taping the colored papers to windows, instead of a bulletin board.

Guard against sweeping conclusions from this experiment. Although darker colors often tend to fade more rapidly than bright colors, the color "fastness" and composition of materials vary so widely that no reliable single generalization can be drawn.

Inform the class that when light strikes a colored substance over a period of time, a chemical change may take place in the colored dye of the substance. Light energy may cause the atoms to become rearranged in the molecules of the dye, giving new molecules of a different color. This change is permanent.

2. *Materials:* piece of flat glass, about 8 inches by 11 inches; several sheets of blueprint paper; pan of water; leaves or other relatively flat objects; sheet of cardboard.

Explain to the children that chemical reaction to light can be speeded up by treating paper with special chemicals. This is done in camera film and blueprint paper. Now they will have a chance to take and develop "pictures" with blueprints.

Dim the room light. Remove a sheet of blueprint paper from the package. Place its sensitive side up on cardboard or other stiff

backing. Put a leaf, an old film negative, or other object to be outlined on the paper and cover with glass. Expose the paper to sunlight or strong artificial light until it turns blue. This may take five or more minutes, depending on the intensity of the light.

Now the blueprint is ready for developing. Remove materials. Place the print face down in a pan of water for five minutes, or run water over it for the same time. Let it dry face down in a dark place or in a drawer. A clear outline of the leaf or other object will be recorded. Eventually, the outline loses distinction if exposed to much light.

Extending activities

1. Visit a nearby greenhouse. Let children learn how light, shade, and temperature are controlled throughout the year.

2. Have someone report on how films are developed.

3. Encourage children to look for examples of fading through light. Discuss each example to determine if another factor may have been responsible. Let them look for controls. For example, blue jeans will fade with repeated washings. But looking at the cloth inside a back pocket will help reveal the effect of sunlight. In other words, a sample is valid only when it contains faded and unfaded portions, and when both portions have received the same treatment, except for light.

evaluate critical

We have stated that the speed of light changes as it travels in media of different densities. If a light beam enters or leaves a different medium at a slant the uneven change in speed may cause the beam to *refract*, or change direction of travel.

This phenomenon is readily observable. A pencil half-placed in water looks bent. Distant images shimmer through unevenly heated air as we drive along a hot road. The scenery looks distorted through a cheap glass window, since its thickness is uneven. Interestingly, the function of an automobile windshield wiper is to restore the rainy, outside surface of a windshield to a plane surface. As rain is wiped away, the light rays enter the plate glass at a uniform angle, rather than unevenly.

Man has learned to control light refraction with lenses. Magnifying glasses and optical instruments of many descriptions extend the power of sight far beyond that available to the unaided eye. In this section there are opportunities for children to work with both convex and concave lenses, the two principal types.

BASIC GENERALIZATION IV: Slanted light rays are refracted when they pass from one medium to another of different density; lenses are made to control refraction

Contributing idea A. Slanted light rays bend when passing from one medium to another of different density.

1. *Materials: straight* yardstick or pointer; flat-sided aquarium tank, two-thirds filled with water; white button or chalk (placed inside the tank); book.

It will be interesting to start this sequence with a bridge that leads into a problem and a need to understand why the problem has occurred. You might say, "Who likes to go fishing? What else do people fish with besides a rod and reel? (Bring out that some people spear fish while standing in a boat or on a dock.) Spearfishing is fun, but you are likelier to get good results if you know how light travels. Who thinks he can spear the 'fish' (chalk or button) in this tank?"

Accept several volunteers, but let each observe only his own trial. Let one child sight along the yardstick. (He should use the wide portion, rather than edge, for his sighting. If the yardstick is slid into the water on its edge, the extra width of wood may permit him to hit his target even though his aim is off.) When his angle of aim is set, ask how a control can be developed to insure that the angle does not shift when the stick enters the water. A book may be used for this purpose. Hold it firmly while the yardstick is slid down a groove formed by the outside covers.

select procedures

Have the class observe silently while each volunteer consistently goes over the target. Ask for hypotheses to account for the misses. Let the pupils discuss each hypothesis. Three reasonable guesses are:

suggest hypotheses

a. The volunteers could not aim. (This is unlikely, because several were used and all missed.)

b. The stick is bent. (This can be checked. If necessary, the stick can be turned over and tried again.)

c. Something happens to the light when it enters or leaves the water. (Let them discuss this briefly; then move to an explanation of the principles involved.)

Bring out that anything in motion will slow down or stop when something is in the way. It is easy to run across an empty room at top speed. But scatter some people around it and the runner must slow down. If the room is completely filled, it is impossible to run across it. The population of the room has become *denser* each time. A greater amount of matter is taking up the same space.

Continue by stating that a similar thing happens with light as it travels through air, water, and glass. Water is denser than air—it has more molecules in the same space—and glass has more density than water. When light enters a denser medium, it slows down. The reverse is also true.

2. *Materials:* chalkboard sketches of Figure 3-11 A-B.

Exhibit sketch A. Explain that two wheels attached to an axle are rolling freely in the direction indicated. Bring out what happens when the leading wheel strikes a sandy road. The device moves on, but at a slightly different angle. Now show the reverse. If the wheel-axle device travels diagonally upward, one wheel will hit the paved portion sooner. The direction will again change, but in an opposite way. Inform the class that a similar change in directions takes place when a beam of light enters and leaves materials of unequal density.

draw conclusions

Place sketch B next to A. If your pupils are alert thinkers let them study this drawing for a moment. Can they provide an explana-

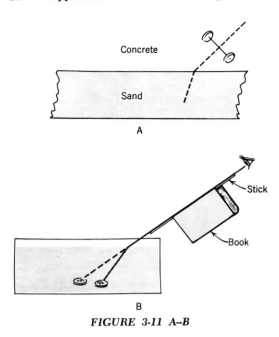

FIGURE 3-11 A–B

suggest hypotheses tion of why the "spearfishermen" consistently overshot their mark? It may be worthwhile to use small discussion groups to form explanations.

Develop that, as light leaves the water, it changes directions slightly. We sight along a path where the button seems to be, because it seems to be in a straight line. But when our stick enters the water, *it continues at the same slant as it began.* Therefore, it overshoots the target.

draw conclusions Have the children apply their thinking. How should the aim be changed? Be sure they reason this through, as now it is easy to suggest only altering the aim. By aiming below the target, accuracy should improve. Let class members try it.

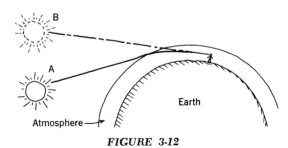

FIGURE 3-12

3. *Materials:* shallow paper cups, or shallow teacups; straws, or pencils; paper towels. (Two paper cups, one three-fourths filled with water, and one straw are needed for each experiment. It is desirable to have children do this activity in pairs.)

It will be most interesting to the class if everyone can try the above "spearfishing" activity in miniature. At the same time, this will provide an opportunity to discover that light "bends" only when it enters or leaves water at a slant.

If children are to work in pairs or groups, remember to review briefly standards and procedures. Paper towels should be available to soak up any spilled water.

Have children draw a pinhead-sized circle on the inside bottom of each empty paper cup. It should be reasonably centered. (If ceramic teacups are used, substitute a small pebble or coin. Secure with cellophane tape.) These cups should be placed on desks and viewed from an angle, so that the penciled circle just barely disappears from view. Direct partners to pour water slowly from the unmarked cup into the marked cup. Viewers should keep their heads perfectly still. As water is poured in, the circle will appear, slightly farther away and higher than before. Let partners trade roles and try this demonstration several times.

draw conclus Bring out that light must have bent slightly as water filled the cup; the penciled circles obviously could not move.

draw conclus Permit children to sight their target through straws and try to hit it from all angles. Again a book can be used to maintain an unchangeable angle once a sighting has been made. Pupils will discover that when they are directly over the target, there is no difficulty in hitting it. The circle is where it appears to be. They should realize no bending occurs unless the light enters or leaves at a slant, even though its speed changes.

4. *Materials:* sketch of Figure 3-12.

Pupils will be interested in another application of refraction. We can observe the sun a few minutes after actual sundown, because its light changes directions when entering our

*draw
clusions*

atmosphere from airless space. Exhibit the sketch. Let class members try to explain what happens at sunset. Can they explain why the light rays are curved, rather than straight, as they travel through the atmosphere? (Our atmosphere gradually gets denser closer to the earth.) Rays from A traveling to our eyes finally enter from a direction that is slightly above the horizon. Therefore, the sun seems to be at B.

Caution your class against observing the sun at any time except briefly when it is very near the horizon. Damage to the eye's interior may result.

Contributing idea B. A convex lens converges light rays; lenses with shorter focal lengths magnify more than those with longer focal lengths.

1. *Materials:* hand magnifying lenses of varied thicknesses; ruler; sheet of lined paper; sunshine or flashlight; sketch of Figure 3-13 A-B-C.

Many children are surprised to learn their magnifying "glasses" work because of refraction. The next several activities will help them see why.

Have everyone recall how they use a hand lens to focus the sun's rays. If necessary, someone can demonstrate this. Show your sketch, and indicate drawing B as a *convex* lens refracting light rays. Explain that the sun's parallel rays enter the glass and are refracted or bent when entering and leaving. Once again it will be helpful to draw or use an axle with two wheels to show how the refraction takes place. Some teachers use a large cardboard cross section of a lens, with a toy wheel and axle combination, so pupils may see this more clearly.

Once the children understand how the refraction takes place, move to drawing A. Most of the light rays enter the eye from two opposite slants. As the eye follows these slanted rays to the lens they seem to continue outward, and so form an enlarged image of the object.

Compare drawings B and C. Bring out that the two lenses are different in thickness, al-

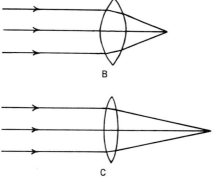

FIGURE 3-13 A–B–C

though their diameter is the same. Each will bring the sun's rays to a point or *focus* at a different distance. Distance from point of focus to the lens is the *focal length*.

Develop conjecture as to whether lenses with shorter focal lengths give more powerful magnification than those of longer focal lengths. Encourage the children to use drawings A-B-C as they reason this through. Extend the angled lines in B and C from the focal points outward, as in A. They should reason that B would be more powerful than C. Challenge them to test this notion.

*suggest
hypotheses*

The first step is to determine focal lengths for each· hand lens available. This can be done quickly with rulers and lenses in the sun. (Caution pupils not to focus on any flammable substance while measuring.) If there is no sunshine, substitute a narrow-beam flashlight. Darken the room and place the flashlight in a parallel position at least 15 feet away from the lens. Hold the lens in the light beam and focus it on a wall. A lens is focused when the light rays are converged to

FIGURE 3-14

reason quantitatively the smallest point. Most focal lengths will be about 4 to 8 inches. Of course, written notations will be helpful to keep track of lenses and their focal lengths.

Magnification can be tested by placing a lens parallel to and over lined paper, as in Figure 3-14. Put an X on the paper. Center it in the lens. Move the lens up and down until the X is most clearly defined. This distance will be somewhere between the paper and the lens' focal length. Count all the lines visible through the lens. Then count all lines outside the lens that fall between the first and last lines visible through the lens. Divide the *reason quantitatively* larger figure by the smaller. This provides the

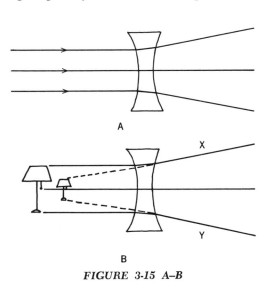

A

B

FIGURE 3-15 A–B

lens' power of magnification. In Figure 3-14, lens power is 2. Images would be twice life size.

2. *Materials*: various clear drinking glasses and jars with straight sides, containing water; pencils.

Mention the story of a woman who purchased "giant-sized" olives in a narrow, round bottle, only to find them much smaller when taken out of the bottle. Let pupils explore the refraction characteristics of many glass containers by placing pencils, fingers, and other objects inside and in back of them. Have them note the greater refraction—and *draw conclus* so magnification—present when two containers of water are placed together, one behind the other. Many other interesting observations may be noted. Glasses and jars containing transparent liquids are spherical lenses; they converge light rays similarly to convex lenses.

Contributing idea C. A concave lens causes light rays to diverge; therefore, images appear smaller.

Materials: sketches of Figure 3-15 A-B; concave lens. In your sketch of A, leave out the diverging lines. It will be challenging for your pupils to draw these in later.

Exhibit sketch A, but withhold B at this time. Tell the class this is a cross section of a *concave* lens. An easy way to remember the shape is with the words "caved in." A concave lens has a caved-in center. Invite someone to *suggest hypoth* predict where the parallel lines will go after they enter the lens. Again a wheel-axle device may be used. After diverging lines have been drawn, emphasize the opposite curvature of *draw conclus* this lens in contrast with that of a convex lens. Since they are curved in an opposite manner, the refraction is also opposite. Convex lenses *converge* light rays, or bring them together. Concave lenses cause light rays to *diverge*, or spread out.

Now show sketch B. Help pupils think through what happens when an object is *draw conclus* viewed through a concave lens. Most of the rays slant outward, as in X and Y. As the eye follows many of these slanted rays back to the lens, they seem to continue inward at a slant, and form a smaller image of the object.

Allow pupils to look at objects through a concave lens. If none is available, perhaps substitutes can be provided. Thick drinking glasses often have concave-shaped bases. Check by seeing if images are smaller when viewed through them. Nearsighted children who wear eyeglasses are another available source of supply. It will be worthwhile to record, but temporarily postpone, questions about why some eyeglass lenses are concave. This will be taken up shortly in an overall and applied context when the eye is studied.

Extending activities

1. Almost everyone has seen wavy, shimmering images produced when viewing objects through heated air. A similar effect can be achieved by a hot plate. Place a picture in back of a hot plate before and after it is turned on. The children should understand that the effect is produced through air convection. Warm air rises and is continually being replaced by cooler air of different density. Light rays passing through the area of unequal density are refracted unevenly.

2. Any transparent, convex object may produce magnified images, including a water drop. Pupils will profit from making their own hand lenses from improvised materials.

a. The simplest lens is a drop of water on a clear glass slide or similar glass piece. Water drops may be placed either on top of or underneath a slide by an eye-dropper. A slightly better lens is provided with a "hanging drop" technique, but it is less convenient to handle.

b. A desirable substitute can be made with cellophane tape and a stiff card. Cut a 2-inch square piece of card. Snip out a small center portion. Cover each side with one strip of cellophane tape, sticky sides together. Be sure not to get fingerprints on the center portion, as it will interfere with viewing. Place several water drops on both the glass and cellophane slides. One drop is almost sure to magnify better than others.

c. Make a "wire loop" water lens. Form a loop of thin, soft wire around a large nail. It is important to get the loop perfectly round, as otherwise a distorted image results. For best results, use only enough wire to close the loop without having any wire left over. Pliers will help. Scoop up a drop of water in the loop. Surface tension will hold it in place.

d. A more elaborate setup may be constructed for viewing thin cross sections of objects. In this case it is important to have strong light going *through* the objects. Place a clear glass slide bearing the specimen on end between two small stacks of books. Position a small mirror at an angle underneath the specimen. Prop it with an eraser or stack of cards so light is reflected strongly upward through the specimen. View with any of the lenses previously suggested. (For an illustration, see page 415.)

When ancient man saw a rainbow, he was probably inclined to give a magical or supernatural explanation to account for it. Later, people thought that the colors came from the rain droplets through which the sunlight passes. It was not until Isaac Newton (1642–1727) performed experiments with prisms that it was realized these colors were the components of visible sunlight itself.

There are seven universally recognized colors in the visible color spectrum of sunlight: red, orange, yellow, green, blue, indigo, and violet. (Many teachers remember these colors and their spectral order through the name Roy G. Biv.) Since indigo is virtually indistinguishable from its adjacent colors, it is common to exclude indigo at the elementary level of study.

A prism separates light because each color has a different wavelength and rate of vibration. Red light has the longest wavelength, with about 30,000 waves to one inch. Violet light has the shortest wavelength, with about 60,000 waves to one inch. As a light beam passes through a prism the longer waves are refracted least, the shorter waves most.

Differences in colors are often compared with pitch differences in sound. A low sound is a result of relatively slow vibrations. Its visual counterpart is the color red. A high sound results from fast vibrations. Its counterpart is violet.

If white light consists of all the spectral colors, why don't all nonluminous objects bathed in this light look white? The answer lies in the selective absorption properties of these objects. A pure white object reflects all seven spectral colors. Nonwhite objects reflect only certain colors and absorb the rest. A blue suit looks blue because the atomic structure of the blue pigment absorbs every other color, but rejects blue. The same process is true of other colors. On the other hand, pure black is a result of total color absorption, with no reflection. The main reason a pure black object is visible is because it is usually outlined in a nonblack surrounding.

Colored cellophane filters are similarly subtractive in nature. For example, a pure red filter placed over a white light lets through only the red waves.

Some interesting experiments help verify this theory of color. If a red light shines on an object with a "red-hating" pigment, it looks red. If a green light shines on this object, it looks black, since it absorbs green. There is nothing to reflect. All other colors but red would be similarly absorbed.

Even the best artificial light does not contain the exact colors of sunlight. For this reason, we can never be sure a garment purchased at night will look the same in daylight. For example, most white light bulbs are somewhat deficient in blue. Therefore, a blue garment will look a bit darker under this light than in daylight. Fortunately, many clothing retailers recognize this problem and install lights whose color qualities differ only slightly from sunlight.

Visible light is only a small portion of the radiant energy received by the earth. The fact that something can exist without their being conscious of it is difficult for many children to understand. It is helpful to remind them that radio waves are in the air, although we cannot feel them. Germs exist, although we cannot see them. However, with the proper instruments to extend our senses, these phenomena are detectable.

Observe closely the spectrum cast by a prism, and you can notice that the red and violet ends do not end sharply, but trail off into invisibility. In 1800, the famous British astronomer William Herschel discovered that a thermometer became warmest when placed just below the red end of the spectrum. He realized that invisible infrared radiations were probably responsible. A German scientist, Johann Ritter, discovered ultraviolet waves about the same time. His method was to place a light-sensitive chemical just beyond violet in the spectrum.

With the development of refined instruments, scientists have become able to discover a huge range of radiations. All radiations appear to be different variations of electro-magnetic energy found in atoms. Their differences appear to be mainly those of wavelength and frequency of vibration.

Radiations beyond the violet end of the visible spectrum continually increase in frequency and penetrating power. This is why X-rays can penetrate flesh, while visible light is "blocked" by an opaque barrier. Interestingly, however, infrared radiations easily slip through a hazy or foggy atmosphere while shorter, visible light waves are blocked and reflected. Since many infrared radiations are emitted by any warm object, excellent pictures can be taken with heat-sensitive film in hazy weather, or even at night.

Have all radiations been detected by now? How can we be sure? This leads to another question. What else is "out there" that we have yet to discover? Perhaps one day some of today's pupils will be instrumental in finding out.

BASIC GENERALIZATION V: White light is composed of different colors; the color of objects depends on which colors are transmitted, reflected, and absorbed

Contributing idea A. A prism separates white light by refracting the colors of which it is made.

1. *Materials:* glass prism; sunlight (or film-strip projector and darkened room); sketch of Figure 3-16.

Begin by asking if anyone has seen a rainbow. Continue: What makes a rainbow? Where do the colors come from? Develop that it is reasonable to think they may come from the sunlight itself. Mention the children can find out for themselves with several activities. In the first one they will use a glass *prism*. Show them a prism.

Exhibit your simplified sketch. It shows a greatly magnified ray of white light going through a prism. Bring out that the lower part of this ray strikes the prism before the upper part. Use the wheels-axle analogy to show the direction of bend. Have the class notice also that the lower part of the ray must travel through more glass than its upper part. Therefore, it makes sense to assume the prism's shape will spread the light beam apart. If there are colors in the light, will they be revealed when they leave the prism?

Hold the prism in sunlight and rotate it slowly until a spectrum appears on a wall or ceiling. (If there is no sunlight, hold the prism in front of a filmstrip projector beam.) Have pupils identify the colors: red, orange, yellow, green, blue, and violet. There appear to be six main colors (excluding indigo) in sunlight. If a projector light is used, its spectrum will be similar.

Return to your sketch; let the children help complete it. Draw in three more lines (or four, to include indigo) and label each, beginning with red and ending with violet. Elicit that red was refracted least and violet most when going through the prism.

But perhaps these colors came from the glass. Encourage pupils to think of a way in which they could be reasonably sure this was not the case. When needed, provide hints. If light can be taken apart, then we should be able to put it back together. How could *two* prisms help?

Establish now, or later through authority, that although difficult to do in a classroom, light refracted into separate colors can be reconstituted. Two prisms are used, the second

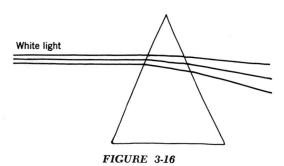

White light

FIGURE 3-16

in reverse position of the first. The end product is again white light.

2. *Materials:* cake pan of water (or other shallow container); small mirror; sunlight (or filmstrip projector and darkened room).

Remind everyone that they are still concerned about understanding rainbows. How can a glass prism help in explaining what happens? Encourage discussion. Elicit that two factors are always present in rainbows: sunshine and water in the air. Can water act like a prism? They can find out now. *draw conclusions*

Place a container of water in sunlight (or projector beam) and lean a mirror against the rim. Light must strike part of the mirror below the water's surface. Depending on the angle of light, a beautifully clear spectrum will appear on a nearby wall or ceiling.

Stir the water slightly and have the class note that white light appears. When the water becomes still, the spectrum again appears. Bring out that colors were recombined when the water was stirred.

3. *Materials:* attached garden hose, with fine spray nozzle; slanted morning or afternoon sun. (If the sun or school custodian are uncooperative, children can do this activity at home sometime after its introduction.)

Briefly review what they have learned: White light is composed of rainbow colors. White light can be separated by a prism. Water can act like a prism. But water in the air is made up of fine droplets. Rainbows appear when the sun is at an angle. Can tiny droplets act like prisms in slanted sunshine?

Encourage pupils to think of what to do. Give clues as needed. When are the sun's rays slanting? (Morning and late afternoon.) *select procedures*

What can break up water into tiny droplets? (Garden hose and spray nozzle.) Where is the sun when they see a rainbow? (In back or at an angle.) If essential factors are observed—slanted sun in back of the observer, and fine spray—a rainbow will be observed.

Contributing idea B. An object's color depends on the color of light striking it and the color it reflects.

1. *Materials:* glass prism; filmstrip projector and white screen; three small sheets of cellophane, red, blue, and green; three sheets of construction paper, red, blue, and green; darkened room.

Shine the projector on a white screen. Draw out that the children are viewing all the rainbow colors combined to form white light. Now place a double thickness of red cellophane over the lens. Invite anyone to explain why there is now a red light shining. "Is the red cellophane turning the rainbow colors to red? Or is the cellophane letting just the red through? Let's see if we can figure out what is happening."

Take off the red cellophane and place the prism in the white light beam. Hold it on end as steadily as possible. If manageable, place the prism on a pile of books to achieve perfect stillness. Reposition the projector so that a spectrum appears on the white screen. Ask pupils to note carefully the exact position of red in the spectrum. Place red cellophane between the prism and screen. All but the red part of the spectrum will disappear. The position of red in the spectrum will be identical before and after red cellophane is interposed.

draw conclusions Invite pupils to use what they observed in explaining how the red cellophane functioned. Guide them to reason that the cellophane probably prevented all but the red waves from getting through. Additional trials with green and blue cellophane blocking spectrum colors may be tried, but will probably be less successful. It is difficult to obtain perfect filtering action with ordinary cellophane.

2. Ask, "When the sun shines, do you feel warmer in a dark blue sweater or a white sweater?" (Blue.) Develop that only one color, blue, is being reflected and all other spectrum colors absorbed.

draw conclusi "If blue is the only color that can be reflected, what color must shine on the sweater to see it?" (Blue.) Hold up a blue sweater or, preferably, blue construction paper in front of the projector. (If there is inadequate darkness place the paper inside a large, empty carton or wastebasket. Lay it on its side and shine the projector light into it.) Put folded blue cellophane over the lens. The construction paper will continue to be visible and blue in color.

suggest hypothe Raise conjecture about the paper's color if red and green lights are used. Try each in turn. Bring out that these colors were absorbed. Since there was no blue light in either color, the paper looked black. Objects appear black when there is no (or very little) reflection of light waves.

3. *Materials:* filmstrip projector; variety of colored cellophane sheets; variety of colored construction paper; darkened room; empty carton or wastebasket (if needed).

Mention that even a careful person can make mistakes when buying colored clothing in stores with inadequate artificial lighting. Challenge the class to detect the true colors of the construction paper samples as they are exposed to various colored lights. Be sure to mention that neither cellophane paper nor construction paper will be perfect in filtering and absorbing colors. Therefore, resulting colors should be unpredictable.

Have someone change construction paper samples as you change cellophane filters. Use one colored filter for a whole series of construction papers, then another, and so on. It will be especially interesting if a guess-verification procedure is adopted. For example, have pupils keep their eyes closed while the paper sample is changed. Show the example in colored light. Let each pupil write his guess. Then remove the filter and let the children see the paper in white light. After sufficient practice, they should have little difficulty in understanding that color is a function of the light striking an object as well as the color it reflects.

4. *Materials:* microprojector (microscopes are less adequate, hand lenses least adequate); several colored pictures from magazines featuring these colors: orange, green, purple, and brown; three sheets of colored cellophane, yellow, red, blue, cut in circles of identical size; one large sheet of white paper; several straight pins.

Fix a large sheet of white paper on a bulletin board. Remind pupils that they have worked with water colors and tempera in art. How did they get various colors? Review their experiences briefly.

Hold up the three-colored cellophane cutouts against the white paper. Bring out that they are the three *primary colors* for mixing paints or pigments. Combine the three pieces of cellophane as in Figure 3-17. Elicit the combinations of colors:

yellow + red = orange
yellow + blue = green
blue + red = purple or violet
blue + red + green = black

Say, "In printing colors in comic books and magazines, all colors are shown. Let's discover how the printers do it." Place a small sample of orange between two slides, and project it with the microprojector. If only hand lenses are available, place two together for higher magnification. Let several children at a time examine a sample. They will probably see many separate yellow and red dots. Help them understand that our eyes combine these separate dots into orange when they are viewed from a distance.

suggest
otheses
Now refer pupils to the pieces of colored cellophane. Have them predict how green and purple are formed. Test predictions by view-
draw
lusions
ing appropriate samples. They will discover that other colors are formed in like manner. For example, brown is a combination of the right number of blue, red, and yellow dots.

Many printed illustrations employ three slightly different basic colors. However, chil-
draw
lusions
dren should understand that virtually any color can be produced by varying the number of dots in just several different colors.

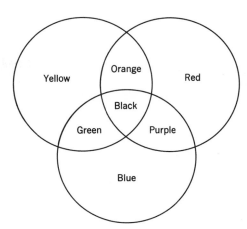

FIGURE 3-17   Combining primary pigments.

Contributing idea C. Visible light is only a small portion of the radiant energy received by the earth.

1. *Materials:* hot plate (the kind with an exposed heating element); sketch of Figure 3-18.

You might use this bridge:

Back in 1800, an English astronomer, *William Herschel*, made an amazing discovery. He knew absorbed light energy changes into heat energy, but he wanted to find out which colors made the most heat. He blackened the bulb of a thermometer and placed it in the different colors of a spectrum made by a prism. The temperature rose in every color, but he noticed a strange thing. As the thermometer was moved closer to red, the temperature became higher and higher. Finally, when he placed his thermometer *outside* the red color, the temperature was highest. Why do you think this happened? What did this show him?

suggest
hypotheses

FIGURE 3-18

Scene photographed with normal film.

Electric iron photographed in the dark.

Same scene photographed with infrared film.

Car photographed in darkness.

FIGURE 3-19   Infrared.

Develop in the discussion that a reasonable guess is that some *invisible* form of radiation was present. This radiation is now called *infrared* radiation—"infra" meaning below red in the color spectrum. It is present in sunlight, but also in many other things. Tell the pupils in a moment they will feel infrared radiations for themselves, but first it would be helpful to know more about the color spectrum.

Exhibit your sketch. Explain that this is an imaginary interpretation of what happens when sunlight is separated into colors. Point out in any color the distance from the crest of one tiny wave to another. Identify this distance as one *wavelength*. Explain that scientists believe different colors have different wavelengths. Mention that wavelengths are greatly exaggerated in the drawing. They actually range from about 30,000 red waves to about 60,000 violet waves in one inch. Emphasize that short waves vibrate much faster than longer waves, so they must have more energy.

Ask, "Since infrared comes just before red in the spectrum, would you expect its wave-

draw
*clusions*length to be longer or shorter than red?" Produce a hot plate. Tilt it, or place it on a side so that the wire heating element is visible. Bring out that a hot plate converts electrical energy to heat energy. The heat energy it gives off is infrared radiation.

Have someone place his hand about six inches away from the hot plate. Direct him to withdraw his hand immediately when he feels the infrared radiation.

"What did he feel? (Heat.) Did you see any heat? (No.) What would happen if we let more and more electrical energy into the wire? (There will be more heat.) What else? (Light.)"

Snap on the electricity. Direct the child to put his hand out farther and farther from the hot plate as it grows hotter. Gradually, the hot plate will glow red, then red-orange if the electricity remains on for a period of time. Disconnect the electricity. Have the class notice the reverse sequence of colors as energy is withdrawn; also, that infrared radiation continues for some time after visible radiation has ceased.

Develop that, as more energy is introduced into the hot wire, additional waves of greater frequency than infrared waves are sent out. These waves are visible.

Emphasize that infrared waves are like visible light waves, except they do not vibrate fast enough for our eyes to see them. An infrared source may be given more energy, however, and so produce visible waves we recognize as light.

2. Develop that nearly all substances emit some infrared waves. This is most noticeable when the air temperature is colder than the radiating body. Have the children place their open palms very close to their cheeks. They will feel heat resulting from the infrared waves coming from their skin.

Remind them that when they are "fighting" a cold they get a fever. Or when they exercise, they feel warmer. Both conditions result from a faster "burning" of the body's fuel; in other words, using up energy faster than usual. As a result, the body radiates more "heat" (infrared waves).

3. *Materials:* opaque projection of Figure 3-19.

Exhibit these photographs as examples of how infrared waves are used to take photographs during hazy conditions in daylight, and at night. Explain that special films sensitive to infrared waves are used. Discuss why some parts in these photographs are much brighter *draw conclusions* than others. (They are warmer, and so emit more infrared radiation.)

4. *Materials:* previous sketch of Figure 3-18; projection of Figure 3-20.

Through a pupil report, or your exposition, inform the class that Herschel's extension of the spectrum was only a beginning. Shortly after his discovery came another, this time at the spectrum's opposite end. *Johann Ritter,* a German scientist, sprinkled a light-sensitive chemical (silver chloride) on some paper and exposed it to a spectrum. To his surprise, the chemical blackened first just beyond the violet end, and then later in the spectrum itself.

He reasoned from this that a more power-

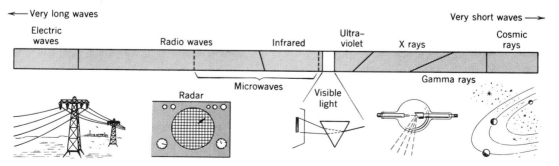

FIGURE 3-20 Electromagnetic spectrum.

ful but invisible radiation was striking the chemical, an *ultraviolet* radiation. Bring out that "ultra" means beyond. Discuss the appropriateness of this name. Develop that through the use of two instruments—a simple thermometer and a light-sensitive chemical—man was able to extend his senses.

Bring out some common uses of ultraviolet light. It tans skin and helps our bodies to manufacture Vitamin D. When radiated from special lamps, it destroys germs.

Show Figure 3-20. Indicate other forms of radiation scientists have discovered, and their uses. Emphasize that all are basically the same except for vibration rate and penetrating power. If desired, indicate that the entire extended range of radiant energy is called the *electromagnetic spectrum.*

Extending activities

1. Build a discussion of the following situation. It may be helpful to write some material on the chalkboard. A child asks two scientists the question, "Are there any other forms of radiation?"

Scientist A replies, "At the present time, we have been unable to discover that any other forms of radiation exist."

Scientist B replies, "There are no other forms of radiation because we cannot find any more, even with our most advanced instruments."

evaluate critically Challenge pupils to choose the better reply, and then justify their choice. After some discussion ask, "Which of these two replies could have been written 100 years ago without being wrong, according to what we now know?"

2. Ultraviolet light is largely stopped by ordinary window glass. Children can find this out for themselves through reading or through an experiment as they attempt to cope with the following problem:

A man developed a tan in the summer and wanted to keep it during the whole year. To do this, he got a job in a glass greenhouse. In spite of being in the sun nearly every day as he worked that winter, he lost most of his *suggest hypotheses* tan. Why?

To test if glass blocks ultraviolet light, someone can tape a glass slide to his upper arm or other portion of his body which is usually covered, and expose it to sunlight for a half-hour to forty-five minutes. The glass covered area will be noticeably light-colored a day later, while the surrounding skin is reddened.

3. Encourage an open-ended color-mixing *select procee* activity that employs the blending of colored dots. Have children compose colors of any combination by varying dots of yellow, blue, and red; or green, purple, and orange. Use crayon or colored pencil on squares of white paper. These should be viewed at a sufficient distance for color-blending to occur.

The closing generalization of this unit gives children the opportunity to learn how their eyes function, and to apply some ideas previously encountered. Although the eye has many parts, we shall concentrate on three directly involved in sight: the *iris, lens,* and *retina.* (See Figure 3-21.)

The iris contains pigment which absorbs some colors and reflects others. Since the kind and amount of this coloring matter varies in individuals, some eyes appear brown, some blue, and so on. Two sets of tiny muscles control the size of a small hole (pupil) in the iris. This regulates the amount of light entering the eye.

The eyes of cats have a capacity for pupil dilation far in excess of humans. This is one reason why they see better than humans in near darkness. A dramatic example of this capacity appears when the headlights of an automobile suddenly shine into the eyes of a cat on a dark night. The two shiny round spots we see are the headlight reflections from *inside* the cat's eyes.

Our eyes make a second important adjustment when light varies in brightness. The retina contains two light-sensitive cells, named *rods* and *cones.* Cones are less sensitive than rods and are clustered near the back of the eyeball. They function most efficiently in strong light, and enable us to see color. Rods are distributed in other parts of the retina and are sensitive to dim light. Chemical changes sensitize either rods or cones under appropriate conditions. For example, when we walk into a dark theater on a sunny day, it takes several moments before the rods work well. To achieve optimum sensitivity, up to a half-hour may be required.

It is thought that cones are most sensitive to three basic colors—red, green, and blue. According to this idea, we see many colors because the basic colors are seen in various combinations. An experiment is provided to test this theory.

An eye lens is convex in shape and works like any other convex lens—with one important difference. A muscle permits it to change shape. If a large, close object appears before you, the lens thickens. This refracts light rays entering the eye sharply enough for a focus to occur on the retina. However, light rays from a small or faraway object enter the lens in a near parallel fashion. Only a small refraction is needed to bring the rays to a focus on the retina. Look at a distant object, then suddenly look at something a foot away. Do you feel the tug of your lens muscles pulling the lens? Do you find the near object is fuzzy for the brief instant it takes for the muscles to adjust lens thickness? In a camera, of course, focusing is achieved by moving the lens back and forth.

Two principal defects in vision are introduced in this section. In *nearsightedness*, the lens may be thicker or the eyeball longer than normal. This causes an image to focus before the retina. In *farsightedness*, the lens may be thinner or the eyeball shorter than normal. In this case, an image can be focused only some distance in back of the retina. Activities are provided to help children apply this knowledge of lenses in correcting these defects. This may be an ideal time to help pupils develop a mature attitude about the wearing of eyeglasses.

An excellent example of how the brain and eyes work together takes place when we judge distance. Each eye sees an object from a different angle. The closer the object, the more each image appears to be different. We actually see a tiny bit "around" the object. At the same time, we feel our eyes turn inward. With greater distances, the angle gets smaller. The brain interprets this accordingly.

Beyond about 50 yards, we rely mainly on size to judge distance. A small telegraph pole looks far away mostly because we know that telephone poles are large. We also use such other clues as increased haze and the surrounding perspective.

Several activities are provided to acquaint children with the subjective nature of vision. A study of common optical illusions can cause them to become more aware of how these interesting phenomena occur.

The apparent motion of a motion-picture projection results from *persistence of vision*. It takes about one-sixteenth of a second for an image to fade from our vision after it is withdrawn. By flashing twenty-four images a second on a screen, a projector creates the illusion of motion.

It took some experience before the present speed of projecting individual motion-picture frames was adopted. Early motion pictures were photographed and projected at much slower speeds. The short, unlighted pause between frames was noticeable. This is how the term "flickers" got started.

Develop with pupils the necessity for protecting and conserving their eyes. Particular care should be taken with sticks, stones, and other potentially dangerous objects. Children should consult an adult when a foreign object is imbedded in an eye. Good lighting is important in reading and studying. Television watching should take place a reasonable distance from the screen. At night, an extra light will soften the harsh contrast between the screen and surrounding darkness. Be alert for signs of eyestrain or poor vision. The school nurse can decide if medical attention is necessary.

Your class will find it interesting to learn that the eyes of certain animals are peculiarly adapted for how or where they live. A snake's eyes are protected by a horny, transparent cover. The hippopotamus and alligator have eyes on top of their heads. The excellent side vision of rabbits makes it difficult to approach them undetected. So-called "flatfish," such as the flounder and halibut, lie on one side. Both eyes are arranged on one side of the head. Since these fish are typically bottom-dwellers, this eye arrangement permits greater vision.

BASIC GENERALIZATION VI: The eye is a complicated organ that operates with the brain

Contributing idea A. The eye has three main parts—iris, lens, and retina—each of which works in a special way.

1. *Materials:* large sketch or projection of Figure 3-21; pencils; paper.

Have your pupils recall what it is like to go into a darkened movie theater from the bright outdoors and the reverse. Briefly pursue an explanation of what happens when their eyes "get used to" the light or darkness. Mention that a demonstration will help them to understand one important adjustment of the eye.

Let pupils work in pairs, facing each other. Each should cover one of his own eyes with a hand, and wait fifteen or more seconds. Then have each remove his hand quickly and note if his partner's eye changes in any way as it undergoes sudden exposure to light. After several trials most pupils will realize that the black spot (pupil) changes in size.

draw conclusions

Exhibit your sketch. Identify the *pupil* and *iris.* Help the children understand that the pupil of the eye is an opening in the iris. Develop that the pupil looks larger and smaller because the iris automatically adjusts in size as the brightness of the light varies. When it is dark, a larger opening helps us to see. If it is very bright a smaller opening prevents us from being temporarily blinded. Explain that chemical changes inside the eye are also involved in its adjustment to light and darkness. Emphasize that eye pupils change size very quickly, but that the chemical changes take much longer.

Acquaint the class with other eye parts:

Cornea—a transparent covering in front of the eye. It gives protection to more delicate parts beneath it, and partly focuses entering light rays. Let the children examine others' eyes from the side. The cornea is easily seen.

Lens—a transparent convex-shaped part through which light passes into the eye. Mention that they will investigate this part more closely later.

Vitreous humor—a jellylike material that helps the eyeball keep its shape.

Retina—nerve fibers sensitive to light. When light strikes any portion of it, a signal is sent to the brain through the *optic nerve,* which is connected in back of the eyeball.

Children will be interested in learning that there is a blind spot in the retina where the optic nerve is connected. Have them pencil on paper a dot at left and a cross at right, about three inches apart. With the left eye closed, they should stare at the dot with their right eye. The paper should now be slowly drawn closer to the eye. At some point, the cross will disappear.

2. *Materials:* two hand magnifying lenses; piece of white tagboard; sketch of Figure 3-22 A-B-C.

Remind the children that in the previous sketch, a convex lens was shown in back of the iris. Have them recall a common convex lens they used before—a hand magnifying lens. Does it work like the eye lens?

To find out, have someone with a hand

FIGURE 3-21

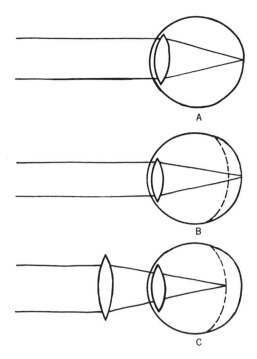

FIGURE 3-22 A–B–C

*valuate
itically*

lens stand 10 feet or more from an open window and focus the window image on a piece of tagboard or wall. The proper distance for focusing probably will be under 12 inches. Draw out the analogy: a hand lens for the eye lens; a piece of tagboard for the retina.

Most children are surprised to find the image is upside down. Is this also true in our eyes? Let them find out that it is. The brain learns by experience how things are really arranged, and we adjust our thinking accordingly.

Ask why some people wear eyeglasses. Develop that images often appear fuzzy or blurry to them; eyeglasses help make these images sharp and clear. Exhibit your sketch of Figure 3-22 A-B-C. Explain that drawing A shows a normal eyeball with an image properly coming to a sharp focus on the retina. However, drawing B shows what happens when an eyeball is shorter than normal. Help pupils explain what is happening. (The image must be blurry, because it has not yet been brought *draw* to a focus.) Assist them in explaining C. (A *usions* convex lens slightly converges the light rays

before they enter the eye. This helps the eye lens to converge the light rays a little sooner, and thus achieve a proper focus.)

Tell the children their explanations may appear reasonable, but should be tested for accuracy. They can use two hand lenses and a piece of tagboard.

Guide an experimenting child to parallel the drawings closely. A clear focus of the window on his tagboard represents a normal eyeball. When he brings the card closer to his hand lens the image is fuzzy, or out of focus. When a second lens is held in front of the *draw* first, a sharp image appears on the shortened *conclusions* "retina." If there is a farsighted child with glasses in the room, one lens of his glasses will dramatically substitute for a hand lens.

3. *Materials:* one hand lens; a concave lens (use a nearsighted person's eyeglasses); sketch of Figure 3-23 A-B-C.

Exhibit your sketch as an example of how eyeglasses correct for the opposite problem— an eyeball that is longer than normal. The children should have little difficulty in ex- *suggest* plaining these three drawings. Again challenge *hypotheses* a test of their explanations.

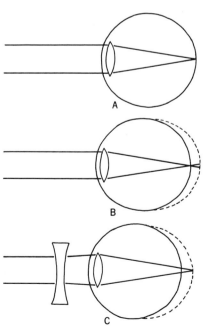

FIGURE 3-23 A–B–C

A proper focus on the card represents a normal eyeball. Moving the card a few inches farther away will lengthen the "eyeball" and cause a fuzzy image to appear. When a concave lens is held in front of the convex "eye" lens, a sharp image appears on the card "retina."

These experiments may be verified through reference to authority. Also, it will be worthwhile to develop briefly that our eye lenses continually change shape to accommodate for viewing objects at varying distances. When eye lenses cannot accommodate satisfactorily, proper glasses will help to achieve a proper focus. Thus, lenses correct both eyeball and eye-lens defects. (Many children find it difficult to understand lens accommodation at this level. Therefore, it may be better to treat this aspect as a readiness experience rather than a definite teaching objective.)

4. *Materials:* several small, colored objects; sketch of Figure 3-21.

Show the sketch of Figure 3-21 again. Point out that the retina contains millions of nerve fibers which react to different amounts of brightness and color. However, color sensitivity appears to be largely clustered in back, near the optic nerve.

Aid them in thinking through the implications of this idea. If we are to see color, some colored light must reach the back of the eyeball. But what if we view a colored object from the "side" of an eye? When we are first able to detect it is there, can we also tell its color?

To test this, a child can stare fixedly at a designated spot while a colored object is slowly moved forward at the side of his head. When he barely detects the object, he should immediately say so. The object then is held motionless, while he tries to detect its color, eyes still staring fixedly on some forward spot.

Let other pupils try it in pairs. But first, draw out needed controls. The viewer must not know beforehand what colors are used, and must stare fixedly forward. They will find color is detectable only after the object is moved some distance forward of where it is first noticed.

5. *Materials:* three flashlights (identical, if possible); three sheets of colored cellophane —red, green, blue; large sheet of white paper (for a screen).

Have pupils recall their previous experience with separating white light into colors with a prism. Remind them that scientists can recombine the separated colors with a prism; that they, too, did this in their water prism simply by stirring the water a little.

Now ask, "What color would we see if we shine six colored flashlights, each having one color of the spectrum, on a white screen? (White.) How about three colors?" (Answers will vary.)

Cover each of the three flashlights with a different colored cellophane filter. Fold for double thickness. Darken the room and project all three flashlights on a white screen. Leave some overlap so color combinations are noticeable. Results will be similar to Figure 3-24 if the flashlights are equally bright and cellophane filters reasonably effective. Record these colors on a chalkboard as they appear in Figure 3-24.

Encourage conjecture briefly as to why white light is obtained with only three colored lights when presumably six are needed. Through reference to authority, or your exposition, develop these ideas:

Many scientists believe the color portion of the retina is mainly sensitive to three basic colors—red, green, and blue.

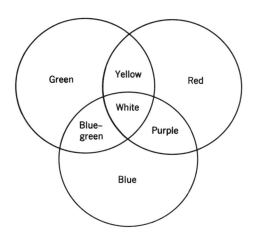

FIGURE 3-24 The primary colors.

We are able to see many different colors because the three "retinal" colors are seen in different amounts.

6. *Materials:* large, white paper screen; three large circle cutouts of colored construction paper—green, red, blue; sketch of Figure 3-24.

Ask the children to look at the white paper screen. Establish that it looks white because nerves are stimulated in the retina which are sensitive to red, green, and blue. Have children note that in the sketch the three-color combination results in white.

Speculate what "white" light would look like if we were able to see only two of these colors. Elicit these combinations and record them on the chalkboard:

a. If we could not see blue, white light might look yellow.

b. If we could not see red, white light might look blue-green.

c. If we could not see green, white light might look purple.

Inform the class that there is a way of temporarily tiring the nerves which are sensitive to colors. This can be done for each color, so that only two groups of color nerves operate together, instead of three, when white is observed.

Pin a blue circle in the center of the white screen. Have everyone stare fixedly at it for about thirty seconds. Now quickly remove the colored circle, while everyone continues to stare at the same spot. A yellowish circle will appear on the white paper. Try the other two colors, but allow several moments between trials for discussion and eye rest. Have pupils reason through what happened in each case.

draw *usions*

Contributing idea B. Two eyes are better than one for judging distance.

Materials: pencils.

Discuss some of the many reasons we must be careful with our eyes. Bring out problems that might emerge if only one eye were operable, rather than two. Bridge into the story of a baseball player who temporarily wore a bandage over one injured eye. He began hav-

ing trouble catching high pop flies. The ball kept dropping in front of him.

Do two eyes make a difference in how we judge distance? Have each pupil hold a pencil vertically at arm's length away from his face. With one eye closed, let each try to touch the pencil with a finger of the opposite hand. The finger should be held sideways, parallel to the body, and brought down slowly over the pencil. The children will be astonished at how difficult it is. Bring out the need for trying it with two eyes, also.

evaluate *critically*

Before inviting the class to explain why two eyes make judging distances easier, provide some input:

Tell children to look down a pencil, eraser end placed against the nose, with fingers holding the sharpened tip. How many pencils do they see? (Two.)

Ask everyone to look at a room corner. With one eye closed have them line up a thumb with the corner, then alternate the other eye. Elicit that the thumb seems to move.

With both eyes open, have each child look over a thumb at a corner. Each will see two thumbs.

Guide them to express why judging distance is better with two eyes. Each eye views an object from a slightly different perspective; often this helps us to see slightly "around" an object. Through reading or other reference, bring out that this advantage decreases with distance. Decreased size of objects and other cues are likelier to be important in judging distances.

Contributing idea C. We cannot always believe what we see.

1. *Materials:* paper; pencils; sketch of Figure 3-25 A-B-C.

Remind the children that their past experience has been helpful in judging size and distance. Now they are going to apply their experience in judging size and distance in another way.

Exhibit your sketch of Figure 3-25 A-B-C. Ask these questions, and urge rapid responses.

suggest *otheses*

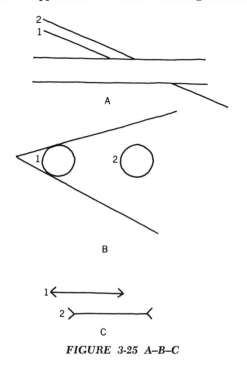

FIGURE 3-25 A–B–C

evaluate critically For A, "Which top slanted line belongs with the lower slanted line, one or two?"

For B, "Which circle seems larger, one or two?"

For C, "Which inside line seems larger, one or two?"

After children commit themselves, let them connect the lines in A with a yardstick, and measure sizes in B and C. Most will be surprised to discover slanted line 1 connects to the lower slanted line in A, and circle sizes in B and C are identical.

Help pupils understand what happened. They are accustomed to using many cues in interpreting things. Ordinarily, this is helpful. In some cases, however, the cues can mislead us.

evaluate critically Discuss how moods may also influence perceptions. Bring out examples: When are some people likely to interpret a white sheet as a "ghost"? When does a cold glass of lemonade appear the most refreshing? Help the class realize that the eye is only a gateway to the mind; it is the mind that sees.

2. *Materials:* reel of motion-picture film; small paper pads; pencils; projector; crayon; watch with second hand.

Introduce motion-picture projection as another case in which we see something that is different from reality. Have some children unwind several feet of film and examine the individual frames of a sequence in which action is occurring, such as a moving vehicle. *draw conclus* They will note that in each frame the vehicle appears in a slightly different position.

If small paper pads are available, guide children to draw a head-on view of a bird with wings, on the bottom and center of the first page. A small circle for the body and two curved lines for wings will do. On succeeding pages, in the same spot, have them draw the wings in ever higher positions. Subsequent drawings should show the wings in gradually lower positions. A total of twenty pages is more than adequate. When the pad pages are flipped over rapidly, a sequence of flapping wings appears.

Through reading or your exposition, bring out these facts:

a. We observe a series of rapidly flashed still pictures in a "motion" picture.

b. Our eyes cannot see more than about sixteen separate images in one second. When more than that number appear, the pictures appear to run together.

Get pupils to reason: We cannot see more than sixteen separate images in one second. If true, would motion pictures be flashed on a *draw conclus* screen faster or slower than sixteen frames per second? (Faster: twenty-four frames.)

Now present this problem: How can we discover the number of frames flashed through a movie projector each second? (Lightly mark with crayon the film frame *select proced* closest to the projection slot. Run the projector for exactly 10 seconds. Mark with crayon the frame just beyond the slot. Count the number of frames between the crayon marks and divide by 10.)

Challenge the class to calculate how many *reason quanti* separate frames are flashed in an hour-long movie. (24 frames × 60 seconds × 60 minutes = 86,400 frames.)

Extending activities

1. Invite a school nurse to give an illustrated talk on eye safety and care.

2. Let children investigate insect eyes with hand lenses. Some are compound eyes, as in the housefly. Each of the hundreds of facets seems to record a separate image.

3. Encourage several children to check encyclopedias and trade books for information on animal eyes. Have them report on the special ways in which such animals as snakes, cats, rabbits, and bottom-dwelling fish benefit from their visual organs.

Magnets Have Force

(Primary)

At the primary level magnets are probably studied more widely than any other topic. Growing numbers of young children have their own magnets and magnetic toys. Many learn something about magnets even before enrolling in school. For these reasons, we shall go into the subject more deeply than is customary at this level. The force of magnetism is our theme. Among other things, children will learn how magnetism attracts through different materials;[1] how it can be studied although invisible; and how it is preserved or destroyed. If only several magnets are available for this unit, encourage pupils to bring theirs from home. Many forthcoming activities are suitable for either group or individual participation.

BASIC GENERALIZATIONS

I. Magnets attract things made of iron and steel.

II. A magnet attracts things without touching them because there is a field of force around it; the field is most powerful at the ends, or poles.

III. The force of magnetism can attract through many materials.

IV. Iron or steel can be magnetized by a magnet; steel holds its magnetism longer than iron.

[1] Wristwatches should be removed before working with magnets.

V. The field of force around a wire carrying electricity can be used to magnetize iron or steel objects.

VI. Compasses are magnets that show directions because of the earth's magnetism; unlike poles of magnets attract, like poles repel each other.

VII. Dropping, heating, or storing a magnet improperly will weaken its force.

There is no scarcity of magnets about us for examples in teaching. In kitchens, cloth pot holders containing magnets are placed conveniently on the sides of stoves. Automatic can openers contain magnets to hold opened can lids. Cabinet doors remain closed because of magnets. Many women wear magnetic earrings. Beauty operators use magnets to pick up dropped hairpins. Physicians sometimes employ them to extract pieces of metal from wounds. Toy stores contain a variety of toys that in some way use magnetism.

In nearly all these cases, the metals attracted to a magnet are iron and steel. Less well-known magnetic metals are cobalt and nickel. Among the commoner metals not attracted by magnets are brass (an alloy of copper and zinc), aluminum, tin, silver, stainless steel (an alloy of several metals), copper, bronze (an alloy of copper and tin), and gold.

It will be helpful to know several facts which may cause some confusion in this unit

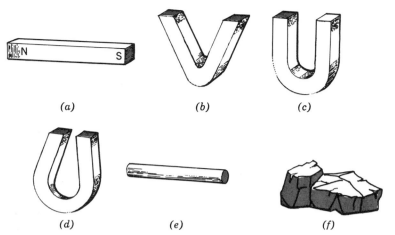

FIGURE 4-1 Magnets. (*a*) bar, (*b*) V, (*c*) U, (*d*) horseshoe, (*e*) bar, and (*f*) lodestone.

unless they are understood. For example, gray-colored, World War II pennies are attractable, since they were made of zinc-coated steel at a time when copper was in short supply. The zinc prevents rust. All other United States pennies are made of bronze, an alloy of copper and tin.

A question may arise about so-called "tin" cans. These are made of thin sheet steel and coated lightly with tin. Although tin is not attractable, steel is. Confusion may also result if some straight pins are attracted by a magnet and other identical-appearing pins are not. Scraping off some silver coating on the nonattractable pins will usually reveal that they are made of brass. Also, whereas pure nickel is ordinarily magnetic, our five-cent piece is largely composed of copper and so should not be used as an example.

Natural magnets are sometimes called "lodestones," or "leading stones," perhaps because ancient mariners used them as crude compasses. Lodestones are composed of magnetite, an iron ore found in different locations on the earth's crust. Since only some of these deposits are magnetized, theories have been developed to explain this phenomenon. One such theory holds that lightning may have been responsible. It is thought that electricity discharged into the ore may have arranged many atoms within the ore in a manner similar to that found in magnets. Traces of magnetite are common in soils. A magnet dragged along the ground or in a playground sandbox may attract many particles. These particles can be an effective substitute in experiments where iron "filings" are used.

Man-made or artificial magnets are often composed of steel and magnetized by electricity. Named for their shape, there are *bar*, V, U, *horseshoe*, and *cylindrical* magnets, to give the more familiar varieties. Each of these magnets attracts substances most strongly at the ends, or poles. The U, V, and horseshoe magnets are more powerful than the others, when all factors are equal; they are bent so two poles attract instead of one.

Powerful *alnico* magnets are now available to teachers at scientific supply houses and in commercial kits. These are made from aluminum, cobalt, nickel, and iron. Alnico magnets are used for such home and commercial purposes mentioned at the beginning of this section, as well as for a variety of others.

Thus far, we have described permanent magnets. Though useful, they do not compare with the enormous importance of temporary magnets, or more accurately, *electromagnets*. These will be discussed more fully later.

BASIC GENERALIZATION I: Magnets attract things made of iron and steel

1. *Materials:* several magnets; 3-inch string; numerous attractable and nonattractable objects—paper clips, pins (use steel only), rubber bands, pennies, and so on. (Have at least several nonattractable metals.) Write on the chalkboard material such as the following:

Name:	Made of:	We think:	We found out:
nails	iron	–	–
comb	rubber	–	–
pins	steel	–	–
hair curler	aluminum	–	–
penny	bronze	–	–
scissors	steel	–	–
coat hanger	iron	–	–

If your class cannot read, just place these or similar materials on a table.

You might begin with this bridge: "A boy was walking around on some very large rocks one day. He had a penny in his pocket. When he jumped from one big rock to another, the penny fell out of his pocket and down in between two big rocks. The space between was too small to get his arm into. How could he have gotten his penny back?" *suggest hypotheses* If no one suggests using a magnet, point to the string and magnet. "Could he have used *select procedures* these things in any way? How can we find out?"

Let the children use several magnets to attempt attraction of some bronze pennies. After failure is experienced, point to the chalkboard or table and ask them to make *suggest hypotheses* specific hypotheses about each of these materials in place of the penny. Before and after each one is tried, write "yes" or "no" in the appropriate columns.

Guide the children to observe that the objects tested successfully were made of iron and steel. Help them to conclude that the boy probably could not use a magnet to get his penny back; but if he had dropped an *draw conclusions* object made of iron or steel, a proper magnet may have been used successfully.

2. *Materials:* nail file, or small coarse rock; magnet; several identical-appearing straight pins of brass and steel. (Test with a magnet to determine which are steel.)

Ask someone to put some straight pins in a box. Have him use a magnet to make the task "easier." When failure is experienced with the brass pins, let the children first de- *define problems* fine the problem, then raise hypotheses as to why failure occurred.

Their previous input with nonattractable *suggest hypotheses* objects including metals should prompt some children to guess that the pins are made of different metals. If not, review their initial experience. If this guess is made, ask for a test.

Attracted and unattracted pins may be *select procedures* rubbed against a nail file or rough stone. As the thin coating is worn away, steel pins will appear dull gray, and brass pins yellowish. Let the test continue until a pattern develops. All attracted pins will be one color, all un-attracted pins another. This will help verify the hypothesis.

Bring out that some pins were made of *draw conclusions* steel, and some of *brass*—a metal that is not attracted by magnetism.

Extending activities

1. Encourage children to bring in other materials and magnets that have not been tested. This is an open-end activity. Follow *draw conclusions* a similar hypothesis-test procedure.

2. Acquaint the class with some standards for the care and keeping of magnets. It is suggested that no attempts be made at this time to reason through these standards, as this requires input that will be acquired in the unit. However, tell the children that these standards will help keep their magnets in good condition. See Figure 4-2 A-B for some model charts. Chart A uses soft iron "keepers" in two instances. If regular keepers are not available, nails or other soft iron objects will do. Two strips cut from a tinned can work well with bar magnets.

WHEN WE PUT OUR
MAGNETS AWAY

FIGURE 4-2 A

Magnets Take Care

- Never drop or pound them.
- Never heat them.
- Use a keeper.
- Put the N and S parts together.

FIGURE 4-2 B

3. If possible, provide several different kinds of magnets for exploration. Teach their proper names. Some magnets might be brought by class members.

As children explore with magnets, they will observe that a magnet will attract from a distance. For example, a small nail or paper clip will "jump" to the magnet. They will also see that the attractive force is strongest at the poles. This offers an opportunity to illustrate the field of force surrounding a magnet.

Although it is impossible to see the field directly, its presence may be inferred. Sprinkle iron filings on a sheet of paper placed over a magnet. Observe that their distribution is orderly, with the greatest concentration of filings at the poles. Theoretically, a magnetic field extends outward to an infinite distance. But for practical purposes the field ends where its presence is no longer detectable.

BASIC GENERALIZATION II: A magnet attracts things without touching them because there is a field of force around it; the field is most powerful at the ends, or poles

Materials: container of iron filings (a salt shaker is useful), or a handful of tiny nails (brads); a sheet of stiff, white paper; several paper clips; a powerful magnet.

Place the foregoing materials on a table.

Besides revealing fields of force, iron filings in this picture indicate that like poles of magnets repel and unlike poles attract each other.

FIGURE 4-3

Hold up the magnet and ask, "How close must this magnet be to attract iron or steel things?" Allow several children to try different distances with a magnet and paper clips. Have them determine which part of the magnet appears most powerful. If several magnets of differing strengths are available, let the children demonstrate that some will attract over a greater distance than others. "How is it possible for these magnets to pick up things without touching them?" After the class reacts, you might remark, "Here is a way we can find out."

Lay the magnet on a table and place the white paper over it. Explain that the container holds small bits of iron, called "filings." Sprinkle some filings on the paper above the magnet. Tap the paper gently to assist in the distribution of filings. Have the children observe that the filings are arranged in an orderly pattern some distance around the magnet. Tell them that this area is the magnet's *field of force*. The idea of field (area) and force (push or pull) might be explained simply here, if needed.

*draw
clusions* Note that concentrations of lines of force seem greatest at the poles. Bring out that this is probably the reason the ends of the magnet seemed more powerful than its other parts. Observe that this force is invisible, but that we can see what it does through this demonstration. Help the class to realize that an iron or steel object can be attracted without being touched as long as it is within the magnet's field of force. Point out that the magnet's strength and weight of the attracted object determine whether this attraction becomes visible.

Extending activities

1. Make permanent records of lines of force with different magnets. Sprinkle iron filings on blueprint paper laid over a magnet. Place carefully in a sunny area, without disturbing the pattern. Expose for 5 to 10 minutes. Brush or shake the filings off and run cold water over the blueprint. A permanent blue and white record of the lines of force will be recorded.

2. For a variation of this activity, use a plastic spray to fix the filings on a sheet. Hold the aerosol can at sufficient distance so filings are not blown away. (Plastic spray is handy for many activities in science, as well as the commoner art uses.)

An intriguing phenomenon of a magnetic field is that it can pass through many substances without apparent loss of effect. This makes it possible for magnetic earrings to be worn, and for wristwatches to be affected unless precautions are taken. Plumbers may use magnets in locating pipes (iron or steel) behind walls or under floors. In fact, the field of force will penetrate any nonmagnetic materials the class may test.

Materials of iron and steel are considered "opaque" to this force, since the force passes inside them and back into the magnet.

BASIC GENERALIZATION III: The force of magnetism can pass through many materials

Materials: flat, thin pieces of glass, steel (can tops), plastic, aluminum or aluminum foil, wood, and so on; magnet; string; paper clip; ruler; books. (Place the objects on a table and set up the magnet as in Figure 4-4. However, leave the attached paper clip lying on the table until after your bridge.)

Say, "Once a man had a waterpipe leak in his house. The pipe was inside a wall and he could not find it. He didn't want to tear down his whole wall just to find the pipe. *suggest hypotheses* What could he do?"

FIGURE 4-4

If no one guesses, have the class recall the previous demonstration, where iron filings were attracted through paper. Continue questioning until it is reasoned that perhaps a magnet's field of force could go through a wall.

Now, suspend the paper clip, and elicit that the magnetic field is attracting it through air. *select procedures* "How can we use this setup and materials on the table to see if magnetism will go through things?"

Have some children try slipping various flat objects in the space between the magnet and paper clip. Relate their findings to the initial problem.

draw conclusions When a can top is placed in the space, they will note that the paper clip falls. Guide them to understand that magnetism will penetrate nonmagnetic materials, but will not pass through magnetic materials unless an attracted object is actually touching them.

Extending activity

Let the class set up an experiment to determine whether magnetic force will penetrate water. *select procedures* (Hint: How will a bowl of water, magnet, and paper clips help?)

A magnet can be made from a piece of iron or steel by stroking it in one direction twenty or more times with one pole of a permanent magnet. If a long piece is used, stroke with one pole from the object's center outward for twenty strokes. Repeat the procedure on the remaining half, but this time with the magnet's opposite pole. This should produce a strongly magnetized object. Be sure to lift the magnet at the end of each stroke before bringing it back to start another. Merely rubbing it back and forth will produce unsatisfactory results.

Although it takes longer to induce magnetism in steel than in iron, steel retains its magnetism longer. Common materials made of steel include scissors, some knitting needles, sewing needles, screwdrivers, hacksaw blades, and knife blades. Perhaps the commonest ex-

amples of soft iron are nails and wire coat hangers.

A more efficient way to induce magnetism is by using electricity. This is developed in another basic generalization of the unit.

BASIC GENERALIZATION IV: Iron or steel can be magnetized by a magnet; steel holds its magnetism longer than iron

Materials: several large and small nails; magnets; steel straight pins; paper clips; steel knitting or darning needles; screwdriver; or similar objects.

Place your materials on a table. Invite a child to pick up a small nail and try to attract another nail with it. Then have him use a magnet to attract a nail. Guide him to build a "chain" of nails, using each magnetized nail to attract another. Permit him to continue until the chain is broken.

If a powerful magnet is available, suggest that a nail be held near it. Magnetism will be induced in the nail by the magnet's field of force. Ask the child to build a chain of nails, if possible. "What could we call each nail *draw conclus* that attracted another nail? Was each nail a magnet to begin with? What caused each nail to become a magnet?" Point out that magnets can be made out of steel and iron objects.

Now demonstrate how to induce magnetism in several objects. Use a large nail, a steel knitting or darning needle, or similar materials. Show first that these are not magnetized by touching them to a paper clip. With either pole of a magnet, stroke the object its entire length *in one direction only*. Call this to the children's attention. Lift the magnet at the end of each stroke for about twenty to thirty strokes. Demonstrate that the object is now a magnet.

For additional activities, say, "Here are some questions that need experiments to find the answers. Let's see if you can think of ways we can find these answers." (Each experiment will need controls the children can construct, if they are guided to see the necessity for them. After each question, briefly discuss how the experiment should be done. Substitute appropriate materials where necessary.)

select cedures   a. "Will this nail's magnetism get more powerful the more it is stroked?" (First, test the nail for magnetism by seeing if it attracts paper clips. It should not. Test again after each ten strokes with a magnet.)

select cedures   b. "Which can be magnetized more easily —a soft iron nail or a knitting needle made of hard steel?" (Each object is first tested for magnetism, stroked once before each test, tested again with paper clips, and so on.)

select cedures   c. "Which will keep its strength longer— the magnetized, soft iron nail, or the magnetized needle made of hard steel?" (Same procedure as above is followed, except that objects are initially stroked more times and tested after a 5-minute or longer interval.)

select cedures   d. "Will a magnet you make be more powerful if stroked in one direction or back and forth in two directions?" (Use two identical nails. Test to see if magnetized. Stroke both thirty times—one in both directions and one fifteen times each way. Test with paper clips.)

If you have a capable primary class, assign the problems to various small groups so procedures can be thought through. Allow enough time for thinking to take place, and for the experiments to be tried several times.

Discussion afterward can begin by asking first for the problem, then for specific procedures followed in individual groups. With your aid, procedures can be constructively *valuate* analyzed by the children. After discussion of *itically* specific findings, summarize by asking, "How *draw* can a magnet be made?" and "How can a *lusions* long-lasting magnet be made?"

Connect a wire to a flashlight battery or dry cell, and the wire will attract iron filings. It is an *electromagnet*. If the wire is fashioned into a coil, this concentrates the effect, making it a more powerful magnet. Other ways of boosting magnetic force are to use an iron or

A wire carrying electricity makes an effective electromagnet when wrapped 20 or more times around a large nail.

FIGURE 4-5

steel core in the coil, and to increase the flow of electricity going through the wire.

Variations and applications of electromagnets are virtually endless—motors, doorbells, generators, telephones, and so on—some very complicated. One of the easier and more interesting applications for children is the electromagnetic crane. (See Figure 4-6.)

Basically the same things are present in the crane as are needed in a related, upcoming lesson: a source of electricity, wire to carry the current, and a soft iron core around which the wire is wrapped.

Children need to be made aware that a soft iron core is used in electromagnets rather than hard steel, since steel tends to become permanently magnetized. If they have studied the previous generalization, most should have no trouble understanding this fact. They will also realize the advantage of having a magnet that can be shut off or turned on whenever needed.

A question may be raised if certain lightweight materials such as tacks or pins continue to be attracted to the electromagnet after electricity is shut off. This is due to "residual" magnetism, or the small amount that remains for a while in the soft iron nail or core. These materials will usually fall off when shaken slightly.

BASIC GENERALIZATION V: The field of force around a wire carrying electricity can be used to magnetize iron and steel objects

1. *Materials:* 4-inch length of insulated bell wire (Remove an inch of insulation from each end so proper contact can be made when it is connected to a dry cell.); a large iron nail, a steel rod (a screwdriver will do); several tacks or steel straight pins; a No. 6 (one and one-half volts) dry cell; a projection of an electromagnetic crane, as in Figure 4-6.

define problems Show your class the crane sketch and ask, "What is happening in this picture?" If necessary, draw attention to the manner of lifting. Scrap metal objects appear to be sticking to the device suspended from the crane. Bring out that probably some kind of large magnet is attached to the crane and its apparent purpose is to move scrap iron and steel from one place to another.

suggest hypotheses "If this is a big magnet, how can the crane operator remove materials from his magnet?" Observation of the electric wire may help the children in guessing. Guide toward a hypothesis that permits the crane operator to turn the magnetism on and off. Ask *how* this is possible. If no one knows, tell the class the crane has a magnet attached to it that operates through electricity. It is called an *electromagnet.*

Using the sketch, point out three features: (1) a metal core; (2) wire wrapped around inside the core cover; and, tracing the wire from the core to the crane's cab, point out (3) a place where batteries or generators are kept to provide electricity. Indicate your materials and ask, "How could these things be used to make an electromagnet?" *select proced*

A pupil may need assistance in connecting the wire properly to the dry cell. Only one terminal screw of the dry cell should be used to hold down an end of the wire. The other end should be touched to the remaining terminal. A direct connection of this kind will completely drain the power of a dry cell if left for a length of time. Some teachers remove one screw to make this less likely.

Let pupils experiment with the number of turns of wire. They will observe that increasing the number of turns increases power. *reason quantit* Several children can try touching and removing the wire alternately from the screwless terminal. They will note that nails or other attracted objects fall off after the wire is disconnected. (Remember, if lightweight objects are used, residual magnetism in the electromagnet may continue to attract them for a time even after the wire is disconnected.)

2. Review that in a previous lesson they had magnetized hard steel and soft iron objects. Steel retained its magnetism longer. Ask which metal should be used in the core of *evaluat critical* an electromagnet to work properly. Encourage reasons for answers. Guide toward the hypothesis that a steel core will become a permanent magnet but that a soft iron core will lose its magnetism quickly. Invite a group to *select proced* set up an experiment to find out.

FIGURE 4-6

A large nail and small screwdriver can be used for the cores. Guide the children to realize needed controls: same wire and number of turns on each core; cores should be about the same size; the same dry cell should be used, and same objects attracted. Both iron and steel cores must be tested for magnetism before the experiment.

draw
lusions

Children should find that a steel core will become a permanent magnet, and is therefore unsatisfactory for this purpose.

Extending activity

To magnetize various objects by electricity, use the following activity. (See Figure 4-7.) Provide a cardboard tube 8 inches to 12 inches long and about 2 inches in diameter, such as found with paper toweling. Also at least 30 feet of insulated bell wire; two dry cells; and some steel objects to be magnetized (screwdrivers, hacksaw blades, rods, and so on).

Wrap wire closely around the tube. Strip insulation from both ends of the wire. Connect one end to a terminal of the dry cell. Place objects to be magnetized in the tube, and within the wire-covered area. Briefly touch the unconnected end of the wire to the other terminal; objects will be magnetized.

Suspend a bar magnet from a string in North America and a curious thing happens; it points toward the north magnetic pole. Do the same in South America and it points toward the south magnetic pole. (This assumes no interference from nearby metal deposits or objects.) A magnetized needle placed on a floating wood chip or bit of cork also points toward a magnetic pole.

To see why this is so, consider the poles of a magnet. When another magnet or magnetized object is held near a suspended or floating magnet, the like poles (north-north or south-south) repel each other. The opposite poles (south-north or north-south) attract each other.

The earth itself acts like a giant magnet. No one knows why, but there are some theo-

FIGURE 4-7

ries. One explanation holds that several parts of the earth's interior rotate at different speeds. The resulting friction strips electrons from atoms. This causes an electric current to be generated which creates a magnetic field. Since the earth's core is supposedly made of nickel-iron, the effect is that of a huge electromagnet buried within the earth.

Lines of force from the earth's magnetism run roughly north and south far into space and then loop down to concentrate at the north and south magnetic poles. Therefore, a freely swinging magnet—bar, horseshoe, or any other type with dominant poles—tends to assume a direction parallel to these lines of force. Since lines of force terminate at the magnetic poles, properly following a compass in the northern hemisphere eventually results in arrival at the north magnetic pole. This is located above the upper Hudson Bay region of Canada. If a southernly direction is taken, the trip terminates near Wilkes Land, a portion of Antarctica.

The north and south *magnetic* poles should not be confused with the north and south *geographic* poles. The geographic and magnetic poles are actually more than 1000 miles apart in the north and 1500 miles apart in the south. In other words, when a compass points north, it does *not* point true north, or toward the north star. Charts must be made for navigators which show the angular variation between true north and the direction

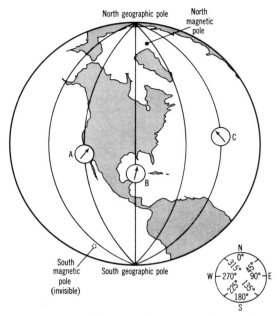

Note in A, B, and C an angle between the meridian on which the compass is located and the direction toward which the needle points. These are variations that must be added or subtracted from a compass heading to determine true north. For example, true heading for A, B, and C should be 0°, or north. Actual readings are 35°, 5°, and 315°. A chart would indicate the need to subtract 35° from A, 5° from B, and to add 45° to C.

FIGURE 4-8

toward which a compass points. These charts must be periodically changed, as the magnetic poles are slowly but continually shifting. (See Figure 4-8.)

Many persons are surprised to discover that a bar magnet or compass points with its "N" or *north* pole toward the earth's *north* magnetic poles. Yet it is known that *like* poles *repel* and unlike poles attract. How is this apparent paradox explained? The answer lies in antiquity. Compasses were used long before reasons for their operation were understood. Thus it became customary to speak of the end of a magnet that points northward as the north pole. It is more accurately called the *north-seeking* pole, and its counterpart the *south-seeking* pole.

Of course, these explanations of magnetic variation and misnaming of the magnet's poles are intended more for your background than for presentation to most pupils at the primary level.

BASIC GENERALIZATION VI: Compasses are magnets that show directions because of the earth's magnetism; unlike poles attract, and like poles repel each other

1. *Materials:* two bar magnets (or two magnetized steel knitting needles, or rods, or hacksaw blades); 18-inch string; four cards marked *north, south, east* and *west* respectively; cork; needle; glass bowl; masking tape; compass.

Place directional cards prominently on the walls. If the walls are not aligned with reference to a cardinal direction, cards can be affixed to chairs or taped down on the floor.

You might ask, "What do you notice today in our room that you have not seen before? What do these words tell us? Who lives north of our school? South? East? West?"

Draw a chalkboard sketch of the school and two main streets that run north-south and east-west. If this is impossible, use a sketch of Figure 4-9.

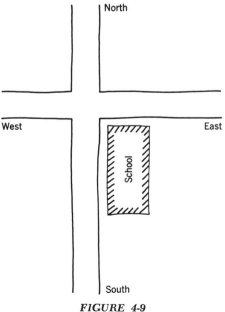

FIGURE 4-9

Picking out various locations on this "map," ask the children directions they would take to come to school, go home, and so on. Continue until it is obvious that most everyone knows the four cardinal directions.

2. Suspend by a thin thread a bar magnet or substitute. For a stand, use an overturned wooden chair, or pile of books with a ruler tucked part way into the top book. Cover the magnet's poles with masking or adhesive tape, so that pupils will need to identify poles for control purposes. To save time, it will be helpful to set up these materials before working with the class.

Ask a child to spin the magnet around *lightly*. (Otherwise the spinning takes too long to stop.) After the magnet stops, ask the class toward what main direction the magnet is pointing. Repeat this procedure. When the children again say the magnet points north, *select* ask how they can be sure, since both taped *cedures* ends are alike. They should then see the need to mark one end for control purposes.

Use the same procedure with another suspended magnet (at least 10 feet away). Are similar results obtained? (Make certain no iron or steel objects are close enough to affect the magnets.) Elicit that these magnets seem to point reliably in one direction. De- *draw* velop that if one direction is known, then *lusions* other directions are also known.

3. Continue this sequence with a floating needle demonstration. Have ready a needle, a magnet to magnetize the needle, a cork, and a *glass* bowl. (Remember, an iron or steel container will "block" magnetism.)

Hold up the needle, and ask someone to magnetize it. To avoid confusion, the needle should be stroked from its blunt end to its point with the magnet's "N" pole. This will insure that the sharp end points north. Develop speculation as to whether it will point north if pushed into a cork and floated in water.

Again an approximate north-south align- *draw* ment should be indicated. Elicit that a mag- *lusions* netized needle can also point out directions.

(Sometimes this demonstration is interfered with by the cork's tendency to drift against a container's sides. This is caused by the attraction of the water molecules to the sides, which creates a slight rise around the rim of the water line. Since a floating object always floats to the highest possible point, it naturally drifts toward a container's sides. If a little detergent is mixed in the water, it reduces the force and so "flattens out" the water line. This should take care of the problem.)

4. Keep the bar magnets in activity 2 and needle in activity 3 set up and pointing northward. Produce a compass. Establish that it is pointing in the same direction as the other materials. Elicit that it, too, is probably a magnet.

Set up some hypothetical situations in which the children can use a compass. For example, they are at sea; no landmarks exist. They know, however, land is northward. In what direction shall they sail? Continue with south, east, and west. Use at least several compasses, if possible, for maximum pupil participation and understanding. For further clarification, draw a simple chalkboard sketch of a compass, with only four principal directions and a needle. Bring out the advantages of being able to use a compass when lost in a wooded area, sailing at sea, or flying at night.

5. *Materials:* two bar magnets, one suspended from a string.

If the class is above average, it will be worthwhile in this and the next activity to go into *why* magnets point north. With one magnet suspended and the other in his hand, have a child demonstrate what happens when the like poles are brought together. Have him try opposite poles. Use often and together the words "pull" and "attract," "push" and "repel" until the children are reasonably aware of their meaning. After several trials, bring out as clearly as possible the fundamental law of magnets: unlike poles attract and like poles repel each other.

6. Ask someone to explain why magnets point north-south, rather than in other directions. A satisfactory explanation will probably not be given. Now draw a chalkboard sketch of Figure 4-10.

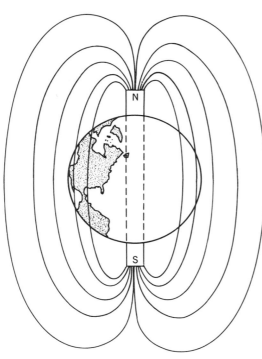

FIGURE 4-10

Explain that deep inside the earth are huge amounts of magnetized metals. Although these metals do *not* look like the big bar magnet drawn in the picture, they do attract and repel magnets in much the same way. Have the children recall how they previously discovered that magnetism could penetrate many substances. Bring out that the earth's magnetic field of force exists everywhere on earth. Its effect can be seen with magnets or compasses, whether underwater, in the air, or on land.

Extending activities

1. Discuss the difficulty of finding one's way without landmarks. Inform pupils they can help several classmates find their way out of an imaginary, unfamiliar forest. Provide one compass and two large cardboard boxes with open tops. Take the class to the playground. Let two volunteers place the boxes over their heads. Give the compass to one child. Each child should walk straight ahead for 300 steps, then retrace his steps. The child with the compass should follow its needle due

north, then due south after he makes a turn-about. The object, of course, is to see which child will come closest to the starting point.

Take caution to insure that ground markings, noises, and so on do not give directional clues to the participants. A discussion in the room before the demonstration, about procedures and needed controls, will be worthwhile.

2. For an agreed time period, have all those with compasses try to discover a location where their compass needle will not point north. Caution them about nearby interference from iron or steel objects, or let them discover such faulty procedure for themselves.

Important as magnetism is, science has yet to provide a satisfactory explanation of its cause. One theory, capable of being understood by young children, is based on observations they make for themselves. It has been known for many years that heating or repeatedly dropping a magnet will cause it to lose its magnetic properties. And, although a magnet may be broken into smaller and smaller pieces, each fragment continues to have a north and south pole.

It is believed that small clusters of atoms within these materials each contain north and south poles. Such clusters, called *domains*, are normally randomly arranged. When an object is stroked in one direction with a magnet or otherwise magnetized, the domains tend to line up in a single direction. Heating a magnet forces the domains into more violent motion, and so they are likelier to become disarranged. Repeatedly dropping a magnet jars the domains out of line, with the same result. Since steel is harder than soft iron—the molecules exert a more powerful attractive force on one another—it is more difficult to rearrange the domains' makeup. But once this is done, magnetism is retained longer for the same reason. (See Figure 4-11.)

The closing experiments of this unit are based on standards for magnet care. They can be performed at an earlier time, but placing

select proced

evalua critica

them at the end permits more pupil planning and thinking than would be possible without prior experiences. It is recommended that only the effects of heating and dropping magnets be tested. Experiments on improper storage and use of a keeper are too subtle and time consuming for most primary classes.

BASIC GENERALIZATION VII: Dropping, heating, or storing a magnet improperly causes it to lose its magnetism

1. *Materials:* candle; two identical, steel knitting needles (or hacksaw blades or screwdrivers); magnet; pliers; paper clips.

Try this bridge: "You have learned that to take good care of magnets they must be stored properly, and never dropped or heated. What do you think would happen to a magnet that is dropped a few times?" (Pause for comments, then hold up the needles or substitutes.) "Rather than perhaps ruin our regular magnets, what could we do with these materials?"

select edures To avoid confusion, treat the magnetizing of the needles and "dropping" test as two distinct activities. Make sure both are stroked the same number of times, and tested with paper clips. The same number of clips should be attracted in both cases. If not, apply additional strokes as needed.

With the "dropping" test, drop only one magnet, from twenty to thirty times. This should produce a noticeable difference in its attractive force. Help pupils to record their pretest and post-test results in this or a similar way:

	Dropped Magnet	*Other Magnet*
Before:	5 clips	5 clips
After:	3 clips	5 clips

reason atively Help them reason that dropping one magnet probably causes the difference in clips attracted. To gain additional assurance of this *draw usions* conclusion, guide them in testing the second (control) magnet in an identical manner.

2. Remagnetize the needles. Develop a similar procedure with heat as the critical

A

B

Atomic domains represented are not literal illustrations.

FIGURE 4-11   An unmagnetized (A) and magnetized (B) steel rod.

factor. Pliers or tongs should be used to hold the magnet while it is placed in a candle flame. A minute is usually long enough for significant results. As before, use paper clips for pretest and post-test comparisons. Follow *draw conclusions* through by testing the control magnet to affirm conclusions.

3. *Materials:* opaque projection or sketch of Figure 4-11.

If some pupils have played with broken magnets, have them recall that these parts continued to attract objects. Tell the children that when a magnet is cut into smaller and smaller pieces, each piece retains its magnetic properties, and continues to have two poles. Present the projection or sketch. Explain it shows an unmagnetized and magnetized steel rod. Develop the following ideas:

a. Magnets have inside them tiny, invisible particles called *domains*. Domains in the sketch do not look like real domains. They are drawn that way to help pupils learn what happens when something is magnetized.

b. When domains are lined up, they act like tiny magnets which are pointed in one direction. Stroking a needle or nail with a magnet is one way to arrange them in a line.

c. When heated or jarred, the domains get out of line and repel each other. Storing like poles together pushes the domains out of alignment, too. This causes a magnet to lose some of its force.

Extending activities

1. Try "faulty procedure" with able pupils in the dropping and heating experiments. Use

evaluate critically large nails instead of steel objects. Challenge them to determine why the unheated and un-dropped nails also lose some magnetism. If necessary, remind them of their experiments with electromagnets.

2. Invite the class to draw their versions of a *partially* magnetized steel rod. In this case, some "domains" should appear aligned and some unaligned.

3. Have a display of many magnetic toys gathered by the children. Each should be explained before exhibited. Where possible, bring out ideas learned during the entire unit as such explanations are made.

The Energy of Electricity

(Upper)

One way to appreciate the advantages of a ready source of electricity is to count the number of electrical devices in a modern home and then try to devise nonelectrical substitutes for them. Yet appliances alone do not represent the full importance of electricity in our lives. The atom itself is composed of electrical particles and forces. Thus it seems that anything that exists cannot escape the influence of electricity. In the study of this unit, children should begin to understand and appreciate not only that there are instruments to make electrical energy available, but also why.

BASIC GENERALIZATIONS

I. Current electricity flows when there is a complete circuit; circuits may be opened and closed through the use of switches.

II. Circuits may be designed in series and parallel.

III. The kind, size, and length of materials used all affect the flow of electricity.

IV. Short circuits and overloaded circuits may create dangerously hot wires; fuses or circuit breakers are used to eliminate this danger.

V. Electromagnets can be made because a magnetic field is generated around a wire carrying electricity; electromagnets may be used in many ways.

VI. Matter contains electrons which may be accumulated through friction into electric charges; unlike charges attract, and like charges repel one another.

VII. An electric current may be generated by changing chemical, mechanical, light, or heat energy into electrical energy.

Each time we push a button or flip a switch that "turns on" electricity, billions of tiny electric particles called *electrons* begin flowing in the wires connected all the way from the generating plant to our appliance and back again to the plant. On a smaller scale, much the same thing happens when a dry cell is connected to a miniature lamp. If there is a continuous connection between the source of electricity and the appliance or device using it, lights go on, bells ring, or motors spin.

Children may recognize the need for connecting a bell or a lamp in a complete circuit with a dry cell without realizing that such a circuit is also needed in the home or school. The probable reasons are that appliance wires in the home are usually bound up in a single insulating sheath or casing, lending the appearance of a single wire. Then, too, most of the other wires in the circuit are located inside the walls, not readily available for examination.

Regardless of their shape, size, or method of operation, electric switches serve only to open or close a circuit. They offer a safe and convenient method of supplying the flow of electricity when we want it by merely providing a metal bridge over which electrons can flow to the connecting wires.

A miniature bulb and socket

An improvised socket and bulb

FIGURE 5-1

Much of the work in this unit calls for the use of dry cells, bell wire, and flashlight bulbs. Number 6 dry cells are often used because they are safe, fairly long lasting, and relatively inexpensive. When fresh, they deliver one and one-half volts of electricity, as contrasted with 110 to 120 volts or so supplied in the home. In other words, it would take as many as 80 of these cells connected together to have a force usually supplied by the current found in the home. The same is true of regular flashlight "batteries," though being smaller they become weaker and wear out faster than the larger dry cells. Incidentally, although individual flashlight cells are often called "batteries," it is correct to use the term "battery" only when a combination of two or more cells is used.

Since the unit calls for experiments with miniature bulbs, or flashlight-type bulbs, it will be helpful to understand how to use them properly. Miniature bulbs are designed to be used with a specified number of one and one-

FIGURE 5-2 A wirestripper.

half volt dry cells. Thus there are 1-cell, 2-cell, 3-cell, etc. bulbs. One-cell bulbs are marked "1.2v," 2-cell bulbs "2.5v," and so on. If three dry cells are connected to a 1-cell (or 1.2-volt) bulb, it is likely that the thin tungsten filament in the lamp will burn out quickly. So it is best to use the proper bulb for the number of cells employed. Too many cells will cause the bulb to burn out quickly; too few will cause it to glow too feebly.

Many of the demonstrations include the need for miniature bulbs and sockets. If these are unobtainable, an effective substitute can be made. As materials, use some bell wire, a small aluminum or metal foil strip, two paper clips, a small piece of wood, and two tacks or nails. Bend the wire around a pencil to make the screw-in base for the bulb, and assemble as shown in Figure 5-1. The paper clips will permit easy attachment of lead-in wires by merely slipping them under the elongated "loop." The wire base may need a little bending to make a secure contact with the metal strip.

The experiments in this unit have been carefully worked out to help insure teaching success. However, occasionally an experiment may not go as planned. If this happens, use the occasion as an opportunity for learning. Most difficulties with materials in this unit can probably be handled by posing one or more of the following questions. Through knowing about them in advance, you should experience little difficulty in tracing the source of the "trouble."

Bulb—Is it screwed in tightly? Burned out? Is there correct voltage?

Wire—Is it in good condition? Is the insulation stripped from the ends where contact is made? Is a complete circuit made? Short circuit?

Dry Cell—Is it in good condition? Is it powerful enough for the circuit?

Connections—Are they secure? Is enough contact being made for the current to flow easily?

Other Materials—Are the devices used in good operating condition?

As in the other units, there will be some necessity for the use of several tools. A very useful tool will be a "wirestripper," shown in Figure 5-2. It can be purchased inexpensively at most hardware stores. With it, insulation can be quickly removed from wires and wires can be cut with ease.

BASIC GENERALIZATION I: Current electricity flows when there is a complete circuit; circuits may be opened and closed through the use of switches

Contributing idea A. Current electricity flows only when there is a complete circuit.

1. *Materials:* table lamp and cord (optional); No. 6 dry cell; bell wire; miniature bulb and socket; 12-inch piece of house appliance wire; knife.

Exhibit a lamp with plug-in cord or a sketch of one on the chalkboard like the following:

FIGURE 5-3

"How can we get this bulb to light up?" Permit a child to plug in the lamp or tell how to do it, in the case of a sketch. You might ask, "What three things do we need to make a bulb light?" Draw out from the children: a "good" bulb, connecting wire, and a source of electricity. Point to a dry cell, *one* wire, and a miniature bulb and socket. "How are these things like those we just mentioned? How can we make this light go on?"

Allow a child to attempt a connection between the bulb and dry cell with the *one* wire.

When the bulb does not light, get hypotheses as to the reason from the class. To save time, you may wish to counter each reasonable hypothesis with a reasonable reply. For example, for the hypothesis "Maybe the bulb's no good," you might reply "We could test this, but the bulb was working just a moment ago." If nobody guesses or knows that another wire may be needed, inquire as to why there may be *two* binding posts on the dry cell and *two* attachments on the bulb socket. Produce another wire when the class surmises it is needed. *(margin note: suggest hypotheses)*

When the bulb lights, teach the meaning of the words *complete circuit*. Do this by asking someone to trace the apparent flow of electricity from the outside post of the dry cell through the wire, bulb, wire, and to the center binding post. Compare a complete circuit to an unbroken ring or a rubber band—there is a continuous connection at any part to the other parts.

Now hold up the house appliance wire and ask the children why *two* wires were needed in the previous activity when apparently only a single wire is needed in any appliance wire. If no one knows or guesses that there are two wires within the wrapping of the cord, cut off a few pieces and pass them around. After they have observed the two wires, explain that house appliances also need a complete circuit. *(margin note: suggest hypotheses)*

2. *Materials:* a clear (unfrosted) light bulb or flashlight bulbs; hand lens.

Examine a clear bulb. Trace the apparent path of electricity through it. Or, flashlight bulbs may be examined with a hand lens.

3. *Materials:* No. 6 dry cell; flashlight cell.

Show the class a flashlight cell and observe that it is very much like the larger dry cell used. Explain that it will not last as long as the large cell, but when new has the same force as the large cell. Point out that both cells have *terminals*, or places where the electricity leaves and then enters again in a complete circuit. Both cells have the *positive* terminal in the center of the top part. The other terminal, called the *negative* terminal, is located on the outside rim on top of the dry cell. However, the negative terminal of the flashlight cell is located at the opposite end. Mention that the terminals of the large dry cell are often called *binding posts* because this is where wires are fastened. Emphasize that when connected in a circuit, electricity flows from the negative terminal through the wire and back to the positive terminal.

4. *Materials:* paper clip; flashlight cell; 1.2-volt bulb.

Bring out again what is needed to make a light go on: a bulb, source of electricity, and a complete circuit. Challenge the children to make a flashlight bulb light with a paper clip and a flashlight cell. Assist them in thinking through what would be a complete circuit before they try. Perhaps the following sketch for the chalkboard will be helpful, if further assistance is needed.

FIGURE 5-4

5. Draw on the chalkboard the following sketch of a 2-cell flashlight. The class should

now be able to trace the circuit by drawing in a dotted line with colored chalk.

FIGURE 5-5

Contributing idea B. Switches are used to open and close circuits conveniently and safely.

1. *Materials:* bell wire; miniature bulb and socket; No. 6 dry cell; scissors. Have the lamp connected and glowing.

Ask the children how they turn on the electricity at home. Elicit a variety of means:

flipping a switch, pushing a button, pulling a string, turning a switch, etc. Point toward the demonstration lamp and ask how it might be turned off. The children will probably indicate that the bulb might be unscrewed slightly and that a wire can be disconnected. After trying it, draw out that in each case the circuit was broken.

Inquire as to how the scissors might be used to break the circuit. Permit a child to cut a wire. Strip off an inch or so of insulation from each end of the severed wire, and have someone alternately touch and pull apart the ends, causing the bulb to light and go out again. Bring out the inconvenience and hazard of closing a circuit in this manner with regular house current. Help the class to conclude that house switches are a safety factor as well as a convenience.

2. *Materials:* paper clip; piece of cardboard; two paper fasteners; two tacks; strip from a tinned can; piece of wood; several commercial switches (optional).

If several kinds of switches are available, have the children examine and connect them to the broken circuit. Since the children will also profit from making some switches, challenge them to make a switch from a paper clip and two paper fasteners mounted on cardboard. Another may be made from two tacks and a strip cut from a can and mounted on a piece of wood. (See Figure 5-6.) If the strip has ragged edges, smooth with a file. The strip should be bent upward slightly and just

A paper-clip switch

A metal-strip switch

FIGURE 5-6

FIGURE 5-7

loose enough barely to swivel. This way the end can be tucked partly under the head of the tack to maintain a closed circuit without the need to press down continuously with the fingers.

3. *Materials:* two metal strips; six tacks; two pieces of wood; bell wire; miniature bulb and socket; No. 6 dry cell.

Ask the children if they have a hall or stairway light that can be turned on and off by either of *two* switches. Sometimes it is necessary to turn off one of the switches by flipping it up *or* pushing it down. Encourage anyone to draw on the board a possible circuit that would illustrate how it works. If no one can, draw a sketch (see Figure 5-7) on the chalkboard and invite someone to draw switches and connections that might indicate what happens. Do not include the parts shown in dotted lines unless needed.

Putting the two tack-contact points in the extreme corners may be enough of a clue. If more clues are necessary, add to the sketch the two bottom contact points, and then the connecting wires. When the class reasons the switch will be successful, have several children assemble it according to their diagram. Let them demonstrate and discuss the conditions under which the light would be turned on by moving the switches either up or down.

Extending activities

1. Ask the class to make a list of all the places in the home where switches are used and how they are turned on and off.

2. Have the group examine different kinds of flashlights and make diagrams of how they work.

There are only two basic ways to connect electrical devices in a circuit: through series or parallel wiring. In series wiring, all of the usable electricity flows through each appliance. Figure 5-8 and activity on page 212 should help make this clear to your class. A chief disadvantage of this circuit is obvious to anyone who has had a bulb burn out in a series-type string of Christmas tree lights. When one bulb burns out the circuit is broken and all the lights go out. All the bulbs must then be tested to discover which one needs to be replaced.

To avoid the difficulties of series circuits, most wiring for home and commercial use is parallel wiring. In this kind, electricity flows through a main wire and through branching wires connected to it as well, as shown in Figure 5-10. If a light or other fixture should burn out, no other light or fixture is affected. They receive electricity whether or not the others are in use.

Hooking up dry cells in series increases the *voltage*, or pressure, behind the flow of electrons. In contrast, arranging several or more dry cells in parallel makes available a longer lasting supply of current without increasing the voltage. For example, a bulb connected to three dry cells in series will burn much brighter than if the cells were connected in parallel. However, the bulb will burn about three times longer with the parallel arrangement.

When switches placed in the main part of a parallel circuit are opened, the current is prevented from flowing to any part of the circuit. If switches are placed solely in the branches of a parallel circuit, only the appliance next to it is affected. This is why shutting off a desk lamp, for example, does not shut off all the other appliances, too. For a sketch of how this works, see Figure 5-13.

BASIC GENERALIZATION II: Circuits may be designed in series and parallel

Contributing idea A. A series circuit is designed to channel all of the usable power through a single route.

FIGURE 5-8

1. *Materials:* three miniature lamp sockets; three 1.2-volt bulbs; three 2.5-volt bulbs; No. 6 dry cell; bell wire. Have the following series circuit set up and connected. Large sketches on the chalkboard of this and other circuits used will be helpful to the children's thinking.

Ask the class to trace the apparent flow of electricity, beginning with the negative binding post of the dry cell. Raise conjecture as to *suggest hypotheses* what would happen if one of the bulbs were to be partly unscrewed. Press for reasons, then allow a child to try unscrewing and screwing back each of the bulbs. Draw out that in each case the circuit was opened, preventing a flow of electricity.

2. *Materials:* 2.5-volt bulb; two No. 6 dry cells; bell wire; miniature socket.

Hook up the bulb to a single dry cell. Have the children observe its brightness. Attach another dry cell in series, as shown here.

FIGURE 5-9

Again the brightness should be observed. Children can read to confirm their conclusion that *draw concl* increasing the dry cells in series will increase the electrical pressure, or voltage, thus causing the light to burn brighter.

Contributing idea B. A parallel circuit is designed to channel usable power through a main route and branching routes.

Materials: three 1.2-volt bulbs and miniature lamp sockets; two No. 6 dry cells; bell wire.

FIGURE 5-10

Assemble the three bulbs and a dry cell in parallel, as in Figure 5-10. Request a few pupils to trace the apparent circuit. Develop predictions as to what will happen if one or more bulbs are unscrewed. Try this, and observe to confirm or reject the predictions. Lead pupils to understand that the current divides into several pathways—one that goes down past the branch sockets, and others that go through each branch socket.

Add another dry cell in parallel, as illustrated in Figure 5-11. Help the children to

FIGURE 5-11

note that there is no increase in brightness, as was the case with the series circuit.

Contributing idea C. Dry cells are set up in series for additional voltage.

Materials: three 1.2-volt bulbs; three 2.5-volt bulbs; two No. 6 dry cells; bell wire.

Ask several pupils to set up circuits that have the bulbs in series and the dry cells in parallel. Then reverse the procedure, with the bulbs in parallel and the dry cells in series. Be sure to use the 2.5-volt bulbs whenever two dry cells are used, to avoid the chance of burning out the bulbs. Children might read to confirm that cells in parallel insure a longer lasting supply of electricity, but do not increase the pressure or voltage.

Contributing idea D. Switches set up in series in the main circuit break the entire circuit; switches set up in parallel branches of a circuit break only a part of the circuit.

To show the effect of switches in the main and branching parts of a circuit, the following

FIGURE 5-12

activities should be helpful. In both cases large sketches on the board will be desirable to use in reasoning through hypotheses before they are tried with actual materials.

1. *Materials:* three paper clips; bell wire; three miniature bulbs and sockets; No. 6 dry cell.

Set up a circuit as in Figure 5-12 with paper-clip "switches" at the numbered spots. (Three will be needed.) Have pupils trace the circuit carefully, beginning with the negative (outside) binding post. Starting with switch 1 encourage them to predict what will happen if it is opened. Let someone follow through with the actual materials. Do the same with switches 2 and 3. In each case the circuit will be broken and the lights will go out. Bring out the consistency of these findings with the children's previous observations of circuits.

2. *Materials:* same as above.

Sketch a parallel circuit as in Figure 5-13

FIGURE 5-13

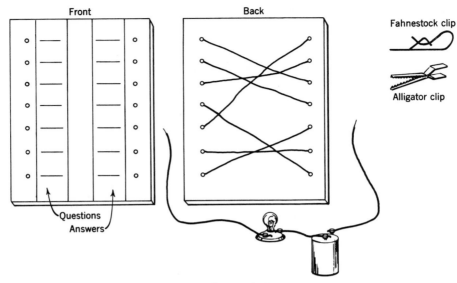

FIGURE 5-14

with the same kinds of paper-clip switches at the numbered places. (See inset for how to hook up the parallel wires when using the materials.) Explain that this is still a parallel circuit, but the parallel branches have been extended slightly to allow room for switches.

suggest hypotheses

Permit someone to trace the circuit carefully, beginning at the negative post of the dry cell. Entertain predictions as to what will occur when switches 1 through 4 are opened; then follow through with real materials. Only when opening switch 1 will all the lights go out. Elicit why: It alone has all of the usable current flowing past. Opening each of the other switches will result only in each adjacent light going out.

draw conclusions

Extending activity

Let the children construct an electrical questioning board, as in Figure 5-14. Use chipboard, masonite, or plywood for the base, bell wire for the circuits. Paper fasteners are useful for terminals, but stove bolts and nuts are more durable. To permit easy interchange of the bell-wire pieces, Fahnestock clips or alligator clips are more satisfactory to use than nuts. Nuts must be loosened and tightened each time the wiring setup is changed to avoid the possibility of children memorizing the

correct positions of the connectors, in place of knowing the correct answers. Fahnestock clips and alligator clips may be purchased at radio-TV repair stores.

An easy way to prepare questions and answers is merely to type them on two long sheets of paper, with spaces between questions and answers corresponding to the spaces between the connectors on the board. Sheets may be fastened with a tack at each end. Be sure that the answers are "scrambled" out of order with regard to the questions.

When children prepare questions and answers, it is convenient to have them written on 3- by 5-inch cards, which are then tacked next to the terminals.

The term "conductor" is usually given to any substance that permits an easy flow of electrons. Metals are by far the best conductors of electricity and so are commonly used for wires. Although several of the precious metals are better conductors, copper is most often used as it is comparable in efficiency and yet cheap enough to produce in quantity.

We often hear the term "nonconductor" applied to such materials as rubber, glass, plastic, cloth, and other nonmetallic substances. This is a misnomer, as virtually anything will conduct electricity if given sufficient voltage. These materials may be more properly considered as poor conductors, or *insulators*. This is why electricians may wear rubber gloves, and electric wires are covered with cloth, plastic, or rubber. This is why appliance plugs are covered with rubber or plastic and glass separators used on telegraph poles to keep apart high voltage lines.

Some poor conductors become good conductors when wet. Pure or distilled water is a poor conductor, but with the addition of dissolved minerals it becomes a fairly good one. Wet human skin is a far better conductor than dry skin. For this reason it is safer to turn appliances on and off with dry hands.

Although metals conduct electricity much better than nonmetals, there is still some resistance in metal wire to the flow of electrons. Obviously, the longer the wire the greater will be the resistance. You may have experienced the gradual dimming of lights in a theater or adjusted the brightness of dashboard lights in an automobile. The change in both cases was probably achieved by a *rheostat*. A rheostat is a device that increases or decreases the length of wire through which electric current flows, thereby increasing or decreasing the wire's resistance. A simple model is shown in Figure 5-15.

Some metals have so much resistance to the flow of electricity that they glow brightly when there is enough electrical pressure or voltage to force relatively large quantities of electron movement in them. Unfortunately, most metals melt or evaporate within a short period of time when hot enough to give off light. This caused an agonizingly long search by Thomas Edison for materials to be used as bulb filaments before he was able to achieve reasonable success. Some of the materials he tried indicate the exhaustive character of the search: bamboo slivers, sewing thread, even human hair were carbonized and tested!

Tungsten, sometimes called wolfram, is the metal used in *incandescent* bulbs today. (Any bulb that gives light from a very hot filament is called an incandescent bulb.) With a melting point of almost 6200 degrees Fahrenheit, tungsten is well able to withstand the temperature caused by the movement of electrons through its highly resistant composition. An inactive gas, such as argon, is pumped into the bulbs to help prevent burning away of the filament. However, some of the tungsten evaporates eventually and the filament is separated, breaking the circuit. The ever-darkening appearance of the portion of the bulb next to the filament indicates the deposition of the evaporating tungsten. Most house bulbs will burn for about 1000 hours.

Electric heaters also have wires of highly resistant metal. Most heaters today use nichrome wire, a combination of nickel and chromium.

Thus far, length and composition of wire have been mentioned as important factors in resistance to the flow of electricity. Another factor is the diameter of the wire. Perhaps the use of an analogy here will be helpful in explaining why size of wire affects resistance. Imagine part of a large crowd in a sports stadium converging into a narrow passageway. As some of the people begin to enter the passageway the forward speed of the crowd slackens. At the end of the passageway the forward pace again picks up.

FIGURE 5-15 A simple rheostat.

A thick wire presents a broad pathway for the flow of electrons. A narrow wire constricts the flow of electrons. In the "effort" to crowd through the narrow pathway much friction is created and the wire grows hot. If thin enough and when made of material such as tungsten, it can also produce much light as it glows.

Most devices that produce heat, such as heaters, toasters, and electric irons, have relatively thin, long, highly resistant wires. The wires cannot be as narrow in diameter as a light filament—one reason is that they are exposed to the open air and would rapidly evaporate away—but they are relatively thin compared to other wires designed to carry a similar voltage.

It would be helpful when teaching this section of the unit to acquire some real examples of toasters and heaters for observation. Discarded electric irons, toasters, and heaters can often be obtained free of charge from electrical repair shops. These can be taken apart and closely examined—something that perhaps better not be tried with someone's new appliance!

Sometimes children inquire about the operation of neon and fluorescent lamps when they study about electricity. Neon lamps and signs are simply narrow tubes of glass formed to fit the purpose for which they have been designed. After the air has been pumped out, a small amount of neon gas is introduced. When an electric current is sent through the tube, the electrons strike the rarefied gas and produce a red glow. If argon is used, near-white light is produced. Sodium vapor gives off a yellow light under similar conditions.

Fluorescent lamps are made from glass tubes coated on the inside with a light-sensitive chemical, such as phosphorus. Also inside the tube is a small amount of mercury. When electricity heats the filaments at each end of the tube, the mercury vaporizes. An automatic switch then permits the current to flow through the entire tube. The bombarded mercury vapor begins to emit invisible ultraviolet light. This light strikes the fluorescent internal coating and causes the lamp to glow brightly. Fluorescent lights are becoming in-creasingly used because of their superior lighting efficiency at reasonable cost.

BASIC GENERALIZATION III: The kind, size, and length of materials used affect the flow of electricity

Contributing idea A. Conductors are materials through which electricity passes freely; materials that tend to block the flow of electricity are called insulators or nonconductors.

Materials: poor conductors (insulators), such as plastic, wool, cotton, glass, chalk, paper, rubber, etc.; good conductors, such as carbon (from an old flashlight cell), graphite (from a pencil); metals, such as copper, aluminum, silver plate, nickel, dime, etc.; miniature bulb and socket; bell wire.

Hook up a simple circuit with a bulb in socket, wire, and dry cell. However, do not scrape off the insulation on the wire where it makes contact with the socket, or on the binding posts of the cell. Inquire "Why doesn't the light go on?" Allow a child to correct the difficulty when it is diagnosed. Mention that the material covering the wire is called an *insulator*—something that tends to block the flow of electricity.

Mention that materials that permit the easy passage of electricity are called *conductors*. Discuss the kinds of materials they have observed covering plugs, commercial switches, or other devices that must be touched by the hand or foot to be operated. These are insulators, for safety reasons.

Point to a table on which many materials are displayed and raise conjecture as to which are conductors or insulators. The materials may be divided tentatively into two piles before testing. Get class members to think of a method for adapting the circuit setup they used before to test their present hypotheses. A pair of scissors on the table next to the circuit may help them realize that if the wires are cut and insulation is stripped from each end, materials may be tested by merely touching each end of the bared wire to the material under consideration.

Contributing idea B. Thinner wire has more resistance than thicker wire.

Materials: several worn-out light bulbs; bulb with transparent glass (if possible); paper bag; hammer; short strand of iron picture wire; dry cell.

Let the class examine a transparent light bulb to observe the filament. If no transparent bulb is available, get a worn-out bulb and place it in a bag. Holding it downward and against a wall or other solid structure, tap it lightly with a hammer until it breaks. The filament may now be observed. Ask the class why it is so thin. When someone hypothesizes that a thin wire will "light up" faster than a thicker wire, point to the strand of picture wire and dry cell. Ask if an appropriate experiment can be performed with these materials.

A thin strand may be unraveled from the picture wire for the smaller diameter wire. The remainder of the strand can serve for the larger diameter. Each strand (start with the thin one) may then be placed across the posts of the dry cell to observe how long it takes to glow. Holding the thin wire across the posts too long may make it melt from the heat. Therefore, record the amount of time needed for the wire to glow for the thin wire first; and abandon attempts to make the thicker wire glow after it becomes obvious that it is taking longer. *Caution:* Use pliers or clothespins to hold the wires, as the wires will heat up fast. Hold the wires on the post as short a time as possible, since this quickly dissipates the cell's energy.

Let pupils read to confirm their tentative conclusion that thinner wires offer more *resistance* than thicker wires.

Contributing idea C. Longer wires offer more resistance to electricity than shorter wires made of the same material.

Materials: straightened-out iron hanger; dry cell; miniature bulb in socket; two wires connected to socket; and dry cell.

Use the analogy of a garden hose to help the children think through the next experiment. Inquire whether a very long hose would

suggest hypotheses

select procedures

draw conclusions

FIGURE 5-16

have as much pressure at the nozzle as a short one. Point out that the friction taking place inside the hose as the water slides along gradually reduces the force of the water. Now, raise conjecture about whether longer wires have more resistance to electricity.

evaluate critically

Connect the materials as shown in Figure 5-16; slide an end of the connecting wire up and down the hanger. Encourage the pupils to observe keenly the brightness of the light. If the hanger wire is painted, scrape or sand off the places where contacts are to be made. Explain that this is a *rheostat*—a device that decreases or increases current by decreasing or increasing the resistance to the flow of electricity.

Have the children read to confirm the conclusion that the length of the wire affects the resistance.

draw conclusions

Contributing idea D. Some metals have more resistance to electricity than others.

Materials: dry cell; straightened-out iron hanger; bell wire; miniature bulb and socket; two wires connected to socket.

Set up this demonstration just like the previous one, except now place alongside the hanger wire a piece of bell wire (insulation stripped at each end) of equal length. Have the children observe the brightness of the bulb as the connecting wires are touched to each of the separate wires. The bulb should burn more brightly with the copper bell wire.

draw conclusions   Ask the children what can be concluded from their observation. They may be unaware that size might also be a factor. If so, you might ask them to recall what they previously learned about wire and resistance. Ideally, now is the time to have pieces of iron picture wire and copper bell wire of equal diameter and length for testing. If not, the class might read to confirm that the composition of the metal does affect its resistance to electricity.

Contributing idea E. Devices that produce heat, such as heaters, toasters, and electric irons commonly have relatively thin, long, and highly resistant metal wires or ribbons.

Materials: new or old toasters; electric heater; hot plate; worn-out electric iron that may be taken apart.

Review with the class that size, length, and kind of wire affect resistance. Have the children recall that greater resistance resulted in greater heat. Bring up the idea that man attempts to apply the scientific principles he may learn about. Ask the children for some *suggest hypotheses* names of devices that provide heat. Invite them to predict what the heating elements would look like.

draw conclusions   Let them observe the above devices for confirmation or rejection of their predictions.

It will be helpful to use several questions to stimulate their thinking during the observations of these devices. For example:

Why aren't the wires as thin as those in the bulb? (They would otherwise burn out soon in the open air.)

draw conclusions   Why are the wires a different color from bell wire? (They are made of a different material, nichrome, a combination of nickel and chromium, which is highly resistant. Bell wire is copper.)

Why are the wires partly coiled or zigzagged? (This enables more wire, and thus heat, to be provided in the available space.)

Extending activities

1. Invite someone to report on Thomas Edison's invention of the first practical incandescent lamp. Emphasis might be on the long and frustrating search for materials that would not quickly burn away, with illustrations of these materials where possible.

2. Let someone report on how neon and fluorescent lights work.

3. Have an interested child read to learn why bulbs appear to explode when dropped. (They are filled with nitrogen gas to retard *evalu* the burning of the filament. If the filament *critic* were not enclosed and surrounded by this gas, it would quickly burn out—oxygen supports burning.)

We have seen that when appliances are wired into a circuit they show great resistance to the flow of electrical energy. At the place where this energy enters the resistors, however, a transformation of energy takes place—some of the electrical energy becomes converted into heat (if it enters a heater) or light (bulb) or sound (radio) or motion (motor). In other words, a significant amount of electrical energy is "used up," or changed. Suppose, however, there is no resistor connected in the circuit. Since the copper wire has relatively low resistance, a great surge of electricity flows through the wire. The wire now heats up rapidly, even though it normally offers little resistance to a current.

In house and commercial circuits intense heating of the wires is likeliest to come from either of two causes: a "short" circuit, or "overloading" the circuit. A short circuit may occur when two bare wires touch each other, thus preventing the main supply of current from flowing through the resistor. Since the resistor is bypassed, a huge amount of electricity flows. A common cause of short circuits occurs when an appliance cord is placed under a heavily traveled rug. If the insulation between the two internal wires wears away they may touch and a "short" develop.

Overloading a circuit is perhaps an even more frequent cause of wires overheating. Many older houses, for example, were wired when only a few of today's common appliances were in widespread use. Small-diameter, lightly insulated wires were formerly adequate.

However, as more and more appliances in modern times continue to be plugged in, more and more electric current is caused to flow through these circuits. A constant pressure of 110 to 120 volts is maintained by the power source. The intense heating that occurs from the friction of too much electricity forced through the wire is a potential source of fire.

Fuses and circuit breakers protect us from the fire hazard. A screw-in type fuse contains a narrow metal strip that melts at a fairly low temperature. When a fuse is placed in a circuit, the electricity must travel through the strip. Should the wire heat up dangerously, the strip melts and the circuit opens, thereby shutting off the current.

Occasionally, someone will replace a burned-out fuse with a penny to avoid the "inconvenience" of another fuse burning out. Unfortunately, if the initial source of the difficulty is not corrected the wires may grow so hot the house may catch fire. An acceptable fuse has two requirements: it must be a good conductor, and have a low melting point. A penny only meets the first requirement!

Often a bimetallic strip circuit breaker is used instead of a fuse. This consists of two thin, metal ribbons fused together. The ribbons are made of two different metals. When placed in a circuit and heated, the bimetallic strip bends away from one of the contact points, opening the circuit. The bending, as mentioned in Unit 1, is due to different expansion rates of the metals.

Another type of circuit breaker works from the fact that any wire containing current electricity generates some magnetism. Increasing the supply of current has the effect of increasing the magnetism. When contained in a coil of wire placed in a circuit, a movable steel rod may be pulled upward as the current (and magnetism) increases. If the rod is connected to a contact point, its upward movement will result in the circuit being opened. A spring catch that can be reset by hand is used to prevent the rod from dropping down again. An electromagnetic device that operates this way is called a solenoid or "sucking coil."

There are many opportunities in the lessons that follow to emphasize safety with electricity. It is perhaps better to do this in context as the opportunity occurs, rather than to make a long list of "rules" to follow. Such a list can be begun early in the unit and added to as study progresses.

Children can be taught to find out a number of resistors that can be safely placed in a circuit. In order to do this they will need to be acquainted with the terms *ampere, volt,* and *watt.* An *ampere* is the rate of flow of electricity. Technically, it is defined as the flow of 6.3 billion billion electrons per second past a given point. This figure can be presented to the class (a six, followed by eighteen zeroes), but, of course, will be meaningless. The idea to stress is that ampere means the rate of flow. If a fuse is rated at 15 amperes, then only those appliances can be operated whose total rate of current used is under 15 amperes.

We have indicated before that the term *volt* is a unit of pressure. A dry cell has an electrical pressure of one and one-half volts, house current 110 to 120 volts. Sometimes a special line which carries 220 volts is attached to a house circuit for such heavy users of current as electric clothes dryers and ovens.

The term *watt* is used to indicate the amount of electricity used. It is found by merely multiplying amperes by volts.

Activities are included in this section to help children understand how electric power company bills are calculated for consumers.

BASIC GENERALIZATION IV: Short circuits and overloaded circuits may create dangerously hot wires; fuses or circuit breakers are used to eliminate this danger

Contributing idea A. A short circuit results when a resistor is largely bypassed; the increased flow of electricity increases the heat of the wire.

Materials: miniature bulb and socket; bell wire; dry cell; small knife or wire stripper.

To lamp

Wires touch here

FIGURE 5-17

Have on the chalkboard the sketch shown in Figure 5-17.

Use this bridge: "We are often warned not to place electric wires under a rug, particularly where they are liable to be stepped on or pushed down a lot. Why is this so?" Discuss this for a moment. Now turn to the sketch and inform the class that it shows a table leg pressing on a wire whose insulation at one point has gradually worn away. Explain that the lines to represent the wires are drawn as broken lines; this shows that the wires are invisible because of the insulation. Point out *suggest hypotheses* that electricity is streaming into the top wire. Encourage the pupils to hypothesize as to the probable path of the electricity at point X, where contact is made. Also, seek a prediction as to whether the lamp will light at this time.

select procedures Indicate the materials and ask how they can be set up to test the hypotheses. Help the children to scrape away the insulations on the two wires where contact will be made. The assembly may look like Figure 5-18. *Caution!* Do not permit anyone to hold the bare wires at the contact point, as the wires will quickly grow hot. It will also be best to do this experiment fairly quickly, to avoid greatly draining the cell's energy.

After it is observed that the light goes out, have several children feel the insulated part

of the wire in front and in back of the bare contact point. Have someone notice that the short-circuited part is hot while the wires beyond the contact point are cool. Draw out from pupils that this helps confirm the *draw conclus* hypothesis of electricity not flowing beyond the contact point. It should be pointed out, however, that there is a very small current still flowing through the other part.

Bring out that this experience is an example of a *short circuit*. Try to elicit a reasonable explanation as to what happened. Let the children read to understand that when a resistor such as a lamp is bypassed, a huge amount of current will surge through a wire when contact is made; there is very little resistance to check its flow. Again call attention to the great heat produced as a result of this short circuit.

Contributing idea B. Fuses are designed to open a circuit that is heating up before it becomes dangerous.

1. *Materials:* dry cell; miniature bulb and socket; bell wire; metal foil strip (from a gum wrapper); scissors; small piece of wood; two nails; hammer.

Get your pupils to speculate about the fire hazard when a short circuit takes place. Bring out that, because of the hazard, measures are taken to avoid it. Ask the children if any heat would occur if the circuit were opened. Ask for a logical way a circuit might be broken with heat. Help them reason that any device introduced into the circuit which would conduct electricity well and yet have a low melt- *draw conclu* ing point would be applicable.

Prepare some materials now for a demonstration. Pound two nails into the wood a few inches apart, stretch a foil strip between the two nails and secure fast. To help insure that the middle of the strip will melt, narrow it by cutting away portions with scissors. It may take a little trial and error to find the proper size. Use the same circuit as before, except now include the fuse in the circuit by fastening each wire to a nail as in Figure 5-19.

Before touching a loose wire to a binding *sugges hypot* post and completing the circuit, ask the chil-

FIGURE 5-18

dren what they predict will happen to the fuse if there is no short circuit. (Nothing.) Ask again prior to making the short circuit. (The fuse will melt, the light will go out.) Help them conclude that the fuse is an important safety factor when short circuits occur.

2. *Materials:* same as above; substitute a penny for the foil.

Review two reasons the fuse worked: (1) it conducted electricity satisfactorily while the circuit was normal; and (2) having a lower melting point than the copper wire, it melted when the increased current created increased heat. Now repeat the previous demonstration, but this time place a penny between the two nail heads. The nails, of course, now have to be placed closer together. The penny should begin heating up. (*Caution:* The wires, too, will become hot.)

Bring out that while the penny is a good conductor, it has a high melting point. Ask the class if it would be sensible to substitute a penny in place of a fuse when it burns out. Bring out the foolishness of ignoring a warning sign or symptom by "correcting" the symptom and not the cause.

3. *Materials:* various commercial fuses.

If several commercial fuses are available, it would be especially helpful to show them at this time. Electrical shops may be good sources for worn-out fuses.

Contributing idea C. Overloading a circuit with too many resistors may also overheat the wires.

1. *Materials:* two dry cells arranged in series; five miniature 2.5-volt bulbs and sockets; bell wire; foil fuse.

Ask your pupils if they have heard that attaching too many appliances to a house circuit may cause the wires to overheat and the fuse to "blow." Remind them that a house usually has parallel wiring. Inform them that the power station maintains a fairly steady voltage in the house circuit regardless of the number of resistors used. Invite them to try hooking up the materials in parallel to see if they get an overheated circuit. Start with one lamp,

draw conclusions

evaluate critically

FIGURE 5-19

and gradually increase the number until the fuse melts.

The children might trim the center width of the fuse until they have "designed" one that will melt according to some agreed specification—such as a two "appliance" fuse, four "appliance" fuse, etc. Point out that, in a more refined way, it is possible for engineers to design a fuse that will melt at a specified temperature or amount of current.

select procedures

2. Draw on the board the sketch shown in Figure 5-20.

Introduce the idea that the circuit could also be broken by a bimetallic strip circuit breaker. Point out that the strip is composed of two different metals fastened together. Mention that when heated, the metals expand at different rates and cause the strip to bend, thus breaking the circuit.

To circuit

To circuit

FIGURE 5-20

If a bimetallic strip is available, attach a wire at one end and lay the other end over the second wire. In this manner, it will be free to bend and disconnect the circuit. Several or more dry cells arranged *in series*, plus a short circuit, may be needed to achieve a noticeable bending of the strip.

Contributing idea D. Arithmetic may be used to find out the number of resistors which can be safely placed in a circuit.

1. Develop the idea that we do not need to leave to chance whether a fuse or circuit breaker will open a circuit. If a 30-ampere fuse is available, mention that the label reads "30 A." Otherwise, mention that there are 30 A fuses. Such fuses melt when 30 amperes flow through the circuit. Explain that the safety margin can be calculated through the use of arithmetic. To understand how to do this, first the term *ampere* must be learned.

Begin with the analogy of two water hoses. Both are the same length. But one is a narrow garden hose and the other a wide fireman's hose. Both are hooked to the same fire hydrant. Ask which has the larger amount of water flowing out of the nozzle and why. (The larger hose, because it can carry more water.) Apply the idea to electricity now, and acquaint pupils with the word ampere, used to mean the rate of flow. Tell them that one ampere is a flowing of more than six billion billion tiny particles of electricity a second. Have them recall their previous experiment with thick and thin wires. Will a thick copper wire have more flow or amperes of electricity than a thin copper wire of the same length? (Yes.) Mention some typical house appliances, and the amount of electricity each might need to operate. For example:

draw conclusions

	Amperes
Coffee maker	5
Toaster	5
Waffle iron	8
Sun lamp	5
	23

Point out that by adding the amperages of these appliances one knows whether they are totally within the capacity of a 30-ampere fuse.

Have the pupils add an 11-ampere iron and five 1-ampere bulbs to the list. Inquire if the new total will exceed the rated capacity of a 30-ampere fuse.

reason quant

2. Continue with the analogy of the water hose. Many children have noticed the water pressure varying to some noticeable degree while playing with or using a hose. This happens when someone else in the house or a neighbor is also using outlets. Point out that sometimes the water will shoot out powerfully for a great distance from the nozzle, but sometimes only a short distance. Mention that the push or force behind the water is greater in one case than the other. Would more water flow into a bucket within 10 seconds with a forceful stream than with a weaker one? (Forceful stream.)

Help the children to summarize the two ways they could increase the amount of water flowing at any time: by using a bigger hose, to provide a wider pathway; and by increasing the push or pressure behind the water. Continue by making the application to electricity. Point out that the unit of pressure is the *volt*. Have someone read the voltage rating of a No. 6 dry cell (one and one-half volts). Bring out that the pressure of house current is about 120 volts. If class members can work with decimal divisors, request them to calculate how many new dry cells it would take to equal this voltage by dividing 120 by 1.5. (80 cells.)

draw concl

Remind the children that in the lessons on series and parallel wiring they have already learned how to increase the voltage of dry cells by attaching them in a series. Have them recall that the light got brighter as the second cell was added in series, but that the brightness did not change as the cell was added in parallel. Repeat this demonstration, if needed.

3. *Materials:* three dry cells; a 1.2-volt bulb; bell wire.

If a 1.2-volt bulb can be sacrificed in the interest of science education, let the children connect the bulb to a dry cell, and then gradually add more cells in series until it burns out. Allow a minute or so of lamp burning for each additional cell. Three cells will probably have more than enough voltage to burn out the lamp.

4. Mention that sometimes household appliances do not have the amperage rating stamped on them, but have instead the number of *watts* used. Explain that the wattage is merely the flow of electricity times the pressure, or amperes times volts. Thus, 5 amperes × 10 volts = 50 watts. In other words, a watt tells how fast electricity is being used. Show the class that it is possible to figure out amperes if the voltage and wattage of the appliance is known. Write on the board the formula:

$$\text{Amperes} = \frac{\text{Watts}}{\text{Volts}}$$

Pose some problems such as the following:

reason tively An electric drill uses 240 watts on regular 120-volt house current. How many amperes does it use?

$$\frac{240 \text{ W}}{120 \text{ V}} = 2 \text{ A}$$

An electric iron uses 1200 watts on regular house current. How many amperes does it use?

$$\frac{1200 \text{ W}}{120 \text{ V}} = 10 \text{ A}$$

5. Ask the class to calculate the following problem to determine if all the appliances could be used without overloading a house *reason tively* circuit. (Assume a 120-volt supply.) The circuit breaker is rated at 30 amperes.

	Watts
Coffee maker	360
Waffle iron	960
Toaster	600
Iron	1200

The class should total the wattages (3120 W) and divide by 120 V. The answer is 26 amperes. It would not actuate the circuit breaker.

Extending activities

1. Invite the pupils to find out the rated capacity of the fuse or circuit breaker used in their home or apartment. Have them find the wattages or amperes used by the lights and appliances and total them. The total may *reason quantitatively* then be compared with the circuit capacity. If a few children are unable to find the wattage rating of some appliances, perhaps the following list of typical appliances may be convenient to use.

	Watts
Electric blanket	600
Electric frypan	1100
Dishwasher	1200
Oven	3000
Washing machine	1600
Electric dryer	5000
Vacuum cleaner	700
Waffle iron	1100
Iron	800

2. Pupils who excel in arithmetic may wish to determine the quantity of volts, watts, or amperes used when only two of these factors are known. Present the formula $A = W/V$. Next to it place $4 = 8/2$. Tell them that these numbers can help them to think through the relationships of the symbols in the formula. Now ask them if they can discover a formula *reason quantitatively* that will determine volts, if only watts and amperes are known. In a like manner the other quantities may be thought through.

3. Invite a local fireman to class for a talk on safety with electricity. This courtesy is extended by many fire departments as a public service.

4. The class may be interested in determining how electric power bills are calculated by the local power company. The essentials of *reason quantitatively* the arithmetic involved are to multiply watts times hours, which yields watt-hours. Dividing this figure by 1000 gives the kilowatt-hours. This figure is then multiplied by the kilowatt-hour rate.

Example:
1700 watts for 200 hours = 340,000 watt-hours

$$\frac{340,000 \text{ watt-hours}}{1,000} = 340 \text{ kilowatt-hours}$$

$$\begin{array}{r} 340 \text{ kilowatt-hours} \\ \times \quad 0.05 \text{ per kilowatt-hour rate} \\ \hline \$17.00 \text{ charge} \end{array}$$

In 1820 a professor of physics at Copenhagen made a discovery that opened up for development one of the most useful devices ever conceived: the electromagnet. *Hans Christian Oersted* had believed for years that there was a relationship between magnetism and electricity. In spite of much research, however, Oersted had not succeeded in discovering a useful connection between these phenomena. One day, while lecturing to a class, he noticed that a wire carrying electric current was deflecting a nearby compass needle. Oersted realized immediately that the wire was generating a magnetic field. His subsequent experiments, writings, and lectures helped spread to the world the new concept of electromagnetism.

The telegraph, telephone, electric motor, and many other indispensable tools of modern living had their origin in Oersted's work and related discoveries. This section of the unit goes into some detail on how these devices work. It would be most helpful to the children if the tremendous impact of these inventions on their lives can be discussed as they are studied.

BASIC GENERALIZATION V: Electromagnets can be made because a magnetic field is generated around a wire carrying electricity; electromagnets can be used in many ways

Contributing idea A. A magnetic field is generated around a wire carrying electricity; the strength of the field can be increased in several ways.

1. *Materials:* dry cell; bell wire; iron filings; compass and mirror; large nail; paper clips.

Connect one end of the bell wire to the dry cell and hold a section immediately over a compass. Ask a child to touch the other end of the wire to the remaining binding post. Hold the mirror at an angle in back of the compass so the class can observe what is happening to the needle without crowding around the compass. Class members will notice that the compass needle is suddenly deflected. Do this several times and ask them

what they see. Explain that this demonstration is much like the method used by the nineteenth-century Danish scientist *Hans Christian Oersted* when he discovered that a wire through which electricity was flowing produced a magnetic field.

2. *Materials:* compass; magnet; mirror.

Ask how Oersted realized it was magnetic attraction he was viewing. Answers may vary. Encourage a pupil to use a magnet to attract the compass needle. The class will observe similar deflections of the compass needle.

3. *Materials:* bell wire; sharp knife; iron filings; two dry cells; paper clips; large nail.

Strip off a few inches of insulation from the middle of the wire. Place the stripped part over some iron filings, but connect only one end of the wire to a dry cell. The class will note no attraction. Now, complete the circuit and the filings will be attracted. Try attracting paper clips. They will probably be too heavy to lift. Ask for ideas as to how the magnetic field could be strengthened.

Have someone wrap about ten turns of bell wire around a nail, connect one end of the wire to the cell, and touch the other end to the remaining binding post. If the nail is brought near the clips, they will be weakly attracted. When the free end of the wire is lifted from the binding post, the clips will fall. (If there is some residual or "left over" magnetism, shake the nail slightly.)

Let the children experiment with more turns of wire on the nail, and with hooking up more dry cells in series, to increase the force of the electromagnet. Encourage them to note any relationships between the number of turns and number of clips picked up, number of cells used and number of clips picked up.

Contributing idea B. Door chimes and electrical circuit breakers may operate through electromagnets.

1. *Materials:* two clean, empty tinned cans; piece of stiff paper about 4 inches by 2 inches; cellophane tape; large nail; bell wire; two dry cells; switch, if desired.

Assemble the materials according to Figure

5-21. Point out that the iron nail is fitted loosely in the paper cylinder. Ask the class to predict what will happen when the circuit is completed. Use two dry cells, if needed.

suggest theses

The top can may be held by someone or suspended by a string. Use cellophane tape to fasten strings. Let the children point out that this device resembles door chimes at home.

2. *Materials:* as used in the previous activity; substitute a can lid for the cans.

Using the same "sucking coil" as in the previous demonstration, assemble materials as in Figure 5-22.

suggest theses

Invite the class to trace the circuit in the construction and to predict what will happen. Since it may be difficult for all to see well, a simple sketch on the chalkboard may be helpful. A weak dry cell, heavy nail, or insufficient turns of wire all could prevent movement of the nail in the coil. Any one of these contingencies would be excellent for analysis of faulty procedure.

evaluate critically

After doing the demonstration, help the children to conclude that they have seen a circuit broken. Bring out that real electrical circuit breakers operate on the same principle, but that a spring catch closes after the iron core is activated, thus preventing its return. Recall with them that much electricity surges into a wire when there is a short circuit and overloaded circuit. Ask them how the increased electricity affects this kind of circuit breaker. From their experience with making electromagnets more powerful, through the addition of cells, they should quickly see that a similar relationship exists here.

draw conclusions

draw conclusions

This demonstration can be improved if pupils place a miniature lamp in series in the circuit. Opening and closing the circuit thereby becomes more obvious.

select procedures

Contributing idea C. A telegraph uses an armature that is attracted by an electromagnet.

Materials: six large nails; two 12- by 4- by 3/4-inch blocks of wood; two small pieces of scrap wood to mount switches; large tinned can; tin shears; bell wire; six large tacks; hammer; two dry cells.

FIGURE 5-21

Let several children build the telegraph set illustrated in Figure 5-23 and tell the others how it works. Let them discover that to maintain a complete circuit, the person receiving the signals must keep his key closed. As with a previous activity, a switch, or "key" in this case, may be left just free enough to swivel under the head of the contact point. In this way, it can close the circuit without any need for holding it down by hand.

draw conclusions

Caution the children that the wire must be wrapped around the front nails in *opposite directions*. This gives the electromagnets *opposite poles*, which are much more powerful than two like poles. Forty turns of wire around each nail should be adequate.

Explain that pauses made by delaying or speeding up clicks of the "sounder" (armature) against the nail can be interpreted as dots and dashes. The Morse Code may be used to send messages. However, the diffi-

FIGURE 5-22

FIGURE 5-23

culty of interpreting signals satisfactorily can lead to a need for an improved sounder, shown in the next activity.

Morse Code

A . –	B – . . .	C – . – .
D – . .	E .	F . . – .
G – – .	H	I . .
J . – – –	K – . –	L . – . .
M – –	N – .	O – – –
P . – – .	Q – – . –	R . – .
S . . .	T –	U . . –
V . . . –	W . – –	X – . . –
Y – . – .	Z – – . .	

Contributing idea D. Electromagnets may be used in the construction of an interrupted circuit for a bell or buzzer system.

1. *Materials:* same as in the previous activity, plus a door bell.

Have some children build a telegraph set that gives a buzzing signal. However, suggest they use only *one* sounder and key, as this circuit is easier to analyze. Let them use a projection of Figure 5-24 to build their set and explain how the circuit works. Have

them test the set and observe closely. Make sure they understand that this circuit is alternately opened and closed as the contact point opens and closes at the nail head. The end of the tin strip must touch the bottom of the nail head. If it does not, tap the nail down with a hammer until it touches.

2. Remove the cover of a door bell. Compare the telegraphic buzzer and bell. (See Figure 5-25.) Develop that the circuitry is practically identical. The main differences are in materials used and sounds made.

Contributing idea E. Telephone receivers contain electromagnets that help change spurts of electrical energy to sound energy; the transmitter uses sound energy to turn on electrical energy.

1. *Materials:* carbon rod from an old dry cell; hammer; two 25-cent pieces; bell wire; cellophane tape; dry cell; miniature lamp and socket; large sketch of a telephone transmitter and receiver; if possible, a real telephone. (Local telephone companies are usually cooperative in lending many useful materials to schools.)

sugge *hypo* *draw* *concl* *evalu* *critic*

FIGURE 5-24

Begin by asking the pupils if they have ever made a long distance call on a telephone. Bring out distances involved. Cite the case of a person who phones someone 2250 miles away. The two people seem to hear each other instantly. Yet it is known that sound *reason* travels about 750 miles per hour, about the *atively* speed of some jet aircraft. What is the prob- *define* lem? (How is it possible to hear a person al- *blems* most instantly when a telephone is used?)

uggest It is doubtful that your pupils' explana- *theses* tions will be entirely correct. However, ask which explanation seems most reasonable, then continue. Tell them they now have al- most enough background to understand how a telephone works, and will be able to figure out shortly for themselves what happens when a telephone is used.

It will be helpful to begin the sequence with a demonstration. Show that the amount of electrical current sent through a wire can be varied by increasing or decreasing the dis- tance between conductors. Recall the chil- dren's previous experience with a rheostat, where length was an important factor in vary- ing the resistance. In the following demon- stration with carbon granules, the varying dis- tance of the granules to one another will alter the amount of electrical current that flows in

the circuit. This will cause light to burn with varying brightness.

Place the carbon rod on some paper and

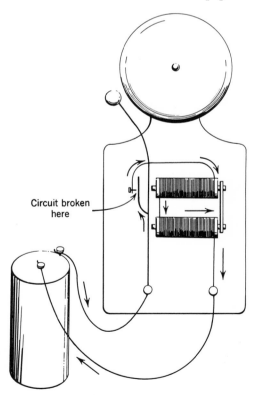

Circuit broken here

FIGURE 5-25

FIGURE 5-26

break it into small pieces with a hammer. Take two large coins, and attach the bared ends of two wires with cellophane tape to the coins. Complete the rest of the circuit as in Figure 5-26, placing the carbon granules between the coins to make a "sandwich." A small, clear, plastic container will keep the granules from scattering and yet permit observation. Tell someone to press down on the coin gently, then harder. Ask the children to tell what they see and to explain why it hap-

draw conclusions pens. (More electricity is conducted when particles are squeezed together; this makes the light brighter. The opposite happens when the particles are not squeezed together.)

2. Have the children recall the ways in which an electromagnet can be made stronger. Emphasize that increasing the current by hooking up more dry cells in series makes an electromagnet more powerful. Ask if an electromagnet would gain or lose power *evalua* through the same reason that the light's *critica* brightness varies. If there is any difficulty at this point, substitute an electromagnet for the light. Note its varying power of attraction with paper clips as the coins are pressed and released.

3. Place on the chalkboard or project the sketch of a telephone transmitter and receiver in Figure 5-27. Point to the two diaphragms and inform the class that they are made of very thin metal that can *vibrate*, or move back and forth rapidly. Note that the carbon granules or particles in the transmitter are like those used in the coin "sandwich" demonstration. Now ask the class to study the sketch and give an explanation of how the telephone works.

With a little assistance, it should now be *draw* clear to the children why its is possible to *conclu* hear someone speaking over the telephone almost instantly. Sound vibrations from the voice variably squeeze the carbon granules. This causes the granules to conduct variable electrical impulses, rather than a steady current. The electrical impulses rather than the voice itself are transmitted in the wire. There-

FIGURE 5-27   A telephone circuit.

FIGURE 5-28

fore, they travel thousands of miles almost instantly instead of at the much slower speed of sound. The varying currents or impulses cause the electromagnet in the receiver to set its diaphragm vibrating. This creates the sounds. To summarize, you might emphasize the idea that one kind of energy may be changed to another. In this case, sound energy is used to provide the electrical energy, which is then used to provide sound energy. For reinforcement of learning, this would be an ideal time for pupils to read a textbook explanation.

evaluate critically If an actual telephone is available for inspection, unscrew the transmitter and receiver. Let pupils compare the parts with those in the sketch.

Contributing idea F. Electric motors spin because they contain electromagnets which alternately push and pull as their poles change.

1. *Materials:* two bar magnets; string; electromagnet; dry cell.

Tell the children that one of the most important applications of the electromagnet is in electric motors. Draw out names of common appliances that use electric motors, such as sewing machines, washers, fans, etc. Mention that the class will begin to understand how electric motors function after the following demonstration.

Suspend a bar magnet from a string. Bring the opposite pole of the second bar magnet close to the suspended magnet. Demonstrate that unlike poles attract each other, and like poles repel each other. Now start the suspended magnet rotating in one direction by alternately attracting and repelling each pole. Twist the bar magnet so the poles are attracted at first, then repelled. If timed properly, the suspended magnet will rotate somewhat uniformly.

Now demonstrate a similar technique with an electromagnet. First, find the pole on the electromagnet that is the opposite of the bar magnet's nearer pole. It will attract. Next, reverse terminal connections and the poles will also be reversed. The nearer pole will now be repelled. (See Figure 5-28.) It should be possible to rotate the suspended magnet smoothly by touching the binding posts—first one way, then the opposite way. (A child can do this at a given signal.) Explain that in

FIGURE 5-29   A St. Louis motor.

electric motors there is a device which reverses the current automatically, and thus reverses the poles. The alternating attraction and repulsion of the poles keeps the motor turning.

2. *Materials*: commercially made St. Louis motor; bell wire; dry cell.

A St. Louis motor is excellent for illustrative purposes. (See Figure 5-29.) Point out the *armature*, which is a rotating electromagnet, and the *commutator*. This latter device automatically reverses the armature's current —and thus its poles—just as the poles line up with the poles of the *field magnets*. These two permanent magnets are fastened on opposite sides of the armature. Also point out the *brushes*, which enable electricity to flow through the commutator to the electromagnet and back again.

Extending activities

1. Have short reports on contributions of the following men to the technology of communication:

Samuel F. B. Morse (invented the first practical telegraph and code for each letter of the alphabet).

Cyrus W. Field (major contributor to research information used in laying telegraph cables across the Atlantic Ocean, through which messages called cablegrams are sent).

Guglielmo Marconi (invented the wireless telegraph, making possible transmission of electrical waves through air for communication purposes).

Alexander Graham Bell (invented the first practical telephone).

Hans Christian Oersted (conducted early experiments in electromagnetism).

2. A few advanced pupils may wish to build their own electric motor and demonstrate it. Directions for construction of simple motors may be found in many children's books on electricity.

Almost everyone has experienced some form of *static electricity*: the crackling sound of

hair when it is combed after having been washed and dried; the slight shock felt when a metal door knob is touched after scuffing across a rug; the flash of lightning that briefly illuminates a darkened sky. In each case an electric charge appears to build up on an object and then stay there (hence the name static) until a conductor provides a route through which the charge can escape. Although forms of static electricity vary considerably, their causes are fundamentally the same. To understand these causes, it will be helpful for us to peer briefly into the composition of molecules and atoms.

We know that most matter is made up of *molecules*. A molecule is the smallest bit of any substance which retains the appearance and chemical characteristics of that substance. If we subdivide the molecule further, it no longer resembles the original substance; we have arrived at the atomic level.

Only two of the particles of which an atom is composed need concern us here: *electrons* and *protons*. Each of these particles has a tiny electric charge that is the opposite of the other. The electron's charge is called a *negative charge* and the proton's charge a *positive charge*.

In their "normal" state, atoms possess as many electrons as protons. Since these particles attract each other with equal force they balance or neutralize each other. The atom is said to be *neutral*, or uncharged. However, electrons are easily dislodged or torn away from atoms by rubbing and by other means. Free electrons, as these dislodged particles are called, may be attracted to another atom. If an atom loses one or more electrons it will have an excess of protons, and hence a positive electric charge. If it gains one or more electrons the atom will have an excess of electrons and a negative electric charge.

When unlike materials are rubbed together one tends to lose electrons to the other. For example, when a hard rubber rod is rubbed with a wool cloth, the cloth loses some of its electrons to the rod. This gives the cloth a positive charge and the rod a negative charge. When a glass rod is rubbed with silk, however, scientists have found that some electrons leave the glass and go onto the silk cloth. This gives the silk a negative charge and the glass a positive charge. Although almost any unlike materials rubbed together will produce some static electricity, the above materials usually yield the most satisfactory results.

A modern conception of the atom is needed to understand reasonably well the nature of static electricity. But early scientific discoveries helped at least to make it a less mysterious phenomenon than it must have been to primitive man. Benjamin Franklin's contribution to the understanding of static electricity is an interesting example.

To determine if lightning was associated with electricity, Franklin flew a kite during a thunderstorm. Attached to the kite was a metal rod, and at the end of the string a key was fastened. Franklin hypothesized that a spark would jump to the key as electricity traveled down the string. To avoid being shocked, he held the key by means of a silk ribbon. (Silk is a fairly good insulator.) Franklin took the additional precaution of standing under a shelter so the ribbon would remain dry. He realized that moisture increases conduction of electricity. His success with this and other experiments helped prove that lightning was a form of static electricity.

(Discourage anyone from trying Franklin's experiment. We know now that a severe electric charge would have electrocuted him in spite of the silk cloth insulator.)

What causes lightning? Basically, it is produced by friction. A cloud contains varying amounts of dust particles, rain drops, air (gas) molecules, and sometimes ice crystals. When violent air currents occur in clouds, these substances rub together in various combinations. If a huge electric charge is built up, it may be attracted by an oppositely charged cloud, or the ground. When this happens, we see lightning.

Since metals are excellent conductors, usually anyone is safe from lightning in a steel-framed building, or in a building equipped with a lightning rod. If the object is struck, the charge is harmlessly conducted by the metal down into the ground. Electricity always takes the path of least resistance. Teach children to stay away from tall trees and other tall objects during a storm, especially if these are isolated and wet. The least resistance effect occurs here, too.

Static electricity can be dangerous or annoying in other ways. When spots or stains are rubbed off clothing through use of a flammable fluid, sparks may ignite the explosive vapor. Air inside flour and grain mills is often laden with fine particles of dust. Almost any material is highly combustible if reduced to small enough particles. Again there is danger of a spark causing an explosion.

Gasoline trucks have a strap or chain dangling from the chassis to the ground. This drains off static electricity built up from the gasoline jostling around in the tank. Toll booths on bridges and highways usually have thin metal rods imbedded in the ground immediately before each station. These rods drain off whatever static charges a vehicle has accumulated, thus preventing either driver or attendant from receiving a shock when the toll is paid.

Experiments with static electricity may be disappointing unless performed on dry days. Cold days are often ideal, because the air holds less moisture than on warmer days. When there is much moisture in the air, whatever static charges are built up may leak off rapidly into the air and ground.

BASIC GENERALIZATION VI: Matter contains electrons which may be accumulated through friction into electric charges; unlike charges attract, like charges repel each other

Contributing idea A. All matter is made up of atoms which contain tiny particles of electricity called electrons and protons.

1. *Materials:* rubber comb; small bits of tissue paper; wool cloth; new balloon.

Invite a child to rub a comb briskly over some cloth and then place the comb near some tissue paper. The two will be attracted.

Have another pupil rub a balloon with cloth and then place the balloon against the wall. It usually will stay there. Ask the class what is causing these phenomena to occur. They are almost sure to say "electricity."

Mention that this kind of electricity is called *static* or *frictional* electricity. Briefly, go into the meaning of the two words. Continue by inquiring whether someone has washed his hair a day or so previously. Have him recount what he noticed if he had brushed or briskly combed his hair after it dried. Invite the children to tell of other instances when they have noticed static electricity. They may mention experiences of sparks after rubbing their pets' fur, or sliding across a plastic automobile seat and then touching a metal door handle. Someone may have scuffed across a deeply piled rug and then touched a metal door knob.

evaluate critically

After experiences have been told, develop that in each case rubbing one thing against another brought on a charge of static electricity. Now, ask the children where the electricity came from. Some may volunteer an explanation. Perhaps no one can. This will arouse the need for finding out how electric charges are built up on objects.

2. Permit the class to read or view visual materials to find out about the electrical particles of which atoms are partly made. Or, your simplified exposition will help. Some ideas to stress are:

a. Everything in the world is made up of atoms. Atoms are very, very tiny. No one has ever seen one. But scientists have formed some ideas about them through their experiments and mathematical calculations.

b. Atoms have two different kinds of tiny electrical particles, of equal but opposite forces. One kind is the electron, whose electric charge is called a *negative* or minus (−) charge. The other is the proton, whose electric charge is called a *positive*, or plus (+) charge.

c. Electrons may whirl in many different orbits around the center of an atom. Protons usually stay located in the center of the atom.

d. Different atoms may have different amounts of electrons and protons, but usually they have an electron for every proton. When there is a balance of this sort, the atom is said to be *neutral*, or *uncharged*.

e. Protons usually stay where they are. However, some electrons are rather easily removed from atoms by an outside force, such as rubbing. When that happens, there is no longer a balance of electrical charges.

f. When electrons are rubbed off a neutral object, there are more positive protons left than electrons. The object has a positive charge.

g. A neutral object that gains negative electrons now has more electrons than protons. It has a negative charge.

h. Therefore, objects that have more electrons than usual have a negative electric charge. Those that have fewer electrons than usual have a positive charge. Atoms that have the same amount of electrons and protons have no charge, or are neutral.

Review to insure understanding. Place on the board the material in Figure 5-30:

A   B   C

FIGURE 5-30

Atom A has four electrons but only three protons. What charge, if any, does it have? (Negative.)   *draw conclus*

What charge, if any, does atom B have? (Positive.)

What charge, if any, does atom C have? (It is neutral, or uncharged.)

Contributing idea B. Materials which have unlike charges attract each other.

1. *Materials:* glass rod (or piece of glass tubing or test tube); piece of silk; rubber comb; piece of wool cloth; new balloon; 18-inch string.

Suspend a balloon by a string from an upturned chair or other support so that it hangs freely. Have someone rub the balloon with a cloth. Explain that wool loses electrons easily and that electrons are going onto the balloon. Ask the class what charge the balloon may now have. (Negative.)

Permit a child to rub a glass rod with some silk. Explain that silk can remove electrons from a glass rod. Ask what charge the rod now has. (Positive.) Inquire as to what the children think will happen when a positively charged object (glass rod) is brought near a negatively charged object (balloon). After *draw* trying it, elicit that the objects tested had un- *clusions* like charges, and therefore attracted each other.

2. *Materials:* glass rod; string; silk cloth; rubber comb; woolen cloth.

Suspend the rod from a string. Charge it positively with the silk cloth. Let someone charge a rubber comb negatively by rubbing it on some wool. Be sure everyone knows the comb is negatively charged and the rod is positively charged. Have someone explain what is happening to the electrons. Again request the children to predict what will happen when the unlike charges are brought close *draw* together. After they find the same result, draw *clusions* from them the idea that unlike charges attract each other.

Contributing idea C. Materials which have like charges repel each other.

1. *Materials:* balloon; wool cloth; rubber comb.

Allow a class member to suspend the balloon again and recharge it with the wool cloth. The comb should also be recharged with the wool cloth. Make sure that everyone understands both items are negatively charged. Invite predictions as to what will happen if two negative charges are brought *draw* near each other. After trying it, draw from the *clusions* group that the two negatively charged objects pushed or repelled each other.

2. *Materials:* two glass rods; silk cloth; string.

Let a glass rod be suspended again. Have both rods rubbed with the silk cloth. If only one-half of each rod is rubbed, make sure

that only those parts are brought near one another, as the charge will be built up only on the portion of the rod that is rubbed. Again call for predictions of what will happen when two positively charged objects are brought close together. After trying it, draw *draw* from the children that the two positively *conclusions* charged objects repelled each other.

Recall with them the previous experiment. Through questions, bring out that in both experiments the objects had the same charges; in one case, negative charges, in the other, positive charges. Press for a tentative conclu- *draw* sion which states that like charges, whether *conclusions* negative or positive, repel each other.

At this time, or perhaps after the children try several of the extending activities, discuss the difficulty of using static electricity in productive ways. Stress the need for a sustained and reliable source of electrical power. Draw out the name of one fairly good source of power the class has been using in experiments —the dry cell. Mention that this source and other sources of electricity will be investigated closely in lessons to follow.

Extending activities

1. Get a child to find out what causes lightning and what safety precautions may be taken to protect people and property.

2. Invite someone to report on how Benjamin Franklin experimented with a kite to find out about lightning. Have the class discuss the danger of this experiment and the danger *evaluate* of flying kites near power poles. *critically*

3. Draw up two teams. Each team can find out how the following things or places may be affected by static electricity; also, what precautions are necessary to prevent static charges from piling up. Develop with the class criteria *evaluate* for choosing valid and reliable information *critically* sources. Illustrative questions to pose before the pupils begin their search will also be helpful.

Dry cleaners	Spray paint shop
Flower mill	Gasoline truck
Automobiles	Highway and bridge
	toll stations

4. Let a very able child locate a scientific explanation for the auroras found in the northern and southern hemispheres.

5. Challenge some pupils to build up a static charge on a metal conductor. (Hint: They may have to use a nonconductor or insulator to keep the charge from leaking into their hands.)

select procedures

When you use an electric appliance to buff a waxed floor, electrical energy is changed into mechanical energy, or energy of motion, thus saving you some labor. This is an everyday event. What may not be so obvious is that the process may be reversed; mechanical energy—indeed, other kinds of energy as well —may be changed into electrical energy.

Children are usually very curious about how a dry cell can "make" electricity. Some think it is stored as water might be stored in a tank. Beginning from such early experiments as those of *Galvani* and *Volta*, described in the following activities section, the science of electrochemistry has furnished explanations for many interesting electrical effects.

It has been found that an electric current can be generated by placing two dissimilar metals in a solution of acids, bases, or salts. The stronger the solution, the greater will be the current. Also, the greater the difference in "activity" potential of the metals, the greater will be the current. Consider these metals, for example:

1. aluminum   2. zinc   3. iron
4. nickel   5. tin   6. lead
7. copper   8. silver   9. gold

When placed in solutions of acids, bases, or salts, greater chemical reactions will take place with the metals high on the list than with those lower down. The farther apart the metals are on the list, the higher the voltage produced when they are placed in a *wet cell*, as such a cell is called.

Any solution of salts, acids, or bases of sufficient concentration to conduct electricity is called an *electrolyte*. Since all that is required for electrochemical action to take place is an electrolyte and two dissimilar metals, this action is likely to turn up in the strangest places. For example, if a dentist places a gold and silver filling next to each other, the mouth's saliva may act as an electrolyte, setting up a slight electric current. In some cases, this might eventually cause so much deterioration of the silver filling that replacement (with another substance) may be necessary.

The chemistry of what takes place in a wet cell is complicated. But a general idea may be helpful. When two metal strips are placed in an electrolyte, the more active (higher on the preceding list) of the two metals begins to break down. If zinc and copper are used, for example, the zinc begins to dissolve in the electrolytic solution. As it dissolves, electrons from the dissolving atoms remain on the zinc strip. The surplus of electrons gives it a negative electric charge. At about the same time, the copper strip is left with a surplus of protons and has a positive charge. Since unlike charges attract each other, connecting the two metal strips with a wire enables the electrons to travel from the negatively charged strip to the positively charged one. This creates an electric current.

The same basic chemistry takes place in a dry cell. (See page 238 for sketch.) The cell consists of a moist paste made of ammonium chloride, carbon powder, manganese dioxide, and water, placed in a zinc container. The zinc container functions as the negative connection. A carbon rod is used for the positive connection instead of a copper strip. The zinc container is shielded from the chemical paste by porous paper. This permits the solution to make contact with the zinc. Hydrogen gas bubbles may form on the carbon rod, thus insulating it from the electrolyte. Manganese dioxide is placed in the paste to oxidize the hydrogen gas into water. Prolonged use will cause hydrogen to form more quickly than it can be dissipated. If this happens, the cell stops generating electricity. In addition, drying out of the paste or sufficient "eating away" of the zinc will also prevent the cell from working.

Also notice in the sketch an air space next to the top of the cell. If the cell is used for long periods without disconnection, materials inside heat up and expand into this space. Occasionally, expansion may be great enough to rupture the seam of the cell and cause some materials to ooze out.

Dry cells are convenient for classroom demonstrations, but are too weak and expensive for widespread home or commercial application. Mechanical energy—the energy of motion—is by far the widest used source of generating electricity. On page 194 is a demonstration that clearly displays the lines of force around a magnet. By interrupting these lines of force through revolving or pushing a coil of wire in the field, electrons are caused to flow in the wire.

Today, most of our electricity is generated by transforming the energy of fuels and falling water. In hydroelectric power stations, water falls on the blades of huge wheels, causing them to revolve. Other power stations may use oil, coal, or natural gas to heat water into steam. The steam forces giant turbines to whirl. In both cases, large magnets are spun around rapidly inside a wire coil (or vice versa), thus inducing electrons to flow into the wire.

Either alternating current or direct current can be produced by a generator. This depends on how connecting wires are arranged. In alternating current, the flow of electricity alternately changes directions, usually sixty times a second. In direct current, it flows continuously in one direction. Since electricity is transmitted more easily and safely over long distances with alternating current, this type of current receives much greater use. Direct current is usually produced by smaller, or emergency-type generators.

Thus far in the United States, other forms of energy have not been widely used to generate electricity. It is known, for example, that electrons flow when light energy strikes certain light-sensitive chemicals. But the principal applications of this phenomenon have been in solar cells for space satellites and photographer's light meters. Direct production of electricity through heat has also been used only in specialized ways.

One unusual way of generating electricity is available to children through construction of a *thermocouple*. That is, when two dissimilar metals are joined and heated, electrons flow from the hotter to the cooler metal, thus creating a current. Apparently, the heat lends enough additional velocity to the electrons that some escape from one wire and transfer to the other.

Other methods are being examined with much interest by scientists. For example, fuel cells and "plasma" (electrically charged gas) are now rather remote from our daily experience. But perhaps they are important methods for the future.

Many activities in this section involve production of electric currents so weak that only the use of a sensitive current detector will determine if current has actually been produced. Such a detector, called a *galvanometer*, can be constructed by you or a member of the class. (See page 236.) You recall that a wire carrying an electric current has a magnetic field. By coiling the wire, the field can be made more powerful, just as an electromagnet can be strengthened by wrapping more turns of wire around a nail. Thinner wire works better than thicker wire. Increasing the number of turns in a coil also helps to increase sensitivity. When a compass is placed inside such a coil, even a slight current may cause the needle to deflect, thus indicating the presence of electricity.

BASIC GENERALIZATION VII: An electric current may be generated by changing chemical, mechanical, light, or heat energy into electrical energy

Contributing idea A. A compass galvanometer operates because a wire that carries an electric current has a magnetic field.

Materials: compass and mirror; two pencils; 20 to 30 inches of No. 28 insulated wire or

FIGURE 5-31   An improvised galvanometer.

bell wire; dry cell; cellophane tape; two tacks; small piece of wood; two paper clips. (To save time, have the galvanometer assembled as in Figure 5-31, prior to the lesson.)

Tell your pupils it is easy to take for granted discoveries of early scientists which make today's realities possible. Further, it is easier to find answers to problems when we have the discoveries of other people to help us. As an example, hold up a dry cell. How can they tell when a steady electrical current is being produced by it? They can use any information *select* they have acquired in the unit to answer the *procedures* question. Answers will probably include lighting a bulb, operating an electromagnet, and heating up a wire with a dry cell.

Now inquire how they would know a current was being produced if these materials had not yet been invented, including the dry cell! After answers, if any, inform them that they will learn more about how early discoveries made further developments possible.

Recall the name of Hans Christian Oersted, and his discovery that a wire carrying a current produced a magnetic field. Develop again how he knew it was magnetism by the deflection of a compass needle. Bring out that the electromagnet was a logical consequence of this observation. Have the children recall how an electromagnet's power is increased. Inform them that when scientists learned these facts it made possible the development of a sensitive electric current detector, called the *galvanometer.*

Produce the assembled galvanometer. Mention again that the galvanometer is used to detect an electric current. Ask why a compass is used, and why there are so many turns of wire. Invite a prediction as to what will hap- *suggest* pen to the compass needle if wires connected *hypoth* to a dry cell are briefly touched to the galvanometer's paper-clip leads. Try it. The needle will deflect sharply.

Now attach the wires at the paper-clip leads. Touch and alternately cross and uncross the wires at the dry cell's terminals. Note opposite deflections of the needle. Help children reason that reversing the flow of current also reverses the direction of deflection. *draw* Again, the use of a mirror held at an angle *conclus* above the compass will permit easy viewing.

Contributing idea B. Electricity can be produced by chemical energy.

1. *Materials:* five iron washers or five dimes; five pennies; glass containing a heavy salt-water solution; paper towels for blotters; galvanometer and mirror.

To begin this sequence, you or a child who has read about it might tell briefly the story of *Luigi Galvani,* an Italian scientist, and his accidental discovery in the year 1780. Galvani had prepared some frog legs for study in his laboratory and had placed them next to an electrostatic generator—a machine that can produce static electricity by friction or rubbing. When the frog legs were touched with a small knife, a spark jumped from the machine down the knife and into the frog legs. The legs jerked suddenly as though they were alive! Later, Galvani discovered he could do the same thing by touching frog legs with the ends of two wires made of iron and copper.

Although Galvani was not sure about what had happened, another Italian scientist, *Alessandro Volta,* thought carefully about it. He reasoned that the frog legs contained some salts and acids that might help cause the reactions. He tried making batteries that contained two different metals separated by material soaked in salt water. These batteries came to be known as *Voltaic piles.*

Allow several children to make Voltaic piles by alternately placing pennies and dimes in a pile. Between each coin there should be a piece of toweling or blotting paper that has been soaked in salt water. Iron washers may be substituted for the dimes. The more coins and washers used, the more powerful the battery will be. Have someone hold the battery "sandwich" between his moistened thumb and forefinger. A slight electric shock will be felt with about four or five pairs of these metals. If little or no current is detected, try cleaning the coins and washers with scouring powder or soap to remove insulating grease and dirt.

Show the children how the current can be detected with the galvanometer. Slip two small wires into the paper-clip leads of the galvanometer. Touch the other ends of the wires to the bottom and top of the Voltaic pile. The compass needle should deflect slightly. Bring out that a chemical reaction takes place in the Voltaic pile and chemical energy is thereby changed to electrical energy. Try using just one kind of metal or coin. Let the children hypothesize if it will work. Try it. There will be no visible reaction.

2. *Materials:* copper strip (or carbon rod from a dry cell); zinc strip (from an old dry cell); quart jar or beaker; vinegar; bell wire; galvanometer and mirror.

Develop the idea that many years ago much experimentation took place to produce current electricity with *Voltaic cells*, commonly called *wet cells*. Bring out that this was the next step in developing ways of changing chemical energy into electrical energy. Now the children will have an opportunity to work with these cells.

Place a zinc strip and carbon rod in a jar containing vinegar, and connect these terminals as in Figure 5-32. Explain that because of chemical action on the two different metals, electrons are flowing from the zinc strip through the wire and galvanometer, and back through the vinegar. Introduce the word *electrolyte* as a name for a solution used to conduct electricity. Explain that vinegar is a weak acid, and an electrolyte.

In simple terms, explain in more detail what is happening:

a. When the two different metal strips (or metal strip and carbon rod) are placed in the solution, chemical changes begin taking place.

b. The chemical energy causes a surplus of electrons to develop on the zinc strip and leaves a shortage of electrons on the other strip (or rod). Therefore, the zinc strip becomes negatively charged and the copper strip positively charged.

c. Electrons on the zinc strip repel or push ahead electrons in the wire. About this time electrons are attracted at the copper strip. Like charges repel and unlike charges attract.

d. As far as we know, current electricity is just a flowing of electrons from a place with extra electrons to another place that has a shortage of electrons. In this case, the flow takes place through a wire.

3. *Materials:* same as above; also orange or lemon juice; table salt; ammonia.

The same procedures as above can be used with other mild acids. Table salt (a neutral substance) and ammonia (a basic substance) *evaluate* may also be used to round out the different *critically*

FIGURE 5-32   A wet cell.

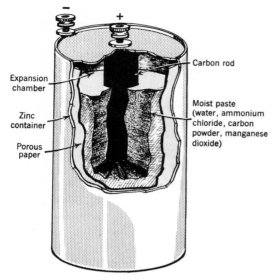

- Expansion chamber
- Zinc container
- Porous paper
- Carbon rod
- Moist paste (water, ammonium chloride, carbon powder, manganese dioxide)

FIGURE 5-33 A dry cell.

kinds of electrolytes which may be used to help conduct and generate electricity.

4. *Materials:* sketch of a dry cell (see Figure 5-33).

Bring out the inconvenience of having a wet cell. Discuss the convenience of having a source of electricity in a dry cell. With a sketch or opaque projection of a dry cell, point out the several materials it contains and their functions.

5. *Materials:* three-fourths pound ammonium chloride; miniature bulb and socket; two connecting wires; a zinc and copper strip (or carbon rod); quart jar three-fourths filled with water.

If it can be obtained, three-fourths pound of ammonium chloride, purchasable at drug stores, will permit an interesting demonstration of how the principal chemical ingredient in the dry cell works in a "wet" cell.

Set up materials as before, but in place of the other electrolytes use ammonium chloride. Connect the bulb in place of the galvanometer. The lamp should glow for a short while until hydrogen gas accumulates around the positively charged copper strip, thus insulating it and stopping the flow of electrons. If available, about a tablespoon of manganese

dioxide dissolved in the water will slow down accumulation of hydrogen.

Contributing idea C. Electricity can be produced by mechanical energy.

1. *Materials:* galvanometer and mirror; bar magnet; 30-inch bell wire.

Tell the class that when a lower-grade pupil learned that dry cells produced electricity he searched all over the school, but could not find the dry cells he thought furnished the school with electric power. Ask the children if they could help the pupil by telling him where the school's electricity comes from. Prepare to receive many different interpretations of how power is generated, some more accurate than others but probably all quite incomplete. Tell the children that by repeating a famous experiment, they will find out how another way of generating electricity came to be understood.

To get into the proper mood for this experiment, they must go back in time over one hundred years, to the year 1831. The experimenter was *Michael Faraday*, an English scientist. Faraday was familiar with the experiments of Oersted. He knew from his work that an electric current produced a magnetic field. But he reasoned that if this could happen, why couldn't a magnetic field produce an electric current? He tried many experiments that gave him more understanding of how this could be done. One day, he tried one of his most famous experiments. Faraday made a coil with some wire and connected the coil to a galvanometer. He picked up a magnet and pushed it into, then pulled it out of, the coil. (See Figure 5-34.) Now direct this question to the class: "What do you think he saw?"   *suggest hypoth*

After a brief discussion, have several "Faradays" try the experiment and variations. These questions may be useful guides:

What happens to the direction of the pointing needle each time? (It changes direction.) Bring out what this means with regard to the direction of flow. (It is also changing directions.)

What happens when speed of the movement is increased? (The needle is deflected more.)

What happens when the coil is moved and the magnet is still? (There is no difference.)

What happens when the coil has only half as many turns? (The needle barely moves.)

Continue by informing the class that Faraday's discoveries paved the way for production of electricity by *mechanical* energy—in other words, by using machines that provide motion to generate electricity. Bring out that only three things are necessary for this to occur:

a. There must be a magnet.

b. There must be a coil of wire.

c. Either the coil or the magnet must move so that the lines of force of the magnet are broken.

2. The class may acquire additional information through reading or viewing materials as to how mechanical energy is changed into electrical energy. Perhaps someone can demonstrate a simple bicycle light generator. The use of falling water or burning fuels to turn generators in huge power plants offers an especially important illustration of man's ability to apply his scientific ingenuity for everyone's benefit.

Contributing idea D. Electricity can be produced by light energy.

Materials: light meter, such as that used by photographers; flashlight.

The children may have heard or read about solar batteries used in space satellites, but may be unaware that these batteries function somewhat like an ordinary light meter:

If a light meter can be borrowed, take light readings in various parts of the room in daylight. Shine a flashlight on the meter; the reading will change. Someone might look up in a trade book or encyclopedia (or you might explain) such facts as these about light meters and solar batteries:

a. They are usually made of a thin coating of selenium or specially treated silicon. Both are nonmetallic elements.

b. When light strikes them, electrons are released from the coating.

c. Solar or light batteries are presently very inefficient; only ten per cent or so of the light energy is actually changed to electrical energy.

Contributing idea E. Electricity may be produced directly from heat energy.

1. *Materials:* Bunsen burner (a candle will be a less effective substitute); galvanometer and mirror; 18-inch copper wire; 18-inch iron or steel wire (picture wire or metal clothes hanger will do); pliers.

Review a previous lesson in which it was found that heat from fuels was used *to* boil water *to* make steam *to* turn a turbine that finally turned the electric generator! Point out that in this case heat is used only in an indirect fashion. Now the class can demonstrate a direct method of converting heat energy into electric energy.

Scrape off insulation from the copper wire and paint from the iron coat hanger for at least 4 inches. Take the bared ends of these wires and twist them together as tightly as possible with pliers. Scrape off enough insulation on the other ends to insure good contact, and connect these ends to the galvanometer. With the pliers, hold the twisted

draw
lusions

FIGURE 5-34 A simple generator.

evaluate critically

ends in the flame of a gas burner. Have everyone note the effect on the galvanometer. Then use a candle flame for contrast.

Develop that heat energy gives additional speed to electrons in the ends of the wires. This causes them to move from the hotter to the cooler of the two metals, thereby creating an electrical current. Point out that this, too, is an inefficient method of generating electricity and has only special uses. Mention that scientists are continually working on other methods of generating electricity. Someday the children may find electric power commonly produced in very different ways from those now usually found.

Extending activities

1. "Rehabilitate" an old dry cell that it too weak to light up a bulb. Punch several holes with a nail in the bottom of the cell. Leave it for several hours in a container partly filled with water. Absorbed moisture may activate the electrolyte enough to make a connected bulb glow weakly for a short time.

2. Do some open-end experiments with different concentrations of several electrolytes and dissimilar metals. The purpose is to discover which combinations of metals and solutions develop the highest voltage. See page 234 for metals which might be tested.

draw conclu

3. Take a study trip to a nearby electric power plant. Before going, prepare the children for what they will see by giving them a simplified explanation of the plant's operation.

4. Invite an able child to investigate how storage batteries operate and are recharged.

5. Have a committee make a report and devise an accompanying bulletin board on how electric power is transmitted from the generating plant to the home.

Machines and Force

(*Primary*)

Imagine a parade of the world's machines—airplanes and tweezers, bulldozers and baby carriages, computers and egg beaters—an almost endless line of inventions, without which we would fare far less well. But perhaps the most remarkable aspect of these applications of man's ingenuity lies in their construction. All machines, no matter how complex, are made from variations of just six so-called "simple machines." These are the inclined plane (ramp), screw, wedge, lever, wheel and axle (windlass), and pulley.

Many scientists classify simple machines into only two types—inclined plane and lever. To them, a screw and wedge are only variations of the inclined plane, and a windlass and pulley variations of the lever. Our agreement with this idea is reflected in the sequence adopted in the unit. However, each of the six machines initially mentioned will also be examined separately.

When simple machines are taught, we are often tempted to plan for an analysis of more complex types. This is not advisable with primary children, except perhaps for some familiar tools and less complicated machines. Variations and combinations of simple machines are limitless and hard to perceive, unless pupils have much experience and thorough understanding.

Although anyone who has just sat and thought hard for a while may disagree with this definition, to a scientist "work" can only be an applied force that moves a resistance over a distance. Force applied is measured in pounds, and distance measured in feet, to yield foot-pounds of work.

For any machine to do work, force must be exerted to overcome gravity, inertia, or molecular attraction. (*Friction* can be considered a form of molecular attraction; another is *cohesion*, the binding force that holds materials together.) Machines may be used to (1) reduce the force needed to do work, (2) speed up work, or (3) change the direction of a force.

The following lessons concentrate on making work easier, or more accurately, how to reduce applied force. Children will learn that it is possible to gain an advantage of force in each case, but this is done at the sacrifice of moving a resistance over a greater distance than before. They will also see that friction is a counteractive force which reduces efficiency of machines. *The trading of distance for force and the inhibiting effect of friction should be brought out in each lesson, where applicable.* If these ideas are coupled with the following generalizations, pupils should learn many significant relationships. These should provide preparation for more precise ideas in later experiences.

BASIC GENERALIZATIONS

I. Force needed to use an inclined plane changes as its tilt is changed.

II. Force needed to use a screw changes as its pitch is changed.

III. Force needed to use a wedge changes as its sharpness is changed.

IV. Force needed to use a lever changes as length of the force arm is changed.

V. Force needed to use a wheel and axle (windlass) changes as size of the wheel is changed.

VI. Force needed to use a pulley changes as the number of ropes supporting the load is changed.

Although they may not have thought about it, even small children have had such experiences with inclined planes as climbing stairs, walking up a hill, coasting down a slanted driveway on roller skates, and the like. They known from these experiences that it is more difficult to climb a steep hill than a gradual hill. Boys and girls may even unknowingly use the idea that distance may be increased to decrease force, as when a bicycle rider rides diagonally up a hill, back and forth. This background of common experiences permits us to focus on relationships fairly quickly in the present generalization. It should also permit relatively easy applications of learnings to the wedge and screw, since these machines are variations of the inclined plane.

Perhaps it is wrong for us to say that an inclined plane or other simple machines make work "easier," if by that we mean that some effort is saved. In terms of work, or force moving a resistance over a distance, it is impossible to get out of a machine any more than is put into a machine. Another way of saying this is: *effort times distance equals resistance times distance,* or *ED = RD.*

Let us apply this idea to the inclined plane in Figure 6-1.

FIGURE 6-1

We wish to push a 50-pound barrel to a height of 5 feet and the inclined plane is 10 feet long. A measure of the force required to roll the barrel up would theoretically average out at 25 pounds. Using this figure and the distances involved, it can be shown that the total effort is the same:

By using the inclined plane—Effort (25 pounds) times Distance (10 feet) = 250 foot-pounds of work.

By lifting straight up—Resistance (50 pounds) times Distance (5 feet) = 250 foot-pounds of work.

The foregoing assumes that we are physically capable of performing the work in both cases. However, it is physically easier for us to apply less force for a longer distance and time. Muscles become tired quickly when subjected to heavy work. This is mentioned because many persons think that since the total foot-pounds of work are equal in both cases of a comparative situation, a simple machine never makes more actual work possible.

Thus far, we have omitted reference to friction. In reality, there would be some friction between the barrel and board. Since this would increase the actual resistance, effort would also need to be increased. In the lessons that follow, roller-skate wheels are used to reduce the friction factor with a pushed box.

The reduction of force provided by a simple machine usually is called its *mechanical advantage.* This is found by *dividing force of the resistance by the effort.* In the foregoing example the mechanical advantage is

$$\frac{R(50 \text{ pounds})}{E(25 \text{ pounds})} \text{ or } 2$$

In other words, it is twice as easy to lift the barrel with the inclined plane as without it. Or we can say it takes half as much effort. Since distance for both resistance and effort varies inversely in each case, inverting the two distances and dividing can also reveal the mechanical advantage. Thus

$$\frac{10 \text{ feet}}{5 \text{ feet}} = 2$$

However, this disregards friction.

By including frictional resistance with the resistance of the load moved, and by measuring actual effort needed to overcome this combined resistance, the real mechanical advantage is found. Since this would differ greatly with many objects moved—for example, a box with wheels, and an equally heavy box without wheels—it is the preferable way to measure mechanical advantage.

Friction makes it impossible for any machine to produce exactly as much work as the effort put into it. Since work "spread out" over additional time is easier, and because today so many machines use other than muscle power, this fact is not quickly obvious.

Of course, no one properly expects typical primary children to be taught mathematical formulas in this exposition. But pupils can make many crude measurements and perceive, in a limited way, some of the relationships involved. For instance, a string can be employed to note relative distances. A rubber band with a ruler can be used to measure different degrees of applied force in terms of "stretch." Or a spring scale will be even more effective than a rubber band. However, forces translated into ounces or fractions of a pound tend to have very limited meaning for young children. This is especially the case when differences of only a few ounces are involved.

We suggest that only whole numbers be used in gathering data, unless pupils are quite advanced. If measurements are awkward and difficult with a ruler because of the relatively wide spaces between numbers, cut out a cardboard "ruler" with numbers at half-inch intervals or less.

BASIC GENERALIZATION I: Force needed to use an inclined plane changes as its tilt is changed

1. *Materials:* cardboard box weighted with books; smooth, sturdy board about 4 feet long; 9-inch piece of string; low table. Also, several pictures of inclined planes from magazines, perhaps including a stairway, a gangway for ships, an airplane ramp, and a trucker's loading ramp. In the absence of pictures, copy the upcoming sketches in Figure 6-2 on a chalkboard or chart. (Use an opaque projector for easy tracing.)

Ask such questions as, "How do people leave this house?" "How do they get on a ship?" "Airplane?" "How is the man getting the heavy barrel onto his truck?"

Now inquire, "What seems to be about the same in all four of these pictures?" Bring out that in each picture there is a slanting   *draw conclusions* way to go up and come down. If no child knows, the proper inclusive term for the four devices is a *ramp* or *inclined plane*. The children may need help to understand that a plane is any flat surface, and that inclined means a slanted or tilted condition.

Take a string and stretch it from the upper end of the first inclined plane straight down to the ground.

Holding the string between the thumb and forefinger of each hand to mark the distance, place it over the inclined plane itself. Guide   *reason quantitatively* the children to note that the distance is greater. Follow the same procedure in each picture.

Say, "We have seen that in each picture the people are walking farther than they need to. Why don't they climb straight up a ladder? It would be shorter, wouldn't it?" Someone will probably hypothesize that it is easier to walk or push a load up an inclined plane   *suggest hypotheses* than to walk or pick something straight up. Ask the pupils how they could find out with   *select procedures* the board, box of books, and low table.

Help them to reason through the experiment. Two children might first attempt to lift the books onto the table. Then the board can be placed against the table, and the box of books pushed up onto the table. Take care to hold the board so that friction between box and board does not cause the board to slide upward. Bring out from the two participants that it was somewhat easier to use an inclined plane. Encourage others to repeat

FIGURE 6-2

the experiment to see if they get the same results.

reason quantitatively   Permit someone to measure with string the distance from table top to floor, and then along the ramp. Develop that while it was *draw conclusions* easier to use an inclined plane, more distance had to be traveled to get the load onto the table.

2. *Materials:* cardboard box of books; 4-foot board; pair of roller skates; low table.

Draw out that although the inclined plane was easier to use than lifting the box of books straight up, there was still a fairly large effort needed to push the box onto the table. Bring *draw conclusions* out that the box and board are rubbing together when the box is pushed. Inform the class that rubbing action is called *friction—* whenever two things rub together there is friction. Inquire as to whether it would be easier to push the box up the ramp if there were less friction. Question how grease, butter, or banana peels could ease the sliding. Since no one wants to make a mess in the classroom, is there another way to reduce friction? If unmentioned, hold up the skates. How could they be used?

Again, guide the children to think through *selec* a procedure. First, the box will be pushed up *proc* the ramp without wheels, then with wheels. Several children may repeat the experiment to verify accuracy of findings.

Now is a good time to introduce the idea of force within an understandable context. Explain that when we push or pull something we use *force*. A hard push needs a large force behind it. An easy push needs less force. Ask if more or less force was used to push the box when the skates were placed under it. Inquire as to why less force was needed. (There was less friction.)

Bring out that now the children have *draw* found two ways to make work easier: take a *conc* longer distance to lift something, and lessen friction.

3. *Materials:* roller skates; 4-foot board; a durable rubber band; ruler.

Have everyone recall the ramps shown in the introductory pictures. On the chalkboard, develop that the angles of ramps differ somewhat. Sometimes ramps are slanted like this ⟍. Others are slanted like this ╱ and this ╱ . Raise conjecture as to whether the degree of slant is related to the force needed to travel up a ramp. You might say, "If we want to get something like this skate onto our table, does the way the board is slanted make any difference in the force we must use? How many slants should we try?" Perhaps no more than three or four positions should be tried as the differences in force must be large enough to be readily noticeable.

gest
eses

Pupils will probably hypothesize that more force will be required as the slant becomes steeper. Press for why they think this is so. It may be helpful to give them such forced choices as: "Does it take less force to walk up a short, steep hill or a longer, less steep hill?" "Do you go down faster on a steep slide or a longer, less slanty slide, if both are the same height?"

Tell the children that since there will be several slants, it may be hard for everyone to see the amount of force required unless they use something to help them. Hold up the rubber band and ask how it can help. Let a child hold the band and stretch it gently, then harder. Ask the class if more or less force is being used the second time. Now, hold a ruler in back of the band and have another pupil read the number closest to the end of the band as it is stretched. Bring out that a larger number is indicated as the stretch is increased, showing that more force is used.

elect
ures

Encourage class members to plan how they will record the numbers they observe each time the skate is pulled with the ruler held alongside the rubber band. They might begin with either the steepest or the least steep slant, but, of course, should continue in serial progression. Tell them to ignore any part of the board that might project above the table in several positions. A chalk line drawn across the board at table height **in each** position

might help them to understand that they are solely concerned with the portion of the board below the table top. A record on the chalk board might read:

Board	Rubber Band
Very slanty	4 inches
Less slanty	3 inches
Least slanty	2 inches

Ask the children what the findings seem to mean. Help them conclude that decreasing the slant of an inclined plane reduces the force needed to use it, and that the converse is also true. Develop that increased distance is the price paid for decreased force. A simple way to summarize this is, "The less the slant the easier it is, but the distance is greater."

reason quantitatively

draw conclusions

4. A variation of this activity is to fasten one end of a rubber band with a nail or tack to the top of the inclined plane. The attached skate will stretch the band to varying lengths depending upon the angle of inclination. Of course, recording the degree of stretch is easier when the band is static than when it is in motion. Therefore, you may find this variation better suited for less capable children.

5. For additional application, draw a hill on the chalkboard with zigzagged lines, as in Figure 6-3.

Inquire if anyone has seen animal trails on steep hillsides that look like the lines in the sketch. Why do animals seem to choose a longer, zigzagged route rather than a shorter, straight-up route? Again bring out the sacrifice of distance to secure decreased effort.

draw conclusions

Extending activities

1. Ask your class to find pictures for a scrapbook or bulletin board showing how inclined planes are used in everyday life.

2. Encourage individual children to look for many examples of inclined planes. Each should be ready to tell the class where and how they are used.

FIGURE 6-3

"The screw is just an inclined plane wrapped around a nail." This is what one child said, and it's a fairly accurate description. A common conception of the screw is that of a naillike object with a spiral thread which holds together pieces of wood or metal. But other applications of this machine are all around us. There are spiral staircases, roads that wind around a steep hill or mountain, vises for work benches, clamps to hold things together, adjustable piano stools, and the adjustable parts of wrenches, to name just a few. Sometimes its appearance is not readily detectable, as in propellers for ships and airplanes.

When used to lift things, the mechanical advantage afforded by the screw is the greatest readily employable of any simple machine. It is relatively easy for a small woman to lift up the front of an automobile with a screw-type jack, and jackscrews employed by house-movers actually lift entire houses off their foundations. As with an inclined plane, however, the price paid for such a gain in force is distance.

Each time a screw is given a complete turn, it advances into a piece of wood or lifts an object only as far as the distance between its threads. This distance is termed *pitch*, and is illustrated on page 249. The paired sketches show that two screws of similar size, but different pitches, would vary in the number of times turned if screwed into some wood or employed to lift something. We expect a short, steep inclined plane to require more effort than a longer, gradual one when used

to ascend to the same height. Likewise, the steeper the pitch of a screw, the more force is needed to make it rotate. However, it advances farther and faster than one with a narrower, more gradual pitch.

Although beyond most primary children, the mathematical relationships involved are identical to those of other simple machines. Actual resistance times distance traveled (pitch distance) is equal to actual effort times distance traveled (distance of one rotation). Mechanical advantage is again found by dividing resistance by effort. Sometimes mechanical advantage is calculated by merely dividing the distance of one turn of the screw by its pitch. Since this ignores friction, it is likely to be almost useless for practical application.

We shall use several paired comparisons in this section to go from the familiar inclined plane to the screw as a related device. Use such a procedure frequently with younger children. It helps them to grasp the logic which links related applications of an idea.

BASIC GENERALIZATION II: Force needed to use a screw changes as its pitch is changed

1. *Materials:* a large sketch for each pair of simple machines shown in Figure 6-4. (Use an opaque projector for easy copying.)

Show sketch A. Which inclined plane needs the least force for a barrel to be pushed to the platform? Establish that though less *draw concl* force is necessary to use the longer inclined plane, the load must be pushed a longer distance.

Show sketch B. How are the two staircases like inclined planes? The class should be able to respond from previous lessons that a staircase is an inclined plane with steps. Which side requires the least force in order to walk to the top? Again establish that additional *draw concl* distance is traveled to gain decreased force.

Exhibit sketch C. Point out that two lighthouses are pictured with inside stairways visible; these, also, are examples of inclined

FIGURE 6-4

planes. Emphasize that these inclined planes wind around in a *spiral*, and are called spiral staircases. Draw out similar illustrations the children may have seen. Encourage them to indicate the staircase that would require the least force. They should easily recognize that again distance is traded for force.

draw sions

2. *Materials:* two identical pencils; two tacks; two inclined planes cut from white paper, both 4 inches high, one 6 inches long and the other 9 inches long (Draw a heavy colored line on the outer edge of the long side on each cutout.); two large wood screws of equal size but different pitches; screwdriver; hammer; two small blocks of soft wood (Screw down one end and nail the other end with a nail of about the same length as the screw.); a chalkboard sketch of Figure 6-5.

Hold up a wood screw. Ask what it is and its purpose. Bring out that screws of this kind are usually used to hold things together. Develop places where it is used; the classroom alone should contain many examples.

aluate tically

Hold up the fastened blocks. Have children observe that one end is nailed and the other screwed down. Which end can be most easily pried apart? Let someone slip a screwdriver in the ends and try. Do not permit the end initially pried to be opened too far. The opposite end will be loosened too greatly for a valid comparison. This difficulty can be avoided, of course, if another set of identical wood blocks is used just for the screw or nail. But a little care should make it unnecessary to locate another set of wooden blocks. Help the class understand that a screw holds things more securely than a nail.

Exhibit the screw sketch. Bring out visible differences in *threads* of the screws; one has more spirals or turns. One has a steeper *pitch*, or greater distance between threads. Bring out that the steeper pitch is a steeper "slant." This will help the class to relate the threads to the previous example of inclined planes. Ask the pupils which previous sketches the spiral threads recall for them. Have someone select the paired lighthouses from among the previous sketches, so that they may be visually compared with the paired screws.

aluate ically

FIGURE 6-5

Let children hypothesize as to which screw in the sketch would be easier to screw into a piece of wood, and which would take more turns of a screwdriver. They should choose the screw of lower pitch. If not, review the paired lighthouses again. Now hold up the two actual wood screws and have someone put each under the sketch example that is most like it. Their previous hypothesis can be tested now with the actual wood screws.

Permit a child to screw the wood screws into one block. (It will be helpful to start the screws for several turns before a child attempts it.) Have the children count the number of turns made by the screwdriver as the screws go into the wood. Which screw turned most? Ask the demonstrating child to indicate if the screw with the most turns was easier to screw in. If he indicates otherwise, permit several others to try it. "Faulty procedure" can result when a child's hands have become tired, one screw is much thicker or longer than the other, screw threads are dull, or when the wood used is of unequal softness.

reason quantitatively

select procedures

Why was the screw with more turns of thread easier but longer to turn? Explanations may be fairly, but probably not wholly, accurate. Use some cut paper inclined planes to insure clear understanding.

draw conclusions

Place the smaller inclined plane over the larger, as in Figure 6-6. Review that the longer inclined plane would require less force, but would take longer. Now hold up two pencils. How could two "pretend" screws be made with them and the paper cutouts? Assist two volunteers to roll the paper tightly and

select procedures

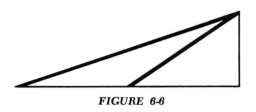

FIGURE 6-6

evenly around each pencil. Secure paper at the bottom with a small tack or piece of cellophane tape. If both pencils are rolled clockwise, results should look like Figure 6-7. Help the group to summarize: A screw is an inclined plane wound in a spiral. Force required to turn a screw is lessened as pitch is lessened, but the number of turns (distance) is increased.

draw conclusions

3. *Materials:* piano stool or screwtype auto jack; or pictures of these and a housemover's jackscrew. If available, it would be most interesting for the children to manipulate a piano stool and auto jack (minus the auto!) to observe how screws can be used for lifting heavy objects. Pictures are helpful, also. If possible, locate a picture of a housemover's jackscrew "in action." The class will be impressed with its tremendous mechanical advantage.

Extending activity

Let class members locate many actual examples of screws for an exhibit table. Have them tell how each screw is used. Some easy-to-find examples where screws may be wholly or partly employed are the screw-top lid, corkscrew, monkey wrench, C-clamp, nut and bolt, propeller for a toy airplane or boat, desk chair, bit (of a brace and bit), vise, electric fan, and meat grinder.

eval criti

A wedge can be thought of as two inclined planes placed back to back. Although the classic use of this machine has waned along with professional railsplitters and woodchoppers, the wedge principle is employed in numerous other ways. For example, "streamlining" is a way of better enabling objects to pierce air and water. Thus more speed can be achieved with the same amount of applied force. Paper cutters, knives, pencil sharpeners, nails, needles—all these are everyday wedges used for cutting or piercing functions.

Friction and force applied in wedges are likely to be varied or uneven. Hence it is difficult to calculate the actual mechanical advantage of this machine under conditions of practical use. However, a theoretical mechanical advantage can be calculated in the same way as with the inclined plane and screw.

The following activities show why a wedge performs like an inclined plane, along with practical applications.

BASIC GENERALIZATION III: Force needed to use a wedge changes as its sharpness is changed

1. *Materials:* Figure 6-8 A–D; wedge, or sketch A; ax, or sketch B; paper cutout of a wedge as illustrated in sketch C; two sturdy wood stakes, sawed as illustrated in D; 2-inch strip of masking or cellophane tape. (Make this into two small loops with the sticky side out. Place on the back of each cutout. These will then adhere to a chalkboard or other surface.)

Exhibit a real wedge or sketch A to the children. What can this object be used for?

FIGURE 6-7

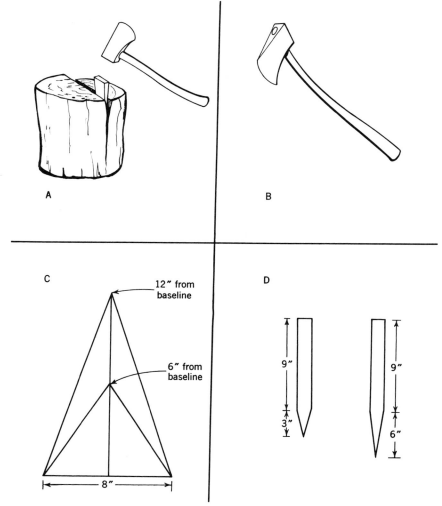

FIGURE 6-8 (A) Wedging apart a log, (B) an axhead is a wedge, (C) a paper wedge (cut out around the outside lines, then cut in two down the center line; the two smaller inside lines are only for comparison purposes), (D) two wood stakes.

In the unlikely event that no one knows, tell them. Write *wedge* on the chalkboard. Ask them how a wedge is able to split things apart when struck forcefully.

Show the children a real ax or sketch B. Guide children to note the resemblance between a wedge and an ax. Help them understand that the head of an ax is an example of a wedge. Briefly discuss how an ax is used, and the caution that should be taken with a sharp ax. Take one-half of the paper cutout (sketch C). Stick it to the chalkboard. In-

draw *sions*

quire whether a longer or shorter route would require a lesser force to move an object up. Draw out again the idea of a longer distance traveled for a gain in force.

draw conclusions

Now place the other half of the wedge next to the first half. Pause, then reposition both halves together on the chalkboard, sharp end pointing downward. Elicit that a wedge is really two inclined planes placed together. Ask a child to trace the shorter outline of one wedge with his finger, then the longer outline of the other wedge. Although both are identical in thickness, one is sharper because it is longer. Which one would be easier for splitting things? The class should select the longer, or sharper, one. If not, review.

Ask if anyone has gone camping and pitched a tent. Bring out how ropes are tied to stakes (sketch D) to prevent the wind from blowing over a tent. Pick up the two wooden stakes and place them next to the cut paper wedge. Which would be easier to drive into the ground, if the class wants to set up a tent?

Let them think through "faulty procedures" in this experiment. For example, a patch of ground will need to be selected which is of fairly uniform consistency where each stake is driven in. With properly cut stakes, the longer will go in more easily. Draw out that a longer length was required to gain force in pushing apart the ground. The ground was "split" exactly the same width in both cases.

2. *Materials:* knife; scissors; needle; nail.

Invite different children to describe why these materials can be considered wholly or partly wedges. Have them compare the cutting or puncturing effect of the regular (sharp) and opposite (dull) portions of these materials.

Extending activity

Set up a bulletin board of pictures that illustrate many "unusual" wedges. Let pupils explain why each is partly a wedge. Some examples are the front of an airplane, the bow of a boat or ship, animal claws (especially digging claws), woodpecker's bill, teeth, plow, head of a rake, spade, carpenter's plane, chisel, can opener, fork, hoe, bulldozer front, trowel, sickle, and saw.

No one knows who actually first contrived it, but apparently the lever has been known and used for a very long time. The ancient Greek scientist Archimedes is supposed to have said he could move the world, if given an appropriately long lever, fulcrum, and place to stand. It is widely assumed that primitive man also had knowledge of levers, but probably solely in a functional way.

The principles of this simple machine are used in so many ways that a moment's reflection can produce somewhat surprising examples. Thus, the venerable Japanese sport of judo is based on knowledge that the human skeleton is comprised of lever systems. Also, a golfer with long arms is able to develop a speedy club-head movement more easily in his swing than one with shorter arms.

This section begins with an example quite familiar to children: the seesaw. All three parts in this lever will need to be introduced briefly at a suggested time in the first lesson: (1) *fulcrum*, or point on which the seesaw pivots; (2) *force arm*, or that portion of a lever whose end bears the exerted force; and (3) *load arm*, that portion of a lever bearing the resistance or load to be raised.

As with other machines, effort times distance equals resistance (load) times distance. "Distance" in this case is the space from the ground to either raised lever arm. As for mechanical advantage, in our previous discussion of the inclined plane it was suggested that actual mechanical advantage could be found only by dividing resistance by effort. In the case of levers, friction is usually so minor that mechanical advantage can be found fairly accurately by dividing force-arm length by load-arm length. Thus, when an effort arm of a lever is 6 feet and load arm is 3 feet, mechanical advantage equals 2.

Levers are found with parts arranged in three different combinations called *classes*. This is unnecessary to bring out with primary children. But it is helpful to know for further understanding of simple machines. Notice the three arrangements in Figure 6-9.

Seesaws, crowbars, and can openers are first-class levers. Two levers of this kind are placed together in such tools as scissors and pliers. By varying the force-arm length, you change the amount of required force, or gain in speed and distance. This type also changes direction of movement. You exert force in a direction opposite to which the load moves. If both effort and resistance arms are equal, however, a first-class lever can change only the direction of a force. Neither reduced force nor gain in speed and distance takes place.

Second-class levers are illustrated by the wheelbarrow and post-puller. A nutcracker illustrates joined, double levers of this type. Speed or distance are not as likely to be considerations when employing a second-class lever as in the previous case.

Should you forget third-class levers, just think of your arm! Your elbow is the fulcrum, your bicep provides the effort at a point just below and opposite the elbow, and your fist represents the resistance. Other common applications are found in the broom, baseball bat, fly swatter, and fishing pole, to name just a few. Sugar or ice cube tongs represent double levers of the class. Analysis of this lever reveals that force is sacrificed to provide added speed or distance. With a fishing pole, for example, you want to increase the speed of your hands to hook a nibbling fish securely before it can react and get away.

In several following lessons, use, if possible, a sturdy 4-foot board for experiments. It is often more dramatic and understandable to primary children when large, actual materials are used rather than small, analogous models. For a fulcrum, nail a piece of dowel to a block of wood. If a strong, cylindrical pint or quart can is available, it may be used effectively as a fulcrum. Wedge two pencils underneath to prevent rolling. Often primary room block-play sets include round blocks. One of these may serve well if wedged properly.

Although not as desirable, a yardstick or similar stick may be substituted for the board. A bookend or cylindrical can may serve as a fulcrum. One difficulty will be to prevent the load lifted from falling off the yardstick. Clay, or anything that will resist sliding off, may be serviceable. While books are sometimes used, they must be secured firmly or else are unsatisfactory.

BASIC GENERALIZATION IV: Force needed to use a lever changes as length of the force arm is changed

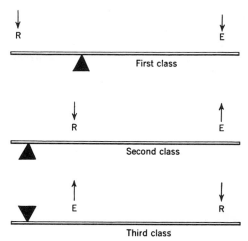

FIGURE 6-9   Three classes of levers.

1. *Materials:* sturdy 4-foot board and fulcrum (See preceding exposition for substitute suggestions.); chalkboard sketch of Figure 6-10 (The three parts of the sketch should be drawn as indicated in the following bridge.)

Begin with a "chalk talk" bridge such as this:

Let's see the hands of everyone who likes to play on a seesaw. (Pause for responses.) Fine! Well, I'd like to tell you about two boys, *Frank* (write the word), and *Bill* (write the word). They like to play on a seesaw, also—but they have a problem. Frank is quite large and heavy (draw figure). But Bill is smaller and lighter (draw figure). Here's a picture of their seesaw (draw a level seesaw). If both get on it at the same time, what will happen? (Pause for responses.) But we've seen children playing on the seesaw who are of different weights. Is there a way it could be fixed so they will *balance*— so that the board will stay level—the way it is now? Who would like to draw the way this seesaw should be?"

FIGURE 6-10

select procedures Encourage several children to draw positions. Elicit the position that seems most reasonable to the class. Press briefly for why it seems best. It is unlikely that the true nature of the fulcrum and force-arm relationship. will be expressed by pupils at this time. But this may increase their readiness to perceive the reason later. If a drawing is attempted where the figures are moved instead of the board, permit this. But try to bring out why it works when both the figures and the board are moved.

Now remark, "It seems that the seesaw might be even or balanced this way. But would it be possible to arrange it so that Bill could push down and actually lift Frank up high? How?" Watch for consistency of direction as another board and fulcrum are drawn *evaluate critically* by a child. If the fulcrum is moved right, whereas it was moved left before, pursue the questionable logic of this action.

select procedures Produce the board and fulcrum from the materials. How may they be used to see whether the drawings are correct? If a large child and a small child are chosen for demonstrating a seesaw in action, make sure neither is psychologically oversensitive. Each should hold on firmly to the arm of another person to prevent slipping, should the board slide on the fulcrum.

As children give directions, they will probably refer to the fulcrum by several names. Call attention to this and tell them the proper name is *fulcrum*. Establish that the side of the board on which force was applied is called the *force arm*, and a seesaw is an example of a simple machine called a *lever*. If continual reference is made to the portion of the board carrying the load, introduce the words *load* *draw conclusions* *arm*. Finally, establish that increasing the board length from the fulcrum (force arm) made the load easier to lift.

2. *Materials:* hammer; nail partly driven into a block of wood.

Point to a table on which the above materials are gathered and tell the group that it is going to discover more about levers. Begin with the hammer and nail-in-wood example. Request someone to pull out the nail with his fingers. When he fails, ask which simple machine could help. As the claw of the hammer is placed under the nail head, and he begins applying force to the handle, stop him before the nail can be extracted. Note that his hands are near the end of the hammer handle. (We have yet to see a child apply force near the hammer head.) Ask why. Have the child shift his hand and apply force at the beginning of the handle, next to the hammer head. It will be difficult, if not impossible, to extract the nail. Inquire as to how extraction of the nail can be made easier. The class will probably advise applying force at the end of the handle.

Now help the children apply their previous knowledge. Point out that the hammer is a lever. Rock the hammer back and forth on its head; help them determine where its fulcrum is. (Where the hammer head claws touch the wood.) Guide them to observe that the handle functions as a force arm. Remind everyone what happened previously when the force arm was made longer. (Force was increased.) Will it be easier to extract the nail if the force arm is lengthened in this case, too? Now have the child easily extract the nail. Develop that increasing the force-arm length makes it possible to exert less force. *draw conc* Work is made easier.

3. *Materials:* can opener; small adjustable-end wrench; clean, discarded, tinned can with one end intact; thick rubber band (It may take a trial or two to get the best size.); ruler.

Point to the materials. Ask the children to demonstrate that increasing force-arm length permits work to be done with less force. Provide assistance and clues as needed. It should *selec proc* be easy (with help) for them to design a demonstration that includes, first, an attempt to pierce the can end with the can opener, then another with the adjustable-end wrench attached to its handle. The wrench, of course, is used to lengthen the handle (force arm). A rubber band can be affixed to the end of the handle in both cases to show amounts of applied force. If desired, a ruler may be used to record approximate amount of stretch (force) required to pierce the can in both cases. If a rubber band is used, it may be too difficult actually to pierce the can end. In any case, the can should be held down firmly by another person each time the can opener is used. See Figure 6-11 for this demonstration.

4. *Materials:* thin rubber band; thumb tack or masking tape; ruler; classroom or closet door; chalkboard sketch of a door top as in Figure 6-12.

Raise conjecture as to what the chalkboard sketch shows. If needed, give a few clues: The children are looking down on it; it can be opened and closed; there are two or more in the classroom. When it is identified, ask them which of the several simple machines is most like a door. (Lever.) Help them find the fulcrum. (Hinges.) Ask how they could reduce friction at the hinges if they were squeaky and hard to turn. (Use oil.)

Let someone indicate the door knob in the sketch. If the children do not know, explain that the perpendicular, dotted lines indicate the door's position when opened. Starting with the largest arc, trace the path one's hand follows as the door is opened and shut. Now show that if a door knob were placed in position A, the arc distance for opening and closing the door would be lessened. Show that it would even be less for B. Raise conjecture as to why a door knob or handle is usually placed near the outside end of a door. If someone mentions that it makes latch placement more convenient, acknowledge this is true. But press for another reason. If none is forthcoming, ask if it might have anything to do with the amount of force required to open and close a door.

Invite some children to experiment with a rubber band at three different positions. Use a thumb tack to attach the rubber band to the door. A ruler may be employed to assist in recording each degree of stretch (force) needed to move the door. (*Caution:* Pupils should be out of the way in case the tack comes out.) Instead of a rubber band and ruler, perhaps a child can push gently with a finger at the three locations.

To conclude, bring out that increasing force arm length again permits less force to be exerted in doing work. Also develop that a

FIGURE 6-11

greater distance is traveled to reduce effort.

Now inquire as to whether greater distance was also needed to gain force in the previous experiments with levers. Let several children quickly perform these experiments again to see if the class can point out the lengthened distances through which effort was applied to gain force. In the several paired cases, a lengthened arc in each second example should be easily detected.

5. *Materials:* nutcracker; several nuts; scissors; tinner's snips (optional but helpful—try asking the custodian); piece of cardboard; chalkboard sketches as in Figure 6-13.

Show the materials as examples of *double levers,* or two levers put together. Permit pupils to point out the fulcrum, where work is done, and force arms. If they cannot, show them. With the nutcracker, let children hypothesize whether A or B would be the

FIGURE 6-12

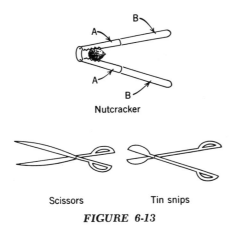

Nutcracker

Scissors   Tin snips

FIGURE 6-13

suggest hypotheses best place to apply force. Make sure they think this through in terms of increasing force-arm length.

If tinner's snips are available besides regular scissors, establish that the greater distance *draw conclusions* from the fulcrum (i.e., longer force arms) would probably make tin snips more powerful than scissors. Either wire or metal from a can may be used in the comparison.

suggest hypotheses If scissors alone are available, ask pupils to hypothesize whether it would be easier to cut cardboard at the tips or closer to the fulcrum. Make sure they realize that placing ma- *draw conclusions* terial to be cut close to the fulcrum has the effect of increasing force-arm length. (This will be difficult for many classes.) Use thick

enough cardboard so the difference in ease of cutting can be readily seen.

Extending activity

Invite everyone to gather materials or pictures that are wholly or partly levers. Divide the class into groups and assign each several *evaluat* examples. Each group cooperatively locates *critical* the fulcrum, force arm, and where work is done. This information can be reported in turn to other groups. Examples are the broom, shovel, crowbar, fishing pole, pliers, hedge clippers, ice cube or sugar cube tongs, baseball bat, paper cutter, tennis racket, golf club, hockey stick, bottle cap opener, tweezers, canoe paddle, and boat oars.

The wheel and axle (windlass) is a commonly misunderstood simple machine. Although similar in appearance to a wagon wheel and axle, a windlass is distinctly different. We put wheels on a wagon, for instance, to reduce friction by lessening the surface area that comes in contact with the road. Its axles are stationary. Greater "leverage" is indeed present in a large wheel, as contrasted with a small wheel. This is why a large wheel can roll over uneven ground more easily than a small wheel. But usually a wagon wheel and axle combination is not regarded as a simple machine.

In a windlass the axle and wheel are firmly fixed together. Spinning the axle causes the wheel to rotate, and the reverse is also true. By turning the axle, force is sacrificed to gain an advantage in speed and distance on the outside of the wheel. By turning the wheel, an advantage in force is gained, while speed and distance are sacrificed at the axle.

A windlass can be visualized properly as a continuous lever on a continuous fulcrum. Thus, when a handle is placed anywhere on the wheel it becomes the end of the force arm. The axle's center is the load arm. Figure 6-14 provides an illustration of this idea.

The theoretical mechanical advantage in a windlass is calculated as with a lever. If the

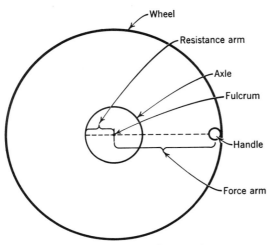

Wheel

Resistance arm

Axle

Fulcrum

Handle

Force arm

FIGURE 6-14   A windlass is a lever.

force-arm length is 18 inches, and resistance arm length is 2 inches, mechanical advantage equals 9. Because friction is so much greater with a windlass, however, actual mechanical advantage is found only through dividing resistance by effort.

Our following lessons develop the same relationship brought out in the lever. Placing the windlass handle ever farther away from the axle increases force. At the same time, it increases the distance through which force is applied. But in this machine the wheel's radius is a lever. Distance traveled is thus the wheel's circumference. To build readiness for understanding this relationship, an analogy is used in the beginning lesson. Several children are described as running around a circular pond. Knowledge gained from analysis of this activity is transferable later to the windlass itself.

Applications of the relationships involved make it easy for children to understand why a meat grinder needs a longer crank than a pencil sharpener, for example, and why a large steering wheel is easier to turn than a smaller one.

It will be convenient to construct a simple windlass, as in Figure 6-15, before starting this unit section. This requires four 12-inch or similar-sized pieces of wood, one 18-inch piece of dowel, and five nails. Bore holes as shown near the ends of three sticks. Here the dowel will be inserted. The handle arm hole should be made slightly smaller, to give the handle a tight fit. Place nails where indicated. Tack a rope or line to the center of the axle for load attachment. (This apparatus must be held down on the table when used to prevent it from tipping over.)

Make a cardboard wheel to preserve the illusion of a windlass. Later, it can be discarded to show that this machine is actually a lever. Cardboard or heavy tagboard will do. Measure with string the distance from the axle center to the handle. Using the string for the radius, tack one end down to the cardboard, the other to a pencil, and draw a circle. For comparison purposes, do this again one-third, then two-third's distance between

FIGURE 6-15

handle and axle. But draw dotted circular lines now. Cut out the large wheel and tack it to the handle. Pound large nails into the handle at points A, B, and C. These may be used as handles or points where rubber bands can be attached for comparative experiments.

BASIC GENERALIZATION V: Force needed to use a wheel and axle (windlass) changes as size of the wheel is changed

1. *Materials:* homemade windlass and cardboard "wheel" (See preceding exposition for construction details.); rubber band; ruler; three tacks; strong twine; several books tied together (or any convenient object to be used as a load); chalkboard sketch A, and chart sketch B, as in Figure 6-16.

An indirect approach may be useful to introduce the sequence. Put sketch A on the chalkboard. To draw circles, use a piece of

FIGURE 6-16

string with one end tied to the chalk, and the other end stretched and held down to the chalkboard with a finger. Cover the sketch until needed with a pulled-down map or screen.

To begin, you might say,

Let's see the hands of anyone who has ever tried to run faster than somebody else. Fine. Well, I'd like to tell you something very odd. There were three girls. All three could run at the same speed. One day, they decided to have a foot-race. They lined up evenly, started off at the same time, and then ran around a small, round pond. Even though each ran as fast as the other, one girl finished first, another second, and one was last. If they ran equally fast, why didn't they finish at the same time?

suggest
hypotheses
Pause for responses. If some know, un-cover sketch A and invite someone to use the chart as he explains what probably happened. If they do not know, ask how sketch A could be used to help explain what happened. If needed, give such additional assistance as pointing out the "pond," girls a, b, c, etc.

After the children understand that different relative distances were involved, ask them what would be needed for girls b and c to finish at the same time as a. Girl b would need to run faster than girl a, and girl c would need to run faster than both a and b. (If letters seem confusing, substitute girls' names for them.)

draw
conclusions
To bridge further to the windlass, say, "If you had run as hard as those girls, you would probably want a nice, cool drink of water. An old-fashioned well like this (show sketch B) might have such water. How would you get

it?" Let a pupil or two describe the method used. Make sure they include pushing the handle around. If they do not know, tell them that this is an example of a simple machine called the *wheel* and *axle*, or a *windlass*. Guide observation of the axle and wheel. Briefly establish that they are attached and therefore are unlike a wagon wheel and axle.

evalu
critic

Call attention to the handle location at the wheel's outer edge. Mention that it is com-mon for a well windlass to have the handle near the wheel's outer edge. Press for reasons. Someone should hypothesize that less force would be necessary. If not, point out the distances from the center. Ask what the chil-dren have previously found out about re-quired force when distance is increased.

sugge
hypo

Exhibit the model windlass. Have the class compare it with sketch B in Figure 6-16. Establish that its handle would probably be at point C (Figure 6-15). Will less force be required as handle distance from the axle is increased? What must be done to see? A rubber band and ruler can again be used to measure the amount of force required to lift a load of books at handle positions A, B, and C.

selec
proce

Have the class describe accurately what it saw. Bring out the main, but still tentative, conclusion that should be drawn: lengthening the handle distance from the axle made it easier to lift a load.

draw
concl

Now take off the cardboard wheel. Show that only a single spoke is necessary to have a wheel and axle machine. Let someone point out where the axle is rubbing and how fric-tion can be reduced. These ideas will enrich understanding.

2. *Materials:* door knob; screwdriver; broom, or any sturdy, polelike object of similar size; masking tape. (Mark the center of the broom-stick. Place two pieces of tape 6 inches and 18 inches to the right of the center mark, re-spectively. Do the same left of the center mark. See Figure 6-17.)

Inform the pupils that there are many wheel and axle examples around them. Peer intently at a door knob on the door. Invite them to tell what the example is you are look-

FIGURE 6-17

ing at. Unscrew the knob and take it off. Have someone identify the axle (the part the knob is fastened to) and wheel (the knob itself). Let several pupils try to turn the latch first without, then with, the door knob. Develop the idea of distance and force again.

Hold up a screwdriver. Let a child identify the wheel (handle) and axle (shaft). Request the children to hypothesize as to whose applied force would be more powerful if one child held the shank, another the handle, and each tried to turn the tool in opposite directions. Can they detect that unequal friction of the two surfaces is a lack of control? Masking tape around both parts can help reduce any friction discrepancy. Also note if pupils plan to have the two experimenters reverse their roles. (Strength is a factor, also.)

Exhibit the broom or pole. Refer to the chalkboard sketch. Explain that this can be considered a spoke of two steering wheels, one large, one small. Question if a larger, rather than smaller, steering wheel makes it easier to turn a car or truck. Entertain hypotheses. Ask how two children could find out with the broomstick.

Lead them to understand what must be done. One child will hold the stick at the inner markings and another at the outer markings. Upon a given signal, each will try turning the broom evenly and steadily in opposite directions. (A few words from you can prevent this experiment from becoming a wrestling match.) Stress that force should be applied smoothly and without excessive strain. Note if reversed roles for the experimenters are planned to control the strength factor. The distance-force relationship should now be quite clear.

Extending activity

Invite everyone to find examples of machines that are at least partly the wheel and axle kind, and explain how they work. The children can bring to class names, pictures, or real examples of these machines. Items to look for are a meat grinder, pencil sharpener, tricycle (front wheel), pepper mill, wall can opener, eggbeater, wrench (in use), skate key (in use), radio and television dials, hand drill, and fishing reel.

In a previous exposition, it was suggested that miniature models were less usable than larger, real-life materials. Perhaps nowhere is this more applicable than with pulleys. Tiny pulleys that use thread, currently offered by many scientific supply houses, simply are not practical at the primary level. Often worse are homemade varieties fashioned from wire hangers and thread spools, or similar devices. They are apt to be cumbersome and exhibit much friction. A better solution is to use ordinary clothesline pulleys, or purchase at a hardware store two single pulleys of moderate size. Sash cord, or something similar, can serve for rope.

Single pulleys contain but one grooved wheel, or sheave. Some pulleys possess two or more sheaves for combined use with other pulleys in heavy lifting. As its name implies, a *fixed pulley* is securely fastened to some object. A *movable pulley* moves vertically (or laterally as the case may be) with the load.

The pulley's similarity to a lever and windlass is diagramed in Figure 6-18. As with a windlass, the wheel-like arrangement is really a continuous lever. Observe why a fixed pulley can do no more than change the direction of a force. Like a seesaw whose fulcrum is centered, the force arm and resistance arm are of equal length. There is no useful mechanical advantage. If one foot of rope is pulled downward, the resistance moves upward one foot. This happens, for example, when a flag is raised on a flagpole.

Notice why a movable pulley offers a mechanical advantage of 2. The resistance arm is only half the force-arm length. Like a postpuller, this is a variation of a second-class lever. As with other machines, distance is sacrificed for decreased effort. The rope is pulled two feet for each foot the load is lifted.

By placing a fixed and movable pulley in combination, we are able not only to change the direction of a force, but also to decrease

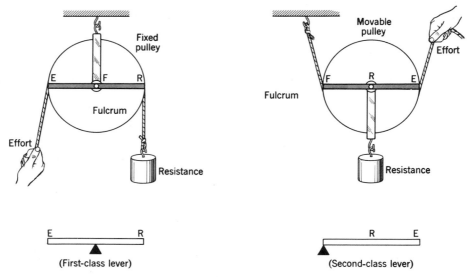

FIGURE 6-18

the amount of force necessary to lift a load. Such an arrangement is called a *block and tackle*. An example of this setup may be found on page 262. By adding more movable pulleys (or pulleys with two or more sheaves) effort can be reduced even further.

Friction ultimately limits how far we can go in adding pulleys to reduce effort. It can be partially overcome by greasing or oiling the axle. Let pupils do this in their experiments.

Since each rope in a block-and-tackle setup supports an equal fraction of a load, it is easy to know the theoretical mechanical advantage. Two supporting ropes have a mechanical advantage of 2, three ropes 3, and so on. For practical purposes, however, mechanical advantage must be calculated through dividing resistance by effort.

Use a rubber band (or spring scale) in the following experiments to measure differences in the force needed to lift things as supporting ropes are increased. Because a rubber band otherwise may be inconvenient to attach, fashion a paper-clip hook. Simply pierce the cord at the place where you wish to measure needed force, and attach a rubber band. As before, a ruler can be provided to record the amount of stretch.

BASIC GENERALIZATION VI: Force needed to use a pulley changes as the number of ropes supporting the load is changed

1. *Materials:* single pulley; strong twine; heavy rubber band; ruler; toy bucket partly filled with rocks, or substitute; paper clip.

Mention that now all but one of the simple machines have been studied. Invite anyone to name or describe the remaining machine. If no one knows, give such clues as: it is used to draw curtains shut; it is used by painters when they paint the outside of a tall building; it is used to raise a sail on a sailboat; it is used to hoist a flag up a flagpole. By the last clue, almost everyone will recognize the machine to be studied. Write *pulley* on the chalkboard and let the class say it aloud. Compare it with a windlass. Now show that a pulley has a movable wheel and stationary axle. Request names of several toys which have the same arrangement: wagons, tricycles (rear wheels), roller skates, and so on.

Point to a hook or nail placed above the chalkboard or other place. Have the class pretend it is alongside the roof of a tall building on which some men are working. Since the men often need materials from workmen below, can the class devise a convenient way in which a pulley and toy bucket can be used to help?

Let the children raise the bucket a few times with a simple pulley. Now, emphasize that all the machines experimented with thus far have made work easier by lessening the force needed to move a load. Ask, "Does it take less force to lift something with a pulley or without one?" Pause for responses. Guide the class as to what must be done to find out. For example, ask how a rubber band and ruler might be employed to measure force in using the pulley and then lifting up the same object by hand. In both cases let someone measure any degree of stretch evidenced by the rubber band. When the rubber band is attached to the pulley string, make sure it is pulled smoothly to reduce fluctuations produced by friction and sudden jerks.

The class will probably be surprised to discover that it requires slightly more force to lift the load with the pulley than by hand. Briefly raise conjecture as to why. If necessary, have the children recall that friction was a retarding force in previous experiments. Bring out how friction might be reduced by greasing or oiling the axle around which the pulley sheave revolves.

Develop that it is more convenient to pull in a downward direction than up because we can use the weight of our bodies to help. Guide pupils to understand that they changed the direction of their applied force. By pulling down, they were able to lift something up. Also, help them to see that there was additional convenience in being able to stay in one spot. For example, discuss the awkwardness of having to climb a flagpole each time a flag is raised or lowered.

Establish that a pulley used in this manner is called a *fixed pulley*—a pulley that stays in one place because it is attached to something. Bring out other common examples of fixed pulleys, such as those used for Venetian blinds, stage curtains, hay hoists, clothes lines, and window weights.

2. *Materials:* two single pulleys; 20 to 40 feet of strong twine; clothes pin; handkerchief.

"Does a fixed pulley always move a load up and down or can it also move a load in other directions? Who has seen a clothes line with two fixed pulleys? How can we arrange these two pulleys so we can move a load back and forth?" Help the class attach the pulleys to two different parts of the room, string the line, and attach the "laundry." Bring out the convenience of remaining stationary while the laundry moves.

suggest *otheses*

select *cedures*

reason *tatively*

draw *clusions*

select *cedures*

draw *clusions*

draw *conclusions*

draw *conclusions*

select *procedures*

draw *conclusions*

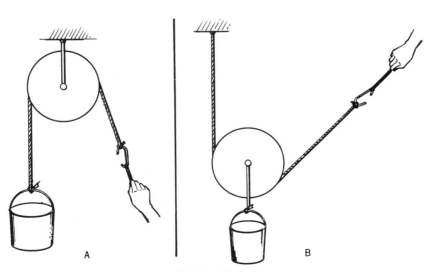

FIGURE 6-19 A–B

3. *Materials:* one single pulley; strong twine; yardstick; toy bucket containing several stones; rubber band; ruler; paper-clip hook.

Introduce the idea of a movable pulley with two demonstrations. These will permit the children to compare different data and draw their own conclusions. Tell them they have seen how a fixed pulley works, and found it does not reduce force. Establish that occasionally a single pulley is so arranged that it moves up and down with the load. This is called a *movable pulley.* Inform the children that you are going to do two silent demonstrations. When you are through, they are to tell why a movable pulley might be used to do lifting.

First demonstrate the degree of force needed with a fixed pulley, then with a movable pulley (Figure 6-19 A-B).

draw conclusions There should be little difficulty in deciding that the movable pulley required less force. Now, help the class understand the reason. Request a child to place a yardstick through the bucket handle and lift it. Have him place one end of the yardstick on a desk top and hold the other end horizontally, with bucket centered. Bring out that now he is supporting only half the bucket's weight.

Establish that in a single, fixed pulley the

FIGURE 6-20

load is supported by a single strand, but that in this movable pulley it is supported by two strands. Therefore, only half the force is required (disregarding friction).

4. *Materials:* one single pulley; yardstick; twine; weighted toy bucket.

Tell the children something is puzzling you. In all their previous experiments they have discovered that whenever force to move a load was made easier, the force was moved over an increased distance. Does the same rule also apply here? How can the yardstick be used to find out? Repeat the demonstrations illustrated in Figure 6-19 A-B, but without rubber bands this time, for greater precision of measurement. Help pupils to measure first the distance the load is raised, then the distance the string is pulled. This should be done with each pulley example. Deal only with whole numbers unless your group is quite advanced. Record data on the chalkboard in this manner: *select procedu*

	Fixed Pulley	*Movable Pulley*
Distance string pulled	1 foot	2 feet
Distance load raised	1 foot	1 foot

reason quantita

Assist the class to interpret data as needed. Conclude that decreased force was gained at the expense of increased distance. *draw conclusi*

5. *Materials:* two single pulleys; twine; rubber bands; weighted toy bucket; yardstick.

Let pupils recall that an advantage of the fixed pulley is that a person can pull downward—body weight assists in pulling. Contrast this with upward pulling when the movable pulley was demonstrated. Ask if the class can invent a way in which a fixed pulley and movable pulley together can be used. This would give two advantages: less effort *select* and a downward pull. *procedur*

If difficulty arises, this may be a favorable time for the children to check books, pictures, a film, or filmstrip. Lend assistance if necessary. (See Figure 6-20.) Once the combination pulley is arranged, draw out that any pulling is indeed downward, and the lower pulley is movable. Encourage measurement

FIGURE 6-21

reason
ntitatively of the relative distances between the rise of load and length of rope pulled. Have children compare force required to lift a load with the combination pulley as contrasted with a single fixed pulley.

Ask pupils to note the two supporting ropes (the pull rope is disregarded). Emphasize that by increasing supporting ropes from one to two, force needed to lift the load is *draw* reduced. Bring out, however, that distance of *nclusions* pull is increased at the same time.

6. *Materials:* two sturdy, round sticks, such as broom handles; clothes line, or other strong rope.

Tell pupils they can see in another way whether adding more ropes to support the load makes it easier to move a load. Tie a rope securely to one broomstick and loop it over the other as in Figure 6-21. Let two boys each hold one broomstick firmly and stand facing each other about 4 feet apart. Instruct a third child to pull on the rope to see if he can force the two boys to come together. They, in turn, are to resist firmly but without excessive strain. (Careful selection of participants in some demonstrations makes the difference between a successful learning experience for all, and unnecessary room control problems.)

It is doubtful whether the boys holding the broomsticks can be pulled together at first. Point out that there is only one supporting *suggest* rope. Have the class predict what may happen *potheses* as more loops are made. Let the children *select* experiment with two, three, and four turns *ocedures* of the rope. Each additional loop will, of course, necessitate pulling in a direction opposite to that of the preceding trial. Care should be taken to insure that the ropes do not cross and bind each other.

Elicit from your rope puller and class that additional turns of rope apparently increased force. You might bring out briefly that the *draw* child had to pull on the rope over a longer *conclusions* distance as well.

If a picture of a heavy block-and-tackle rig is available, it would be most interesting for the class to see the four or more ropes used to support the load. They should learn, however, that there does come a time when adding more ropes will not reduce applied force —friction offsets the advantage otherwise gained.

Extending activities

1. Take a study trip to places where pulleys are used. See them in action. Likely locations are construction projects, boatyards, ships or *evaluate* boats, places where painters or roofers are *critically* working, auto repair shops, heavy moving projects, and factories.

2. Encourage pupils to collect pictures of *evaluate* pulleys used in different ways. *critically*

The Earth's Changing Surface

(Intermediate)

Shifting sand dunes, eroding hillsides, weeds growing on an asphalt playground, muddy water running in gutters—there is evidence all around us that the earth's surface is changing. This unit will help children learn about some of the forces that wear down and build up the earth. In addition, it should increase their understanding and appreciation of soil conservation.

BASIC GENERALIZATIONS

I. The earth is a huge ball composed of a rocky crust, mantle, and core; its uneven surface is surrounded by air and largely covered by water.

II. Weathering and erosion constantly wear down the earth's surface.

III. Topsoil is composed of mineral, vegetable, and animal matter; topsoil conservation benefits everyone.

IV. Lava and magma flows, earthquakes, and crustal movements continually build up the earth's surface.

V. Rocks are formed through the forces that wear down and build up the earth's surface; there are igneous, sedimentary, and metamorphic rocks.

Airplanes cross our continent in four hours. Artificial satellites orbit the earth in less than half this time. It is inevitable for many per-

sons to think of the earth as a small and familiar place. But few of us in a lifetime ever will see more than a small portion of the earth in detail. One reason, of course, is that the earth's surface is simply too large. Over 54 million square miles are taken up by land alone, a mere three-tenths of the entire surface. The earth's oceans and lakes take up the remaining seven-tenths, an immense 143 million square miles. Most of the sea floor remains unknown today, even as we prepare space ships to explore other planets.

Even more of a mystery is what lies beneath the earth's thin crust. The inaccessibility of the earth's interior has compelled geologists to use many indirect methods to gain some clues. Knowing that sound waves travel faster in steel than in wood or stone, geologists rely heavily on the speed of shock waves (seismic waves) from earthquakes and explosions to theorize about the composition of subsurface materials. By timing the different speeds of primary and secondary waves, and noting where some waves seem to be absorbed and bent, they are able to make deductions.

The earth seems to have a solid *inner core* of iron and other heavy metals, with an *outer core* of the same materials in a plastic state. Beyond that is the *mantle*, probably composed of heavy rock. But there is disagreement. One recent theory suggests that a ring of dense rock, some 300 miles thick, separates the core's two parts.

Seismic waves also give clues about the

earth's crust and the way in which it adjoins mantle rock. Wave speeds increase gradually as they go deeper under the crust. This indicates increased elasticity of the rock. However, at certain depths the waves suddenly speed up and change direction. This suggests that the mantle is of markedly different composition from the crust.

Many studies reveal that the crust-mantle boundary lies at varying distances underground, ranging from less than 3 miles beneath parts of the ocean floor to 30 or more miles beneath the continents.

This varying boundary of abrupt change has been named for its discoverer, Andrija Mohorovicic, a Yugoslov seismologist, and is known as the *Moho discontinuity*. There are several projects underway to drill through the discontinuity and into mantle rock.

In teaching the following generalization, we shall attempt to help children develop some conceptions of scaling and relative distances. Although the earth is not a perfect sphere, it is enough of one for us to use circles in representing its several parts. Most children will be surprised to discover that the highest mountains and lowest ocean trenches are mere pin scratches on the scale of an ordinary classroom globe. Even the atmosphere—99 per cent is within 20 miles of the surface—scales down to near invisibility on a classroom globe, unless the 1 per cent extending to altitudes of hundreds of miles is included.

BASIC GENERALIZATION I: The earth is a huge ball composed of a rocky crust, mantle, and core: its uneven surface is surrounded by air and largely covered by water

Contributing idea A. The earth is a huge ball composed of a rocky crust, mantle, and core.

1. *Materials:* large classroom globe; string; crayon.

You might begin by stating that people today are traveling more than ever before. Children in this class may travel as adults even more than their parents. What makes

us want to travel? Bring out such aspects as different scenery, land forms, climates, and so on. Since airplanes are becoming faster all the time, shall we run out of places to visit? Perhaps the globe can help us find out.

Exhibit the globe and string. How many miles around is the earth? Assist a child as he wraps the string around the equator. Mark the distance on the string with crayon. Remove the string and have two pupils stretch it across the chalkboard. Trace a line with chalk along its marked length. This is the *circumference*, or distance around our globe.

But how many miles is it? Bring out the need to consult a scale. Let someone locate the thousand-mile scale on the globe and mark its length with a card or string. Now have him mark and number the chalk line at 1000-mile intervals. This will reveal a circumference of about 25,000 miles. How far is 25,000 miles? Comparing this distance with trips pupils have made will help them understand to some degree.   *reason quantit*

Invite various children to name faraway places they have visited and to measure with string the distances between their points of departure and destinations. In all cases, have the string held up against the chalk-drawn scale and elicit distances traveled. Work toward the realization that it is possible to travel millions of miles, near or on the earth's surface, and still not see everything. The earth is very large.   *reason quantit   draw conclus*

2. *Materials:* globe; large sketch of Figure 7-1; string; chalkboard scale line used on preceding activity.

Yet suppose we could see all the mountains, forests, oceans, continents, islands and so on. Is that all there is to the earth? What's inside the earth? Encourage conjecture. Note children's misconceptions and assumptions. State that it is impossible for us to go down more than a few miles into the earth's solid crust, so we cannot know for sure. But scientists have used some roundabout ways to learn something of what is inside the earth.

Very important findings come from studying earthquakes and their results. Earthquakes and large explosions on the surface

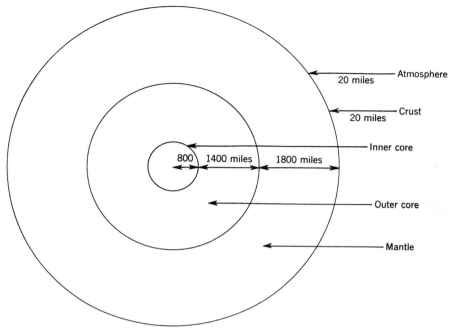

FIGURE 7-1

send shock waves vibrating through the earth. These waves travel at different speeds in some parts inside the earth, just as sound travels faster through an iron fence than a stone wall. Bring out that this may mean there are different materials present.

Display a large, freehand sketch of Figure 7-1 on the chalkboard. Omit any reference to the atmosphere at this time. Point out that the *inner core* may be made of solid iron and other metals. The *outer core* seems to be made of much the same material, but in a near-liquid state. The *mantle* appears to be composed of thick, heavy rock that is probably solid. Above is the earth's *crust*, made of several different kinds of rock, and finally, soil on most of the surface.

Hold up the classroom globe. Elicit that it is much smaller than the chalkboard drawing. How large would the earth's four parts be if we drew another chalkboard sketch to the scale of our globe? Provide assistance where needed. It is 800 miles from the earth's center to the edge of the inner core. Tie a piece of string to some chalk. Place the chalk where

the previously drawn scale begins and stretch the string to a distance of about 800 miles. Can the children interpolate this? The distance should be about four-fifths of the way to the first mark on the chalkboard scale. *reason quantitatively* With this small distance as a radius, hold the string down with a finger and draw a tiny circle with chalk on a nearby section of the chalkboard.

The edge of the outer core is 1400 miles beyond the inner core. How many miles away is that from the earth's center? (1400 + 800 = 2200.) Mark off 2200 miles from the earth's center and draw a second circle around the first. If pupils are able, let them reason *reason quantitatively* for themselves that the radius for the second circle must be 2200 rather than 1400 miles.

The mantle's outer edge is 1800 miles beyond the outer core. A radius of 4000 miles (800 + 1400 + 1800) will be needed for the third circle. Again let the children discover *reason quantitatively* this, if possible.

Now for the crust, which averages about 20 miles in thickness. The children should realize the difficulty of showing a mere 20

FIGURE 7-2

reason quantitatively miles on a scale of this size. Help them to reason that a much larger scale would be needed.

Contributing idea B. The earth's uneven surface is surrounded by air and largely covered by water.

1. *Materials:* as in the preceding activity.

Bring out that the earth also has an atmosphere, which the children might want to show on the present scale. All of the atmosphere but a very tiny amount (1 per cent) is found within 20 miles of the earth's surface. *reason quantitatively* Can this be shown? (Not unless the scale is enlarged or drawing instruments improved.) Have someone look up the height of the highest mountain, Mt. Everest (five and one-half miles). Can it be shown? (No, same problem.)

2. *Materials:* globe; sketch of Figure 7-2. (Leave off the recorded data.)

Exhibit the globe. Besides the solid part of the earth, and the air, there is a third part the children have not yet considered. (The ocean.) From their previous information, have them speculate about its average depth.

Note obviously wild guesses. Get them to *suggest hypothe* reason. Is it likely the ocean could go deeper than the crust?

It's easy for us to observe how rough or smooth is the earth's land surface, but how about the ocean bottom? How can this be done? Some children may suggest using a *select procedu* long line dropped from a ship. This indeed was the only method used for a long time. Have someone find out that now most depth recording is done by sound waves. A sound wave is sent from a ship to the ocean bottom. It bounces back to the ship a short time later.

Give a problem for clarification. Sound travels about 5000 feet per second in water. If a sound goes from the ship and bounces *reason* back in 2 seconds, how deep is the water? *quantit* (5000 feet.)

Display a chalkboard or chart sketch of Figure 7-2. It will show the depth recordings of a ship taken at 1000-foot intervals along the surface. Help pupils to plot the following data:

Initial sounding 2000 feet, then 3000, 3500, 3000, 4000, 5000, and 5500 feet.

Then 5500 feet, 6000, 6500, 6000, 6500 and 7000 feet.

Then 7000 feet, 6500, 10,000, 10,000, 8500, and 8000 feet.

reason critically Help them interpret these data. Where is the deepest place? Steepest drop? Most level parts? and so on.

Inform the class that actual soundings are taken at much shorter intervals, with some depths recorded to an accuracy of several feet. Get the children to reason how this would change the profile from a relatively smooth to a more jagged one. Let someone find out that ocean depths average less than 3 miles. The deepest part seems to be about 7 miles, located in a narrow trench off the Mariana Islands. Have a child find these South Pacific islands on a map or globe. If pictures or sketches of the ocean floor are available, this would be an excellent time to show them.

Exhibit the globe. Rotate it slowly. Tip it to show the southern and northern hemi-*reason critically* spheres. Have the children estimate (in fourths) the proportion of water compared to land. Bring out that nearly three-fourths of the earth is covered with water. Even with automatic sounding equipment, it is likely that most of the profile of such a vast ocean floor will be unknown for many years.

Develop that as we learn more about the earth's surface, the more we realize it never stays the same. Over thousands and millions of years, action of forces within and outside the earth's surface keep changing its appearance. What these forces are, and how they slowly change the earth's surface, will be the important things they will learn in this unit.

Extending activities

1. Show a sketch or opaque projection of Figure 7-3. Point out that this is a cross section of a large part of the earth's crust. Mention that scientists want to drill through the earth's crust into the mantle—something never done before. Samples of mantle rock will provide needed information about how our earth was formed. But drilling through rock is very difficult. Challenge your pupils *evaluate critically* to select a place to drill on this profile and to justify their choice. Many will select the narrowest part of the discontinuity. Draw out the enormous difficulty of drilling from a floating platform. Even so, it should be easier than drilling through much more rock. Tell them that rock formations at the narrowest portion shown total 2 to 3 miles in thickness. Perhaps someone can report on the present progress of *Project Moho*.

2. Present a film or filmstrip on the composition of the earth's interior. If the subject matter scope is too broad, be selective. Show only those portions that relate to the lesson's specific objective.

The close interaction of the earth's three parts—land, water, and atmosphere—is re-

FIGURE 7-3

FIGURE 7-4   Lichens play a part in weathering rock.

vealed in the forces that weather and erode the land. Strictly speaking, *weathering* refers to the breaking down of rocks into smaller parts through action of such agents as plants, chemicals, frost, and changes of temperature. *Erosion* is the process of transporting weathered material from one location to another, as in the action of running water, wind, and glaciers. However, the distinction blurs in actual cases, as we shall see.

Plants break down rock in several ways. Growing roots may wedge deeply into a cracked rock and force it apart. As dry plant seeds absorb water, they swell with surprising force, and may perform a similar wedging function. Tiny flat plants called *lichens* grow on bare rock. Acids released by these plants decompose and soften the rock. Larger plants may then follow in a long succession, each contributing to the rock's destruction.

Oxygen and water in the air combine with rock surfaces to produce "rust." Reddish soils, for example, usually contain oxidized iron compounds.

Falling rain picks up a small amount of carbon dioxide in the air and forms carbonic acid. Although it is well diluted, this substance slowly wears down limestone. Older limestone buildings and statuary have a soft, worn look from the dissolving effect of acidic rainwater. This is especially noticeable in England, where coal burning has been so prevalent. Abnormal quantities of carbon dioxide in the air increase the acidic content of rain and hasten weathering.

Rainwater that percolates into ground may encounter a limestone formation and dissolve some of it, thus forming a cave. This is how the Carlsbad Caverns of New Mexico, Luray Caverns of Virginia, and Mammoth Caves of Kentucky were formed. Since the surface appearance of a rock is somewhat altered by chemical weathering, we must often chip or break it to note its natural coloration.

Frozen water also contributes to weathering. Many rocks are relatively porous. Water, remember, is one of the few substances that expand in freezing. As absorbed water expands, bits of rock are broken off. In addition, ice may wedge apart cracked rocks.

Stones placed around campfires are sometimes cracked because rocks conduct heat poorly. The difference between a hot surface and cooler interior may produce strains which cause parts to flake off. But some of this *exfoliation*, as it is called, may be from expansion owing to release of pressure. Rocks formed underground are subjected to great pressures. When they finally appear on the surface, because of erosion or other means, there may be a tendency for these rocks to "unsqueeze" slightly, thus starting some cracks.

Moving water is no doubt the most erosive force on earth. Abrasive, waterborne rocks and particles have gradually formed the Grand Canyon over millions of years. Millions of tons of soil daily wash from banks and hills over the world into streams, and are eventually carried into the ocean. Ocean waves unceasingly pound huge cliffs and boulders into sand.

Water running down hills characteristically forms gullies. As the slope angle increases, water moves more swiftly, thus hastening erosion. Rain splashing on near-level fields has a different erosive effect. Broad sheets of soil wash off into lower places without obvious gullying.

Wind erosion became dramatically apparent to millions of Americans in the "Dust Bowl" years of 1934–1935. Prairie lands originally covered by a grassy sod had been broken up for agriculture. A combination of dry weather and marginal farming practices resulted in the most destructive dust storms ever seen in the United States.

Glaciers also contribute to land erosion. Huge snow deposits build up when snowfall exceeds the melting rate. Gradually the snow compacts into ice and flows slowly downhill, in the case of mountain valley glaciers. Continental glaciers are much larger, ranging to thousands of square miles in size. Today, much of Greenland and Antarctica are covered by such glaciers. Gravity forces these glaciers to spread out as more and more snow piles on top.

When glaciers move, they scour the land under their tremendous weight, scooping out basins and leveling hills. As they melt, huge deposits of soil and rocks are left at the sides and leading edge. Effects of glaciation may be seen in many parts of our country, particularly in New England.

Although most of the following activities on weathering and erosion can be conducted in the classroom, it will be desirable to use local resources outdoors in teaching them. Signs of weathering and erosion are everywhere. Pupils will be delighted to help look for them.

BASIC GENERALIZATION II: Weathering and erosion constantly wear down the earth's surface

Contributing idea A. Plants, chemicals, frost, and temperature changes break down solid rock.

1. *Materials:* small glass jar with screw top; plastic bag; pan; lima beans (Soak several beans in a glass of water overnight. They will absorb water and swell somewhat. These will be used for comparison with unsoaked beans.)

Inquire about the children's observations of road cuts, deep excavations for building sites, and river banks. Perhaps pictures can be shown. Develop that there is loose soil

FIGURE 7-5 **The last ice age advanced deeply into what is now the northern United States.**

and rock only a few yards deep. Below that is solid rock. Why isn't it all solid rock? Why is there loose soil and rock on the surface? Encourage conjecture. Bring out that hard rock is probably being broken up in some way. What might do this? Compile a list of possibilities on the chalkboard. Add others, if needed:

suggest hypotheses

Can these things break up rocks?
   (1) Plants
   (2) Chemicals
   (3) Frost
   (4) Changes in temperature

If such erosive agents as running water and glaciers are suggested, add them to this list. Or use a separate column and handle them in the B section of this generalization.

How can plants break up the soil? What have they observed? Someone may mention seeing a sidewalk cracked by the growing roots of a tree, or plants growing between rocks. Weeds may be growing in sections of the school's asphalt playground area. If there are examples on or near the school grounds, take the class on a short walking trip.

Mention that sometimes seeds are dropped or blown into a partly cracked rock. Sometimes the crack gets wider and the rock splits even before the seeds grow. How is this possible? Invite discussion. If a clue is needed, display the soaked and dry beans. Is the swelling powerful enough to crack rock?

Point out that it will be easier to make a test of the seeds' swelling power with a glass jar instead of a rock. How shall the jar and other materials be used? (Fill the jar about half-full of water and place inside all the beans it can hold. Screw the cap on tightly and enclose the jar in a plastic bag. Place this material in a pan, to contain water leakage.) Next day, the glass jar should be broken. Caution about jumping to conclusions. This is an analogy. How is it like a real rock? How is it different? Let children read to confirm their inferences.

select procedures

evaluate critically

draw conclusions

2. *Materials:* radish or bean seeds (radish seeds usually germinate in two to three days

—about half the time beans need); pie tins; plaster of Paris; paper toweling.

Some plants seem to grow on rock. Are the roots strong enough to wedge into rock? To find out, seeds can be placed on top of dried plaster of Paris formed inside pie tins. Mix the plaster with water to the consistency of thick cream. It will set firmly after about 20 minutes. Sprinkle with radish seeds. Place several layers of paper toweling on top and keep soaked with water. One or two waterings a day should suffice. In a few days the tiny roots of some seeds will have penetrated into the plaster.

If there are some lichens nearby, perhaps someone can bring in a sample. Scrape some off. Have pupils notice that some rock disintegrates at the scraped place. Is it the plant action that crumbles the rock, or is the rock just soft? How can we tell? (Scrape a part that does not have lichens on it.) Inform the pupils that the tiny plants release certain acids which break down the rock. It seems that plants use chemical action, too. Are there other ways chemicals break down rock? They will see another way now.

select procee

3. *Materials:* vinegar; small sea shell or piece of limestone; glass container.

Encourage class members who have visited some of the nation's famous limestone caverns to describe these underground wonders. Develop that some of these caves were hollowed out over thousands of years as rainwater soaked deep into the ground. When the water soaked into the soft rock, it slowly dissolved. How can water dissolve rock? Rainwater has a tiny bit of acid in it.

Demonstrate what happens when vinegar, which is a weak acid, comes into contact with a calcium carbonate. Point out that a sea shell is composed of about the same material as limestone. Pour some vinegar in the glass and immerse the sea shell. Have some pupils listen to the bubbling sounds. Place it on a table for others to examine later.

The next day—or now, if another shell has been previously soaked for 24 hours—scrape the shell with a knife. It will crumble and break much more easily than a control

draw conclu

shell that has not been soaked in vinegar.

4. *Materials:* two small glass jars with screw-top lids; various small rocks (Ask the children to bring these to school.); several containers of water; two heavy paper bags.

suggest theses

How might frost or frozen water break up a rock? Encourage conjecture. Is there anything in the children's experience that might help explain this? Maybe someone has seen frozen milk push out of a milk bottle, or frozen water burst a pipe. It seems as though the water expands. But don't things usually contract, or get smaller, when they get cold?

select edures

Perhaps the best thing is to experiment. This can be done at home. How can the glass jar be used? (Fill one with water, and cap tightly. Put it and an empty capped jar —this is a control—in separate paper bags, to contain possible broken glass. Place both in the freezer section of a refrigerator.)

select edures

How can the rocks be used? (Answers will vary; provide clues, if needed.) Which rocks are likelier to break, those that soak up much water or a small amount of water? (Much water.) How can we find out which are the most porous, or filled with air? (Place rocks in water and note the bubbles.) Use committees to test and select the most porous and cracked rocks when there are many specimens. Softer rocks will work best. These can be soaked for at least several hours, bagged, and placed in freezer compartments at home.

Similar but unsoaked rocks should be used as controls, to see if the cold alone is responsible for any cracking.

draw usions

Request reports on results the following day. Probably all the water-filled glass jars used will have burst, and a small percentage of soaked rocks will have cracked and chipped. Let the children show their materials and discuss the results. Emphasize that water is one of the few materials known that expands rather than contracts as it freezes. This expanding action is powerful enough to split rocks, especially over a long time.

5. *Materials:* candle; matches; one clear glass marble (ask a child); glass of water; pliers.

Have someone tell the class a safe way to make a campfire. One technique is to use stones to rim the fire. How about extinguishing the flame? Rangers recommend dousing with water and covering the remains with dirt. Have the children noticed that sometimes stones rimming an extinguished campfire are cracked? Why?

suggest hypotheses

Guide an experiment to test the effects of extreme temperature changes on a simulated rock—a glass marble. How shall it be done? (Hold a marble with pliers in a candle flame for ten seconds or so, then thrust it into water.) Exhibit the results. Many tiny cracks will appear in the marble. Compare this analogy to campfire rocks.

select procedures

evaluate critically

Develop that rock breaks through the continual expansion and contraction caused by extreme differences in temperature. Where are great temperature differences common? Much rock disintegration of this type occurs there. Often gravity assists this action, as when a piece of a rock falls from a high cliff and cracks apart again when it strikes other rocks below.

Emphasize that the actions of plants, chemicals, frost, and temperature changes in breaking down rock are collectively termed *weathering.*

Contributing idea B. Moving water, wind, and glaciers wear down and move rock.

1. *Materials:* areas on the school grounds and in the adjacent neighborhood which bear some signs of hillside and sheet erosion.

Have the children recall how places subjected to water runoff look after a heavy rain. Gutters run deep with muddy water. Soil particles and pebbles are strewn in the streets. Where do the soil and rock fragments come from? Encourage discussion. Elicit that the wearing down and shifting of rocks and soil is called *erosion.*

Take the children for a short walk around the school grounds and adjacent land. Have them notice such things as hillside erosion and gullying. Let them see erosion on a steep and a gradual slope with similar or no ground cover. Point out any miniature alluvial fans—fan-shaped depositions of soil and

evaluate critically

rock at the base of a gully. Have them compare a slope without ground cover to one protected by a profusion of plants or grass. Look for signs of sheet erosion on relatively flat land. Some signs are the partially exposed, upper portions of tree roots, coarser than usual soil, and sparse or no ground cover. Perhaps mud splashes are visible around the bases of some buildings.

If you are unable to leave the classroom, perhaps pictures and slides can be shown. Have pupils recall and discuss their previous observations of these phenomena.

2. *Materials:* glass of water; piece of black construction paper; a weed or similar plant, carefully dug up to preserve soil adhering to the roots; sprinkling can of water; four large cafeteria trays (or cookie or television trays), one containing a sample of soil covered with grass, another containing a sample of similar but loose soil. (Perhaps the school custodian can be coaxed to spade up a square foot or so of grass—enough to fit the dimensions of the tray. Or, at least three weeks prior to this experiment, plant some rye grass seed in one of the two soil-filled trays. Pupils will enjoy seeing the seeds germinate and watering the soil each day. Leave near a window for light and warmth during the day. Fill the second tray with soil until it is level with the top.)

Permit the class to recall some of the possible factors of erosion. Which hillsides had the deepest gullies, those with or without ground cover? (Without.) What effect did greater slope steepness seem to have? (Gullies were deeper.) How can the materials be used *select procedures* first to test for the effect of ground cover? (Prop up or hold both trays at the same angle, with trays below to catch any runoff water. Sprinkle the same volume of water over each. Note any gullies and muddiness of runoff water.)

select procedures

How can we set up another experiment to see the effect of slope steepness? (Clean all trays. Put bare soil in two trays. Hold or prop at different angles with trays below as in previous experiment. Pour equal volumes of water over trays containing soil. Note the difference in gullies and runoff water.) If get-

ting additional soil for two trays is inconvenient, simply have the children note the changing speed and more rapid erosive effect of poured water as one tray is held at a low and high angle.

Invite pupils to explain why a planted hillside erodes less than a bare one. Exhibit the weed roots. Point out the clinging soil. Gingerly soak the roots in a glass of water until the soil washes away. Lay the plant on some black construction paper. The intricate, soil-holding network of delicate roots and root hairs will be visible. A hand lens will help the viewing. Leave these materials on a *draw conclus.* table for everyone to examine.

3. *Materials:* two clean, flat sticks (tongue depressors are a bit small, but should do); tray of grass sod; tray of soil; several pop bottle caps or coins; sprinkling can of water. (The following activities may be done outdoors at appropriate locations, and with a garden hose.)

Bring up the common observation of mud *define problem* splashes around the lower portions of buildings. What is the problem? Develop the erosive nature of falling water. What can be *select procedu* done to prevent splash erosion? (Plant a thick ground cover to break the impact of the falling raindrops.) How efficient is a grass cover? Invite a test with the trays of grass sod and *select procedu* soil. Have the children do the planning. A stick can be placed upright in each tray sample and equal volumes of water poured from an equal height. Let them note and evaluate *draw conclus.* the differing degrees of mud splashes on the sticks.

Is there much erosion from falling water when the ground is fairly level? Or does the mud just splash? Place several coins or pop bottle caps on the soil tray. What will happen if water continues to pour onto the soil? *suggest hypoth.* Tilt the tray very slightly—virtually no field is absolutely level—and have someone sprinkle several or more cans of water directly over the caps. Remove the caps and have them notice the pedestal effect. This makes it eas- *draw conclus.* ier to note the *sheet erosion* that has taken place.

4. *Materials:* wall map of the United

States; a quart size or larger can with lid (discarded tobacco, coffee, or paint can); ten to fifteen small rocks (most should be rough, several smooth and rounded); water.

Invite someone to locate the Mississippi River on the wall map. Bring out that often it is called the "Muddy Mississippi." Where does the mud come from? Develop that this river washes thousands of tons of eroded soil into the Gulf of Mexico. This stream can be considered a gigantic "gully." Let class members identify other significant rivers. Bring out how each river begins as a small stream *draw* at an elevated location, gradually increases in *clusions* size, and ultimately empties into the sea.

Do rivers just carry soil to the sea? Or do they also break down rocks and soil? Hold up some smooth rocks. How did they get that *suggest* way? Guide the children to reason that, as *otheses* the rock is pushed along by the river current, it rubs and knocks against other rocks. Also, that a fast current probably breaks down the rock faster than a slower one.

Ask the children to think of a way the weathering effect of rocks rubbing in water might be simulated with the available materials. (Put stones in the can. Half fill with *select* water and shake.) They may not realize the *cedures* necessity of shaking the can many hundreds of times. This can be done by volunteers during the day at recesses.

Request everyone to note how the smaller rock particles gradually increase in number as the rough rocks get smoother. This would be an excellent time to show a picture of the Grand Canyon, if one is available. The class should be impressed by this majestic example *draw* of the cutting power of a stream carrying *lusions* abrasive materials. Be sure to bring out, however, that millions of years were needed.

Why are ocean beaches so sandy? Develop that a similar abrasive effect occurs when waves smash along the shore. Rock particles grind against other particles. Perhaps a picture can be shown in which wave action is undercutting a cliff. Or draw a rough, chalkboard sketch. Pupils will see how continued erosion at the cliff base eventually will cause the jutting, top-heavy portion to collapse into the

sea. Here it will be gradually pulverized into *draw* sand after many years. *conclusions*

5. *Materials:* sheet of black construction paper; two identical flat stakes about 36 inches long; masking tape or cellophane tape; outdoor lawn and bare soil areas; windy day; desert sand dune picture (optional).

Act puzzled. You can see how rivers and ocean waves grind rock into sand, but why are deserts so sandy? Everyone knows that deserts receive very little rain. Show the desert *suggest* picture, if available. Invite hypotheses. If clues *hypotheses* are needed, remind the children that deserts usually have wide temperature ranges. Many children at this point may name expansion-contraction as the main factor. Show them the sand dune picture again or discuss sand dune appearance. Are there any clues which *evaluate* seem to go against this guess? (The sand is *critically* distributed into uneven piles, like snowdrifts.) By this time, most pupils will think of wind as a possible factor. Wide temperature ranges create strong winds.

Gradually develop that windblown soil or sand is highly abrasive. Some pupils may describe the stinging sensation on their faces when walking into wind whipped dust and sand. Sand blasting crews cleaning building surfaces or removing painted traffic guides from streets may be familiar. Perhaps a child's relative has had a pitted windshield replaced or automobile repainted after a desert or prairie windstorm. Point out that windblown sand can gradually erode away the base of a high cliff. The top-heavy overhang then crashes down and is gradually worn down into sand.

Why isn't wind erosion a major problem *suggest* where there is more rain? Guide toward the *hypotheses* hypothesis that rain permits more vegetation to grow. Perhaps ground cover holds down the soil more than dry, bare terrain or sand. Challenge the pupils to design an experiment to test this notion. Indicate the available ma- *select* terials, if needed. *procedures*

Cellophane or masking tape can be fastened —sticky side out—almost the full length on both stakes. One stake should be placed upright in a dry, bare soil area; the other in a lawn. There are so many possibilities for controls it may be wise to divide the class into small discussion groups to plan this experiment before meeting together to decide on the best plan. Or perhaps several plans can be used.

Help the children if needed. Do the sticky parts on both stakes face the wind? Are both exposure areas about equal in size? Is exposure time the same? Long enough? Are the test areas side by side, or could the wind blow from the bare spot onto the lawn area or the reverse? Are both areas unobstructed? Are the stakes the same height? What do we mean *define* by "height"? An operational definition is *problems* needed. Perhaps we should measure from the soil upward in both cases; the grass top may be several inches above the soil. Use as many possibilities for thinking as the class seems able to profit from and enjoy.

If this experiment is done indoors, use the following materials: an electric fan; cellophane tape; two identical trays (one containing soil, one grass sod); two large cardboard boxes. Fasten tape—sticky side out—on the inside bottom portion of both boxes and tip on the side. Place a tray partly into each box. Turn on the fan before one tray, then before the other tray. Use the same distance, force, and time.

draw Assist pupils in evaluating their data. Many *conclusions* more particles should appear on the bare soil sample. What conclusions might be drawn about vegetation and wind erosion?

This experiment might be extended. Why are the bases of high desert cliffs usually eroded away sooner than the tops? Taller *select* stakes may be needed to note that more and *procedures* heavier sand particles blow at a lower height *draw* than higher up. *conclusions*

Yet another experiment might be tried with tray materials. Does soil dryness make a difference? Use a tray of dry soil and one of damp soil, both firmly compacted. Help the *draw* class to realize that moisture increases the *conclusions* cohesiveness of soil particles.

Bring out that, in addition to grass lawns and other ground cover, cities and towns have many paved areas and structures which reduce wind erosion. However, even populated areas have many dust particles in the air. Place a piece of black construction paper on a table. Leave exposed to the air a few days. Have pupils observe daily the growing amount of *draw* dust that settles on it. *conclu*

6. *Materials:* wall map of North America.

Trace an imaginary line along the northern United States. Establish that there are huge boulders and rocky soil along this area, especially in the New England States. But these materials are different from the underlying rock. How did the huge boulders get there? Weathering? The boulders are of differing *evalua* composition. Running water? Is it likely that *critica* rivers could move so much rock over so widespread an area?

Develop that *glaciers* were responsible. Of what are they made? From where did they come? Through reading and discussion, bring out some important ideas. Glaciers form when the rate of snowfall exceeds the amount that can melt each year. As more snow piles up, the tremendous pressure turns much underlying snow into ice. The pull of gravity causes the glacier to move. Thousands of years ago, a series of great *continental glaciers* advanced and retreated over much of North America.

Bring out how these huge ice sheets scoured the land, crushing and picking up boulders, rocks, and soil. What are some likely clues of glaciation? Huge deposits of boulders, soil, *evalua* and rock left along the sides and ends of *critica* glaciers as they melted in warm climates; deep, parallel scratches in hard rock layers or boulders; many lakes. Point out the large number of lakes in Minnesota and adjacent states. Develop that there are also smaller, *valley glaciers*. Icebergs are glaciers that reach the coastline, break off, and fall into the sea. Glaciers and icebergs exist today, though not nearly to the extent that they did when the climate was colder.

Draw a rough outline sketch of a valley. Put a glacier outline between the two mountains. Introduce a problem for discussion: The speed of glaciers varies widely, from 6 inches in a year to more than 50 feet in a day. Some glaciers are miles across, and not all parts of a large glacier's front edge move at the same rate of speed. How could poles or stakes be used to check if different parts of the front edge are moving at different speeds? (Drive a series of stakes into the ice in a straight line near the edge. Observe any changes in alignment.)

select cedures

Summarize the study of weathering and erosion. Guide statements about how these forces work together to change the earth's surface. Bring out that we try to understand the earth's history by using what is happening now as a guide.

Extending activities

select edures

1. Mention that the materials of which rocks are composed are called *minerals*. Salt is one of many minerals found in rocks. Rains dissolve a tiny amount of salt in the rocks; eventually rivers carry this water to the ocean. But why is the sea so salty when the salt content in river water is so slight? What happens to salty sea water exposed to the air? (It evaporates.) Does salt? Encourage a test. Have someone evaporate a strong solution of salt water. A hot plate will speed this up. Let everyone note the white mineral residue left behind. A taste will confirm it is salt. The seas are gradually getting saltier because most of the salt stays behind as sea water evaporates.

draw lusions

valuate tically

2. Encourage children to bring in old magazine pictures that feature weathering and erosion effects. Help them plan a bulletin board organized around the factors they have studied.

3. Reinforce and extend their study with a film or filmstrip on weathering and erosion.

aluate tically

4. Suggest reading about the great "Dust Bowl" wind erosion disaster of the thirties. What caused it? What measures are being taken today to prevent a recurrence?

aluate tically

5. Man changes the earth's surface, too. What evidence can pupils find of this?

Weathering and erosion wear underlying rock into small particles. But it is not until decomposed plant and animal matter is added (or man-made chemicals provided) that the soil becomes productive enough to support agriculture. *Humus,* as this organic matter is called, supplies plants with nitrogen, phosphorus, potassium, and other essential elements. The decomposition of organic material is done by soil bacteria. Acids released in decomposition also dissolve other minerals in the soil particles. Humus retains water well, and so keeps soil from drying out rapidly. The darkish color of humus-laden soil absorbs sunlight efficiently, and so it is warmer than light-colored soil. This speeds up plant growth and reduces seed failure.

Earthworms are important to soil for several reasons. They help break up the soil, which permits air, as well as water, to reach the plant roots. Root cells die unless they absorb sufficient oxygen. And, as earthworms eat through soil, they leave castings which contain rich fertilizing ingredients.

The mineral composition of soil is easily studied if we mix some earth in a water-filled jar and allow the jar to stand several hours. Gravity causes the several materials to settle in order. Heavier, coarser particles like pebbles settle first, followed by sand, silt, and clay. Any humus present floats on the water surface.

The best soil for most plants is *loam,* composed of sand (30 to 50 per cent), silt (30 to 50 per cent), clay (up to 20 per cent), and abundant humus. Silt and clay have small particles which retain water well. Having been eroded from rocks rich in minerals, they contain elements plants need for healthy growth. Coarser sand particles make soil porous, thus enabling air and water to reach plant roots. As we shall see in a forthcoming demonstration, a soil composed of sand or clay alone lacks the moderate degree of porosity which seems best for watering plant roots.

Soils differ greatly in their degree of acidity and alkalinity. Strawberry plants thrive in acidic soil. Many grasses grow well in alkaline or basic soils. Clover does best in soil which is neither basic nor acidic, but neutral. In conserving soil minerals and fitting proper crops to the soil, farmers may conduct tests to determine the soil's chemical content. An upcoming activity will demonstrate to pupils how chemically prepared *litmus paper* may be used to determine whether a soil is basic, acidic, or neutral.

It may take up to five hundred years for an inch of good topsoil to be produced by natural means. With a rapidly multiplying world population, topsoil conservation is a serious concern. In this sequence, children will be challenged to apply preventive and remedial measures that can be taken in soil conservation. Help them to realize that soil conservation benefits everyone.

BASIC GENERALIZATION III: Topsoil is composed of mineral, vegetable, and animal matter; topsoil conservation benefits everyone

Contributing idea A. Topsoil is composed of a thin layer of mineral, animal, and vegetable matter; soil differences result from differences in these materials.

1. *Materials:* hand magnifying lenses; hand trowel; large bucket of rich topsoil; old spoons; newspapers; several tinned cans.

Briefly review weathering and erosion. Then bridge into the present sequence in this manner: "We've seen how rocks are broken down. Is that all soil is, broken and worn down rock? What do you think is in garden soil? Let's examine some and find out."

If there is enough soil and other materials, a useful arrangement is to have a small pile of soil on newspaper for every three or four pupils. Materials can be picked up from wherever they were prepared in the room and carried to working areas. Besides soil, each group should have something with which to pick apart the soil—old spoons or tongue depressors serve well—also, a magnifying lens, and a tinned can in which to put live insects or earthworms. (A moment to set behavior standards before working will usually prevent any excessive reactions to discoveries.)

Bring out the need to organize the materials found. Parts of the newspaper can be used to hold similar things. Circulate around the room as the children work.

After an appropriate interval, list on the chalkboard specific objects found—leaves, twigs, pebbles, small rock particles, sow bugs, and so on. Help the group to organize these into larger categories. Gradually work into the largest categories: mineral, vegetable, animal. *evalua critica*

Develop that the decaying vegetable and animal matter is *humus*. Water soaks into the humus and helps to decay it into very tiny bits, too small to see. In this dissolved form the humus is taken in by the roots. This provides many materials plants need to be strong and healthy.

Have the children do some thinking:

a. Are we likely to find much humus in the desert? Why or why not? (With little rain, there are far fewer living things to make humus. Also, since there is little water, what humus there is tends to dry up and blow away.) *evalua critica*

b. What, if anything, do earthworms do to the soil? (They burrow into the soil and make holes. This loosens the soil and more air circulates. The humus they eat passes out of their bodies and helps to fertilize the soil. They become part of the humus when they die.) *evalua critica*

2. *Materials:* two Mason jars with screw caps, one half-filled with rich topsoil, the other with poor, coarse subsoil; container of water.

Most children have seen roadside cuts and old excavations which expose the subsoil. Perhaps the following photograph can be projected. Bring out that one seldom sees wildflowers or weeds growing in the subsoil while there may be a profusion of growing things in the topsoil. Raise conjecture as to why. *sugge hypot*

Someone may suggest that seeds cannot get lodged as easily on a vertical or tipped surface. This is a reasonable explanation. Are there others? Exhibit the materials. Have the pupils quickly examine the two soils. If the group is large, it is better to put samples in paper cups and pass these around.

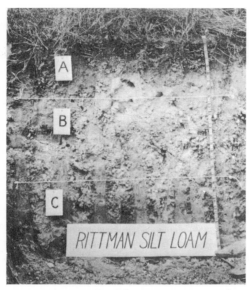

FIGURE 7-6 **A soil profile or cross section. Subsoil becomes coarser and contains less humus with depth.**

*select
dures*

Draw out that the subsoil appears to lack much humus. How can this be tested? Equal-sized samples are necessary. But how can the humus be separated from the rocky grains of soil? Provide clues, if needed. Is humus likely to be lighter than rock particles? Is humus likely to float? What can be done to find out? (Pour water to within several inches of the top in both jars. Shake jars to separate humus from rock particles. Leave until the material settles. This may take several hours.)

*draw
usions*

An examination of the results will show much more humus in the topsoil. But why is topsoil likely to contain more humus than subsoil? Bring out the way humus materials develop.

*draw
usions*

Have pupils describe what else they observe in the two jars. In both cases the soil increases in coarseness toward the jar bottoms. Proceeding from the lower portions of the jars upward, identify the materials: pebbles, sand, silt, clay, and humus. Have the children notice the different proportions of these materials.

*aluate
tically*

Emphasize that topsoil depth averages but a scant 9 inches in the United States. Initiate a discussion as to its great importance to living things.

(Now is a good time for someone to begin a plant growing experiment with radish seeds in humus and subsoil samples.)

3. *Materials*: labeled, capped jars half-filled with samples of topsoils from various locations: forest floor, beach, garden, and so on; water.

Establish that topsoils seem to differ. Some feel loose and crumbly, some closely packed and sticky, and so on. Encourage children to bring in soil samples from many places so that reasons for differences may be examined. Pupils should add water to the samples, shake, and allow the materials to settle overnight, if possible.

At observation time, guide toward an understanding that differences among the samples are mainly the result of differences in the amounts of sand, silt, clay, and humus present. Point out that topsoils often are described as *sandy*, *silty*, *clayey*, or *loamy*, depending upon the relative amounts of sand, silt, clay, and humus particles present. *Loam* is topsoil which contains sand, silt, and clay mixed together with much humus.

*draw
conclusions*

Emphasize through close observation and discussion the different relative sizes of particles in the sand, silt, and clay. Help the

Fill to here with soil

FIGURE 7-7

children to understand that the looseness or compactness of a soil depends greatly on the size of its particles. With a microprojector at hand this would be an excellent time to project dried sand, silt, and clay particles onto a screen.

The next activity will show how three soil samples vary in permeability—the degree to which they retain water.

4. *Materials:* three identical, tinned cans, open at both ends; dried, equal amounts of sand, powdered clay, and loam soil; three small pieces of fine-mesh wire screen or cheesecloth; six pencils; three glass bowls or ceramic cereal bowls; container of water. (Assemble as in Figure 7-7.)

Mention to the children that there is another reason why loam is usually considered the best topsoil for growing plants. They may be able to guess what it is by observing closely what happens now. In a moment they will be asked to apply what they see to a problem.

Carefully pour an equal amount of water into each can. Water will run fastest through the sandy soil, then the loam, and slowest in the clay.

Develop a problem for class speculation: A woman puts three healthy, identical plants in three pots, each containing one of the present soil types. She gives each the proper amount of fertilizer, and the same amount of water each day. After a short while, the clay and sand soil plants die. If she digs up and examines the roots of these two plants, how *suggest* might they look? (It is likely the clay soil *hypotheses* plant roots are rotting away. Roots of the sandy soil plant are probably dry and shriveled.)

draw Bring out that fine clay particles help to *conclusions* hold soil together. But clay alone retains too

much moisture. Larger sand particles are good for drainage, but too much drainage results in too scant a water supply for most plants. Establish that a mixture of these materials usually works best.

Bring out other applications. Dusty, fine-powdered soil stays muddy for some time after a rainstorm. The surface of a sandy beach may dry in minutes.

Contributing idea B. Farmers use several methods to conserve and improve topsoil; this benefits everyone.

1. *Materials:* red and blue litmus paper; salad oil; baking soda; ammonia; glass of diluted tomato or lemon juice; six containers of topsoil samples from different locations; pint of distilled water; paper cups.

Through reading or your information, develop that soils also vary according to certain chemicals they contain. Some soils contain *acids.* Acid solutions have a sour taste. Mention citrus products and vinegar as common examples of acids. Acids will turn chemically treated paper called *blue litmus paper* to red. Demonstrate this by partly dipping a strip of blue litmus into some acidic juice.

Explain that some soils contain *bases.* Basic solutions have a bitter taste. Soap, ammonia, and lye are common examples of bases. (Caution children never to taste lye or ammonia.) Bases will turn *red litmus paper* to blue. Demonstrate by dipping a strip into some ammonia.

Point out that soils that are neither basic nor acidic are *neutral.* These do not change the color of either testing paper. Show this by dipping both kinds of litmus paper in some salad oil.

Indicate the six containers of soil. Labels should identify from where they were obtained. Which are acid, basic, or neutral? Let children test with the litmus paper. Since the soil must be wet for litmus paper to work well, what must be done first? When wetting *evalu* the paper is suggested, see if the children try *critica* to do this without first testing the water with litmus paper. If water is added without testing, how will anyone know whether the water or soil affects the litmus paper? Use distilled water, if the local water supply lacks a reasonably neutral condition.

draw *clusions* Should enough materials be available, have four or five groups testing portions of all soil samples. Chairmen can record findings. These can be summarized on the chalkboard. Where conflicts occur, let the children follow through on retests.

Point out that some crops grow best in one kind of soil, some in another. For instance, clover grows well in neutral soil, certain grasses in basic soil, strawberries in acidic soil. Farmers add materials to the soil to change its chemical content for different crops. Childern in rural areas will be familiar with the widespread practice of distributing powdered lime on fields to reduce soil acidity.

draw *lusions* Encourage class members to try to reverse or change the present chemical composition of their samples by adding small amounts of either baking soda dissolved in water (base), or tomato or citrus juice (acids) to teaspoon-sized samples of identified soils.

2. *Materials:* pictures of contour plowing, strip cropping, terracing, check dams, tall tree windbreaks (all optional, see pages 282–283).

Mention to pupils they know already many things that erode the land. All concern the farmer; to save topsoil he must be able to apply his knowledge of erosion. Can they do the same? Can they suggest solutions to the following problems?

uggest *theses* a. A farm is located on hilly land. Plowing the hill causes gullies to form. Is there a way to plow which will cut down gully formation? (Contour plowing.)

uggest *theses* b. A farm is in a windy location. When corn is planted, much of the soil blows away. How can wind erosion be reduced without eliminating corn growing? (By strip cropping. Alternate a strip of a row crop with much exposed bare ground, such as corn, with a ground cover crop, like clover.)

uggest *theses* c. There is a small but steep hill on a farm. How can the soil be prevented from sliding down? (By a heavy grass cover, or terracing, if a commercial crop is to be grown.)

suggest *hypotheses* d. A gully is increasing in size. Now it is 10 feet across and 5 feet deep. What can be done? (Build check dams of logs and stones. Plant trees and shrubs.)

suggest *hypotheses* e. A field is located where a fresh wind blows from about the same direction much of the time. What can be done to protect the field from wind erosion besides using a cover crop? (Plant a row of trees to act as a windbreak.)

evaluate *critically* Encourage picture research in magazines and books before discussion, if possible. If there is time, it would be desirable to try out experiments in miniature on the school grounds and in the classroom. For example, *select* *procedures* the contour plowing problem can be tested with two small mounds of dirt. One hill should have furrows winding around. The other hill's furrows should go straight up and down. An equal amount of water can be poured upon each hill. The other experiments might be performed on a similarly small scale. Stones, twigs, and sticks make excellent check dams across miniature gullies. A row of wind-breaking trees can be simulated with popsicle sticks, and so on. By this time, the pupils should have sufficient input to think of some *draw* *conclusions* interesting ways to test their notions and make accurate inferences.

3. We have seen some useful ways to save farm soil. But what difference does all this make to people who are not farmers? Why should they care if some farmer's topsoil is washed or blown away? Develop how food *evaluate* *critically* prices and the availability of both meat and vegetable products is related to the abundance of crops. Bring out how various governmental agencies, such as the Soil Conservation Service, have been developed to assist the farmer, and indirectly, everyone else.

Extending activities

1. Have some children study and report on the many different services provided by county, state, and federal agencies for soil conservation. Perhaps they can interview a local agricultural agent.

2. Look into the possibilities of a soil conservation study trip, with a conservation agent

Contour plowing

Strip cropping

FIGURE 7-8 **Ways of Preventing Erosion.**

Terracing

Check dams

Windbreaks

in charge. This service is offered to schools in many parts of the country. Or this person may instead give an illustrated presentation in the classroom.

3. Have ready these materials: two clean half-pint milk cartons with tops removed; water; hand atomizer spray containing some light oil.

Point out that many parts of the United States have severe water shortages. Some farms and most cities depend on water reservoirs for much of their water. Sometimes the water surface of a reservoir is sprayed with a *suggest* very fine, oillike chemical. Why? (Maybe this *hypotheses* slows down evaporation.) Invite a test with *select* the materials. (Fill both containers with wa- *procedures* ter. Spray one lightly with the atomizer. Leave both in the same place, check to see which evaporates faster.)

draw The next day, results should be obviously *conclusions* in favor of the sprayed water. But raise an objection, if no one else does. Doesn't this *evaluate* ruin the water? Who wants to drink water *critically* with an oily chemical in it? If thinking bogs down, have the pupils observe the oil carefully. Pour some into a glass. Does oil seem to be everywhere in the water? How could *select* most of the water be removed from the car- *procedures* ton without getting any oil mixed in it? (From under the surface.)

Have someone with a pencil punch a hole in the oil-sprayed carton near the bottom. Catch some of the escaping water in a clean glass, then replug the hole. Let pupils exam- *draw* ine the water. No oil should appear. Bring *conclusions* out that oil is lighter than water, and does not mix. Underwater pipes can remove clean water from a reservoir. Therefore, we are able to get the advantage of a slower evaporation rate without spoiling the water, except for a tiny amount at the surface.

4. Combine an art activity with science by having children draw a large mural of differ- ent conservation practices of farmers. Much *evaluate* prior picture "research" will furnish ideas *critically* about how to show these practices in pictorial form.

Careful geological studies show that the powerful forces of weathering and erosion should have long ago worn down the earth's surface to a low-lying plain. Then why are there mountains? Part of the answer is seen in volcanic activity. Fiery molten rock formed deep underground, called *magma*, thrusts up through weak spots and fissures in the earth's crust. When this material reaches the surface it is called *lava*.

Sometimes the accumulation of magma and high-pressure gases is so great the molten rock shoots up to the surface in a spectacular eruption. This can occur under the ocean, as well as land. The Hawaiian Islands are the eroded tops of volcanoes, as are the Azores in the Atlantic Ocean.

Sometimes magma may quietly ooze up through great cracks in the crust and spread out over the ground. Large parts of the Pa- cific northwest are covered with hardened lava beds to depths of thousands of feet. Simi- lar lava flows have occurred in Iceland.

Several types of magmatic activity are not directly visible until erosion has worn away parts of the crust. Magma may stop flowing and cool before it reaches the surface. Or it may push up part of the crust, thus forming a dome or *laccolith*.

Where does heat energy for volcanoes orig- inate? This remains a matter of speculation. Since the earth possibly was once a mass of fiery molten rock, perhaps it has not yet cooled in certain portions of the rocky man- tle. But the popularity of this idea is waning. A more prominent theory is that radioactive rocks are responsible. One radioactive ele- ment is uranium, which continually shoots off helium atoms and changes to lead. In the process, a tiny amount of heat energy is gen- erated. If many rocks of this type become concentrated, it is conceivable that they could bring about enough heat energy to melt rocks.

(The known rate of decay of uranium into lead is useful in determining the age of rocks. Since the rate never changes, scientists can determine age by noting the proportion of remaining uranium to lead.)

But magma and lava flows are only partly

accountable for the continued mountainous features of the land. Figure 7-12 illustrates another method which may be responsible. As materials erode from a mountain and wash into the sea, the mountain becomes lighter while the sea floor gets heavier from accumulated sediment. The weight forces down the sea floor, which in turn squeezes the underlying plastic rock into an area of less pressure —under the lightened mountain. A new mountain is not produced, but the "floating" equilibrium developed serves to reduce greatly the leveling effect of erosion.

This interesting explanation was included in a broad theory of *isostasy* (i.e., "equal pressure"), first proposed by an American geologist named *Clarence Dutton*. Although advanced in 1889, it is still widely regarded as an important and useful description of what might have occurred.

Other mountains seem to be made through *folding*. The Appalachians are an example. Unknown subterranean forces push parts of the crust into giant wrinkles. Perhaps immense, slow convection currents of plastic mantle materials are responsible. Solid rock behaves oddly under great pressure. If squeezed hard enough, it acquires some of the properties of a near-liquid.

Earthquakes occur when the crust breaks under the strain of its deforming forces. Parts of the crust may move horizontally, diagonally, or vertically along a huge crack or *fault*. Over a long time *block mountains* may develop through tilted or vertical movements along a fault line. This seems to be how the Sierra Nevada range was formed.

Compare Figures 7-10 and 7-16. Note the correlation between regions of volcanic and earthquake activity. For the most part, these are regions of relatively young, high mountains. These are where the greatest strains on the crust are likeliest. Numerous faults and weak spots occur in such regions. Since magma takes the path of least resistance, it is reasonable to expect that volcanic action would often take place here, too.

BASIC GENERALIZATION IV: Lava and magma flows, and crustal movements, continually build up the earth's surface

Contributing idea A. Lava and magma flows build up the earth's surface.

1. *Materials:* sketch or opaque projection of Figure 7-9; color film or filmstrip or still pictures featuring volcanoes (all optional).

Point out that scientists have made careful measurements of how fast weathering and erosion are wearing down the earth's land surface. According to their findings, all the land by now should be worn down to about sea level. Discuss the two implications of this conclusion. Maybe they are wrong. (But this seems unlikely, because there is general agreement among earth science specialists.) Maybe the earth's surface is built up in some way or ways. Does anyone have some ideas about how this might happen?

evaluate critically

suggest hypotheses

Probably someone will mention *volcanoes*. Should others be mentioned list them on the chalkboard, but defer their study temporarily. Valid ideas will fit into the following B sequence. Invalid ideas can be evaluated after study of both A and B sequences.

Draw out what information pupils have about volcanoes. This is an excellent time to exhibit a film or pictures of volcanoes. Show the sketch of Figure 7-9. Explain that some lower parts of the earth's crust become so hot the rock melts even though it is under great pressure. Melted rock is called *magma* when it is below the surface. If there are weak spots or cracks in the crust the magma may suddenly burst through. A volcano is formed. The hot molten rock—now it is called *lava* —and hot gases, cinders, and ashes gradually build up into a mountain. Emphasize that many volcanoes have more gentle eruptions.

Develop that sometimes lava may also come out of long cracks in the earth's surface. Over many years large flat areas or *plains* of solidified lava are built up. Have someone locate on a map the states of Oregon, Washington, and Idaho. Plains of solidified lava up to thousands of feet deep were formed over large portions of these states.

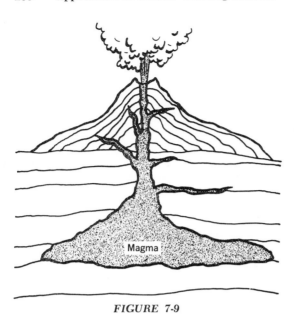

FIGURE 7-9

2. *Materials*: opaque projection of Figure 7-10; large map of the world.

Exhibit Figure 7-10. Acquaint pupils with the world's main distributions of volcano-formed land features. Call attention to Hawaii and the Azores as islands of volcanic origin. Bring out that several volcanoes remain active in these areas.

Have everyone look at the wall map of the world (it should be the physiographic kind, to bring out land surface features) and the volcano distribution map. Help the children recognize the startling correlation between mountainous areas and volcanoes. But caution them about jumping to conclusions. All mountains may not be made by volcanoes. Shortly, they will find out more about this.

3. *Materials*: unopened soft-drink bottle; hand bottle top opener; suitable outdoor location.

Discuss the tremendous explosive power of some volcanoes. Develop that powerful gases in the molten rock suddenly expand when released into the air. Under normal conditions the crust's great pressure keeps both gases and rock from expanding.

Bring out the analogy of a soft-drink bottle. It, too, contains a confined gas. When a pop bottle is opened, gas collected at the top escapes with a "pop" when the cap is released. Rising bubbles indicate that more gas is

evaluat *critica*

FIGURE 7-10   Volcanoes.

escaping. After the gas escapes, the liquid tastes "flat." The gas, carbon dioxide, is responsible for the tingle.

suggest hypotheses

Continue with the analogy: Let's pretend the liquid is magma. What will happen if we mix all the gas throughout the "magma"? (It may "erupt.") Shake the bottle rapidly several times. Have a child hold it firmly at an angle and pointed away from anyone. An outdoor location is best. Anchor the bottle top opener securely, then quickly flip off the top. An impressive eruption will take place.

evaluate critically

Back in the classroom, draw out likenesses and differences of this analogy.

4. *Materials:* sketch of Figure 7-11; wall map of the United States.

Exhibit Figure 7-11. Point out that a *dome mountain* may be formed when magma develops a "blister" in the crust without breaking through. Emphasize that such a mountain may not look like a dome because of erosion. Have someone locate on a map the Henry Mountains of Utah, which were formed in this way. Erosion has since worn many parts of these mountains.

Contributing idea B. Unbalanced forces under the earth's surface cause mountain formation and earthquakes.

1. *Materials:* sketch of Figure 7-12; soft, pliable modeling clay; small glass baking dish; physiographic world map.

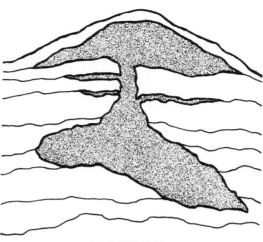

FIGURE 7-11

Explain that scientists have found that not all mountains seem to be made from volcanoes. So additional possible explanations, yet unproved, have been made. The class will now have a chance to develop and test an explanation about how some mountains may be formed.

Reveal your sketch of Figure 7-12. Ask the children to study it for a moment. (With a very bright class omit some details.) Invite them to develop an explanation about how a mountain might continue to stand high even though much of it erodes over millions of years. It may be useful to have several discussion groups each form a theory, followed

suggest hypotheses

evaluate critically

FIGURE 7-12

FIGURE 7-13

by an evaluative discussion with the entire class.

Guide toward a reasonable approximation of the following ideas. Over many, many years, weathering and erosion cause much of the mountain to wash into the sea. The mountain loses much of its weight. As more and more sediment accumulates, the sea floor sinks under the tremendous weight. The weight forces down underlying, soft, heated rock which then flows to where there is less pressure—under the lightened mountain. This material pushes up the mountain again.

select procedures But how can we test this idea? We cannot get a mountain into a laboratory. However, we might use a model. Indicate the materials. Place the soft clay in a clear baking dish. Hold it against the chalkboard and draw an imaginary mountain in the background, as in Fig-

ure 7-13. Place it on a table. Lead pupils to try pushing down on one side of the clay. The other side will rise as the pressed clay flows to the area of less pressure. Help pupils re- *draw conclu.* state what happened, and why, to clinch learnings.

Pull down a wall map of the world's land features. Invite the class to search it carefully for any signs which might give further sup- port to the theory it has just demonstrated. *evalua critica* If clues are needed, remind the pupils that eroded materials were washed into a nearby sea. Be sure to emphasize the mountainous western coastlines of North and South Amer- ica.

2. *Materials:* opaque projection or sketch of Figure 7-14; 2-inch stack of construction pa- per of several colors.

Bring out that many mountains are not along coastlines and are not of volcanic origin. How could these mountains have formed? Project Figure 7-14. It is believed this land was once flat. We saw how hot magma could push land up into a dome. But this seems to have been made in a different way.

Invite the class to speculate how the center portion of the colored construction paper

FIGURE 7-14   An anticline.

stack might be raised. Let someone push the two ends horizontally toward the center. The center will rise into a miniature, humped anticline. Develop that most of this process begins deep under the crust, where the rocks are heated and more pliable. Many mountains are made through *folding*. But scientists are not sure what forces underground cause this to happen.

3. *Materials:* opaque projection or sketches of Figure 7-15.

Present a projection of Figure 7-15 A-B. Bring out that cracks called *faults* sometimes develop in weakened parts of the crust. When this happens there may be a sideways movement along the *fault line*, as in A. Or sometimes an up or down movement develops along a fault line as in B. If the movement is great enough, mountains may form through *faulting*.

Emphasize that faults usually develop when the earth's surface is squeezed or stretched beyond the breaking point. When this happens the rocks suddenly crack and move in a sideways or up and down direction. Shock waves pass along the earth's surface and

FIGURE 7-15   Horizontal and vertical faulting.

through the earth. This is an earthquake. Discuss pupil experiences, if any, with earthquakes.

4. *Materials:* opaque projection of Figure 7-12; physiographic world map.

Project Figure 7-16. Explain that the black areas indicate the world's most intense regions of earthquake activity. Have pupils compare *evaluate* this map with the previous one on volcanic *critically* regions. Use the physiographic map to help them see the correlation between these regions and the world's chief mountain forma-

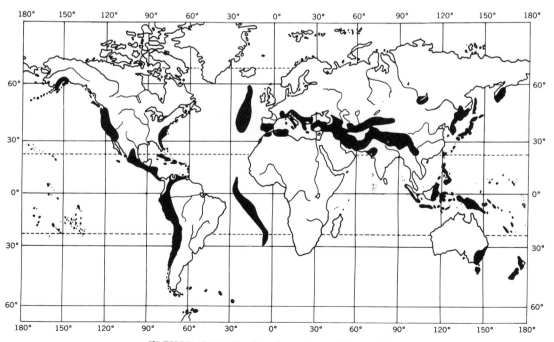

FIGURE 7-16   Earthquake regions of the world.

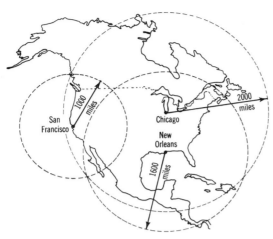

FIGURE 7-17 Finding the epicenter of an earthquake.

draw conclusions tions. Places where volcanoes and earthquakes occur seem to be located mostly where mountain building is taking place.

5. *Materials:* large wall map of North America or world; 16-inch string tied to piece of chalk; opaque projection of Figure 7-17.

Mention that many places where earthquakes begin are unpopulated or under the ocean. How do scientists learn where an earthquake starts? Discuss briefly, then introduce the *seismograph* if no one mentions it. This is a very delicately balanced instrument which continually traces a line on paper or photographic film. Any slight shaking of the earth causes the traced line to become uneven, just as a line drawn by us becomes uneven if someone shakes our desk. Explain that a single earthquake sends out several shock waves, often for thousands of miles on and through the earth, with a time interval between. Since the speed of these shock waves is known, scientists are able to tell how far away the quake is from the seismograph station.

But there is a problem. How can anyone tell where an earthquake is if he knows only the distance but not the direction? Project *suggest hypotheses* Figure 7-17. Ask the children to study it and explain the method used.

Bring out that an individual station can only detect that a disturbance exists some-

where along its recorded distance. This distance becomes the radius of a circle. Two stations narrow the location to either of two places that intersect. A third station verifies the exact location. Identify this as the *epicenter*.

Review until the children have these ideas thoroughly in mind. Now invite them to locate an earthquake on their wall map. They will need a string to measure distances on the map scale and an attached piece of chalk. Put these data on the chalkboard:

Seismograph Location	Distance Recorded (miles)
New Orleans	1000
Chicago	1300˙
San Francisco	1050

reason quanti Have the children discuss how they will locate the epicenter. Help in drawing the circles if the chalk is difficult to see on the map. The three circles should intersect below the Mexican border, near El Paso, Texas. If a perfect intersection does not occur, let the *select procee* class evaluate possible faulty procedures. (The string may have stretched a little; perhaps the scale·was consulted improperly; the distances may be off slightly.) Develop that scientists also make mistakes. But they make them less often and within a much narrower range of precision.

6. *Materials:* wall map of the world.

Invite pupils to solve the following imaginary problem. Tom and Jerry were walking down the street one day. Tom said, "It's so hot and sticky today. It feels like earthquake weather." Jerry said, "That's silly. How can the weather cause an earthquake?" About an hour later an earthquake shook the ground. Who do you think was right, Tom or Jerry? *evalua* Why? How could we find out whether hot, *critica* sticky weather and earthquakes go together? Discuss briefly.

Continue with the story. Jerry thought the weather idea was wrong so he decided to find out more about it. He looked for information and here is what he found (have data ready on the chalkboard but concealed until now by a drawn map):

Place	Earthquake Year	Temperature	Humidity
Coast of Central	1905	warm	high
Ecuador, South	1921	hot	low
America	1940	hot	very high
	1951	hot	low
	1966	warm	medium

Help the children read these data. They may need to know what humidity means, for example. But let pupils draw their own conclusions. Did high humidity go along with earthquakes there? (No.) How about high temperatures? (Yes.) Do earthquakes and hot weather usually go together?

*draw
clusions*

Encourage an evaluative discussion. See if the children detect the flaw in this sample. Lead to an assessment of location. What does a location on the equator usually mean? (Hot weather.) Help them to see the need for further data from other locations not on the equator. Perhaps a temperate zone with all kinds of weather is needed. Where are some temperate zone locations where earthquakes occur? Draw a line below the data and add this information:

*evaluate
critically*

Coast of	1910	cool	very low
Central	1921	warm	medium
California,	1943	cold	very low
U.S.A.	1955	hot	very high
	1965	cold	medium

*draw
lusions*

Now, weather and earthquakes seem unrelated. Bring out that the examination of many more locations and data would be needed for a more definite conclusion.

If the class is able, bring out through discussion the necessity of determining causation even if a correlation could be found between earthquakes and weather.

*valuate
itically*

(Interestingly, one modern theory suggests that large variations in air pressure on the earth's crust may precipitate some tremors. However, this idea is not generally accepted.)

Extending activities

1. Have a child report on Paricutin, a volcano that developed in a Mexican cornfield in 1943.

2. Encourage children to gather magazine pictures of the great Alaskan earthquake of 1964, and more recent earthquakes.

3. Invite pupils to compile from encyclopedias and trade books a list of large volcanic mountains in the United States. Let them make a large map bulletin board with names of these mountains on the side and strings running from the names to locations.

4. Let some able children make a homemade seismograph. Directions may be found in many children's trade books on earth science.

Elementary-school children bring rocks to school by the dozens through the school year. This unit will probably motivate them to bring even more specimens. Of course, the first thing they want to do with their rocks is to identify them. But beyond a few, this is quite difficult.

Rocks are made of *minerals*—natural elements such as copper and carbon, or inorganic compounds such as quartz and mica. The chemical composition of a mineral is much the same anywhere it is found on earth. A pure copper or quartz mineral sample is as recognizable in Asia as in the United States.

Geologists have developed many ways of identifying minerals. These means include noting the mineral's color, luster, hardness, cleavage, fracture, specific gravity (its weight compared to an equal volume of water), certain chemical tests, and crystalline structure. (The interesting, pure crystals into which minerals commonly arrange themselves are a direct result of their atomic structure.)

Of the two thousand known minerals, fewer than one hundred make up most of the earth's rocks. But since these can occur in any combination, it takes much study and practice before we can identify any significant number of rocks through their mineral composition.

It is more productive to begin the study of rock identification on an intermediate level with the three basic ways in which they form. *Igneous* rocks are formed from cooled magma and lava; originally, all rocks were igneous.

Sedimentary rocks are formed largely through deposition of eroded and chemically precipitated materials on the ocean floor. *Metamorphic* rocks are igneous and sedimentary rocks that have been changed through the pressure and heat developed in such crustal deformations as folding.

In this unit we are concerned with teaching basic ideas. Gradually, as children learn to recognize some rocks through the visible clues related to their origins, they can also learn more sophisticated techniques. For most intermediate pupils, however, these techniques will be more properly taught in later school years.

Although colored pictures of rocks are helpful in teaching, there is no comparable substitute for real specimens. A large number is not needed to acquaint children with the three basic rock types. We suggest a dozen. Some, perhaps all, of these rocks may be included in the specimens pupils bring to school. If not, they can be obtained from scientific supply companies, local museums, or rock collectors. If possible, get several examples of each type. This will save time and permit everyone to participate in related activities.

IGNEOUS ROCKS	Description	How Formed
Pumice	Grayish, fine pores, glassy, frothy, light, floats on water.	From rapid cooling of frothy, surface lava containing gases.
Volcanic Breccia	Consolidated fragments of volcanic ash, such as glass, pumice, quartz.	From being exploded high into the air from a volcano and settling.
Obsidian	Black, glassy, no crystals.	From very rapid surface cooling of lava.
Basalt	Dark, greenish-gray very small crystals, may have some holes.	From rapid cooling of lava. (See Figure 7-18A.) Escaping gases form holes.

Granite

Coarse crystals, white to gray, some-times pinkish.

From slow, below surface cooling of molten rock (magma).

SEDIMENTARY ROCKS	*Description*	*How Formed*

Conglomerate

Rounded pebbles, stones, and sand cemented together.

From loose materials compacted by pressure of overlying sediments and bound by natural cement.

Sandstone

Sand grains clearly visible, gray, yellow, red.

From sand compacted by pressure of sediment, bound by natural cement.

Shale

Soft, smells like clay, fine particles, green, black, yellow, red, gray.

From compacted mud bound by natural cement.

Limestone

Fairly soft, white, gray red, forms carbon dioxide gas bubbles when touched with acids.

From dead organisms that used calcium carbonate in sea water in making body parts; from evaporation of sea water containing calcium carbonate.

METAMORPHIC ROCKS	Description	How Formed
 Marble	Different, mixed colors, may have colored bands, medium to coarse crystals, fizzes if touched with acids.	Formed when pure limestone is subjected to intense heat and pressure.
 Slate	Greenish-gray, black, red, splits in thin layers, harder than shale.	Formed when shale is subjected to intense heat and pressure.
 Quartzite	Very hard, white, gray pink, indistinct grains, somewhat glassy.	Formed when sandstone is subjected to intense heat and pressure.

BASIC GENERALIZATION V: Rocks are formed through the forces that wear down and build up the earth's surface; there are igneous, sedimentary, and metamorphic rocks

Review briefly some of the major ideas learned. Emphasize that natural forces are constantly wearing down and building up the earth. These forces also form rocks. How this is done the class will consider more fully now.

Contributing idea A. Igneous rocks are formed from lava and magma flows.

1. *Materials:* pumice, volcanic breccia, obsidian, granite, and basalt rock specimens; hand lenses.

Have the children recall how lava and magma flows build up the land. Rocks made in these ways are called *igneous* or fire rocks. Relate to the word "ignite." Show the five specimens. Indicate all are of igneous origin.

But under what conditions were they formed? Allow time for close observation. Provide two clues. Challenge the class to select two rocks from the five displayed which best seem to match these clues:

a. Small bits of lava and rock materials were thrown high in the air when a volcano erupted. Which rock may have been formed in this way?

b. Some top parts of a lava flow were whipped into a bubbly foam from gases inside the lava. Which rock may have been formed in this way?

To check quickly the individual selections of all class members, number the specimens from 1 to 5. Repeat the first clue. Have pupils indicate their choices by holding up 1 to 5 fingers. Note their choices. Repeat the second clue and again evaluate choices. Identify *volcanic breccia* (a) and *pumice* (b). Set these two samples aside.

*evaluat
critical*

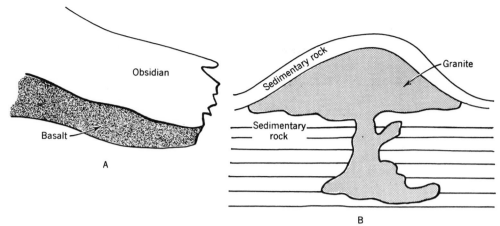

FIGURE 7-18 A–B

Identify the *obsidian* specimen as a type of volcanic glass. This forms on and near the top surface of a lava flow. Just below the lava flow surface, *basalt* forms. Hold up this specimen. Now identify a specimen of *granite*. Develop that it cools under the earth's surface, as when a dome mountain is formed. Sketch Figure 7-18 A-B on the chalkboard if clarification is needed.

Pass around hand lenses and these three rock samples for close examination. Several samples of each type will save time. Help the children notice that obsidian has no viewable crystals, basalt has very tiny crystals, and granite large crystals. Raise speculation as to why these conditions obtain. There are some differences in the mineral composition. Could there be other reasons?

Lead the class to consider the ways in which these rocks cooled. Draw out that obsidian should have cooled fastest, then basalt, and granite slowest. Does how fast a rock cools make a difference in crystal size? The children can do an experiment at home to find out.

2. *Materials:* several ounces of alum (sold at drug stores; or Epsom salts, or sugar, or table salt); tablespoon; two pencils; two paper clips; two coffee mugs; string; small cooking pan; water; stove and refrigerator. (*Stress that this home experiment must be done in the presence of an adult, since it involves boiling water on a stove.* If a refrigerator and hot plate are available at school, it may be done there.)

Through reading or your information, first acquaint pupils with how to grow crystals:

a. Boil about one cup of water in a small pan.

b. Add alum and stir. Keep adding until no more will dissolve.

c. Remove the pan and pour the liquid equally into two heat-resistant cups.

d. Suspend a short, knotted string from a pencil placed across the rim of each cup. (Several knots on the string will permit the crystals to develop a secure footing.) Use a paper clip to weigh down the string.

e. Leave the solutions undisturbed for at least a day. At that time, tiny crystals should be visible on the strings.

Remind the children of the experiment's purpose: they want to see if a difference in speed of cooling makes a difference in crystal size. How can the cooling rate of one solution be increased? (Put one cup in the refrigerator as soon as possible after preparing the hot solutions.)

select procedures

After one or two days, have pupils report on results. It will be most interesting if they have separately tried several of the substances, including alum. The slowly cooled solutions

draw conclusions

should contain larger-sized crystals than the rapidly cooled solutions. Let pupils check authority to relate this analogy to igneous rocks.

Contributing idea B. Sedimentary rocks are formed through the depositing of sediments which are squeezed and cemented together.

1. *Materials:* conglomerate, sandstone, and shale rock specimens; Mason jar about two-thirds full of equal portions of soil, sand, and pebbles. (Put water in the jar, shake, and allow materials to settle overnight before starting this activity.)

Have the children speculate about what happens to the tremendous amounts of soil and rock particles which erode and wash from the land into the seas. Develop that the enormous pressure of overlaid materials gradually causes those deeper down to be squeezed together. Chemicals in the water help to cement the particles together.

Exhibit the materials settled in the Mason jar. Draw on the chalkboard a large diagram of the jar and materials. Let children label the levels of mineral content in order, from bottom to top: pebbles (and a little sand), sand, silt, and clay. (Identify the silt and clay as ordinary mud.) Materials like these settle in large bodies of water and are pressed into rocks.

suggest hypotheses

Show the class the conglomerate, sandstone, and shale specimens. Can anyone identify the jar materials which might, under proper conditions, form into these rocks? Before permitting identifications, pass around the rock specimens to enable close observations. Place some water on the shale and have some children smell it. (It smells like mud.) Let someone rub several pieces of sandstone together. Put a piece of black paper underneath to catch the sandy fragments.

draw conclusions

Let pupils confirm their observations through reading. Pebble and sand particles are cemented into *conglomerate* or *puddingstone*; sand becomes pressed and cemented into *sandstone*; mud becomes *shale*. However, layers may not necessarily form in this order—it depends on which materials erode and settle.

Develop that settled particles are called *sediments.* When hardened, they become *sedimentary* rocks.

2. *Materials:* vinegar; drinking glass; limestone rock.

Have the children learn another major way in which sedimentary rocks are formed. Bring out that in the seas millions of tiny animals take chemicals from the water and make them into shells. When they die these tiny shells settle to the ocean floor and are pressed and cemented into *limestone.* Although limestone does not look like sea shells, we can see how it reacts to the acid test.

Put the limestone in a vinegar solution. Children will notice the bubbles and hear it fizz. Recall with them their earlier discussion of limestone caves. Mention that all sedimentary rock materials made from bones and shells of animals give a similar chemical reaction when touched by acid.

Let children read about how wind and glaciers also may form some sedimentary rock deposits.

3. *Materials:* salt; water; sand; pint or quart milk carton.

Demonstrate how to make artificial sandstone. Half fill the carton with sand. Add a few ounces of heavily saturated salt water. (Hot water will permit more salt to dissolve than cold.) Close the top and shake thoroughly. After the sand settles, pour off excess water. Set materials aside. Any remaining moisture will dry within a few days. Remove the dried "sandstone" by slitting open the carton. How is this like real sandstone? Different? Let everyone compare these materials.

evaluate critical

Contributing idea C. Metamorphic rocks are formed when heat and pressure change sedimentary and igneous rocks.

Materials: limestone, shale, sandstone, quartzite, marble, and slate rock specimens; wire clothes hanger; wax crayon; half-full glass of vinegar.

Have your class recall how modeling clay looks after it has been baked in a kiln. If available, show baked and unbaked pieces of clay. Develop that both sedimentary and igneous rocks can be changed into a third kind, called *metamorphic* rock. Resketch Figure 7-18 B on the chalkboard. Point out that hot igneous rock touches surrounding sedimentary rock inside the dome. The adjacent sedimentary rock is baked and changed, almost as if it were in a kiln.

Remind your group of how the earth's surface may be *folded*. The tremendous pressures bend, squeeze, twist, and heat the rock into changed form. Have everyone observe the effect of bending a solid material. Let a child rapidly bend a wire coat hanger back and forth about twenty times. (See Figure 7-19.) Touch some wax at the point indicated. Wax will partly melt on contact with the hot metal. Bring out that the folding of rocks also produces heat, even though it takes place very slowly. The combined heat and pressure changes the rocks into a new and different type.

Touch with wax

FIGURE 7-19

Pair the sedimentary and metamorphic specimens:

a. *Limestone* can change into *marble*. (Will marble bubble like limestone? Have someone check this. Crushed marble bubbles very well. Wrap a piece of marble in some cloth and crush it with a hammer. Immerse the crushed marble in vinegar.)

b. *Shale* can change into *slate*. (Does wet slate also smell like mud? Let someone check this. It does somewhat.)

FIGURE 7-20 This group is working to identify some rocks brought to class.

c. *Sandstone* can change into *quartzite.* (Get children to notice how the distinctness of separate sand grains has diminished through the crushing action of metamorphosis.)

draw conclusions Have pupils rub the paired samples together and also compare their weights if possible. Challenge them to explain why metamorphic rocks seem harder and heavier than the parent rocks. (The heat and pressure have compacted them more; they are denser.)

Have class members summarize the three main ways in which rocks are formed.

Extending activities

evaluate critically 1. Let the children identify examples of the dozen rocks they have studied from miscellaneous specimens brought to class. Get a few trade books to help make other identifications. Some rocks might just be labeled by the location in which they were found. Individual collections may be placed in egg containers, twelve labeled specimens to a carton.

2. Invite a local rock collector to talk about and exhibit his collection. Give him beforehand a list of questions prepared by the children. Perhaps he can advise children how to begin this excellent hobby.

3. Use a study trip as a culminating activity to observe rock examples at a quarry, road cut, or large building excavations. Let the children note all observations that relate to the major ideas of this unit. *evalua critica*

4. Get a comprehensive film on the earth's changing surface. Use it to help summarize major ideas. *draw conclu*

Air and Weather

(Primary)

In this unit we focus on basic elements of weather. Children investigate the interesting properties of air itself, and develop a heightened awareness of temperature, wind, and the water cycle. The same elements are studied in college courses in meteorology, but of course at a more complex level. There are many occasions for thought-provoking activities in weather study. Few other science teaching areas offer more opportunities to take primary pupils as far as they can go while maintaining real-life observations.

Such concepts as heat transfer, heat absorption, evaporation and condensation, introduced in previous units (Unit 1, page 107 and Unit 3, page 157), are applicable in the present unit. It may be useful and interesting to note differences among the several levels of presentation.

BASIC GENERALIZATIONS

I. Air is real because it moves things and we can feel it; air also has weight and takes up space.

II. Air is found almost everywhere around us.

III. Air presses in all directions around us.

IV. Wind is moving air; it changes in force and direction.

V. Temperature is how warm something is; a thermometer reading changes with the temperature.

VI. Water evaporates into the air; evaporation is affected by wind, temperature, and amount of water surface exposed to the air.

VII. Air contains moisture which condenses when it cools; water evaporates and condenses, over and over.

There are so many printed and spoken references to the earth's "ocean of air" it is easy for us to get the impression that pure air is a uniform compound, such as pure water. Actually, the air we breathe is a mixture of several separate and distinct gases, of which the three most important to survival are oxygen, nitrogen, and carbon dioxide.

Oxygen makes up about 21 per cent of the air, and nitrogen 78 per cent. Oxygen is essential to us because it combines readily with sugars in our body cells and releases heat energy. Nitrogen is essential because it is necessary for plant growth. It also dilutes the oxygen we breathe. Continual breathing of pure oxygen speeds up metabolic processes to the point where the body cannot get rid of waste products fast enough to survive. The small amount of carbon dioxide in the air, about $\frac{3}{100}$ of 1 per cent, is needed for photosynthesis to occur in green plants. In addition to these gases, there is less than 1 per cent of such gases as argon, krypton, helium, neon, radon, and xenon. All these atmospheric gases are remarkably well mixed by winds, up to a height of 5 to 10 miles.

301

But this is not all we breathe. As hay fever sufferers know, there are other substances mixed in the air. Besides the troublesome pollens, there are dust, smoke, and salt particles, water vapor, chemicals, spores, bacteria, and viruses.

Since pure air has no taste, color, or odor, its study at the primary level has an elusive quality not present in many other areas. Therefore, the main intention behind our first sequence of activities is to develop the tangibility of air. Like such other material substances as automobiles, houses, books, and people, air is a real thing. Children can feel it, and see it move things in the form of wind. Air has weight. A blown up balloon shows that air takes up space. Yet no one can see air directly.

The following sequence employs a comparison of air with a real child. It should provide pupils with an understandable, beginning base for further explorations.

BASIC GENERALIZATION I: Air is real because it moves things and we can feel it; air also has weight and takes up space

Briefly acquaint the children with the nature of the unit. Write the two words "air" and "weather" on the chalkboard if the class can read to some extent; otherwise just state them. Get opinions as to what "weather" means. Ask why the words "air" and "weather" appear together. It may be wise to delay any definitive statements at this time. Simply suggest that, as the unit progresses, the class will understand more and more why the two terms go together.

Try the following bridge to move smoothly into a sequence of activities for the present generalization: "Some children say that it is silly to talk about air because they think there *evaluate* is no such thing as air. They say if air is real, *critically* you would be able to see it. Do you think they are right or wrong? Why?"

After a brief discussion, tell the children they may find it helpful in their thinking to decide on what makes something seem real

to us. Ask a child to come before the class. Is he real? How do we know? (He can move things; we can touch, see, and hear him.) Have a strong child lift him slightly—he has weight. Draw a circle on the floor with chalk around where the child is standing. Can someone else stand in that exact space while he is in it? Then he also takes up space.

Put some or all of these ideas on the chalkboard:

We know John is real because: *draw*
  1. We can touch and see him.   *conclu*
  2. He can move things.
  3. He has weight.
  4. He takes up space.

If all the same things are true of air, would air be real? The class can find out now.

1. *Materials:* several leak-proof, clear plastic bags; cardboard fan; some bits of torn paper.

Can we feel air? How can the above ma-   *select* terials be used? Someone may open a plastic   *proce* bag and then twist the top closed to prevent air from escaping. Let pupils push against the bag's sides. Open the top slightly and squeeze the bag near several children. Can they feel the escaping air? Let others try it. Another child may decide to swish the cardboard through the air. The air current result-   *draw* ing will be felt by nearby children.   *conclu*

Can air be seen? Not directly, of course,   *select* but as it moves things. Ask for signs that   *proce* indicate air is moving outdoors. (Leaves moving, flag rippling, smoke drifting.) Someone can move bits of paper by waving the card-   *draw* board close to them. Bring out that air can   *conclu* move things. We can see what air does, although we cannot see air itself.

2. *Materials:* straight pin; two large balloons; string; yardstick; paper clip; tack.

Summarize the preceding ideas. So far, the things that make a child seem real are also true of air. Now the class needs to find out if air has weight. Draw Figure 8-1 on the chalkboard. Explain that two children of similar size and weight are playing on a seesaw. Why isn't the seesaw tipped down on one side? Draw out that the board is *balanced* or even because both children weigh the same. Inquire as to what would happen to one side if the child on the other side suddenly jumped off. (It would go down.)

Set up the materials as in Figure 8-2. Slide an open paper clip along the yardstick to achieve a perfect balance. Ask why the filled balloons seem to be balanced. (They probably weigh the same.) What would happen if the left balloon were removed? (The right side would probably go down.) Would that be a good way to see if air has weight? Encourage conjecture.

luate
ically

Bring out that we know balloons have weight. What is needed now is to find out if the air *inside* has weight. By removing one balloon, the remaining one might go down. But we would have no way of knowing whether the removal of the balloon itself, or the air, or both, made the difference. If needed, gradually help the children become aware that both balloons must remain, but air must be removed from one. If air has weight, letting the air out of one balloon should cause the other balloon to tip down. Invite suggestions as to how this can be done. An easy method is for someone to burst one balloon with a straight pin.

select
dures

draw
sions

Help pupils to reason through what happened. Guide them to a tentative conclusion that air seems to have weight.

3. *Materials:* half-filled aquarium tank (or large, clear glass bowl); small cork; two identical drinking glasses; sheet of paper.

Have everyone recall that a child takes up space. It is impossible to stand where he stands unless he is pushed out of the way. Does air take up space? Everyone will now want to watch the following demonstration carefully.

Hold up an "empty" glass. Bring out that it probably contains air. Turn it upside down. Does it still contain air? Crumple a piece of paper and wedge it far inside the glass. Develop that the glass now contains both air and paper.

Have a child slowly submerge the inverted glass straight down into the water without tipping it. Encourage the class to predict what

FIGURE 8-1

will happen to the paper. Let the glass be withdrawn, again without tipping it. Extract the paper. Press for an explanation of why it remained dry. (The air inside the glass took up space, and the water could not enter.)

suggest
hypotheses

Point out that it was impossible to tell how far the water rose in the glass because both the water and glass were clear (transparent). Put a cork on top of the water. Invite someone to use it to discover the water level, if any, in the glass. By carefully lowering an inverted glass over the cork, it will be possible to push the cork down to the tank bottom. Establish that air kept the water away.

Remove the floating cork. Push an inverted empty glass straight down into the tank until it is completely submerged. Tip it slightly. Have pupils note the bubbles. Elicit that escaping air causes the bubbles. Ask them to observe what happens inside the glass as more bubbles are released. (More water enters.) Lead them to understand that, as air leaves, additional room within the glass is provided for water to enter.

Hold up both glasses. Caution careful observation of what happens next. Invert one glass and submerge it. Tip it so all the air is

Paper-clip
balancer)

FIGURE 8-2

FIGURE 8-3

replaced by water. Invert the second glass and submerge it without tipping. Place the second glass near and slightly under the mouth of the first one. Now tip and pour the air out of one glass into the glass above. (See Figure 8-3.) As one container fills with air, the second fills with water. Reverse the procedure. If no bubbles (air) are lost, the process may be repeated indefinitely. Give pupils a chance to repeat this demonstration. They will react enthusiastically.

4. *Materials:* small flask (or clear glass baby bottle); small plastic or glass funnel; lump of soft modeling clay; large nail; a narrow, short tissue-paper streamer fastened to a pencil end.

This demonstration will present further evidence that air occupies space. (It may be used as a substitute activity for the preceding one.) Place the funnel in the flask opening and seal carefully with clay around the opening's inside edge. There must be no air leakage here. Pour water into the funnel. Some water will fall into the bottle, but this will stop shortly as the air inside becomes com-

FIGURE 8-4

pressed enough to resist any further entry. Fill the funnel. Ask why no water enters the flask. Draw out the probable reason: air is taking up the space inside the bottle. *sugges hypoth*

Challenge pupils to think of what might be done to permit a flow of water into the flask. Guide them to reason that a way must be made for air to escape so water can enter. Encourage use of any materials on the science table. Have many things available, or only one item—a large nail, for instance—depending on the group's ability to think and discriminate. *select proced*

When someone suggests putting a hole in the clay with a nail, develop a method whereby the entire class might observe the escaping air. A small tissue-paper streamer held above the hole should show this nicely. It will flutter in the escaping air stream as water pours into the flask.

Summarize all the preceding activities in relation to the initial statements about the child. Help the class to conclude that air is real, also. *draw conclu*

Extending activities

1. Children will be interested in learning how much space air occupies inside their lungs. Encourage them to measure chest expansions with string.

A more engrossing technique is to set up materials as shown in Figure 8-4. You will need a large bowl; 1-gallon bottle; rubber tube; and two small blocks (on which to rest the bottle opening to avoid pinching the tube). Put several inches of water into the large bowl. Fill the bottle with water. Put your hand or a piece of cardboard firmly over the bottle opening. Invert the bottle and lower it into the water. Have someone position the two small wood blocks under the bottle opening as you take away your hand or cardboard. Be sure to have the bottle opening under water at this time.

Let someone blow one long breath into the bottle through the tube. The water displaced represents his lung capacity. Chalk or crayon marks on the bottle will serve to mark the lung capacities of different children. For *reason quanti* hygienic reasons, dip the tube end in alcohol and rinse with clean water as additional pupils use the tube.

2. Suspend a balanced yardstick as in Figure 8-2; but this time use two suspended, *deflated* balloons. Challenge pupils to think of another way they can demonstrate that air has weight. (One balloon can be inflated.)

select cedures

Space exploration has made us increasingly aware of how dependent we are on our atmospheric environment. Without an air supply, man cannot survive for more than minutes. While we may travel in comfort thousands of miles over the earth's surface, an ascent of only three miles into the sky may require special oxygen apparatus.

How far out does the atmosphere extend? No one knows exactly. But meteorologists have identified four roughly separable layers of differing characteristics, named the *troposphere, stratosphere, ionosphere,* and *exosphere.*

The troposphere extends to a height ranging from five miles at the poles to about ten miles at the equator. This is the region where practically all weather conditions take place. Why the difference in altitudes? Tropospheric air is coldest at the poles and so weighs more per unit than warmer, equatorial air. Also, the earth spins on its axis. The fastest speed of rotation, about 1000 miles per hour, is at the equator. This offsets the earth's gravitational pull to some extent. The speed of rotation decreases as distance to the poles decreases, just as a person who runs on an inside track can slowly jog along while someone on an outside track must run swiftly just to keep abreast. As the rotational speed slows, gravity has an increasing effect. In the troposphere, stable air temperature decreases about 3.5°F for every thousand feet of altitude.

Immediately above is the stratosphere, which reaches to about 50 miles. This is the layer airlines use for long-range cruising when their advertisements proclaim, "We fly above the weather." The cold, thin air is remark-

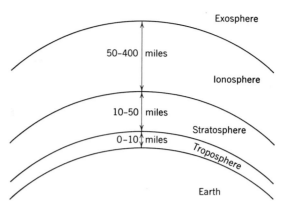

FIGURE 8-5 The atmosphere has several layers.

ably smooth and clear, since vertical movements of warmed air, and atmospheric dust particles, are largely confined to the layer below. Air travelers may note some pale clouds of ice crystals, but these are infrequent.

Between the lower reaches of the stratosphere and the troposphere are found winds that vary greatly in force and direction. Most interesting are the so-called *jet streams*, rivers of high velocity air several miles high, and more than a hundred miles wide. They range to thousands of miles in length, and tend to flow from west to east. A pilot can increase the speed of his plane from 100 to 300 miles per hour by locating and staying within a jet stream.

Beyond a height of about 50 miles, the stratosphere gradually blends into the ionosphere. In this region are ions—electrically charged particles formed from collisions of air molecules with high-energy solar and cosmic rays. These harmful rays are largely absorbed at and below this level. Auroras are sometimes visible. Meteors burn to ashes from friction as they strike scattered air molecules.

The ionosphere is an invaluable aid to radio communication on earth. The earth's surface is curved, but radio waves travel in straight lines. One way of overcoming this problem has been to transmit radio waves to the ionosphere, where they are reflected downward to other points on earth. Since solar "storms" frequently disturb the ionosphere and disrupt communication, this has not proved to be a completely satisfactory solution. Radio and television signals reflected from man-made communications satellites are helping to solve this problem.

The exosphere begins at approximately 250 miles and extends to an undetermined distance. A few air molecules have been detected beyond 500 miles, and it is probable that others are scattered thousands of miles beyond. For practical purposes, this region may be considered the beginning of interplanetary space.

While scientists estimate the entire weight of our atmosphere at an enormous five quadrillion tons, over half of all air molecules are concentrated below a height of three and one-half miles. The combination of this enormous pressure and the unimaginably small size of air molecules results in the presence of air in practically everything on or near the earth's surface. Air is found in most soils, water, and even in some rocks. We shall consider the effects of this pressure more fully in the third generalization.

BASIC GENERALIZATION II: Air is found almost everywhere about us

1. *Materials:* globe; picture of astronaut with helmet (optional).

Ask, "Why does a spaceman wear a helmet?" Bring out that it is probably used to help the astronaut breathe. If available, exhibit a picture of an air tank strapped to a spacesuit. Help the children to realize the significance of a helmet. There probably is not enough air to breathe at some altitude above the earth.

Develop speculation as to how high the air around them extends. Is it as high as the clouds? As high as airplanes fly? Where does it end?

Produce the globe. Help pupils understand it represents the earth they live on, and that the atmosphere envelops the earth. Hold a finger a fraction of an inch above the globe's surface. Inform the children that our atmos-

phere would go to about that height if the earth were actually as small as the globe. Draw an imaginary circle around the globe to indicate that air envelops all the earth. Help them understand that there is less and less air as one goes higher.

Raise conjecture: Since air is so light and easy to move, why doesn't it all blow away into space? Ask a child to jump up. Pretend annoyance when he comes down. You asked him only to jump up! Does this give a clue? The child had weight and is attracted to the earth. Children will recall that air has weight, too. If desired, introduce the word *gravity* at this point.   *sugge hypo*

2. *Materials:* aquarium tank or large glass bowl half-filled with water; small bottle; pieces of brick, chalk, bread, pumice, sandstone, leather, and several coins.

Draw out that since the atmosphere extends all the way around the earth, the children should have no trouble breathing unless they decided to climb the tallest mountains. Air is found everywhere on earth. But how about air *inside* things that are on earth? Hold up a bottle. Is there air inside? Children should recall the preceding demonstration with glasses held underwater. Let a child hold and tip the bottle underwater. Escaping bubbles will indicate the presence of air. The bottle had a large space inside for air to get into.

How about the other materials on the table? Do they contain tiny spaces that air can get into? Which ones? How can they find out? If enough materials are available have several committees test these and then compare results. If disagreements occur, materials can be retested.   *sugg hypo*   *selec proc*   *eval critic*

Virtually all of the above materials except the coins should release some air bubbles when immersed in water. Guide toward the tentative conclusion that they contain some air.   *draw conc*

3. *Materials:* hot plate; flask or small glass bowl (Pyrex); water; fishbowl containing live fish (optional).

Encourage speculation as to whether water contains air. Try to pin down reasons for   *sugge hyp* opinions. Let children carefully observe gill movements of fish, if a fishbowl or aquarium are available. If not, have them recall this phenomenon from past observations. Develop conjecture as to its meaning in the present problem.

Ask the class to observe the following demonstration for signs of air in water. Place a heat-resistant flask or glass bowl on a hot plate. Within a minute or so, tiny bubbles *draw* will appear at the bottom of the bowl, rise *lusions* to the top, and burst. It seems that water, too, contains air.

Help pupils realize that fish need air. When fish stay continually near or break the water surface, this is a clue that points toward an insufficient amount of air (oxygen) in the water. Emphasize that practically all the air in the water would be driven off by boiling the water for a short time.

4. *Materials*: glass bowl half-filled with coarse, loosely packed soil; container of water.

Briefly review the several materials, previously immersed in water, which contained air. How about soil? Are there any signs they *valuate* can think of which might indicate air spaces? *tically* Remind them, if needed, that one sign of air in water was the presence of fishes. Elicit the names of such soil dwellers as insects and earthworms.

select Encourage a test for air in soil. Indicate *edures* the above materials if thinking bogs down. Have your group note the many bubbles that rise to the surface when water is poured onto the soil.

define But isn't there something wrong? What *blems* did the demonstration with water show? (There was air in the water.) How might *valuate* that get the present experiment mixed up? *tically* Bring out that it might be the air in the water, and not the soil, which causes bub-*select* bles. If this is so, what must be done to the *edures* water first? The input children have received about boiling the water should help them come up with this suggestion. To save time, boil and cool the water in a teakettle during another learning activity. When the water is ready, let the children take several moments

out to try their experiment again. Use fresh soil. Bubbles will again appear.

To help clinch this learning, someone *draw* might read a short passage in a trade book *conclusions* or encyclopedia which indicates that earthworms loosen and aerate soil.

Extending activities

1. Help pupils understand that the presence or absence of air in water affects its taste. You will need a clean glass of boiled, cooled water, another glass of water drawn recently from the tap, and a clean Mason jar and lid or substitute. Inform the group that occasionally it is necessary to boil water to destroy harmful germs. Elicit that this practice would also eliminate nearly all the air. Does this make a difference in its taste? Have someone try to distinguish between the tapwater and boiled water. (Several glasses of each will enable more pupils to participate.) The boiled water should taste "flat."

What effect will there be if air is put back into the water? How can this be done? If *select* clues are needed, remind the children of the *procedures* bubbles that appear when frozen orange juice is shaken in a closed container. After the flat water is thoroughly shaken in a jar, pour it into a glass.

Will the taster be able to tell which is *select* which? Draw out that he must be unaware of *procedures* which glass contains the shaken water. Perhaps the class will suggest that he turn his back while the glasses are shuffled. Even if he does detect the shaken water (the use of additional tasters will give more latitude for error) bring out that both glasses of water now taste more nearly alike.

2. Challenge the group to use all the signs it can think of to determine if wood contains air. Some thin, broken pieces of soft wood (tongue depressors are useful), a large bowl of water, and pliers will be needed. Let children split these pieces for examination and *select* then float some of them. Have the children *procedures* speculate about what they see. Eventually guide them toward a test. Someone can hold a small piece of wood underwater while another child squeezes it gently with pliers.

draw conclusions

Tiny air bubbles will rise. Help the children realize that the smallness of the bubbles serves to indicate the tiny size of air pockets in the wood. Guide them to understand that these air pockets contribute to the buoyancy of wood in water.

Since the average weight of air is about 14.7 pounds per square inch at sea level, there may be as many as 20 tons of air pressing against the human body. Why, then, are we not crushed? There are two basic reasons. As with water, air at a given level presses with equal force in all directions. Because there is a counteractive force for every force, the pressure is neutralized. Counteractive pressure also takes place in our bodies. Air molecules are so tiny they dissolve in the blood stream, besides occupying space in our lungs and other body cavities.

Unlike free air, the air in our bodies lags somewhat in building up or reducing counteractive back pressure as atmospheric pressure changes. Have you noticed your ears "pop" while ascending quickly in an elevator of a tall building? This happens because air pressure in the inner ear tends to remain the same while the outside air pressure diminishes with increased altitudes. The result is an uncomfortable outward pushing sensation behind the eardrums. A slow elevator gives more opportunity for inner ear pressure to be adjusted through the Eustachian tube, which connects the inner ear to the nasal passages and mouth.

A similar, but much more dangerous situation is encountered by deep-sea divers. As they descend into the water, air is pumped under increasing pressure into the diving helmet and suit to counteract increasing water pressure. After working for twenty or thirty minutes, the diver's circulatory system contains an abnormal amount of air. If he ascends rapidly to the surface, a region of much lower air pressure, the air in his blood may expand and form bubbles. This causes a very painful and possibly fatal condition known as "the bends."

The lag in adjusting to outside atmospheric pressure may also be an explanation of why some persons complain of aches and pains prior to rainy weather. Outside air pressure usually lessens before a storm. If the body's blood pressure remains the same, the blood will now press outward a little more forcibly than usual against body joints and tissues. It is possible that the slight additional pressure may cause some sensations of discomfort.

At one time, it was thought that atmospheric pressure over any one point was always the same. We now know this is incorrect. Huge masses of air constantly move over the earth, changing the pressure. Cold, dense air piles up in a given area and causes an increase in pressure. In another area, a mass of swirling, warmer air has the opposite effect.

An instrument used for measuring atmospheric pressure is the *barometer*. To understand how it works, let us consider how we drink through a straw. When we draw some air out of a straw, the atmosphere presses down on the liquid's surface and pushes it up into the space formerly occupied by the air.

If you are skeptical, try the following experiments. Place two straws in your mouth, but leave one *outside* the pop bottle or glass. You will find it is now impossible to drink the liquid. Why? Air traveling inward through the outside straw restores the pressure in your mouth and other straw to normal. For the second experiment, fill a flask with water and seal it tightly with a one-hole stopper containing a glass tube. No matter how hard you sip, no water goes up the tube. There is no air pressing down on the water. With a two-hole stopper, normal drinking is possible. Air pressure is exerted through the second hole.

In a *mercurial* barometer, a glass tube closed at one end and about 36 inches long is filled with mercury and inverted into a dish of mercury. While some of the liquid runs out, a column of about 30 inches remains. This indicates the force of air pressing on the liquid's surface. As air pressure increases, the column will rise higher into the vacuum above. The reverse takes place with reduced pressure.

FIGURE 8-6 Homemade mercury barometer and a manufactured aneroid barometer.

Since mercurial barometers are easily broken and cumbersome, many weather observers use the *aneroid* barometer. This consists of a thin, flexible, metal box from which air has been largely evacuated. As air presses on it with varying degrees of force, the box moves in and out accordingly. A clever linkage and leverage system transfers these movements to a movable indicator on a dial. Since air pressure also changes with altitude, aneroid barometers are used in airplanes to indicate altitude. This is done by merely changing the dial to read in feet rather than inches of mercury. Such a barometer is called an *altimeter*.

As with drinking straws, most of the phenomena we associate with "suction" are really due to removing or reducing air pressure from one part of a device. Air pressure on all other parts then pushes and performs the work. In vacuum cleaners, for example, the motor whirls a reversed fan which reduces air pressure at the cleaning nozzle. The surrounding air then *pushes* dirt particles into the nozzle. A plumber's force cup or "suction" cup works in a similar way. By pressing down on the pliable rubber cup, most of the air inside is forced out. Air from all other sides pushes against the cup's exterior and holds it fast to whatever surface it has been pressed.

BASIC GENERALIZATION III: Air presses in all directions around us

Briefly review that air is everywhere around us and has weight. It might be helpful in the discussion to draw a large circle on the chalkboard to represent the earth, and then a larger circle around it to show the earth's atmosphere. Invite pupils to use their knowledge of air to explain the following demonstration.

1. *Materials:* two identical, thin flat sticks about 2 inches long (A produce crate is constructed of such wood.); two large newspaper sheets; rubber band.

Place a wood slat on a table with about one-third of its length protruding over the edge. Open and lay the newspaper sheets over the slat's longer portion which rests on the table. Smooth out the paper as flat as possible to lessen any air spaces underneath. When the slat's protruding portion is struck sharply, the slat should break. The air above the sheets presses down with sufficient resistance to overcome the slat's lifting action. (Since wood varies greatly in flexibility and strength, it will be wise to practice this demonstration, and its forthcoming control, beforehand.)

suggest hypotheses

Entertain hypotheses as to why the slat broke. Guide pupils toward the screening of two likeliest guesses: (1) air pressing down on the sheets broke the stick; or (2) the sheets' weight broke the stick. (In the latter case, "inertia" rather than "weight" would be a more accurate idea. However, this is too subtle for most primary children.)

select procedures

Show the second slat. What experiment can the class do to find out if the weight, or air pressing down, broke the stick? The news sheets can be folded into a small package and fastened to the stick with a rubber band. Fasten it about halfway down the slat's longer portion which rests on the table. Make sure no children or breakable objects are nearby. As the slat is struck, it should remain intact and fly up and away from the table with its fastened news sheets. Help your pupils reason through to a conclusion.

draw conclusions

2. *Materials:* plumber's force cup; a smooth, flat, rigid metal surface (onto which the force cup will be pressed—an upturned dishpan should serve); pencil; toy "suction cup" darts (optional).

Inform your pupils that the next activity will help them learn more about how air presses. Produce the plumber's force cup. Rest it on the upturned dishpan. Draw out that there is air above and inside the cup. What will happen to the air inside when the cup is pushed down? (It will be forced out.) Have someone feel the air as it is squeezed out. Let a child gently try to pull up on the cup. Why is it stuck? Bring out that the air above is pushing down on it.

suggest hypotheses

Invite the children to predict what will happen if some air is allowed to enter between the cup and the metal surface. Let someone take a pencil point and push it gently under

the cup. Have pupils identify the subsequent hissing noise as entering air. The cup will be immediately freed. Lead them to reason that the air below pushed up with the same force as the air above pushed down.

draw conclu

Attach the force cup with the pan held vertically, and then overhead. Allow someone to introduce air with a pencil in each case. No matter in which position it is held, air pushes in that and the opposite direction. Help the group realize this illustrates that air presses in all directions. If we can remove air pressure on one side of a material, air will press on it from all other sides and hold fast.

draw conclu

If a toy "suction cup" dart is available, show it. Or have pupils recall their play with this and similar toys. Bring out that all work on the same principle as the force cup.

draw conclu

3. *Materials:* straw, or glass tube of similar size; glass of water, with food coloring or ink added for easy visibility. (Duplicate materials will permit all pupils to work.)

Announce that the next activity will be done silently. At its completion, the children are to explain what has happened in terms of air pressure. Dip the straw vertically into the water. Lift it straight out. Whatever water enters the straw immediately flows out. Dip the straw again, but now close a forefinger over the straw's exposed end before lifting it out. Water remains in the straw although it is lifted out of the glass. Remove your finger and the water flows out of the straw. Repeat to insure accurate observation. Why does water remain in the straw? Why does it flow out when the finger is removed?

sugges hypot

Develop that air below pushes up the water and keeps it from flowing out. However, when air is free to enter the opposite end it pushes down just as forcefully. Since these forces are balanced, the water's weight causes it to flow out.

draw conclu

This is an ideal time to demonstrate how a dip tube is used to remove small food and waste particles from an aquarium. A straw or glass tube may be used. Scatter a few tiny crumbs of bread in a glass of clear water. Shortly, these will settle at the bottom. Place a finger over the tube's open end before dipping the tube into the water. Position the tube over a particle and release the finger. As the compressed air escapes water will rush into the tube's opposite end and bring the waste material with it. Close the tube's open end again with a finger and remove the tube. Its contents can be released into a nearby container by removing the finger.

Extending activities

1. The following experience will help pupils understand why two holes are often punched into the tops of cans containing liquid. Ask everyone to bring an empty, rinsed-out can which formerly held a liquid. When several cans are assembled, tip them over so pupils may observe the openings made in their tops. Inquire as to what there seems to be in common. (Most have two holes.) Encourage hypotheses to explain. Help the children apply their recently learned ideas in screening hypotheses.

evaluate critically

suggest theses

Encourage tests with liquid poured from one and two holes. Invert the cans after filling them with water and stopping up the previous opening with modeling clay. A large nail and hammer can serve to punch holes easily.

select edures

Elicit that air pressure prevents or slows down the water from leaving when only one hole is made, just as it did with the dip tube. A second hole permits air to enter the can and neutralize this effect.

draw usions

What did the class learn? Many children will say, "You have to make two holes for liquid to pour from a can." Help them see the fallacy in this conclusion by pouring water from a can with only one large opening. Guide toward an amended statement, such as, "There must be enough space for air to enter the can as the liquid is poured."

evaluate critically

draw conclusions

2. Motivate for pictures or names of the many objects around them which use air pressure *inside*. Some examples are bicycle, airplane, and auto tires, balloons, air mattresses, auto lifts at service stations, air drills used by construction workers, and air rifles.

evaluate critically

At early morning off the African coast, hundreds of Arab fishing vessels point out to sea as a fresh land breeze fills their colorful lateen sails. They return in the afternoon with sails taut from a sea breeze blowing in the opposite direction. You have probably experienced a similar shift of winds at the seashore, or by a large lake. How does this happen?

You remember that warmed air expands and is pushed up by denser, colder air which rushes in and replaces it. All winds are caused by the unequal heating and cooling of the earth's surface. During the day, solar radiation is absorbed by the sea and land. But the land heats up much faster. One reason is that the sun's warmth penetrates only a short distance below the land's surface, while sunlight penetrates more deeply into water. Another is the higher heat capacity of water. After a short period of sunlight, air immediately

Day

Night

FIGURE 8-7 Winds are caused by unequal heating and cooling of the Earth's surface.

above the earth is heated by conduction and begins expanding. Cooler heavier air from the sea rushes in and pushes the lighter air upward. The reverse occurs at night and until the following morning. During this period, the land cools quickly and stays cool, while the sea remains relatively warmer. As air warmed by contact with the water expands, it is pushed upward by cooler air rushing in from the cooler land.

These air movements are not confined to land and sea settings. The same basic air movements take place between any surfaces that have a temperature difference. As temperature differences increase, the subsequent wind force increases. This is one reason why a large fire is so destructive. It sets up a powerful, localized wind which fans and spreads the flames.

The world's prevailing winds are caused by the same phenomenon on a grand scale. But the earth's rotation adds a complicating factor. If the earth did not rotate, heavy cold air at the poles would flow due south and north in replacing warmed, rising equatorial air. The rotational effect, or *Coriolis force*, results in a wind deflection to the right in the northern hemisphere. A deflection to the left occurs in the southern hemisphere.

You can see why this happens with a globe and some chalk. Rotate the globe from west to east. While it is moving, draw a line from the North Pole due south toward the equator. Note that the line curves to the right. Draw a line from the South Pole and the curve is reversed.

Detailed understanding of wind patterns requires much more background than we can provide here. For example, we have briefly discussed jet streams. But there are other winds aloft to be studied. It is possible for an airplane pilot to encounter a wind blowing from one direction at 3000 feet and another blowing from another direction several thousand feet higher. It is impossible to explore this subject in detail at the primary level. But it will be worthwhile to help pupils learn that wind direction aloft may differ from surface wind direction.

Meteorologists use measuring instruments to observe small, helium-filled pilot balloons as they rise to various altitudes in calculating winds aloft. A cruder method is to observe cloud movements with a *nephoscope*, a circular mirror marked with the points of a compass. Properly aligned, this instrument can indicate the direction of cloud movement as the cloud reflection moves across the mirror. Pupils may employ a makeshift nephoscope in a forthcoming activity.

It will be most worthwhile in the following sequence to explore and emphasize many observational clues as to wind force and direction. With an able group, this should also be an opportune time to introduce the cardinal directions.

BASIC GENERALIZATION IV: Wind is moving air; it changes in force and direction

1. *Materials:* balloon; cardboard fan; newspaper or tissue-paper sheet; electric fan; toy pinwheel (optional); ribbon.

Ask class members to recall experiences of riding a bicycle or walking on a windy day. Encourage them to define wind. What is wind? Help them to recall several previous activities in which they demonstrated that air could move things. By opening the top of a plastic bag filled with air they could feel the escaping air. By swishing a cardboard through the air they could feel the air on their faces. Now several additional activities will help them to realize more fully that wind is moving air.

Let some air escape from a filled balloon. Direct the air stream against a pinwheel or the hands of several children. Have someone fan a cardboard rapidly, or start an electric fan before the pinwheel or children. Let them feel or see what happens.

Permit a pupil to stand before a moving fan while he holds a single, opened newspaper or tissue-paper sheet against his chest. If the fan is powerful enough, he will be able to release the paper. The wind force will hold it against his body. Let the children compare

*defi-
prob*

this with the experience of the wind outdoors blowing against their clothing.

Tie a ribbon or piece of string to a disconnected electric fan. Have everyone notice how it ripples after the fan is turned on.

Invite the children to tell what happened to the air in every case. (It moved.) Were they able to feel the air or did the pinwheel turn when the air was still? (No.) Would the paper have stayed up without air moving *draw* against it? (No.) Establish that the wind *usions* created in the classroom, and outdoors, are both moving air.

2. *Materials:* hot plate; pinwheel, or narrow strip of thin tissue paper about 4 inches long, tacked to a pencil end.

Express mock puzzlement. You understand how moving air or wind was made indoors with the different materials used, but how about the wind outdoors? What makes the air move outdoors?

After some discussion of this, mention that the following demonstration may help the class's thinking. Slowly pass the pinwheel or tissue-paper strip over an unconnected hot plate several times. Now turn the hot plate on. While the plate is heating for a moment, invite class members to predict what they think will happen when the pinwheel or strip are passed over it.

The pinwheel turns and the strip ripples noticeably as they are passed through the warmed, rising air. As they leave this area, the rippling motion and pinwheel stop. Help pupils understand that cooler air flows into the area from all sides, and takes the place of the rising warm air. It is this flow of air from the sides that is responsible for winds.

If desired, you may substitute two chalk-filled erasers for the pinwheel and tissue strip. Simply clap the erasers near, then over, the hot plate. The vertical movement of chalk dust will be clearly noticeable, particularly against a dark background.

luate But there is no hot plate outdoors. Develop *ically* that the sun provides the heat. As it warms the earth some air rises. Other air rushes in and takes the place of the rising air. To bring out that the ground is heated unevenly, have

FIGURE 8-8

the children recall their experiences when walking barefoot over grass and sand, or other varied ground surfaces. It may be desirable to place a pie plate of soil and one of water in the sun for ten minutes. Pupils can touch the soil surface and water to learn that soil heats up faster. Since the earth's surface heats and cools unevenly, point out that cooler air usually rushes in and replaces warmer, rising air. This causes local winds.

3. *Materials:* electric fan; wind vane (construct from a chalkboard eraser, pencil, straight pin, bead, straw, and feather, as in Figure 8-8); small piece of rope; matches; thin strip of tissue paper or ribbon; small pieces of paper.

Request those who like to fly kites to raise their hands. Point out that when several kites are flown at the same time in the same location, all face in the same direction—against the wind. (If a picture is available of several kites flying together, let all pupils notice this for themselves. Better still, should time and *draw* space be available, let some of them bring *conclusions* kites to school and discover this.)

Bring out that it is helpful to know in what direction the wind is blowing when flying a kite. It is also helpful for sailboat owners and airplane pilots. Ask for signs *evaluate* which might indicate wind direction. Discuss *critically* briefly. Now the class will learn additional things which can indicate wind direction.

Exhibit the above materials. Mention that the electric fan will be the wind source. In-

select procedures — vite the children to use as many materials as possible to indicate wind direction. Before any trials, have them first predict what will happen. The wind vane will always point into the wind. The ribbon or tissue-paper strip will always blow away from the wind, as will *draw conclusions* — smoke from the smoldering rope. Bits of paper will act in the same way when blown.

select procedures — Guide the children to make a list of some things they can observe outdoors which may give them clues about wind direction: flags flying, smoke from chimneys and fires, falling leaves, blown dust or paper, kites flying, clothes on clothes lines, water ripples and waves, wind vanes, and so on. If there is some wind, take them outdoors and let them *evaluate critically* — try to determine its direction. Challenge them to give reasons for their hypotheses, according to the clues just learned.

If your pupils seem able, it will be worthwhile to teach them the four cardinal directions. (Use a technique like that described in Unit 4, page 200.) Develop that a wind is named after the direction from which it comes.

suggest hypotheses — Draw out that wind force is also important when flying a kite. Guide the children to reason about how their wind directional clues would also indicate *no wind*, a *light wind*, a *fresh wind*, and a *strong wind*. If using a daily calendar, extend this information to include the daily weather. It will be more natural and less confusing to pupils to add one item of information at a time as it is studied, rather than to attempt recording everything at once. For example, begin with adding wind force now. Later, include temperature, clouds, and so on. (See page 325 for symbols that can be used for a complete weather chart. If possible, let the children invent some symbols with your guidance.)

Extending activities

evaluate critically — 1. Encourage class members to collect pictures for a bulletin board which indicate the effects of wind. Some scenes might show storm damage, ocean waves, iceboats and sailboats, windmills, kites, clothes on a line, and so on. After exhibiting all the pictures, en-courage the children to classify them in some manner; for example, "pleasant" and "unpleasant" winds, or "light winds" and "strong winds."

reason quanti — 2. Raise the question, "Why do airplane pilots usually land their planes into the wind?" Encourage children to bring their inexpensive balsa wood gliders or stick model airplanes. Guide experiments where distances taken for landing into and with the wind are measured through use of a long string. Help the children see that several trials are necessary and that planes must be thrown with the same force at equal heights. Have them ob-*draw conclu* — serve that the landing speed may be greatly reduced when landing into the wind. This controlled experiment will also provide another opportunity for pupils to estimate wind direction and force for a purpose "that counts" in their view.

3. Acquaint pupils with a homemade nephoscope. This instrument can be used to detect winds aloft by watching the directions of cloud movements. A mirror ($5 \times 6''$ is a useful size), a pencil, and a small white paper cutout of a "cloud" will be needed. Place the mirror on the floor. Have a child kneel by the mirror and watch the cloud reflection as the mirror is moved overhead in a specific direction by another child. Let the observer point to the direction of movement with a pencil without lifting his head. The class can *evalu critic* — verify his accuracy by noting how the two directions compare.

After several trials, let children try to track actual cloud movements outdoors. Encourage all pupils to bring mirrors and compare their results of cloud tracking. When results differ, help them to decide how they will *select proce* — improve the accuracy of their observations. One way will be to use some common reference point. If the class seems capable, this may serve as an excellent purpose to teach the cardinal directions.

In parts of Southern California and Mexico, it is sometimes possible in winter to observe snowy mountain peaks while lying on a warm, sunny beach. Children are curious about conditions like this. ("Aren't the mountain peaks closer to the warm sun?") Most adults know that air temperatures are lower at higher altitudes. But why?

One cause is the varying distance of air molecules from the earth's surface. Air molecules closest to the earth are warmed more easily by conduction and heat waves radiated from the earth's surface than those farther away.

Secondly, as we get closer to sea level, more and more molecules are piled up. This increased weight compresses the air. With reduced space for movement, there is more energy exchange among molecules as they collide. Thus, the heat energy in the denser molecule "population" is concentrated into a relatively low, dense layer.

There is also a third reason. As warmed air rises any great distance it expands and cools as it encounters lower air pressure with the increased altitude. Whatever heat energy is contained in the original air parcel is dissipated throughout an ever larger volume.

The combined effect of these causes results in rising air cooling about five and one-half degrees Fahrenheit with every 1000 feet in altitude. As sinking air is compressed, the opposite happens.

As we saw in Unit 3, our atmosphere is a gigantic greenhouse which retards the loss of heat received from solar radiation. Fortunately, the earth loses and gains about the same amount of heat each day. A narrow temperature range enables life to continue. Since the Industrial Revolution, however, conditions have been developing which may upset this delicate balance.

The increased burning of such fuels as coal and oil to provide heat energy has resulted, after 200 years, in an estimated increase of 2 per cent more carbon dioxide in the air around us. Why is this important? Carbon dioxide is relatively opaque to heat waves radiated from the earth. Therefore, the earth is losing slightly less heat than it gains from solar radiation. The air temperature seems to be rising very gradually. Some scientists estimate that a 10 per cent increase of carbon dioxide will raise the air temperature enough to melt the earth's polar ice caps. If this happens, many great cities along the world's coastlines will be flooded into extinction.

The solution? Some consideration has been given to nuclear energy as a substitute for the fossil fuels. But think of the tremendous difficulties in international economics and diplomacy that first must be overcome.

In the following sequence, pupils can be helped to learn how to measure air temperature with the thermometer. A simple bar graph will show them what happens to air temperature during the day. If desired, measurements can be extended over longer time periods.

Several children may ask why some thermometers have a "silver line" and some a "colored line." Bring out that some contain mercury and others colored alcohol. Whichever is used, be sure that they are placed in the shade, and several or more feet off the ground, when recording air temperatures. When a thermometer is placed in the sun, its glass tube absorbs some heat energy and records a misleading temperature. If too close to the ground, some heat energy coming from the warm ground itself may distort the temperature reading.

Of course, we rely on many indicators other than thermometers to estimate temperatures. Although our skin temperature is a rough but useful indicator, we must rely on other means when observing a distant scene through a telescope or viewing a picture. How people dress, pale slanting sunlight, snowy peaks, denuded trees, the kinds of animal life, and so on, all give temperature clues to the observant person.

Perhaps the most unusual temperature indicator is the cricket. Being a variable-temperatured ("cold-blooded") animal, its basal metabolism rate is slowed or speeded by comparatively small changes in temperature. Some warm evening, count the number of chirps a cricket makes for exactly 15 seconds. Add 37 to this figure, and then check a re-

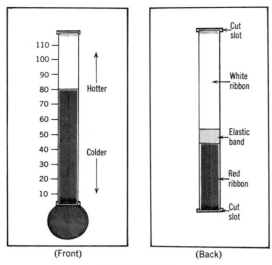

FIGURE 8-9

liable thermometer. Your results should not be off more than several degrees.

BASIC GENERALIZATION V: Temperature is how warm something is; a thermometer reading changes with the temperature

1. *Materials:* two magazine pictures, one showing a child wearing heavy winter clothing, the other light summer clothing; household thermometer; rubber band; glass container of ice cubes and water; candle and matches, or hot plate.

Remind your pupils that they have learned many signs that have helped to indicate the condition of the air. Now they will learn others. Hold up the pictures. What do they probably show about the air? (It may be hot or cold.) Bring out that *temperature* refers to how hot or cold something is.

evaluate critically

Exhibit the thermometer. How does this tell about hot and cold? At least some children will recognize its use, but many or most will be in doubt about how it works. Raise conjecture about the colored line. What happens to it when the temperature gets colder? Warmer? Indicate the materials. How can they be used to check what happens?

select procedures

Before the thermometer is dipped into the

ice water, elicit need for a control. How will the class tell whether the line goes up or down? A rubber band can mark the former place. The same procedure can be used when this instrument is held over the candle flame or hot plate. (Be sure the thermometer is not held too close, as the liquid may rapidly expand and break the tube.)

If another thermometer is available, have the children duplicate the experiment. Will it work the same way? Guide toward a tentative conclusion about how thermometers indicate the temperature.

evalu[ate] critic[ally]

draw concl[usions]

2. *Materials:* large cardboard thermometer model. Construct from a piece of chipboard, red and white ribbons, elastic band. Paint numerals black and the bulb red. (See Figure 8-9.)

Call attention to the model thermometer. Establish that it has numerals similar to those on the real thermometer. Demonstrate how the movable ribbon can simulate a rising and falling liquid column. Have the class practice reading the numerals. Many primary children have no difficulty with multiples of 10. If the class is able, put four equally spaced lines in between the numerals so pupils can make readings in multiples of 2. Multiples of 5 may be more difficult.

Invite someone to look at the real thermometer and adjust the model's ribbon to about the same relative level. A large magnifying glass held over the smaller thermometer will enlarge the numerals for easier viewing by all.

Introduce the term *degrees.* Develop that there are degrees of temperature. Help the children understand that comparisons of temperature in degrees are more useful than the terms "cold" and "hot." Construct questions to get them used to this notion: Is 70° hotter than 80°? Is 40° colder than 50°? What are all the degrees on our model which would be colder than 30°? Warmer than 90°?

reaso[n] quan[titatively]

3. *Materials:* an outside thermometer hung in the shade; scissors; straight pins; thermometer. (See Figure 8-10 for completed version.)

The following activity will help show the children that the daily temperature varies, and will provide them an opportunity to learn how to make and interpret a bar graph.

Initiate a discussion about temperatures during the day. Is the morning cooler than at lunch time? How about dismissal time, etc.? Have children adjust the model thermometer to show the possible temperatures.

Exhibit your chart. Draw out how an hourly air temperature record might be kept for this day. How closely will these temperatures agree with those suggested? Two children can check the outside temperature and *select* then adjust the model thermometer ribbon *dures* accordingly. Strips of red construction paper can be pinned on the chart each time. For proper lengths, first have each strip placed next to the adjusted model thermometer ribbon and snipped off at the proper place. Have one red strip ready for each hour the temperature will be taken.

eason Take a few moments before dismissal time *tively* to interpret the resulting graph. At what time was it warmest? Coolest? What were the two hours that showed the greatest change? Least change? Help the children learn to extrapolate—and learn the dangers of extrapolation. Is the three o'clock temperature likely to be lower or higher than the two o'clock temperature? How can we make sure? (Take a three o'clock reading.)

If weather records are included with the daily calendar, it may now be useful to add the daily temperature. Or a graph similar to the one in Figure 8-10 may be initiated and kept by the children for a week or longer.

Extending activities

1. Have an exhibition of various thermometers: meat, refrigerator, clinical, candy, *luate* aquarium, and household. Encourage pupils *ically* to look at oven and automobile thermometers after school. Have them identify the specific purpose of each.

2. Encourage everyone to bring pictures for a bulletin board. One section might illustrate how people dress when it is cold and warm. Another might show pictures of warm and cold places. Bring out some clues in these pictures which might indicate temperatures:

FIGURE 8-10

vegetation, animal life, snow, slanting sunlight, great heights, and so on. Caution about jumping to conclusions.

Many younger children find it difficult to believe that a tangible substance, such as water, can disappear into air. Therefore, it is advisable to begin a study of evaporation with examples that are well within the scope of their immediate experiences. We begin the next activity sequence with some sketches of an aquarium from which water is disappearing. If an aquarium is handy, it may be desirable to use it for an introductory bridge in place of the suggested sketches.

In Unit 1 (page 115) we saw that both heat and atmospheric pressure have an effect on an evaporating liquid. Increased heat energy increases the speed of molecules. Additional speed enables them to overcome the cohesive forces of nearby molecules and greater numbers leave the liquid's surface than before. Any decrease of atmospheric pressure affects evaporation because it tends to "take the lid off." The counterforce of air molecules pressing down on the surface of an evaporating liquid becomes weaker, and more evaporation takes place.

It is easy to see why increasing a liquid's surface area increases the rate of evaporation. There is greater exposure to the air above and a higher probability of more molecules escaping. This is why we have to add water oftener to a rectangular aquarium than to a

FIGURE 8-11   A homemade psychrometer.

fish bowl of equal volume. The wind speeds up evaporation, too. When air immediately above the surface of an evaporating fluid becomes quickly saturated, the wind blows it away and replaces it with drier air.

Another factor influencing evaporation is *humidity*, the amount of moisture already present in the air. On humid days we feel sticky and uncomfortable because our perspiration evaporates very slowly. We may turn on an electric fan to feel more comfortable. But moving air from a fan cools us mainly because it speeds up evaporation of perspiration from the skin. In the absence of an evaporating liquid a fan has practically no cooling effect at all. This may be seen by putting a thermometer in front of a whirling electric fan. There is no difference in the before and after readings. But dampen some cotton and stick it to the thermometer bulb. The rapidly evaporating water will now cause a noticeable drop in temperature.

The moisture content of air varies considerably from time to time. The capacity of air to contain moisture is related to its temperature—warm air holds more moisture than cooler air. The amount of moisture present in a given volume of air at a certain tempera-

ture, compared to the maximum amount it could hold at that temperature, is called its *relative humidity*. During a period of low relative humidity, our skin moisture evaporates more quickly than it can be effectively replaced. This results in dry, chapped skin.

One reason we have more colds in winter may be directly related to the relative humidity of air in our homes. The cool air of winter holds comparatively little moisture. As it is warmed by heaters, its capacity to contain more moisture increases. Unless the home heating system is equipped to provide additional moisture, the air becomes increasingly dry. The protective mucous film that coats the delicate nasal membrane evaporates, and we may become more susceptible to infections.

Relative humidity is often measured with a wet-and-dry bulb thermometer apparatus called a *psychrometer*. Two identical thermometers are placed next to each other. The bulb of one instrument is enclosed in a wet cotton wick which is immersed in water just before use. The wet-bulb thermometer is fanned rapidly until its reading steadies at some lower point. As water evaporates from the wick, it is continually replaced by water traveling upward through the wick by capillary action. Any difference in thermometer readings is translated into the percentage of relative humidity by consulting a reference table.

We close this section with several possibilities for extending pupils' abilities in data gathering and analysis of faulty procedure (controls). It will be worthwhile to get as many suggestions as possible from the children before providing guidance in these experiences.

BASIC GENERALIZATION VI: Water evaporates into the air; evaporation is affected by wind, temperature, and amount of water surface exposed to the air

1. *Materials:* two identical, wide-mouthed jars with screw caps; water; sketches of Figure 8-12 A-B-C. (Put each sketch on a large, separate card.)

The following bridge may be helpful in getting pupils to identify the problem which leads into the next experiment. We begin with simple evaporation.

"Class, let's say you are in charge of an aquarium for a long time. Here is how it looks." (Show sketch A and have the children briefly identify the two plants and fish. Now put this sketch face down on a table and continue.)

"After a few weeks, here is how the aquarium looks." (Show sketch B but discourage comments. Place this sketch on the table also.)

"After more weeks have passed, here is how it looks. (Show C.) Sometime soon, you are going to have a problem with this aquarium. Does anyone know what it is?"

efine lems

If no one knows, show the cards again in sequence. If necessary, place them side-by-side for easy comparisons. Some children may immediately say, "The tank is leaking." Help them understand that they could be jumping

luate ically

to a conclusion. Do we *know* the tank is leaking from these pictures? Develop that the only thing these pictures show is that the

FIGURE 8-12 A–B–C

water level is getting lower. What seems to be the problem? (Why is the water level getting lower?)

Invite possible causes for this condition:

suggest hypotheses

Maybe the tank is leaky.
Maybe the tank is "soaking up" the water.
Maybe the fish drank it.
Maybe the water is going into the air.

Help the children screen their hypotheses through discussion and experiments. Guide them toward the last idea: What happens to puddles after a rain? Wet clothes on clothes lines? Encourage a test with the two jars. How can they be used to see if water goes into the air?

select procedures

Both jars can be filled to an identical level, with one capped and the other left exposed to the air. Both should be put in the same place, such as a window sill. The next day there should be a noticeable difference in water levels.

Introduce the term *evaporation*. Let children name many familiar situations in which water may evaporate: wet sidewalks and streets become dry; also wet hands, lawns, rivers, ponds, and so on. Water is going into the air everywhere around them.

draw conclusions

2. *Materials*: electric fan, pan of water; two identical handkerchiefs; string; hot plate or sunlight.

To lead into activities showing that evaporation is speeded up by wind and heat, try this bridge. "What are some of the ways in which your mothers dry laundered clothes? When outdoor clothes lines are used, on some days the clothes dry very quickly. At other times, it may take most of the day before they are dry. Why is that?"

suggest hypotheses

Help the children isolate sunny and windy days as possible aids to evaporation. Bring out that sunny days are usually warmer than cloudy days, and that occasionally, wet clothes are hung before heaters. (Develop briefly the possible danger of doing this close to a heater.) Guide toward an experiment with either the hot plate or sun as the source of heat. The two identical handkerchiefs may be soaked in water, and wrung out with equal force. One should be placed on a line stretched over a hot plate or in the sun. The second handkerchief could be placed on the same line but should be away from the hot plate or in the shade.

select procedures

draw conclusions

The same basic procedure will do for testing the effect of wind. Substitute a fan for the hot plate or sun. Guide pupils to do these experiments several times, and to switch handkerchiefs on each subsequent retrial.

select procedures

draw conclusions

To help the group develop beginning notions about the additional effect of humidity on evaporation you might ask: "What are foggy days like? When there is much water in the air will clothes dry as fast as on a sunny, dry day? Whom can we ask to find out? Why would they know? Should we see how many mothers agree?"

evaluate critically

3. *Materials*: cake or pie tin; two drinking glasses; water.

To introduce the idea of surface area as it affects evaporation, try the bridge introduced in Chapter 3:

"Does anyone here own a dog? What does it need to have, especially on a hot day? Let me tell you about a girl who found out something very interesting. Each day, she filled her dog's bowl with water. (Draw a bowl of small circumference on the chalkboard, with a dotted line to show a near-full water level.) At night, it was usually about half empty. (Draw another dotted line halfway down across the bowl.) One day, though, the bowl got lost and she had to use another one. It held as much water as the old one, but it was shaped in a different way. (Draw a picture of a cake or pie tin now. Or postpone this until later, if you wish to provide fewer clues.) Now each night she noticed that the water in this bowl was almost gone. Why was there always less water left over in this bowl than the other one?"

After such logical guesses as the bowl was cracked, the dog drank more water, and so on, help the children focus on the shape of each bowl. For the experiment, guide them to use a glass for one bowl, and a cake tin for the second. Watch for omission of controls. Lead children to determine a way in which equal volumes of water are to be poured into the containers. A bit of tape on the pouring glass can serve to mark any desired water volume.

sugg hyp

selec proc

Have the pupils examine results the next day. Emphasize any disagreement as to which bowl contains the least water. Guide them to see that a precise comparison can be made by carefully pouring the remaining water into two identical glasses. Assist in forming the tentative conclusion that a larger surface area increases evaporation.

draw conc

Guide applications of this idea to pupils' experiences. Why does an opened, spread-out bathing suit dry faster than one that is crumpled into a ball? Why does father sweep out water puddles over a wider area on the drive-

eval crit

way? Let them try some applications with actual materials, if possible.

Extending activities

*select
dures

1. Try this activity to extend pupils' thinking in developing an experiment. Materials needed are a yardstick, two tacks, string, a paper cup filled with weights (such as small stones and paper clips), a towel, and water.

Tell the class, "You have found out that water evaporates. If we wet this towel it will dry. But let's say someone thinks the water just soaks deeply into the towel, so you can't feel it. How could you show him that the water has left the towel and gone into the air?"

Entertain speculation. To provide clues, have someone feel the weight of the towel before and after immersing it in water. Wring it out to prevent dripping. If necessary, suspend the yardstick and ask how it can be used. Pupils' input with previous balance experiments may help them perform a similar experiment now. The wet towel can be tacked on one end of the yardstick, while the cup containing stones and paper clips is tacked on the other end. Once a perfect balance is achieved—the paper clips will help effect small changes in weight—any significant evaporation of water from the towel should cause a noticeable imbalance.

*draw
sions*

After the towel is completely dry, pin a paper cup on it. Lead pupils to see that pouring water into the cup will enable them to rebalance the stick, and also provide a crude measure of the amount of evaporated water. (Bring out that the pin and cup have weight, too.) If some pupils are very able, challenge them to demonstrate a way in which the amount of evaporated water can be found before providing them any guidance.

2. Gather several shallow containers of widely varying circumferences and fill them with *different* amounts of water. Try to keep the differences in water volume from being obvious. Ask the class to predict the correct order of evaporation from these containers, from most to least, in a day. When unexpected results are obtained, challenge the

*'uate
cally*

class to detect why. Encourage repeated experiments before conclusions are drawn.

On many mornings, we see dew drops glistening on lawns, parked automobiles, spider webs, and other surfaces. When the ground cools during the night, its temperature may fall below that of the surrounding air. As the surrounding air loses some heat energy, its molecules slow down. Water vapor molecules in the air slow sufficiently to be attracted to, and condense on, a cool nearby surface. Essentially the same thing happens when water droplets form on a cold pop bottle or cold water pipe.

The relative humidity of air is related to its temperature. Any parcel of air containing some water vapor becomes saturated if cooled enough. The loss of heat energy slows down molecular speed and reduces the range of molecular movement. The attractions of water molecules for one another now draw them together into drops.

The temperature at which condensation takes place is called the *dew point*. In very humid air, as in a steamy shower room, water vapor condenses on walls and mirrors although they may be only several degrees cooler than the air. But comparatively dry desert air may have to be cooled more than 50 degrees before reaching its dew point.

A forthcoming activity calls for observation of dew on the outside of a shiny metal can containing ice cubes and water. If a condition of low humidity exists in the classroom, very little or no moisture may collect on the can unless the can temperature can be reduced. Just add a few spoons of salt to the water. This will cause the ice cubes to melt faster and thus reduce the temperature even more. By substituting dry ice (frozen carbon dioxide), the can temperature will drop below freezing. In this case, condensation will occur in the form of frost. This is what happens to the freezing compartment of a refrigerator; thus, periodic defrosting is needed. Below freezing temperatures also produce frost in place of dew on the ground.

Fog may occur when the surface temperature is low enough to cool air a short distance above the ground to its dew point. In this case, water vapor condenses on tiny specks of airborne dust and remains suspended. Sometimes fog results from the unequal cooling of land and water. Such fog is common over a lake in summer. Cool air from the land flows over warm, moist air rising from the lake. As the warmer air cools to its dew point, condensation occurs and we see fog. Fog can be considered a low cloud.

Clouds at higher altitudes are formed in several ways, but all involve a parcel of air that is cooled to its saturation or dew point. In one method, wind may blow moist air up a mountain slope. As the air rises, it expands because of decreasing air pressure, cools, and condenses on airborne dust particles. If the dew point is below freezing, tiny ice crystals may form. Sometimes air may be pushed aloft when two huge air masses merge. The cooler, heavier air mass will push under the warmer, lighter mass. Again expansion, cooling, and condensation take place. A third method of cloud formation occurs when heat from the ground develops convection currents. The affected air near the ground becomes increasingly unstable, rises rapidly, and cools, and its moisture condenses.

When sufficient moisture is present, the tiny, constantly moving droplets within a cloud collide from time to time and form larger drops. These may fall as rain. In freezing temperatures, ice crystals collect and fall as snow.

Knowledge of the air temperature and its dew point enables us to roughly calculate cloud heights. Here is how it is done. Suppose the outdoor air temperature is now 88°F. Stir a thermometer around in a metal can of ice water. At the exact instant water droplets occur on the can, read the temperature of the immersed thermometer. This is the dew point. Let us say it reads 66°F, which makes a difference of 22°F between the two figures. Remember that rising air cools at about 5.5°F for each 1000 feet of altitude. Dividing 22 by 5.5 gives a quotient of 4. Multiply this figure by 1000. The bases of nearby clouds should be about 4000 feet high.

Although experts have invented over 200 cloud classifications, even young children can be taught to recognize the three basic cloud forms. *Cirrus* clouds are high, wispy formations of ice crystals. *Cumulus* clouds are white, fluffy, and usually associated with clear visibility and fair weather. *Stratus* clouds are lower, darker formations that appear as a dense layer. These clouds may blanket the entire sky and precipitate rain within a short time.

If selected pupils identify clouds, have them use actual clouds and authentic pictures of clouds. Avoid using cotton or hand-drawn cloud models. These seem to develop misconceptions in some children. Should a few able children wish to pursue cloud classification beyond the three basic types, have them consult an encyclopedia for additional illustrations.

The earth's cloud cover provides many clues for weather forecasting. Through use of weather satellites continually orbiting the earth, it is now possible to relay pictures of cloud formations to international data processing centers. As additional information becomes available, increased accuracy of forecasting, particularly long-range forecasting, appears probable.

We shall use several activities in the following sequence to introduce the water-cycle concept. Water evaporates, condenses, and falls without apparent end. The raindrops we see today may have dampened an ancient forest whose remains we now burn as coal. For many pupils, this will be their first conscious encounter with the conservation of matter-energy principle.

It is probable that some children at this level will be unable to understand fully the water cycle or the analogy used to demonstrate how rain occurs. Although it may be too soon to teach for mastery of these ideas, pupils should profit from the present exposure.

Cirrus

Cumulus

Stratus

FIGURE 8-13   **Three basic cloud forms.**

BASIC GENERALIZATION VII: Air contains moisture which condenses when it cools; water evaporates and condenses, over and over

1. *Materials*: spoon; sugar; ink; two clean, identical tinned cans; ice cubes; container of water (at about room temperature).

To lead into experiments on condensation, guide children to discuss their experiences with drinking beverages. Have them recall that sometimes the containers holding these liquids feel wet. Draw out that this seems to happen when a container is cool. Does it *select procedures* have to be cool? Invite a test with some of the provided materials.

Help them plan. Two cans of water will be used, one with and one without ice cubes. Shortly, a beaded film of water should ap-

A

B

C

FIGURE 8-14 A–B–C

pear all over the cooler can. It may be wise to postpone extensive comments until the next activity is concluded.

Introduce a related problem: Where does the water come from? Bring out only two places are feasible, from inside or outside the can. Encourage critical thought: If the cooled *evalua* can is leaking why didn't the other one leak? *critica* Perhaps someone will suggest that the contents of the two cans be switched at this point. The same results should occur.

There are at least three additional ways pupils can test for a leaking can. Give hints *select* if necessary: *proce*

a. Are there water drops *above* the water level inside the can?

b. How can sugar be used to tell?

c. How can ink be used to tell?

Provide needed assistance in if-then thinking. If the can is leaking, then water would probably appear only at or below the water level. If sugar is added to the water inside, and the water outside tastes sugarless, then . . . . If ink is added and the outside water is uncolored, then . . . . Draw out that the *draw* water appears to be coming from the air sur- *concl* rounding the cooled container.

Identify this event as *condensation*—the opposite of evaporation. Moisture in the air can collect on cooler things. Bring out the children's related experiences with condensation. During a shower or bath, warm moist air *condenses* on the cooler bathroom mirror and walls. Warm, moist air inside a house may condense on the inside of a cooler window. Water in the air condenses on cold water pipes in a basement.

2. *Materials*: sketches of Figure 8-14 A-B-C. (Have all the sketches on one large paper.)

The next several experiences will help pupils connect evaporation and condensation to the water cycle. Exhibit the sketches. Bring out that the warm sun is evaporating water from the ocean in sketch A. Raise a question: With water evaporating from the earth all the time, why doesn't everything dry up? The next two sketches will help the children to think about this. Develop that in B the water vapor has risen far away from the warm earth.

Calm   Breezy   Windy

(Use the large, movable thermometer model)

Sunny   Partly cloudy   Cloudy

Rainy   Snowy   Clear

FIGURE 8-15

WHAT IS THE WEATHER TODAY?

The wind is:

The outside temperature is:

The sky is:

The weather is:

Clear

FIGURE 8-16

As the vapor rises higher it gets colder. The vapor now condenses on tiny bits of dust and clouds are formed. More and more moisture collects and many tiny water drops come together and become larger. In C, the larger *draw* drops fall as rain. Point back at A. What hap-*nclusions* pens after the rain? (The clouds disappear and water evaporates into the air again.) Emphasize that this cycle continues without end. The same water is used over and over again.

3. *Materials:* several eye-droppers; several glasses of water; a small piece of waxed paper and a toothpick for *each pair* of pupils (for greater pupil participation).

Distribute the waxed paper and toothpicks among pairs of pupils. Have several children use eye-droppers to place four water drops on each piece of waxed paper, an inch or so apart.

Inform everyone that these materials will help them understand how tiny droplets in a cloud become larger and larger before they fall. Let the children take turns pushing the water drops around the paper. They will dis-

cover that when several water drops are close together they suddenly fuse and become a larger drop. Emphasize that in a cloud, the water drops are much smaller. Also, they move around because of air movements in the cloud.

4. *Materials:* teakettle containing about an inch of water; hot plate; tray or pan of ice cubes; previous sketches of Figure 8-14 A-B-C.

From the sketches, draw out that three *draw* things were needed for rain to occur: water, *conclusions* a source of heat to evaporate the water, and dust particles on which the cooling water could condense. Indicate the materials. Will these act in the same way? We will use the teakettle for water. The hot plate will help the water to evaporate. The cold tray will be used to help the evaporated water condense.

Set the teakettle on the hot plate. When it begins emitting visible water vapor, place the cold tray in the "cloud." Water vapor will soon condense into large water drops and fall as "rain." Carefully review this analogy with *evaluate* your pupils to assist their understanding. *critically*

Extending activities

reason quantitatively

1. It will be interesting and helpful to continue and extend the daily weather chart to include sky and precipitation reports. Figure 8-15 contains examples of useful symbols. Each morning, have the children decide from their weather observations which symbol is most appropriate among the several categories provided. Figure 8-16 reveals a typical chart for primary children.

2. Discuss how weather affects farmers, sailors, aviators, workers in the building trades, road construction, and transportation. Develop how weather affects everyone. Show a newspaper weather forecast. Bring out how the weather bureau is of service in predicting weather. Leave pupils with the realization that in future grades they will learn more about forecasting and other interesting things about the weather.

draw conclus

The Earth in Space

(*Upper*)

"The sky's the limit."

"What goes up must come down."

"Heaven is up above; the other place is down below."

Even tricycle riders today smile at these clichés. Television, space movies, and magazines have given children a beyond-the-earth outlook unknown to previous generations. But few children learn outside of school the basic ideas and physical laws that give meaning to the motions of objects in space. We shall concentrate on several of these in this unit.

Some teachers would ask, "*Can* astronomy units be thoroughly taught at the elementary school level?" Admittedly, there are difficulties. For example, no one can truly comprehend the limitless expanse of space and time represented by the universe. Moreover, tools of instruction are likely to be models and analogies, which demand analytical thinking and reasoned applications—not easy tasks for children.

Yet many teachers do a surprisingly effective job. These persons often use films and filmstrips with their models. They provide for much pupil participation. Their questions are often carefully planned and ordered to help children reason. These practices are especially commended for this unit.

BASIC GENERALIZATIONS

I. The earth's motions in space cause time and seasonal changes.

II. The relative motions of the sun, earth, and moon bring about moon phases, eclipses, the tides.

III. The solar system contains nine planets which revolve at different distances around the sun; the solar system is only a tiny part of a vast universe.

IV. Gravity and the laws of motion affect the movements of planets, satellites, and rockets.

Most upper-grade children know the earth rotates. But few can tell in which direction. Since the rotation apparently causes the sun to rise in a generally eastern direction and set in a generally western direction, at least some good thinkers will figure this out for themselves. Only a west to east rotation produces this effect.

Figure 9-1 indicates how a person on the east coast moves into the sunlight. To him, it looks as though the sun is rising from the horizon, climbing higher as time goes by. Six hours from the time he first observes "sunrise" the sun is closest to being directly overhead. This is noon. Gradually, he continues to rotate counterclockwise. Shadows grow longer. Around 6 P.M. it is almost twilight, and the sun appears to sink into the western horizon. The next 12 hours he spends in darkness, until once again the sun appears to rise. A complete rotation takes 24 hours, or one complete day.

Expect some trouble with the term "day," since it has two meanings—the hours during which it is light, and the time for one complete rotation. Use of the terms "complete day" and "daylight" to differentiate should eliminate confusion.

Of course, the preceding is an incomplete explanation. We know that summer days are longer than winter days, for example. (We shall take up why shortly.) Also, it would be extremely inconvenient to judge time by the sun's apparent passage overhead. Every location more than a few miles away would have a different time as the sun reached its noon position. Though this was not a problem in the days of slow-moving transportation, it became intolerable when railroads were established.

The problem was solved in 1833 by creating four standard time zones in the United States. Figure 9-2 shows those in use today in the continental United States. We set our watches ahead going eastward, and back going westward. The entire globe is now divided into 24 time zones, 15 degrees apart. (This distance was determined by dividing 360°—the earth is a near sphere—by 24 hours.)

Persons in New York on any December 22nd experience about 9 hours of daylight and 15 hours of darkness. Six months later the reverse occurs. To see why, let us first examine Figure 9-3. Notice that the earth's axis is tilted twenty-three and one-half degrees. As the earth revolves about the sun, its axis continues to point in the same direction—north. Check the winter position. Because of the tilt, the northern hemisphere is in darkness longer than in daylight. One can see this merely by checking the length of the top parallel of latitude shown (Tropic of Cancer). In the summer position, we see the reverse. Now the same latitude is exposed for a much longer period to sunlight. At the "in between" periods—spring and fall—day and night periods are more nearly equal.

Also observe that the southern hemisphere experiences opposite conditions to those in the northern hemisphere. While New York shivers in December, the beaches in sunny Rio de Janeiro are crowded with swimmers and sun bathers enjoying their summer.

But there is another reason summers are warmer than winters besides increased length of the days. The sun's rays are more nearly overhead at summer than at other times. Note that we said, "more nearly overhead." Because the earth's axis is tilted, the sun at noon can never be completely vertical (at a 90° angle) north of the Tropic of Cancer or south of the Tropic of Capricorn.

If you ask a pupil to explain why it is warmer in summer than winter, don't be surprised if he replies, "The earth is closer to the sun." This is entirely logical, even though it is wrong. In fact, the opposite is true. The earth's path (orbit) around the sun is a slightly elongated circle, or ellipse, as are virtually all the orbits of celestial bodies. In winter we are 3 million miles closer to the sun than in summer. However, since this distance is relatively small compared to the average distance, about 93 million miles, the effect is generally negligible.

BASIC GENERALIZATION I: The earth's motions in space cause time and seasonal changes

Contributing idea A. The earth's rotation in sunlight causes time changes.

Materials: filmstrip projector; darkened room; sketch or opaque projection of Figure 9-2.

Take time to acquaint the children with their new unit and to gain some insight into what they already know. What does "The Earth in Space" mean to them? How does the earth move in space? How does the moon affect the earth? What causes seasonal changes? What are planets and stars? What problems must be overcome to launch a space satellite?

Mention that the pupils already know some of the earth's motions in space. Review how the earth's *rotation* in sunlight causes night and day. This can be demonstrated with a filmstrip projector and globe. But in which direction does the earth rotate? From west to east, or east to west? Review what *north*, *south*, *east* and *west* mean if necessary.

Have the class remember that the sun appears to rise in the east and set in the west. Tip the globe toward the class, as in Figure 9-1. Where is the east coast of the United States? West coast? Should the rotation be clockwise or counterclockwise? To find out, we can try it both ways.

Let someone darken the room and turn on the filmstrip projector. Rotate the globe counterclockwise. Establish that the east coast is experiencing sunrise as it turns into the light. Continue rotating until the west coast disappears into the shadow. This is sunset. Reverse the rotation. The children should *draw* see that only a counterclockwise rotation *clusions* makes the sun seem to rise in the east and set in the west. Establish that one complete rotation takes 24 hours. This is one *complete day*.

Now that we know where sunrise and sunset take place, where is the United States' east coast position at noon? Guide a child to rotate the globe until the east coast is mid-*evaluate* way between the sunrise and sunset borders. *critically* Slowly rotate the globe in the "sun." At each point where the sun is closest to directly overhead it is noon. The midwest has noon next, and the west coast last.

If noon is always where the sun is highest overhead, how can we know what time it is in another nearby city? A town only a hundred miles west of a location where the sun is highest would not have its noontime until several minutes later. What would happen if everyone set his watch at noon only when the *evaluate* sun was highest overhead? (Everyone more *critically* than a few miles apart would have different times showing on their watches.) Bring out the ensuing chaos in bus, train, airline, television, and radio schedules.

Exhibit a sketch or opaque projection of *draw* Figure 9-2. How is this problem solved? Let *clusions* the children study the sketch. Draw out that the continental United States is divided into four *standard time zones*. The people living in each zone agree to set their watches and

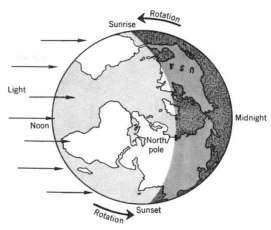

FIGURE 9-1

clocks to the same time, whether the sun is directly overhead or not. In this way, a watch needs only to be changed three times as one flies or drives from one coast to another.

Quiz the children to help clinch their understanding. When it is noon in New York what time is it in San Francisco? and so on.

Write *ante meridien* and *post meridien* on the chalkboard. These are Latin words. The first means before mid-day, the second after mid-day. Can someone guess their abbreviations? Instead of saying or writing "9 in the morning" or "9 in the evening," we use the abbreviations.

Have everyone note that the time zone boundaries are uneven. Help the children notice that otherwise some states and large urban areas would be in two zones, which would be inconvenient. Emphasize that the entire world is divided into 24 time zones of equal size, one for each hour of the complete day.

Contributing idea B. The earth's tilted axis and revolution about the sun cause seasonal changes.

1. *Materials:* slide projector; 2- by 2-inch piece of wire screen; clay; string; globe; darkened room.

Develop that, in addition to rotating, the earth also *revolves* about the sun. Take the classroom globe and, while rotating it slowly, move around a pupil who acts as the sun.

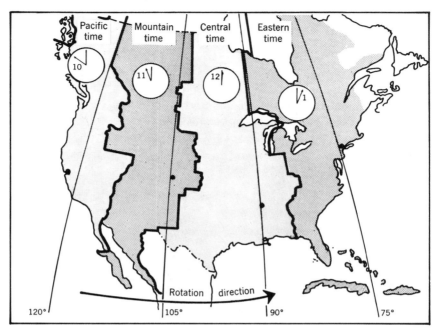

FIGURE 9-2

Emphasize that the earth's tilted axis continues to point in one direction—toward the north star—throughout the revolution. The entire revolution takes about 365 days, or one year. That is, the earth rotates 365 times during one revolution.

Pose a problem. On December 22, New York City has about 9 hours of daylight and 15 hours of darkness. On June 21, it has the reverse. Why? Discuss briefly.

Darken the room. Turn on a slide projector or unshaded lamp. (A projector gives a much sharper definition of light and shadow.) Place the globe in the winter position shown in Figure 9-3. Fix a small lump of clay at the position of New York City, so that it may be easily observed. Slowly rotate the globe at a reasonably uniform rate of speed. Is this location longer in darkness or light? Help someone measure with string how much of New *reason* York's latitude—the forty-first north parallel *quantitatively* —is in darkness and in light. (About 9/24 is in light, 15/24 in darkness.) Chalkboard lines can be drawn to compare these two lengths. For convenience in measuring, reduce these fractions to 3/8 and 5/8. Then

change them to twenty-fourths to represent hours. (This will confuse slower pupils.)

Now place the globe in the June 21 position. Rotate the globe slowly. The forty-first parallel now seems to be longer in daylight than darkness. Measure again with string. The previous findings should be reversed. Bring out that the unchanging tilt of the *draw* earth's axis and opposite orbital positions *conclus* cause the difference.

Let pupils hypothesize about, and then *suggest* measure, portions of light and darkness at the *hypoth* fall and spring positions. They should be *reason* roughly equal in each case. Elicit names of *quantit* the four seasons as the globe is placed in ap- *draw* propriate positions. *conclus*

2. Is summer warmer only because the days are longer? Winter colder only because days are shorter? What might be another reason? Encourage conjecture based on the children's *suggest* observations. Hold up a piece of 2- by 2-inch *hypoth* screen material. Place it in the slide projector slot. Shine and focus the projector on the globe positioned in the December location. A sharp grid effect will be seen. Ask what the pupils observe. (The squares become increas-

ingly elongated toward the top and bottom portions of the globe.) Does this give a clue? *draw conclusions* (The sunlight is more at an angle than at the equator; it is spread out more, and therefore not as intense.)

Have someone place paper over the projected rectangle at New York City and trace it with pencil. Will it be the same size at the June position? Place the globe in the June position. The traced rectangle should now be put in the same location and traced again. It will be appreciably less elongated. What does *draw conclusions* this possibly show about the sun's rays? (In summer, sunlight is more nearly overhead and so is more intense.)

If pupils are unaware that vertical sunlight is warmer than slanted sunlight, use extended activity 3 as an experiment at this time.

Let the children notice that a location in the southern hemisphere receives nearly vertical sunlight when New York has slanted sunlight. When the northern hemisphere has winter, it is summer in the southern hemisphere. Conclude by helping them generalize *draw conclusions* about the causes of seasons. But don't press for precision yet. This is a difficult idea for children.

Extending activities

1. Show a film on time zones and the seasons. If the film is clear and explicit—as many are—you may want to use it first and the models second with a slow class. Pupils' relative success with the models will enable you to determine what points need clarification.

2. Encourage pupils to make a shadow stick for estimating the time. Pound a 12-inch stick vertically into the ground. Make a cardboard marker plate with a hole to fit over the stick. Align in a north-south direction. At each hour, have someone put a dot at the tip of the shadow cast. Children will *draw conclusions* notice that the shadows change in direction and length according to the time of day.

3. Is vertical sunlight warmer than slanted sunlight? Get two identical thermometers and two small pieces of cardboard. Lay one thermometer flat on one cardboard in a sunny place. Next to this, prop up the other cardboard and thermometer against a book so that the sunshine is received vertically. The cardboard pieces will insure a similar background in both cases. A few minutes in strong sunshine should be enough for a sig-

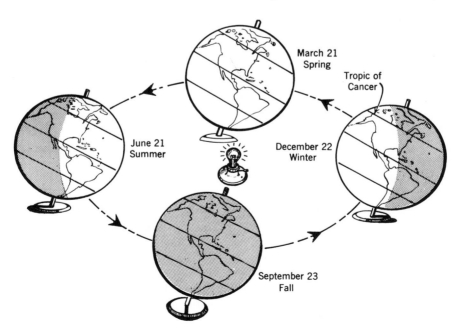

FIGURE 9-3

nificant difference to appear in thermometer readings. If it is cloudy, substitute a gooseneck lamp.

Why does the moon seem to change its shape? Why does the ocean have tides? What causes eclipses? Children are curious about these things. The next sequence presents opportunities for them to learn how the sun, earth, and moon interact. Let us consider moon phases first.

You are aware that the moon, like our earth, receives and reflects light from the hot, glowing sun. Also, the moon revolves around the sun a little less than once a month. Study Figure 9-7 (page 337) for a moment. Inner drawings show the earth and moon as seen from far out in space. Outer drawing of the moon show how it appears as viewed from the earth in each of eight different positions.

Imagine us standing on the earth in the center of this illustration. Gaze at position 1. This is the *new moon* position. The moon's dark side now faces us. But the moon moves on in its orbit. At position 2, we see a *new crescent moon*; at position 3 a *first-quarter moon*. Why not a "half" moon at position 3? There are two reasons. The moon is only a quarter way around its orbital path. Also, only one side of the moon faces the earth in 3. Of this, only about 50 per cent appears to be illuminated from an earthly observation post. At position 4 we see a *new gibbous moon*; one side is now almost fully illuminated. At 5 there is a *full* moon. The other positions reverse the sequence of phases, until once more there is a new moon. Try the moon phase activity on page 338. Compare the phases you see with those in Figure 9-7.

The interaction of sun, moon, and earth also results in tides. Notice the great difference in water level in the photographs on page 335. How does this happen? The law of universal gravitation, first formulated by the great eighteenth-century philosopher and scientist Sir Isaac Newton provides

much of the answer. Briefly stated, *every object in the universe attracts each other; the force of this attraction depends upon the mass of each object and the distance between them.* ("Mass" refers to the amount of material that makes up the object.)

As shown in Figure 9-5, the mutual attraction between earth and moon causes the ocean to bulge at position 1. This is a *direct high tide*. An *indirect high tide* appears at 3 because it is most distant from the moon, and hence gravitational attraction is weakest here. Also, the land surface is pulled slightly away from this region. Positions 2 and 4 have low tides because these are the areas that furnish the extra water making up the high tides.

What causes the tides to rise and fall? Let us put ourselves at the dot opposite position 1. As we rotate on the earth toward 2, the tide will seem to ebb, or fall. We experience a low tide. Moving from 2 into 3, we gradually come into the buldge. It seems as though the tide is "coming in." We experience a high tide. Rotating onward, we have another low tide before once again arriving at the direct high-tide area. In other words, the oceans tend to bulge continually in the moon's direction, while the land part of the earth rotates inside this watery cover. Of course, this is not completely accurate, because about 30 per cent of the earth's surface is land.

Since the earth's rotation takes about 24 hours, high tides occur about every 12 hours. (Remember, there is one direct and one indirect high tide simultaneously.) Six hours elapse between low and high tides. Actually, these times are a little longer because the moon itself moves some distance in its orbit while the earth rotates. Because the tidal bulge moves into alignment with the moon as it advances, the earth must rotate an extra 52 minutes each 24 hours before it is again in the direct high-tide zone.

Twice each month, unusually high and low tides occur. These are called *spring* and *neap* tides, respectively. (There is no connection between "spring" and the season.) Figure

High Tide

Low Tide

FIGURE 9-4 High and low tides.

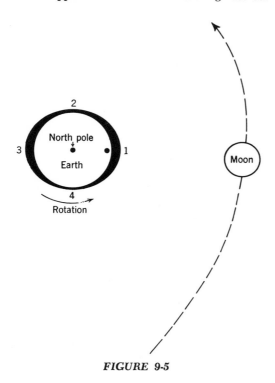

FIGURE 9-5

also huge atmospheric tides, and tiny land tides. All occur through the same interaction of sun, moon, and earth. Accurate measurements show that some land portions of the earth rise and fall more than a foot with the tides.

Causes of eclipses are seen in Figure 9-6. Both earth and moon cast conelike shadows. When the moon is in position 1, the tip of its shadow barely reaches the earth. Persons in this small, shadowy area see a *solar eclipse*. A total eclipse is never more than 170 miles across. Sunlight is cut off except for a whitish halo, called the *corona*. The shadow moves quickly over the ground, since both earth and moon are in motion. Sunlight is never blocked for more than 8 minutes.

In position 2, the moon is eclipsed when it revolves into the earth's large shadow. Practically everyone on the earth's dark side can see a *lunar eclipse*, which may last for 2 hours before the moon revolves out of the earth's shadow. There are at least several lunar and solar eclipses each year.

Notice that eclipses can occur only in the full and new moon positions. Why, then, don't they occur every few weeks? The reason is that the moon's plane of orbit is tilted about 5° relative to the earth's orbital plane around the sun. This usually causes the moon to pass above and below the positions required for eclipses.

A 5° tilt would be only a minor deviation from the earth's orbital plane in Figure 9-6, hardly enough to make a difference. But in proper scale, this small deviation is quite significant. With a scale of 1 inch = 1000

9-10 indicates how these tides take place. When the sun and moon are aligned (A), the sun's added gravitational attraction causes very high spring tides. This happens when the moon is in either the full or new moon phases. Since the sun is so far away, its tremendous mass contributes only an additional one-third to the force of gravitational attraction. When the sun and moon tend to pull at right angles (B), we have neap tides. This occurs when the moon is in its first- and last-quarter phases.

Interestingly, besides water tides, there are

FIGURE 9-6

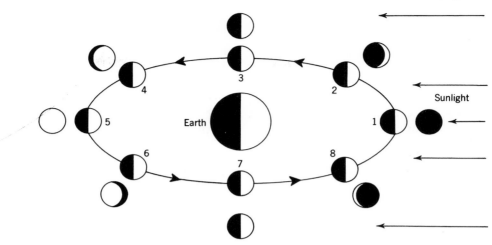

FIGURE 9-7   Moon phases.

miles, the earth's diameter is eight inches, the moon's two inches. Their distance apart is 20 feet. This is seldom realized by children. The sun's diameter and distance at this scale are even more surprising. Imagine a sun model 72 feet across, at a distance of 150 miles!

We tend to think of the moon revolving in a circular path around the earth. But motion is relative to the observer. If we could see the moon's path from far out in space, it would not look circular. Instead it would weave in an S-shaped, undulating motion along the earth's orbit. Since the sun is in motion, a similar pathway is woven by the earth. Is it wrong, then, to say the moon *revolves* around the earth, and the earth around the sun? Not at all. It is just another way of looking at the same set of facts. The closing activity can be used to help pupils learn this idea.

BASIC GENERALIZATION II: The relative motions of the sun, earth, and moon bring about moon phases, eclipses, and tides

Contributing idea A. Moon phases appear when the moon revolves around the earth.

1. *Materials:* slide projector or unshaded lamp; darkened room; globe; white volleyball or substitute; toothpicks; modeling clay; black and white tempera paint; paint brushes; large

chalkboard sketch of Figure 9-7. (At present show only empty circles outside the eight moon positions. Circles may be drawn conveniently by tracing chalk around the base of a large tinned can. Conceal with a pulldown map until needed.)

Ask the children what a *neighbor* is. The earth has a "neighbor," too—a space neighbor. What is it? (Moon.) What makes it shine? Bring out the difference between a body that reflects light and one that generates light. The earth and sun are examples.

Does the moon always look the same? Have children draw on the chalkboard some impressions of their observations. Why does the moon seem to change its appearance? Arouse conjecture. *suggest hypotheses*

Reveal a chalkboard sketch of Figure 9-7. Instruct the children to ignore the outer circles for now. Bring out that the moon is shown at eight different positions as it revolves around the earth. The entire revolution takes a little less than a month. Encourage discussion about how this revolution might change the moon's appearance.

Ask someone to stand in front of the room. He will be an "earthling" looking at the moon as it circles the earth. He will indicate if the moon's shape appears to change.

Darken the room and turn on the slide projector. It should be at the side and pointed toward the child, from at least 10 feet away, to insure a broad field of light. Have him hold a white volleyball "moon" at arm's length and slightly higher than his head. (If the ball is not higher, his head will block off the light as he turns his back to it. Placing the projector at least 5 feet above the floor will also help to prevent light blockage.)

Starting in position 1, let him put the moon through a full revolution as he rotates in place and observes the moon from his position. The other pupils should observe from their seats. Does the moon keep changing shape? The earthling will say "yes." But most of the class should disagree. To them the moon will look much as it does in the sketch. (Turn on the lights for discussion.) *suggest hypotheses* Why is this so? Draw out that the observers are in different relative positions. Perhaps this is the reason. There is a way that all of us can find out together.

Since only one observer or so at a time can observe the present moon setup, suggest that each person use a painted clay ball for a moon. A chalkboard sketch of Figure 9-8 will help the children prepare their moon models. Each child will need some clay to make a ball about an inch in diameter, two toothpicks, a small paint brush, and some black and white tempera paint. Pupils should shape the clay as nearly round as they can, then paint one half of the ball white and the other half black. Guide them to insert toothpicks as shown.

Instruct the children as follows. The white half of the moon model is receiving sunlight.

FIGURE 9-8 A clay model for investigating phases of the moon.

Therefore it must always face toward the sun. Designate one wall as the sun. The top toothpick will remind them to keep the white part facing the proper direction. The bottom toothpick will be used to hold the model.

Have class members stand and view their models at arm's length in position 1. Caution all not to reveal what they see. Have them try all eight positions at least several times. Let each draw his eight observations on a sheet of paper. Walk around and check these drawings; assist individuals in viewing their models as needed. Encourage pupils to make their own observations and record only what they see. *evalua critica*

Ask for a volunteer to now view the projector-volleyball model. Will his observations be the same? At each position, have him stop and draw what he has seen in the empty circle outside each position number on the chalkboard. The class will enjoy noting agreements and disagreements. Follow through with more experimentation using other pupils. *evalua critica*

Acquaint the children with the term *phases of the moon*. The moon's shape appears to go through changes or phases as it is seen in different positions of its orbit around the earth. Bring out the name given to each phase. Write these names next to their proper places on the chalkboard sketch: 1. *new moon* 2. *new crescent* 3. *first quarter* 4. *new gibbous* 5. *full moon* 6. *old gibbous* 7. *last quarter* 8. *old crescent*. Compare and emphasize the full and new moon positions. The understanding of these terms will be helpful in the forthcoming activities on tides. *draw conclu*

Contributing idea B. Ocean tides are caused by the gravitational attraction of the earth, moon, and sun.

1. *Materials:* construction-paper model of earth and its tides (To prepare, see Figure 9-9. Cut out a round piece of tan construction paper about 20 inches in diameter, and a larger blue piece cut into an elliptical form. Number and label as shown. Fasten in the center with a paper fastener. Stick this model to the chalkboard with cellophane tape. Draw on the chalkboard a 5-inch diameter moon

FIGURE 9-9

about 4 feet away. Leave off for now the arc showing part of the moon's orbit.)

Ask pupils to describe ocean tides. Develop that the ocean recedes for some distance from a beach during low tide. At high tide the water may cover most of a beach. If available, show pictures of high and low tides at the same location. (Perhaps you can project the pictures on page 335.)

Direct attention to the earth-tide model fastened to the chalkboard and its nearby moon. Bring out that the mutual gravitational attraction of earth and moon is chiefly responsible for tides. Each body is like a magnet that attracts. However, gravitational attraction is present with all substances, not just metals.

Bring out that the earth's oceans are not sturdily in place as is the land. This causes the ocean to bulge out toward the moon. Why is there an opposite bulge? Help the class to understand that this part is farther away and receives less pull. Also, the land itself at the opposite bulge is drawn slightly toward the moon. Rotate the land part of the model. The land rotates but the bulges tend to stay aligned with the moon.

aluate *tically* Ask questions about the numbered locations. Where is it high tide? (1 and 3; 1 has a direct high tide, 3 an indirect high tide.) Low tide? (2 and 4.) Challenge the children to describe the tides as location X goes through a complete rotation. From 1 to 2,

the tide seems to be going out; it becomes low tide. From 2 to 3, the tide appears to be coming in; actually we are moving into the bulge. From 3 to 4, tide going out. From 4 to 1, tide coming in.

Ask more questions. How long does it take to rotate completely around from one direct high tide to the next direct high tide? (About 24 hours.) From one high tide to the opposite, indirect high tide? (About 12 hours.) From high tide to low tide? (About 6 hours.) *reason quantitatively*

Now pose a problem. According to our figures, there should be 24 hours between one direct high tide and the next direct high tide. (Rotate location X once to demonstrate.) But records show that the actual period between these two direct high tides is 24 hours and 52 minutes. Why the extra 52 minutes?

Arouse conjecture. Challenge the group to show what might cause this delay. If clues are needed, draw in the arc representing the moon's orbit. Gradually develop that in the 24 hours the earth rotates, the moon moves ahead in its orbit. Draw a dotted-line moon about a foot beyond the present moon figure. Unfasten the cellophane tape and realign the water bulges so they are directly aligned toward the moon's new position. However, take care that land position X still points toward the moon's initial location. Now slowly rotate position X until it is in the exact center of the bulge. Bring out that the moon's orbital *suggest hypotheses* *draw conclusions* movement necessitates 52 additional minutes of earth rotation until position 1 is again in the center of a direct high tide. This would then make 12 hours and 26 minutes between *reason quantitatively* a direct high tide and the indirect high tide, and 6 hours, 13 minutes between high and low tides. Let the children calculate these corrected times if they can.

Mention that local land conditions may alter these times somewhat. In a seashore community, have someone consult a news*reason quantitatively* paper for local tide tables. List these data on the chalkboard and let the children calculate and contrast actual times of tides with the generalized times developed before. Discuss *evaluate critically* the importance of ship captains knowing about high and low tides when they enter or leave a seaport. (Water depth and current.)

2. *Materials*: pencils and paper; chalkboard or chart sketch of Figure 9-10. (Omit the tidal bulges for now.)

Introduce drawing A. Bring out that the sun also has gravitational pull. But it is so far away that its pull is much weaker than the moon's, in spite of the sun's far greater size. Emphasize the way that sun, moon, and earth are aligned. Have the children contrast *draw conclusions* this alignment with B. In which situation would a high tide be greater? (A.)

Have the class understand that an extra high tide would also occur in A if the moon were in an opposite position. A very low tide would result in B if the moon were opposite its present position. Emphasize that these

A   B

FIGURE 9-10

positions represent the times when tides are highest and lowest. Extra high tides are *spring tides*. Very low tides are *neap tides*.

Invite pupils to draw pictures of what the *sugges* moon would look like from the earth during *hypoth* spring tides. A new moon would appear in A; or a full moon in the opposite location. With neap tides, there would be a last-quarter moon in B; or a first-quarter moon in the op- *draw* posite location. Walk around and note how *conclu* accurate children's drawings are; review where necessary.

Help them to understand that huge air tides and tiny land tides also occur with water tides.

Contributing idea C. A lunar eclipse occurs when the earth's shadow falls on the moon; a solar eclipse occurs when the moon's shadow falls upon the earth.

1. *Materials*: globe; one-foot string attached by tape to a white tennis ball or baseball; slide projector; darkened room; pictures of eclipses (optional); chalkboard sketch of Figure 9-11. (Omit the two moons and numbers for now.)

Ask the children if they have ever seen an *eclipse*. Show pictures, if any. Develop that the term means "to block off light or cast a shadow." A *solar eclipse* happens when sunlight is blocked and cannot reach the earth. A *lunar eclipse* happens when moonlight is blocked.

Refer to the chalkboard sketch. The dotted circle shows the moon's orbit. Seek someone *sugges* to draw the moon's probable position during *hypoth* a solar eclipse, and lunar eclipse. (Have several moons drawn. Make no comment on accuracy. Position 1 will be needed for a solar eclipse, position 2 for a lunar eclipse.)

Show the materials. How can we test with *select* our models to see if these eclipses might *procee* occur? (Shine a projector on the globe from 10 feet away. Dangle a ball from a string and move it counterclockwise around the globe.) When the moon is between the globe and projector, it will cast a small shadow on the earth. This is a solar eclipse. When the earth *draw lusions* is between the projector and moon, its shadow will obscure the moon. This is a lunar eclipse.

Why is it that persons living on only a small part of the earth see a solar eclipse? (The moon casts only a small shadow—up to 170 miles wide.) Why is it that people on half the earth at one time can see a lunar eclipse take place? (The earth's large shadow blocks off all the moon. Everyone on the *draw* earth's dark or night side can see this hap-*usions* pen.) Draw out that the children's chances of seeing a lunar eclipse are much greater than seeing a solar eclipse. Emphasize that there are only several solar and lunar eclipses a year.

2. Referring to the chalkboard diagram, remind the pupils of their preceding work with moon phases. What moon phase occurs in position 1? (New moon.) Position 2? (Full moon.) There is something odd here. What *define* is the problem? (Why isn't there a solar *oblems* eclipse each month at new moon? A lunar eclipse each month at full moon?)

suggest Encourage hypotheses. If necessary, have *theses* the children recall why the moon-phase demonstrator held the ball slightly higher than his head. Some pupils will immediately suggest a moon orbit above the earth's plane of orbit. Some will have it below the earth's *select* plane or orbit. Let them try these positions *edures* with their models. Both suggestions will permit moon phases, but no eclipses are possible. Encourage discussion and experimentation until the children see the true situation. Only *draw* a moon orbit which is tilted relative to the *usions* earth's orbit around the sun will permit monthly moon phases and occasional solar and lunar eclipses.

Caution pupils never to look directly at the sun during a solar eclipse. Even the use of dark glasses or exposed film negatives may not be completely safe. Show them a safe method for indirect viewing. Punch a nail hole in the center of a small piece of cardboard. With back to the sun, focus the sun's rays through the hole onto another cardboard. During a solar eclipse it will be possible to watch the sun's bright disc on the

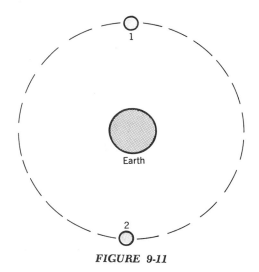

FIGURE 9-11

cardboard being obscured by the passing moon.

Contributing idea D. Relative sizes and distances of the earth, moon, and sun are difficult to draw to the same scale.

1. *Materials:* two small sheets of construction paper, one white and one brown; 20-foot string; yardstick; drawing compass; scissors; paper and pencils for pupils.

Develop that whenever we see drawings of the earth and moon, the moon is usually smaller. Why is this so? (The moon *is* smaller.) Write *8000 miles* on the chalkboard, then *2000 miles.* These are the approximate *diameters* of the earth and moon. Explain this term, if needed. Bring out that, in their eclipse models, the relative sizes of earth and moon are fairly accurate. But how about the distance from earth to moon? How far away is the moon? (About 240,000 miles.) Do the eclipse and moon-phase models give *reason* a false picture? (Yes.) Invite children to *quantitatively* make an accurately scaled model of the earth and moon, and their distance apart, with the available materials.

reason quantitatively

Help them choose a scale: 1 inch = 1000 miles is easy to work with. Let them first calculate sizes. The earth will have a diameter of 8 inches and the moon 2 inches. Have a child draw with a compass an 8-inch circle on the brown paper, a 2-inch circle on the white. Cut these out quickly with scissors. Discard the remaining paper.

reason quantitatively

Now how about the proper distance on this scale? Let the children calculate: 1 inch for 1000 miles. There are 240,000 miles. Dividing 240,000 by 1000 gives 240 inches. How many feet would that be? 240 inches divided by 12 inches = 20 feet. Invite two children to measure off 20 feet of string with a yardstick. Get children to hold the scaled models at opposite ends of the string. Now the earth and moon, and their distance apart, are in proper scale.

It will be instructive to mount the earth and moon models above the chalkboard, 20 feet apart. Have a committee plan and make suitable captions. Labels will be needed for the earth and moon, their diameters, and distance apart. The main caption might read, "A scale model of the earth and moon (1 inch = 1000 miles)."

2. *Materials:* 5-foot string attached to chalk; yardstick; drawing compass (Replace the pencil with a piece of chalk.); a chalkboard at least four and one-half feet high and wide.

reason quantitatively

Write the sun's diameter (864,000 miles) and average distance away (93,000,000 miles) on the chalkboard. Can the same scale of 1 inch to 1000 miles be used in the room for the sun? Let the children calculate. (No. The diameter would be 864 inches, or 72 feet. The distance would be 930,000 inches, over 150 miles away.) Give a familiar referent for the diameter, such as the width of a school building. Have someone indicate on a map a location 150 miles away.

Suggest a scale of 1 inch to 8000 miles. Let the children first calculate the sun, earth, and moon diameters to this scale. Since the sun is 864,000 miles in diameter, this will be divided by 8000 miles to yield 108 inches, or 9 *feet.* The earth's diameter is 8000 miles. Thus it will be *1 inch* on the scale. At a diameter of 2000 miles, the moon will be only *one-fourth inch* across.

reaso quan

Suggest that the children calculate the distance between sun and earth to scale. 93,000,-000 miles divided by 8000 miles = 11,625 inches, or almost 970 feet. The distance between earth and moon is 240,000 divided by 8000, or 30 inches. Since the sun scale is still too large for the room, suggest they make it half as large; that is, have a scale of 1 inch = 16,000 miles.

reaso quan

The above figures are now reduced one-half:

sun   = 4½ feet diameter
earth = ½ inch diameter
moon = ⅛ inch diameter
distance from sun to earth = 485 feet
distance from earth to moon = 15 inches

It appears the playground must be used to show distance. First, however, the models will need to be completed.

3. *Materials:* a string 2 feet 3 inches long tied to a pencil; two 5-foot pieces of butcher paper; cellophane tape; scissors; four bowls of yellow tempera paint; four sponges; white card about 18 inches by 6 inches; 20-foot string; black crayon; yardstick.

A committee can prepare a sun model. Help the members with directions if needed. Connect two 5-foot long pieces of butcher paper with cellophane tape. Draw on this a circle four and one-half feet in diameter with a string connected to a pencil. Cut out the model. Color it with yellow tempera paint. This can be done quickly by applying the paint with sponges. Four children can each take a quarter section, and starting from the center, work out to the edge of the model.

Let someone prepare the earth and moon models. On a white card about 18 inches by 6 inches draw a one-half-inch earth near one end and a one-eighth-inch moon 15 inches away. Label each clearly.

Invite your pupils to show the proper distance between their earth-moon and sun models on the playground. How many times will a 20-foot string need to be stretched to measure this distance? (Slightly more than 24 times.) If the playground is not long enough, perhaps this can be done on a sidewalk in front of or near the school.

reason —tively

After this activity, let the children mount their models on a bulletin board with appropriate labels and familiar referents. A caption might read, "A scale model of the sun, earth, and moon (1 inch = 16,000 miles). At this scale the earth-moon model should be 485 feet away."

Extending activities

1. Encourage pupils to sketch and label the moon's appearance each night at a designated time for 30 days. If near a seaport, have them check in newspapers or port records the correlation between a new and full moon, and spring tides. Do the same with a first- and last-quarter moon, and neap tides.

draw —sions

2. Write on the chalkboard, "The moon changes its shape as it revolves around the earth." Invite the children to state this sentence more accurately. ("The moon *appears* to change its shape. . . .")

luate ically

3. Inform the children that almost one-half of the moon has never been seen from the earth. Yet the moon rotates as it revolves. Why can't all parts be seen? Develop conjecture.

ggest heses

Draw a large circle with string and chalk in front of the classroom. Let someone stand in the center and represent the earth. Have a "moon" child stand on the circle and face him. How can the moon child rotate and revolve in such a way that the earth child never sees the back of his head? (While the moon child revolves he should keep his face toward the earth child.)

select dures

But there may be protests. Some may claim the moon child only revolved; he did not rotate. Have the children invent an operational definition for rotate. ("A body faces all direc-

luate ically

define lems

tions during a complete turn.") Let the moon child try moving around again. Children will see that he faces all four cardinal directions as he revolves. Therefore, he must also have rotated.

Have him try revolving around the earth child while facing only *one* direction, such as north. Now the earth child will see all parts of the "moon." Bring out the reason that only about half of the moon's surface is visible from earth: The moon rotates at the same speed it revolves about the earth.

draw conclusions

Let someone look up in an encyclopedia and exhibit the historic photograph of the moon's opposite face, taken from a Russian space satellite in 1959.

4. The earth is itself moving rapidly in orbit around the sun. This causes many persons to have a misconception of the moon's orbital path around the earth. The next activity can help clarify thinking.

Show a sketch of Figure 9-12. Remind everyone that the earth revolves around the sun as the moon revolves around the earth. The long arc in A, B, and C represents part of the earth's orbit. Since the earth is moving, which one of these three patterns would most nearly show the true path of the moon? Raise conjecture.

suggest hypotheses

Suggest that the children discover for themselves. Each child will need a small piece of construction paper, scissors, a sheet of writing paper, and pencil. Give directions. Cut out a rough earth-moon model from construction paper, as in Figure 9-13. (Show on the chalkboard.) Punch a hole in the earth's center with a pencil. Put an X near the far "end"

FIGURE 9-12

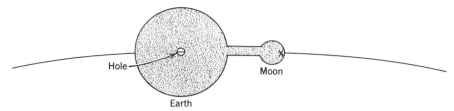

FIGURE 9-13

of the moon. Draw a long arc on the writing paper. Place the paper sideways to provide sufficient space. Align models on the drawn arc as shown, as far to the right as possible.

Have pupils move the earth slowly to the left and revolve the moon counterclockwise. A pencil mark can be made at the X periodi-

draw conclusions cally to trace the moon's track. When these marks are connected with a line, a serpentine path will result, which should resemble C in Figure 9-12.

The earth is one of nine planets revolving around a medium-sized star, the sun. How did the solar system begin? Scientists are not sure. One prominent theory holds that the sun and planets may have been condensed by gravitation from an enormous swirling cloud of dust and gas.

Mercury is the smallest and closest planet to the sun. It rotates very slowly, only two-

thirds around to one complete revolution around the sun. Its small mass results in a surface gravity too weak to retain an atmosphere. As might be expected, Mercury's surface has the largest temperature differences of the planets.

Venus, next in order from the sun, is enveloped in a dense cloud cover. This reflects sunlight so well that, except for the sun and moon, Venus is the brightest object in the sky. The cloud temperature averages about 130°F, but its surface temperature is believed to be much higher.

Beyond the earth is *Mars*. Its reddish appearance may be the result of "rusted" iron compounds on its surface. Of all the planets, Mars most nearly resembles our earth. However, its thin atmosphere, temperature range, and present lack of oxygen make it an unlikely home for any form of life but the most primitive plants. Two tiny natural satellites (moons) revolve speedily around Mars.

Between Mars and the next planet, *Jupiter*,

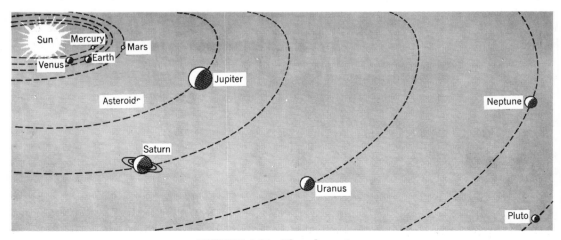

FIGURE 9-14   The solar system.

is an unusually large gap containing several thousand irregularly shaped chunks of stone and metal called *asteroids* (tiny "stars"). Some astronomers think these may be the remnants of a planet which came too close to Jupiter and disintegrated under its powerful gravitational attraction. Ranging from about 1 to 500 miles in size, they are invisible to the unaided eye.

Of the *outer planets,* as the five beyond Mars are called, *Jupiter* and *Saturn* are by far the largest. Saturn is conspicuous because of its rings, believed to be composed of ice particles. *Uranus* and *Neptune* are nearly the same size, about three and one-half times the earth's diameter. *Pluto* is so small and distant it was not discovered until 1930. Its orbital plane is tilted sharply from those of the other planets. All the outer planets but Pluto have natural satellites. All are so distant from the sun, it is probable that at least some of their atmospheric gases are frozen.

Ancient skywatchers were so puzzled by the changing appearance of the planets they named them "wanderers." We realize now that their differences in brightness and position from time to time occur because they revolve at different distances and speeds in their orbits around the sun. But long ago, all such objects were thought to be stars, which ordinarily seem fixed in space. A forthcoming activity will help pupils learn why the movements of planets were misunderstood.

Comets are huge, unstable bodies apparently composed of gases, dust, ice, and small rocks. A few are temporarily visible as they occasionally sweep near the sun and far out again in immense, highly elliptical orbits. They possess so little mass that the pressure of sunlight causes a long streamer or "tail" to flow from the comet head, always in a direction opposite the sun. Like the planets, comets probably originated from the gases and dust of the solar nebula over 4 billion years ago.

Most children have seen "shooting stars." These are fragments of rock and metal, probably mostly from broken-up asteroids and parts of comets, that hurtle through interplanetary space at high speeds. Although most are no larger than a grain of sand, some weigh tons. It is estimated that billions of such *meteors,* as they are termed, daily plunge into the earth's atmosphere and burn into extinction from the heat of air friction. The few that do penetrate to the earth in solid form other than dust are called *meteorites.*

Is there any danger of being struck by a meteorite? Not much. The only recorded instance of anyone ever being injured in the United States was in 1954. An Alabama housewife was grazed by a 10-pound meteorite which crashed through her roof. While records are scanty, it is unlikely that more than one or two additional cases of injury have occurred in recent world history. Since 1900 only two large meteorites have been witnessed to strike the earth, both in Siberia.

By far the most difficult ideas in this unit for children to grasp relate to distances and sizes of objects in space. It will be helpful to their thinking if a large section of the playground can be used in some of the scaled-distance activities that follow. However, even a very large area will be inadequate to demonstrate both distance and size on the same scale. At 1 inch to 8000 miles, for example, Pluto would need to be located about 7 miles away!

Distances are even more astounding as we move beyond the solar system. Now the mile is too tiny a unit of measurement for practical purposes. You will need to acquaint pupils with the *light-year,* defined as the distance a beam of light travels in one year. At 186,000 miles per second, this is almost 6 trillion (6,000,000,000,000) miles. Incidentally, this would be an excellent time to introduce the method used by Olaus Roemer to measure the speed of light. (See Unit 3, page 161.)

It has been said that none but the astronomer-philosopher can ever achieve a "sense of the infinite." Yet even a child can begin to grasp some notion of relative perspectives in the universe. Our earth is a huge planet when compared to the limited area we can personally occupy and closely experience. But it is a smallish member of a large solar family. The gigantic source of its energy, the sun, is only one of billions of stars that make up our Milky Way Galaxy. Millions of galaxies are strewn throughout space at incomprehensible distances, containing further celestial bodies beyond calculation.

BASIC GENERALIZATION III: The solar system contains nine planets which revolve at different distances around the sun; the solar system is only a tiny part of a vast universe

Try this introduction:

Some scientists believe that billions of years ago, there was no earth or sun as we know them. Instead, there may have been a huge, slowly rotating cloud of dust and gas in space. Slowly, gravitational attraction caused these materials to come closer together. The speed of rotation increased more and more. As rotating dust and gas particles rubbed together, much friction and heat developed. A large mass in the center became so hot it formed into the sun. Gradually, most of the remaining materials spread out as a result of their spinning and began revolving around the sun. They slowly shrank and cooled into nine separate masses, which became *planets*. Today, we call these planets and the sun the *solar system*.

Discuss briefly with the children how planets differ from stars. Identify the earth as a planet. Show pictures of the planets, if available. Draw a small sun on the chalkboard with nine surrounding orbits at varying distances. Don't be concerned with scale now. Put a small dot on each orbit in a line. Write nearby the planet names in order from the sun: *Mercury, Venus, Earth, Mars, Jupiter, Saturn, Uranus, Neptune,* and *Pluto.*

Contributing idea A. The planets' different distances from the sun affect their revolution periods and the amounts of solar heat they receive.

1. *Materials:* 20-foot string tied to chalk; suitable playground location.

Write *planetes* on the chalkboard. Identify it as an ancient Greek word which means "wanderer." From it the term planet was derived. Explain that thousands of years ago, no one knew about planets. People thought all such objects were stars. But these so-called "stars" were a puzzle. They never seemed to stay in place, as did the other stars. Sometimes they would appear dim and far away. At other times they would seem near and bright. In short, these objects seemed to "wander" through the sky.

Call attention to your chalkboard model. Under what conditions would some of these planets look nearer and farther away from the earth? Invite speculation. (If the planets moved at different speeds some might get ahead or fall behind others. If they all moved at the same speed, each inside planet would move ahead of its outside partner.)

Keep erasing and changing positions of various planets in their orbits. Have children come up to the chalkboard and measure with string any changing distances from the earth that result. Suggest a larger demonstration with children taking the roles of planets.

2. Take the class to a suitable location on the playground. It will save time if someone previously has drawn with chalk and 20-foot string nine circles of different sizes to represent planetary orbits. Ignore proper scale for now. Orbits about 1 foot to 2 feet apart should be satisfactory. Let the nine planet-children line up in a row. First test to see what happens to their distance from the planet earth child if they move counterclockwise at different speeds in orbit. After a few seconds, have pupils stop and notice the planets' changing distances from the earth.

Now get them to try moving around in orbit at the same speed. Each outer planet will fall behind its immediate inner planet. Again have pupils stop, notice, and measure the planets' changing distances from the planet earth. Mention that the three farthest planets are too distant from earth to be visible with the unaided eye; therefore people of ancient times did not see all the planets.

3. *Materials:* lamp with unshielded light

bulb; large chalkboard graph grid (See Figure 9-15. Leave off all references and recordings for now.); graph paper for pupils (optional).

Point out that Mercury—the planet closest to the sun in our solar system—may have a surface temperature of about 770°F. Pluto, the outermost planet, has a temperature estimated at −400°F. Why the difference? Develop discussion. Bring out it is probable that planets receive most of their heat energy from the sun. So, it is probable that the farther away from the sun a planet is, the colder it is.

draw
sions

Turn on the lamp. Have several children position their hands at various distances from it. Does it feel warmer when one's hand is close to the lamp? Colder when farther away? So far it seems as though distance would make a difference in the heat received. But this is only a model (analogy). They will need to check further. Ask someone to look up the estimated planet temperatures in an encyclopedia, or reveal them yourself. (See below.)

luate
ically

Write the temperature figures on a long sheet of butcher paper in chart form. Leave enough room for such other future data as distance from the sun, diameter, gravity, speed of revolution, number of satellites, and so on. In this way the pupils will gradually develop an awareness of what our planetary system is like. It will also save the trouble of repeatedly writing planet names.

(Add other columns as needed.)

Planet	Temperature (°F)
Mercury	770
Venus	130
Earth	55
Mars	30
Jupiter	−225
Saturn	−250
Uranus	−300
Neptune	−350
Pluto	−400

eason
tively

Suggest that these figures be graphed. How can the chalkboard grid be organized? Help where needed. If graph paper is available, do

FIGURE 9-15

not record temperatures at this time. First let the children prepare their own graphs. Assist where necessary. After pupils have completed this task, have them prepare a master graph on the chalkboard. They should check their individual graphs for accuracy with the master graph.

evaluate
critically

Call attention to Mercury's temperature. Are there reasons other than its closeness to the sun that might account for its very high temperature? Have children speculate, then read to find out. Develop that Mercury turns only two-thirds around on its axis during a full orbit around the sun. This means any portion facing the sun gets very hot before it can rotate away from the fierce heat. Reveal that Mercury's dark side may have temperatures as low as −400°F.

Point to the chalkboard graph. All the other figures are average temperatures. Why don't we record an average temperature for Mercury? (It would be misleading.) Cite the case of two persons, one with a million dollars and one with nothing. Wouldn't it be mis-

reason
quantitatively

leading to say that their average wealth is a half-million dollars? Have the children find Mercury's "average" temperature by counting the number of *intervals* on the graph between −400°F and 770°F and dividing by 2. (Averaging negative and positive numbers may be too tricky for most pupils.) Let them estimate the correct figure. (About 185°F.)

reason quantitatively

Ask the children if they notice anything else that seems unusual on the graph. Bring out that temperatures of the next three planets are relatively close together. But beginning with Jupiter, there is a radical change. Help them realize that there is probably a huge increase in distance from the sun at this point. Suggest that they find the planetary distances by reading or otherwise consulting authority. Write their findings on the chart. Starting with Mercury, the distances (in millions of miles) are approximately: 36; 67; 93; 142; 484; 887; 1787; 2792; and 3672.

draw conclusions

reason quantitatively

Guide the class to understand that, at 484 million miles, Jupiter is more than three times as far away from the sun as Mars. Since there is such a great difference in distances at this point, the first four planets are called the "inner planets." Those beyond are the "outer planets."

Contributing idea B. Relative sizes and distances of the planets are difficult to draw to the same scale.

1. *Materials:* drawing compass; four and one-half feet of string tied to a pencil; two sheets of butcher paper 5 feet long; cellophane tape; scissors; black crayon; white tagboard sheet; previously begun solar system chart; nine sheets construction paper of assorted colors (Tape these along the chalkboard in a row.); several sponges and yellow tempera paint.

Remind the children how misleading their earlier models of the sun, earth, and moon were in size and distance until they were measured to scale. Have them look on the chart at Mercury's distance from the sun (36 million miles), and Pluto's (3672 million miles). Roughly, how many times farther away is Pluto than Mercury? (More than 100 times.) Urge them to recall their playground model of planets. They should realize it was grossly out-of-scale. Suggest they make an appropriately scaled model now for a bulletin board.

reason quan

As before, it will be convenient to start with diameters. Let some pupils look up planet diameters in trade books or other references. Add these to the chart, rounding off figures to the whole number. In miles, they should be as follows: Mercury 3000; Venus 7600; Earth 8000; Mars 4200; Jupiter 87,000; Saturn 72,000; Uranus 32,000; Neptune 27,000; and Pluto 3600 (uncertain). Also have them include the sun (864,000 miles). Suggest that a scale be selected for diameters alone, appropriate for a bulletin board. 8000 = 1 inch should work out well.

reason quant

Show how to estimate diameter sizes from a scale. Draw a line 11 inches long on the chalkboard and carefully mark off each 1-inch interval. Number each interval on top from 0 to 11. Immediately below each number place the appropriate multiple of eight. (See Figure 9-16.) Place a small mark midway between each interval; these will help in close estimations. Label as shown.

reason quant

Ask children to estimate the diameter of Mercury on the scale. It is very tiny; less than the first half-inch mark on the scale. Take the drawing compass and measure half of this for the radius. Draw the diameter with the compass on the first sheet of construction paper. It is difficult with such a small radius. Continue with the others, each drawn on a separate paper. The largest model will be Jupiter, with a diameter of almost 11 inches, drawn from a radius of nearly five and one-half inches. Distribute scissors and let some

Inches
0 1 2 3 4 5 6 7 8 9 10 11
0 8 16 24 32 40 48 56 64 72 80 88
Thousands of miles

FIGURE 9-16

pupils cut out these nine models. Someone can cut out a white ring for Saturn. Make sure planet names are labeled on the back to prevent confusion in later handling. (If enough compasses, paper, and scissors can be provided, it would be ideal for each child to make his own models.)

Have a pupil tape the two butcher-paper sheets together. At this scale the sun will be 9 feet across. With a four and one-half foot string as the radius, draw a quarter of the sun. Use the upper left-hand corner of the paper as the center of an interrupted circle, as in Figure 9-17. This quarter sun should be cut out and painted with sponges dipped in yellow tempera paint. Other pupils may prepare appropriate labels from white tagboard and printed with black crayon. For the present, leave off any reference to scale in distance, as this will be more understandable after the next activity. Mount materials in bulletin board form.

2. *Materials:* previously begun solar system chart; chalkboard scale of 1 inch = 8000 miles

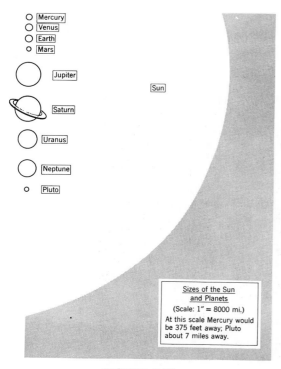

Sizes of the Sun and Planets
(Scale: 1" = 8000 mi.)
At this scale Mercury would be 375 feet away; Pluto about 7 miles away.

FIGURE 9-17

used in activity 1; 50-foot length of string; yardstick; outdoor location at least 50 yards long, preferably 100 yards long (football-field length).

Begin this activity in the classroom: "We didn't have much trouble showing planet diameters on our bulletin board with a scale of 1 inch = 8000 miles. Could we use the same scale to show planet distances from the sun?" (Some should suspect it is impossible.)

Invite discussion. Direct attention to the solar system data chart. How far away from the sun is Mercury? (36 million miles.) How far would that be on the 1 inch = 8000 miles scale? Help the children calculate: 36,000,000 ÷ 8000 = 4500 inches; 4500 inches ÷ 12 inches = 375 feet. Mention that Pluto, at over three and one-half *billion* miles, would be about 7 miles away from the sun with this scale. *reason quantitatively*

Lead toward the adoption of a more usable scale, such as 1 inch = 1 million miles. Children can calculate scale distances by dividing each of the regular distances by 12 inches. Results should be as follows:

Planet	Distances (million miles)	Scale Distances (1 inch = 1 million miles)
Mercury	36	3 ft.
Venus	67	5 ft. 7 in.
Earth	93	7 ft. 9 in.
Mars	142	11 ft. 10 in.
Jupiter	484	40 ft. 4 in.
Saturn	887	73 ft. 11 in.
Uranus	1787	148 ft. 11 in.
Neptune	2792	232 ft. 8 in.
Pluto	3672	306 ft.

reason quantitatively

Invite a committee to mark off appropriate distances on the playground with chalk or pebbles. A 50-foot string and yardstick will be useful for measuring. This can be done at recess or noon hour, if preferred. If the playground is small, omit several outer planets. *reason quantitatively*

3. *Materials:* rulers for each child; ten small tagboard signs, each bearing the name

of a different planet, with one sign for the sun; 25-cent piece; straight pin.

Before going out for a playground demonstration, ask pupils to estimate the sun's diameter on this scale. Let each draw a 1-inch line on paper. This stands for 1 million miles. The sun is 864,000 miles across. How far is that on the line? (About four-fifths.) Hold up the quarter. The sun is about this size.

reason quantitatively

How large is Jupiter—the largest planet—on this scale? (Less than one-tenths inch.) Hold up a pin. It is about the size of a pinhead. Help children realize that the small planets would be practically invisible to the unaided eye.

reason quantitatively

With this perspective established, take the class out to the playground. Place children with signs at the ten appropriate locations. Have the sun child hold up a quarter and the distant Jupiter child a pin. Many children will never forget this sight. The solar system is tremendously large.

Contributing idea C. The solar system is a tiny part of a vast universe.

Materials: opaque projection of Figure 9-18.

reason quantitatively

Discuss the enormous planetary distances represented by the playground scale model. Have the children estimate the amount of time required for a space vehicle traveling at 25,000 miles per hour—that is, 6,000,000 miles a day—to reach Pluto. (About 17 years.) If they could continue on beyond Pluto, what would they find? (Some children will mention the stars.)

How much longer would it take to reach the nearest star other than the sun? Discuss briefly. Note the variety of speculation which probably ensues. Some thoughtful children will want to know how far away the star is before they give a response. Write *Proxima Centauri—four and one-half light-years away* on the chalkboard. Explain that this is the name of the nearest star and its approximate distance from earth.

evalua critica

Let the class try to define a light-year. See if the children can reason why the distance is not given in miles. (Distances to the stars are so great, the mile is too small a unit of measurement.) Is it easier to say, "I took a trip of 6,336,000 inches," or, "I went 100 miles"?

define probl

draw concl

Lead to further understanding of what a light-year means. Light travels at about *186,-000 miles per second*. Let this sink in for a

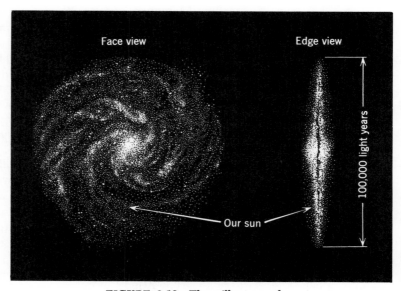

FIGURE 9-18   **The milky way galaxy.**

moment. How could we calculate how far it goes in a year? Guide the children's thinking:

60 seconds = 1 minute
60 minutes = 1 hour
24 hours = 1 day
365 days = 1 year

eason tively

To find out how many miles there are in a light-year we multiply 186,000 miles × 60 seconds × 60 minutes × 24 hours × 365 days. (This calculation should take about 10 minutes. If there is time, it will be worth it. Many pupils will appreciate more fully the enormity of this measurement unit.) The final product is 5,865,696,000,000 miles per year, or almost 6 *trillion miles.*

draw sions

Help them realize that 27 trillion miles of space separate us from the nearest star. On the playground scale of 1 inch = 1 million miles, *Proxima Centauri* would be over 400 miles away. Have someone locate on a map a landmark at this distance. Traveling at 25,000 miles per hour, it would take about 10,000 years to reach this star. Only much greater velocities would permit man ever to travel to the nearest star.

Many pupils will have seen the band of whitish, hazy light in the night sky called the Milky Way. Develop that it is composed of millions of stars in a huge cluster, or *galaxy,* within which the sun and its planets are located.

We can only see part of the Milky Way at any time as we are inside it and the earth is not transparent. Show an opaque projection or sketch of Figure 9-18. Point out that this great galactic cluster is 120,000 light-years long and about 12,000 light-years thick in the center portion. Show the estimated position of the solar system.

Emphasize that there are millions of other galaxies, perhaps more, scattered throughout space. The universe is vast indeed.

Extending activities

1. Is it possible for other planets in the solar system to support human and plant life without special protection? Develop the general requirements for most living things as we know them—water, air, reasonable temperature range, an environment relatively free of hazards, and so on. Have small committees investigate individual planets for data. Emphasize that only *data,* not conclusions, are wanted. The class will weigh the evidence as presented in each case, and try to draw reasonable conclusions. After the class has done so, let each committee reveal conclusions, if any, of qualified astronomers.

evaluate critically

draw conclusions

2. Some children will be interested in learning how astronomers are able to detect temperatures of objects in space. One method is to determine the frequency of radio waves received from these bodies. All objects with some heat energy give off radio waves. The frequency of vibrations increases with increased heat.

Another way to find temperatures is by use of a *thermocouple.* Two wires of different metals are twisted to form a junction. The thermocouple is secured to a telescope which focuses the light (and so some heat) from a distant object onto the junction. The heat causes a very weak flow of electricity in the wires, which is recorded by an attached, sensitive galvanometer.

For a crude thermocouple device, see Unit 5, page 239. Those in use by scientists today can detect heat from a glowing cigarette over 50 miles away.

3. Get several children to report on such other objects in the solar system as asteroids, comets, and meteors. If possible, exhibit pictures of meteorites found in museums, and Meteor Crater in Arizona. Perhaps a study trip can be taken to a nearby museum which houses actual specimens of meteorites.

4. Secure several simplified sky charts that contain directions for locating prominent planets at various times of the year. These are found in many children's trade books, and in such magazines as *Science News Letter.* Point out for pupils approximate locations in the sky and star clues to watch for at a specified time in the evening. Encourage interested, able pupils to learn and report some techniques of "skywatching."

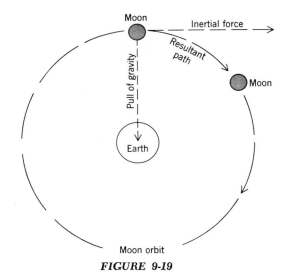

FIGURE 9-19

It is a good idea when teaching astronomy units to avoid becoming deeply involved in the technology of satellites and space vehicles. While this is where the "glamour" is, space technology is intricate and continually changing. It is better for lasting understanding to focus on some principles which undergird technological innovation. The basic scientific laws that govern motions of natural and artificial satellites, planets, and rockets are the same.

This does not mean we should avoid any references to rocket design, propulsion systems, and so on. The motivation and interests of children are broad and should be recognized. And, as suggested in an earlier chapter, the products of technology may furnish a perfect setting through which we can teach principles. It merely suggests where to place the emphasis.

Nobody actually knows what caused the planets to begin moving initially, but the reason they keep moving is readily understandable. There is virtually nothing in space to stop them. But why do they circle the sun? We have already introduced Newton's law of gravitation. Equally important to our understanding is Newton's law of *inertia*. Briefly stated, *any object at rest or in motion remains at rest or continues in motion in a straight line unless acted upon by some outside force.*

Anyone who has ever tried to push a heavy, stalled automobile knows how difficult it is to move a heavy body at rest. It possesses a great deal of inertia. Anyone who has ever tried to stop a heavy, rolling automobile by pushing against it knows how difficult this is. A body in motion possesses the inertia of motion (momentum). The more momentum it possesses, the more difficult it is to stop it.

Figure 9-19 indicates how the laws of gravitation and inertia combine to keep objects in orbit. Although a natural satellite, the moon, is shown in this case, the same factors operate with all bodies that orbit other bodies.

If it were unaffected by our earth's powerful gravitational force, the moon would follow a straight path owing to its inertial momentum. Since it is affected, however, the moon follows a resultant path which may be considered an "averaging" effect of the two forces.

A common example of this averaging effect occurs when a ball rolls swiftly off a table. Instead of falling straight down, the ball's inertia of momentum keeps it going sideways for an instant until gravity forces it to the floor. The resultant path of its fall is an arc.

In our illustration, both forces are equally powerful. If this were not so, the moon would either be drawn into the earth or pull away from it. This is what happens to an artificial satellite that moves too slow or too fast. Clearly, getting a space satellite into a sustained orbit is tricky. Its velocity and angle of entry into orbit must be calculated closely. Since perfection in these matters is virtually impossible, most orbits are markedly elongated (elliptical).

Because gravity weakens with distance, orbital speeds of one body must be slower as distance from the second body increases in order to maintain balance of the two forces. At 22,300 miles from the earth, for example, the proper orbital speed for a satellite results in one complete orbit each 24 hours. Since this is the period of the earth's rotation, a satellite positioned above the Equator will always stay in the same relative position. With several of these satellites, properly spaced, television and radio signals can be relayed to anyplace on earth.

When astronauts circle the earth in a satellite, they have no sensation of weight. This is because the pull of gravity is balanced exactly by the counteracting inertia of motion. This *weightless*, or *zero gravity*, condition we occasionally encounter on earth for an instant when an elevator starts rapidly downward, or an automobile goes rapidly over the crown of a steep hill.

In one science lesson not long ago, a bright child asked his teacher a remarkably astute question: "If we would be weightless in an orbiting satellite, why wouldn't we be weightless on the moon?" The teacher had him reconsider the law of gravitation, especially the part that says ". . . this attraction depends upon the *mass* of each object and the distance between them."

Since the moon has a much smaller mass than the earth its surface gravity is only about one-sixth of the earth's. A 180-pound astronaut would weigh a mere 30 pounds. But the moon's mass is almost infinitely greater than that of a space vehicle. The tiny mass comprising a space vehicle would possess practically no gravity at all.

Since prolonged periods of weightlessness may be unsatisfactory for astronauts, attempts may be made to design space vehicles that create a gravitylike condition. This may be done by rotating the vehicle at a carefully calculated speed. The astronauts' inertia will give them a feeling of gravity as they are slightly pressed against the spaceship's interior. An analogy is the small ball that remains stationary on the rim of a roulette wheel until it stops turning.

Through the ages, men have always yearned to explore what mysteries lie beyond the earth. But until recently, our technology has not been as advanced as our ambitions. Early devices and inventions designed for space travel included such things as hitching a flock of geese to a wicker basket, hand-cranking propellers attached to hot-air balloons, and festooning a box with crude rockets containing gunpowder. Occasionally, such contraptions were personally occupied by their astonishingly daring inventors, some of whom did depart from this earth, although not in the manner intended.

Because space is a near vacuum, no engine that draws oxygen from the air in burning its fuel can serve in a propulsion system. Instead, rocket engines are used; these carry their own oxygen supply. Rockets work because *for every action there is an equal and opposite reaction.* (Newton's Third Law of Motion.) When a rocket pushes hot gases out of its combustion chamber (action), the gases push back (reaction) and thrust the rocket ahead. Additional applications are furnished in the activities that follow.

Most rockets today are composed of multiple stages fastened together in a tandem arrangement. The bottom rocket propels all the stages to a point where its fuel is expended, and then drops off. The remaining stages reach ever higher velocities as the process continues, lightening the load each time. The speed of the last stage represents the accumulated sum of speeds attained by each stage. Perhaps future rockets will be efficient enough to reduce or eliminate the necessity for present cumbersome staging techniques.

Although modern rocketry provides the means to reach beyond the earth, travel for the astronaut poses some difficult problems. As the rocket blasts off in a terrifying surge of power, the rapid acceleration pins his body to the seat with crushing force. Once beyond the earth's atmosphere, he needs oxygen and sufficient pressure to keep his body functioning normally. He needs some means of temperature control. Without air conduction of heat energy the side of the spaceship facing the sun grows red hot, the dark side freezing cold. Because of his weightless condition, the astronaut may eat and drink from plastic squeeze bottles. To prevent the space capsule from being burned to a cinder as it enters the atmosphere, he may slow its

FIGURE 9-20

speed with reversed rocket power and a special parachute. These indicate only some of the problems of space travel.

With so many difficulties, why does man go into space? While his curiousness is one answer, of course, there are many advantages to be gained from continued space efforts. Some additional benefits are improved communications, long-range weather forecasting and possible weather control, astronomers' observation posts beyond the annoying interference of the earth's atmosphere, possible solutions to how the universe was formed, improved mapping and navigation, and more.

Eventually there will be the most important reason of all. It is believed that someday, perhaps two to five billion years from now, the sun's nuclear fuel will be largely depleted. The sun may gradually expand and engulf the planets, or explode in one final cataclysm of fury. Perhaps by then our descendants, whoever they may be, will have found a comfortable haven among the stars.

BASIC GENERALIZATION IV: Gravity and the laws of motion affect the movements of planets, satellites, and rockets

Contributing idea A. Gravitational attraction and inertia of motion cause planets and satellites to orbit in space.

1. *Materials:* drinking glass; child's toy marble; piece of rough cloth about a yard long; chalkboard eraser fastened to a 5-foot string, threaded through a spool, and fastened at the opposite end with two additional chalkboard erasers. (We shall call this contrivance the "orbiting eraser model." See Figure 9-20.)

What keeps the nine planets revolving about the sun? Why don't they slow down and stop? Why aren't they pulled into the sun by gravitational attraction? Encourage speculation for several moments. *suggest hypoth*

Mention that the following demonstration may help the class understand why the planets do not slow down and stop. Lay a large piece of roughly woven cloth on the floor. Put a toy marble in a drinking glass. Tilt the glass over and move it quickly in a line toward the cloth. Stop the glass suddenly at the cloth edge. The marble will continue through the glass opening and roll for a short distance on the cloth. Repeat this demonstration.

Develop the principle shown: A *moving object tends to keep moving unless it is acted upon by another force.* Did the marble keep going when the glass stopped? What finally stopped the marble? (*Friction* from the cloth.) Establish that the tendency of a moving object to keep moving is called the *inertia of motion.* Let pupils recall how they slide forward in an automobile when the brakes are suddenly applied. Help them reason that seat belts are used in automobiles to counter this tendency.

Apply this demonstration to a planet in space. It is moving rapidly. The inertia of motion keeps it going because there is virtually nothing to stop it. Outer space is almost completely empty, and so friction is no problem.

2. But why doesn't the sun's powerful gravity pull the planets into the sun? Why doesn't the earth's powerful gravity pull the moon into the earth? Permit some speculation. Ask pupils to observe a demonstration before they form more specific answers. *suggest hypot*

Taking the orbiting eraser model in hand, hold the single eraser out to one side about 2 or 3 feet from the spool and parallel to the floor. Hold the string at the spool hole to prevent it from slipping through at this time. Release the single eraser. It will swing down, move briefly to and fro, and stop. What prevents it from staying up when released? (Gravity.) What would happen if the eraser were moving around rapidly—if it had the inertia of motion? (It might stay up.)

Start whirling around the eraser slowly overhead. Gradually increase its orbital speed. Slowly the string length beneath the spool will shorten while the horizontal, orbiting length increases. Slacken speed and the reverse occurs.

Bring out that, at first, gravitational force exceeds the force of inertia. Shortly thereafter, this is reversed. Develop that the planets' speeds are fast enough to keep them from falling into the sun. On the other hand, the sun's gravitational attraction is great enough to keep the planets from leaving its effective field. Since the opposing forces are equally *draw* powerful, the planets keep circling the sun. *lusions* Our moon and artificial satellites circle the earth for the same reason.

valuate Make sure pupils understand that the *itically* string simulates the pull of gravity in this demonstration. The children should be familiar enough with magnetism to realize a strong attraction can exist between two objects without a visible connection. But they may need to be reminded.

3. *Materials:* orbiting eraser model (With 3 extra chalkboard erasers. Prepare these for easy attachment to the 2 erasers already suspended by affixing a rubber band and a paper-clip hook to each. Erasers will be added individually as needed.); small red ribbon or piece of yarn; watch with a second-hand; previously begun solar system data chart.

The following activity will teach pupils that planets close to the sun must travel faster than those farther away. If this did not happen, the tremendous gravitational attraction of the sun would pull inner planets out of orbit and engulf them.

Have someone look up the planets' revolution periods around the sun. Add these data to a new column on the chart: Mercury 88 days, Venus 226 days, Earth 1 year (365 days), Mars 688 days, Jupiter 12 years, Saturn 29 years, Uranus 84 years, Neptune 165 years, Pluto 248 years.

Ask pupils why the revolutionary periods of the planets vary so much. Many children will indicate the increasing sizes of orbits. Guide them to reason that the varying periods could also be caused by different orbital speeds, or both factors. Bring out that gravitational force, like magnetism, decreases with distance. Help the class see the significance of this idea. The sun will pull very strongly on such *draw* nearby planets as Mercury and Venus, and *conclusions* more weakly on those farther away.

Can anyone see a problem here? (Why *define* aren't the inner planets pulled into the sun?) *problems* If a clue is needed to elicit a problem statement ask "What would happen if we placed a steel ball close to a powerful magnet?" Encourage conjecture about the stated problem. A reasonable hypothesis is that the inner *suggest* planets' orbital speeds must be greater than *hypotheses* those of the outer planets. Suggest that the children put this idea to a test with the orbiting eraser model and extra attachable erasers for weights.

Guide where necessary. Pupils might have 3 different weights to simulate increased gravitational attraction—a 2-, 3-, and 4-eraser weight. A red ribbon attached to the string about an inch below the spool will remind the model operator to maintain the same orbiting string length in all three trials. Help *evaluate* the children to reason why this control is *critically* needed: They already know that decreasing orbit size decreases the revolutionary period. They need to measure the effect of increased gravity on orbital *speeds*, while holding orbital size constant.

We will want to know the number of revolutions per second. How will the speed of *reason* revolutions be measured? (Count the number *quantitatively* of complete revolutions past a given point for 10 seconds; divide by 10; this will give the number of revolutions per second.) Let the children discover for themselves a useful time period. For example, 1 or 2 seconds will be too short for accuracy. In addition, they might find it useful to average several trials, rather than take only one sample. It will be interesting to have each pupil record his own data, as someone calls out, "Start—stop!" for *define* each agreed time interval. Should discrepan-*problems* cies occur, get the group to determine why.

The children should record their data. For example:

No. of weights	Revolutions in 10 seconds	Revolutions per second
2	21	2.1
3	26	2.6
4	31	3.1

reason quantitatively

It seems as though increased gravitational *draw* attraction does mean an orbiting body must *conclusions* revolve faster to stay in orbit. But this is only *evaluate* an analogy. Do planets behave the same way? *critically* Let someone locate and read the average orbital speeds of the planets. They should be stated in miles per second. Record these on the large data chart: Mercury 29.8, Venus 21.8, Earth 18.5, Mars 15.0, Jupiter 8.1, Saturn 6.0, Uranus 4.2, Neptune 3.4, Pluto *draw* 2.9. The data appear to agree with our *conclusions* analogy.

4. *Materials:* table; rubber ball; picture of an earth satellite (optional); chalkboard sketch of Figure 9-21.

Help pupils understand that the same forces—gravity and inertia—operate on artificial satellites. Roll a ball speedily across a table and let it fall to the floor. Note that it lands a short distance away. Repeat, but now with greater force. The ball will land farther away. Lead children to realize that in each case the ball falls in an arc rather than straight down.

Reveal your sketch of Figure 9-21. Explain that it shows an imaginary child who can throw a ball very, very fast. He throws a ball very swiftly parallel to the ground. It travels parallel to the ground briefly through its inertia of motion, but gravity finally pulls it down. He throws a second ball even harder. Its faster speed causes it to remain parallel to the ground longer. But gravity forces it down at position 2. The imaginary child now throws a ball at 18,000 miles an hour. It now travels so swiftly that its inertial force is as powerful as the earth's gravitational force. It "falls" continuously in orbit around the earth in a *weightless* condition. Bring out that for this to happen the ball would have to be beyond the earth's atmosphere, about 300 miles high. Otherwise air friction would interfere with its movement.

Have the children recall some of their experiences that simulate briefly a weightless condition. Bring out such common examples as being in an elevator that starts descending *evalua* a little too quickly, or riding in a car that *critic* swiftly rolls over the top of a short, steep hill, and starts downward.

Call attention to position 4 on the chalk sketch. In this case the ball is thrown so swiftly that its inertia of motion is more powerful than the earth's gravitational pull. This permits the ball to escape from orbit. Explain that a space vehicle must travel at least 25,-000 miles an hour for this to happen, if it starts from the earth's surface. They should understand from activity 3 that slower escape velocities would be sufficient at increased distances from the earth's surface through lessening gravity.

How are these terrific speeds developed? Draw out that giant rockets are used. How these work they shall consider next.

Contributing idea B. Rockets operate because for every action, there is an equal and opposite reaction; a rocket's speed may be increased by using stages.

1. *Materials:* roller skates; briefcase con-

FIGURE 9-21

FIGURE 9-22

taining several books (or several books tied together); 3-foot rope; bathroom scale; sausage-shaped balloon; cellophane tape; 20-foot piece of strong thread or twine; soda straw. (Assemble these last four materials as in Figure 9-22. Thread line through the straw. Secure one end to a high-up wall fixture and tie the other end to a desk leg. The line should be taut and slanted. Blow up the balloon and attach a paper clip or two on the open end to prevent air from escaping. Secure the balloon to the straw with several strips of cellophane tape. Leave this apparatus set up and ready for demonstrating how a rocket operates.)

Ask the children how rockets work. After a short discussion, suggest that they observe several demonstrations for additional clarification. Request someone to put on roller skates. Have him stand in front of the classroom with his skates parallel to each other. Give him the loaded briefcase. Direct him to hold it to his chest and throw it to you by pushing both hands forward suddenly and releasing it. (Several children should stand ready to assist him in case he loses balance.) Catch the briefcase, return it, and let him repeat this action. Each time he throws the briefcase forward, he will roll back a few inches on the skates. Draw out what happened. For every *action* (his pushing the briefcase away), there was an opposite *reaction* (his rolling *draw* backward). He pushed against the briefcase, *clusions* and it pushed back at him.

Tie a rope to a chair and have a child sit in it to weigh it down. Let another on skates take hold of the rope and tug it briefly several times. He will move forward each time. Bring out the similarity of this and the preceding *draw conclusions* demonstration. He pulls backward (action) and moves forward (reaction). He pulls against the rope and the rope pulls back against him.

Ask someone to step on the bathroom scale. Direct him to hold several books slightly over his head and suddenly thrust them upward while continuing to hold them. He should do this several times as the children watch the scale indicator briefly move higher each time. Again develop what happened. He pushed up against the books (action) and the books pushed down on him (reaction). *draw conclusions*

Draw a chalkboard outline of an inflated balloon with a double-pointed arrow inside along the length. Point to the end through which air will escape. What should happen if the air were suddenly released? The shrinking balloon would push against the escaping air (action), and the escaping air would push back against the balloon interior, making it move (reaction).

Hold the demonstration balloon at the lowest possible point on the line. Remove the paper clip and release the balloon. It should move up the line rapidly, like a miniature rocket. Explain that a rocket works in a similar way. A rocket pushes hot burning gases out of its combustion chamber (action), and the gases push back (reaction), thrusting the rocket ahead.

Let the children read to learn the difference between rocket and jet engines. (Rockets carry their own oxygen supply to support com- *evaluate critically*

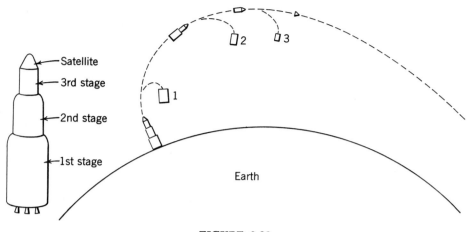

Satellite

3rd stage

2nd stage

1st stage

Earth

FIGURE 9-23

bustion. Jets get their oxygen from the air itself. Since there is no air in space, jets cannot be used for space travel.)

2. *Materials:* playground; piece of chalk; yardstick; 20-foot string; bicycle; rubber ball; chalkboard sketch of Figure 9-23.

Point out on the chalkboard sketch that rockets may be designed to contain three stages. The first and second stages are dropped at certain heights and only the third stage continues in orbit. Or the third stage may release a space vehicle which goes into orbit. *suggest* Why do scientists bother with three stages? *hypotheses* Why not just have one? Arouse speculation.

Some children should suggest that each preceding stage boosts the speed of the last stage. Does this really happen? Have them think of related, analogous situations in their lives. For example, will a ball thrown from a moving bicycle go faster and farther than a ball thrown from a still position? Invite them *select* to plan a test. (Mark a line on the play- *procedures* ground. Have a bike rider pump to a fairly fast speed and coast to the line. As he crosses it, he should throw the ball as hard as he can without losing balance. Measure the distance with a string and yardstick. Have him throw the ball again at the line while sitting on his bike. But this time, the bike is motionless and balanced by a helper. Measure this distance and compare it with the former.)

The additional velocity the thrown ball re-

ceives from the bike's momentum should send *reason* it far ahead in distance. Help the children *quantit.* understand that such extra distance was due *draw* to extra speed. Through a film or follow-up *conclus.* reading and discussion, let them verify their thinking.

Bring out an additional reason why the first two stages of a rocket are discarded. They no longer contain fuel, and so represent dead weight. By discarding these stages the rocket is lighter and thus can go faster. Liken this situation to a runner who must carry someone on his back. He can run faster alone.

Extending activities

1. Present a demonstration of weightlessness. Suspend a book bound with string from a paper clip hooked onto a rubber band. Have a child stand on a chair and hold up this material as high as he can, then let go. Will the rubber band stay stretched as it falls? Have everyone observe closely. (It does not.) De- velop that the rubber band-book "system" was *draw* weightless relative to itself as it fell. *conclusi.*

2. Explain that a weightless or zero gravity condition may be difficult for astronauts to operate in over long time periods. Can arti- ficial gravity be produced? Ask the children to observe this demonstration and tell how the principle it shows might be used in a space vehicle. Punch a hole in the center of a large *evaluate* cottage-cheese container top. Put this on top *critically*

of a phonograph turntable and flip on the switch. Place a marble—explain that this is a man—on the rotating container top and move it out to the edge. The slight ridge around the container's edge will prevent the marble from flying off. The marble's inertia will hold it fast against one section of the ridge.

Develop that, in a similar way, a space vehicle may be rotated just fast enough to produce a gravitylike condition.

3. Let the children study some of the conditions and problems which must be overcome for astronauts to survive a trip into space. Include problems of acceleration, air pressure, oxygen supply, temperature, food supply, waste disposal, radiation, and re-entry into the earth's atmosphere.

Seeds and Plants

(Intermediate)

The opportunities for individual work with open-end experiments are greater in a unit on plants than in almost any other area of elementary-school science. At the same time, there is more need for planning ahead and keeping track of activities, so that they may be interrelated. Living things take time to grow, and growth rates can seldom be precisely predicted. To take advantage of the numerous things to do in growing plants, both in and out of the schoolroom, this unit should be taught in the spring.

There are many kinds of plants. The simplest forms include bacteria, fungi, and algae. These plants lack roots, stems, and leaves. Mosses have stems and tiny leaflike parts, but are rootless. Ferns and their like resemble the most complex plants, except in reproduction.

Most complex and familiar are those plants that produce seeds, of which there are two basic groups. One group is composed of the *gymnosperms*; flowerless, these plants develop seeds which are attached to open scales or cones. Such evergreens as pine, hemlock, spruce, juniper, fir, and redwood are examples. There are about six hundred species. The second and far larger group (250,000 species) is composed of the *angiosperms*, or flowering plants. These form their seeds in closed compartments or cases within the flower. In this unit, we shall concentrate on flowering plants.

BASIC GENERALIZATIONS

I. Some plants grow from seeds; proper conditions are needed for seed germination.

II. Some plants can be grown from roots, stems, and leaves.

III. To grow well, green plants need water, light, proper temperature, and minerals.

IV. The special ways in which the several parts of a plant function keep the plant alive and growing.

V. Plants respond to gravity, light, water, and touch.

Seeds of flowering plants are produced in a central part of the flower called the *ovary*. As the ovary ripens, its seeds become enveloped either by a fruity pulp or a pod, depending on the kind of plant. Apples, pears, and peaches are fruits whose pulp we eat. Beans, peas, and peanuts are examples of seeds enclosed in pods. When we "shell" string beans, Lima beans, peas, or peanuts, we are removing these seeds from their pods.

Seeds come in many different shapes, colors, and sizes. But they have three things in common: a protective seed cover, a baby plant (embryo), and a food supply which nourishes the seed as it pushes up through the soil and grows into a young plant. In some plants,

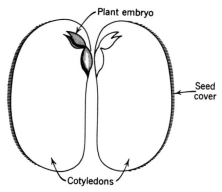

FIGURE 10-1   Parts of a bean seed.

such as the bean and sweet pea, the food supply is located in two seed "leaves" or cotyledons. In other seeds, such as corn and rice, there is but a single cotyledon.

What happens when a seed grows into a young plant or seedling? For an example, look at Figure 10-2. In A, the seed swells from moisture in the soil. The coat softens and splits. A tiny root and stem start to emerge. In B, the upper part of the stem penetrates the soil surface and lifts the folded cotyledons out of the seed cover. In C, the cotyledons and tiny plant leaves unfold. Roots deepen and spread. In D, roots become more extensive. The cotyledons are smaller and shriveled. Nearly all the food supply is consumed. The plant begins to make its own food through photosynthesis[1] within its maturing leaves. In

[1] For a review of photosynthesis, see page 374.

a short while, the shriveled cotyledons, then useless, will drop off the growing plant. This growth process, from seed to seedling, is called *germination*. The total time from A to D is about fourteen days in a bean plant.

Many pupils are surprised to find that seeds and recently sprouted seedlings placed in the dark grow as well or better for a time than those placed in the light. Light energy seems partly to inhibit rather than stimulate growth in many sprouting seeds until photosynthesis takes place.

Some flowering plants produce thousands of seeds a year. If they all grew into plants, before long there would scarcely be room on earth for anything else. Fortunately, a variety of factors enables only a small percentage of wild seeds to grow. Seeds are destroyed by birds, insects, bacteria, and other organisms. And unless proper conditions of moisture, temperature, and oxygen are present, seeds remain dormant. After several years in a dormant state, all but a few kinds of seeds lose their potential ability to germinate. These few, however, may not lose this ability for hundreds of years. Cases are reported of lotus seeds germinating after a dormant period of a thousand years.

Perhaps you have noticed that weeds appear at different times during a growing season. This is because growth conditions of moisture, temperature, and oxygen vary greatly among different kinds of seeds. Of course, this has

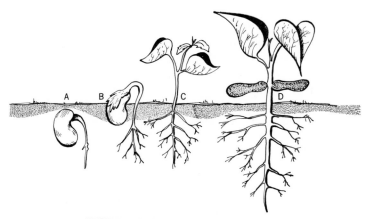

FIGURE 10-2   From seed to seedling.

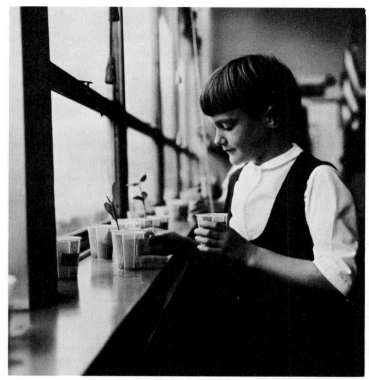

FIGURE 10-3 Simple, improvised soil containers permit everyone to participate in plant experiments.

great survival value. Conditions are never such that all seeds in the soil die at one time.

Two of the most useful seeds for this unit are the Lima bean and radish. Always purchase any seeds for growing plants from a nursery or seed store, rather than relying on those purchased for cooking. The latter are less likely to germinate because of certain food processing methods.

Lima beans are excellent to use because they are large, easy to handle, and start germinating within three or four days. One disadvantage is that they are susceptible to fungus growth if overwatered. Radish seeds start sprouting in about two days and grow fast. One minor disadvantage of these seeds is that they are small and therefore a little harder to handle. Germination may be hastened by soaking seeds in water overnight. However, if left in water too long, most seeds die from lack of oxygen.

Many improvised containers can be used in germinating seeds and growing seedlings— tinned cans, paper cups, half-pint milk cartons with tops cut off, and cottage cheese cartons. In some experiments water glasses permit better observation. Seeds may be planted next to the glass. If black paper masks the roots from light, they should grow a little faster.

All containers may be filled with garden soil, sand, sawdust, or vermiculite—an inexpensive insulating material made from small bits of mica. Only the garden soil will possess minerals needed for healthy growth of plants beyond the seedling stage. For the most part in this unit, however, it will not be necessary to use garden soil as the lessons deal mostly with seedlings. These will still be dependent to a large extent on the plant food within their parent seed. The other foregoing "soil" materials permit more air to circulate around the seed cover and plant roots. They are more porous and hence more difficult to overwater. Plants rooted in these materials may be easily removed, examined, and replanted without serious root damage.

Small holes punched in containers will also aid good drainage. Any water runoff can be caught in a saucer placed below. Water only when the soil surface feels slightly dry.

Guide pupils to plant radish seeds about one-fourth inch below the soil surface. Bean seeds are usually planted to a depth of two inches. In all cases, however, follow instructions on the seed package. Since it takes energy to push through the soil, a small seed planted too deeply runs out of food before it reaches the surface. Also, keep the soil loose.

Because there is a lengthy time lag between the beginning and ending of many experiments in this unit, it will be worthwhile to start some seed germination and grow some seedlings well in advance of need. Specific recordings as to the purposes of experiments will also be necessary. Once into the unit for a week or so, data should be continually materializing. These are the times when carefully written records can prove useful.

BASIC GENERALIZATION I: Some plants grow from seeds; proper conditions are needed for seed germination

Contributing idea A. Seeds need water, air, and the right temperature to sprout.

1. *Materials:* small bag of peanuts; one fresh Lima bean pod, if possible; Lima beans. (Soak some beans overnight to soften the seed coating.)

Ask the children if they have observed their parents or others start a flower garden or new lawn. Develop that seeds are usually planted in the soil. With proper care in a period of time, the seeds will sprout. What's inside a seed that causes it to grow into a plant? Discuss briefly. Hold up the fresh bean pod. Open it and show the Lima beans inside. Explain that some seeds are enclosed in this way.

Distribute one unshelled peanut, and one soaked and one dry Lima bean to everyone, if possible. Bring out that the difference in size and softness of the soaked and dry Lima beans is because the soaked beans have absorbed much water. Help the children open the soaked beans. A fingernail wedged into the rounded or convex portion will force them open without difficulty. The class will immediately notice the plant embryo. Have children agree on names for the seed's three visible parts, such as, *seed covering, seed halves,* and *baby plant.* Help them reason that the seed coat is protective, and that the baby plant grows into an adult plant. However, withhold verification of the seed halves' function for the present. Let them discover this for themselves.

Does a peanut have the same parts? First, have the children remove the protective pod or "shell." It will be easy to identify the reddish-brown seed cover, the two seed halves, and the baby plant. *evaluate critically*

2. *Materials:* paper towels; several drinking glasses; half-pint milk cartons with tops removed, containing soil; water.

Now lead into a problem. There are many weed seeds in the soil of vacant lots and fields. Yet only during certain times of the year do we see a great many weeds growing in these places. Bring out that perhaps proper conditions for seed growth are found only at certain times of the year.

What conditions are needed for seeds to grow? For one clue, have the children again compare the soaked and unsoaked Lima beans. Bring out another clue if needed: What is winter weather like in most parts of the United States? Put the pupils' hypotheses in question form on the chalkboard. Develop discussion about other possibilities they raise that might affect germination. Help the class to plan experiments after all the questions have been raised. Divide the class into small groups to do all the experiments individually and then compare future findings. Some questions and experiments might be: *suggest hypothe select procedu*

a. Do seeds need water to sprout? (Plant several seeds in each of two half-pint cartons of soil. Give water to only one.)

b. Will seeds sprout when it is cold? (Plant several seeds in each of two cartons of soil. Water each. Place one in a refrigerator at school or home, and the second carton in a relatively warm, dark place.)

Bring out that the second carton must be kept in darkness because the refrigerator interior is dark. Since both seeds are underground, only when plant shoots appear above ground would they be directly affected by light.

c. Will seeds sprout whether or not the seed is "right side up"?

d. Do seeds need soil to sprout? (Questions c and d can be tested at the same time. Line the inside of a water glass with several folded paper towels. Wet the paper thoroughly. Leave several inches of water inside the glass. With a pencil push several seeds between the glass and towel. Make sure seeds are in various positions, and that all are above water level.)

e. Will seeds sprout in soil that is underwater? (Plant some seeds in a carton of soil. Water often enough to maintain a pool of water on the soil surface.)

f. Will seeds sprout better in light or darkness? (Line the inside of two water glasses with paper towels or cotton. Wet paper and leave about one-third of each glass filled with water. Using a pencil, push seeds between glass and paper. Put one glass in a dark place and another in a light place of equal temperature.)

Since a week or more may be needed for definite findings in these experiments, get pupils to write and attach carefully to their materials the purpose of each.

Develop children's findings into some tentative conclusions:

draw *clusions*

a. Bean seeds need water to sprout.

b. Bean seeds will not grow when cold.

c. Bean seed roots grow down and shoots grow up no matter how the seeds are placed.

d. Bean seeds do not need soil to sprout.

e. Bean seeds will not sprout properly underwater. There is probably not enough air.

f. Bean seeds sprout a little faster in the dark than in the light.

Acquaint the class with the term *germinate* (also germinating, germination). Invite open-end experiments with other kinds of germinating seeds under these conditions.

select procedures

Contributing idea B. Food material inside a seed provides the energy it needs to germinate.

1. *Materials:* large cardboard carton; six recently sprouted seedlings whose seed halves are above ground, growing in small containers of sand.

Ask pupils to describe a peppy, frisky dog. Explain it has much *energy*—the ability to move around and do things. Where does a dog get its energy? (From the food it eats.) Bring out how humans, too, rely on food for their energy. If animals could not eat, they would gradually use all of their energy supply and die.

How about seeds? Where does a seed get the energy it needs to push up to the surface and grow for the first few weeks or so? Raise conjecture. Develop that we get energy from eating Lima bean seeds. Perhaps the same material in the seed that gives us energy also provides energy for the baby plant. Probably some children will hypothesize that the seed halves contain this food, if there is such. Others may suggest that water is responsible. Some may claim that the soil provides food. If so, have them recall their previous experiments where the seeds grew well for a time without soil.

suggest hypotheses

Have children closely observe seed halves of the six seedlings. Mention that these seed halves seem to be shriveling slowly. What may be causing the seed halves to shrink? (The plant probably is using the food material.) What could we do to see if the seed halves are providing food material for growth? (Remove some of the seed halves from the plants.)

suggest hypotheses

select procedures

Removal of a cotyledon can be easily accomplished by bending it back and forth several times before breaking it off. An effective test would be to leave both cotyledons on two plants, remove one from each of two plants, and remove both from the remaining two plants.

Place all these seedlings under a large, inverted cardboard carton or in a dark closet. This will prevent photosynthesis. (As an explanation for the time being just say it is a good idea to shield the plants as sunshine might affect the experiment. Let the children find out about photosynthesis in a future activity.) Water all plants as usual.

draw conclusions

Within several days, the children will notice that the plants with both cotyledon are healthiest and growing fastest. Those with one cotyledon will be next best. Plants with no cotyledons will be growing the slowest, or not at all.

2. *Materials:* single-edge razor; soaked Lima beans and radish seeds; large, tall glass jar (empty peanut-butter jar), three-fourths filled with sand; black construction paper.

It will be worthwhile to run additional experiments at the same time to cross-check results. Show pupils some radish seeds. Emphasize how much smaller they are than Lima bean seeds. If a seed contains food material for a growing plant, would there be as much in a radish seed as in a Lima bean seed? (No.)

suggest hypotheses

What might happen if we planted both kinds of seeds deep in soil? (The radish plant might not be able to reach the surface.)

Produce a deep glass jar containing sand. Let a pupil push down with a pencil several seeds of each kind to various depths. If seeds are placed next to the glass, it will be possible to observe their growth. Water until the sand is damp, but not saturated. Wrap black paper around the glass to shield the seedling and its roots from the light. Remove paper temporarily as needed for observations. Place on a shelf or table where it will remain undisturbed except for occasional watering.

Within a week or so, results should be clear. The radish seeds planted deep down will have used their food material before reaching the surface. For some confirmation of results, have children check various seed packages for in-

evaluate critically

structions. They will note that instructions for small seeds usually state shallow plantings. Instructions for larger seeds usually specify

draw conclusions

deeper plantings. How does this agree with our findings?

3. Yet another verifying experiment can be run simultaneously. Cut off the bottom half of several soaked Lima beans. Retain the half containing the plant embryo. By opening one bean, you can learn how to align the other beans to cut off the correct half.

Show these seeds to the class. If seeds really contain food material, will these halves grow as well as whole beans? (Probably not.) The halves can be planted next to whole beans about 2 inches down in sandy, damp soil. They will grow more slowly, and into smaller seedlings. The children might also be interested in seeing if the halves that contain no embryo will grow. (They will not.)

Let pupils read or experiment further to confirm and broaden their conclusions.

Extending activities

1. Bring up how seeds "travel." We know that people plant seeds in gardens. But people don't plant weeds in fields and vacant lots. Nor do they plant seeds in many other places where plants grow. Where do these seeds come from? Bring out that seeds are produced by plants, but for the time being, dwell on their means of distribution.

Let pupils read or view a film or filmstrip on how seeds travel. Develop that some seeds travel through the actions of animals and people. The sharp hooks or barbs on the cocklebur, wild barley, and beggar tick cling to clothing or animal fur. Birds eat fleshy fruits but may not digest the hard seeds. The seeds pass out of their bodies some distance away. People throw away fruit pits, which contain seeds, watermelon seeds, and so on. The wind blows many seeds. Some have "parachutes," such as the goldenrod, milkweed, and dandelion. The maple tree seed has "wings." Bring out that water can carry seeds from place to place, since many seeds float. Help pupils understand that seeds travel in many ways.

draw conclus

If possible, have an exhibition of a variety of seeds from green plants. An excellent time to collect many seeds without cost is in the fall. Pupils will be happy to assist.

2. Have an open-end activity to determine

select
·ocedures

draw
·clusions

germination times of many different, common seeds: orange, lemon, apple, pumpkin, barley, corn, oats, and so on. Use half-pint milk cartons filled with clean sand. Have children keep track of germination times. Guide them not to jump to the conclusion that a seed is defective because it has not sprouted right away. Some seeds may take several weeks to begin germination.

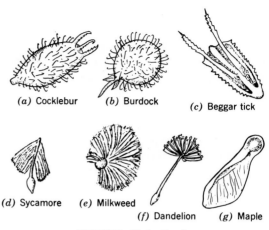

(a) Cocklebur   (b) Burdock   (c) Beggar tick

(d) Sycamore   (e) Milkweed

(f) Dandelion   (g) Maple

FIGURE 10-4 Seeds.

It is common to think only of seeds producing new flowering plants. Yet some of the most useful and interesting means of new plant growth occur through the propagation of roots, stems, and even leaves. This is called *vegetative reproduction.*

Consider the orange-colored tap root of the carrot plant—the part we eat. A carrot plant is usually grown from seed in the spring and harvested some months later. If left in the ground, however, all parts above the soil surface die as the weather becomes cold. No growth occurs during this time. As warmer weather approaches tender shoots grow from the tap root and emerge into sunlight. These grow into stems and leaves. Some time thereafter, flowers and seeds are produced. Like a seed, a tap root provides the food energy needed for shoots to emerge and grow. Parsnips and beets are other examples of tap roots which grow in this way.

New plants may be grown from tap roots in the classroom by imbedding them in moist sand or garden soil. A favorite method of many teachers is to cut off all but the top quarter of a tap root and imbed it in a small bowl containing a layer of pebbles and some water. At least half of the root cutting is above water to assure a sufficient oxygen supply. When sufficient foliage and roots have emerged, cuttings are planted in garden soil for full growth.

A sweet potato is another example of an enlarged root that can propagate a whole new plant. It may be grown in a similar way, described in a forthcoming extending activity.

Most ground cover plants, such as grass,

strawberry, and ivy, spread quickly after planting. Each sends out stems or runners which take root, push up shoots, and develop into new plants. These lateral stems may spread above ground, as in the strawberry plant and Bermuda grass, or below the ground, as in quack grass. The most persistent weed grasses are of the underground-stem variety, as frustrated lawn growers will testify.

New plants may be propagated from stem cuttings of the geranium and begonia. Other common plants whose stems grow independently are the coleus, oleander, philodendron, and English ivy. Dipping the ends of stem cuttings in a commercial hormone preparation may stimulate root growth to occur in half the usual time.

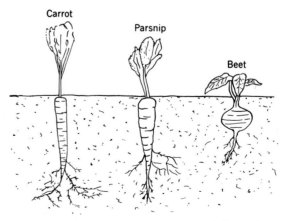

Carrot

Parsnip

Beet

FIGURE 10-5 Carrots, parsnips, and beets have tap roots.

Sometimes upon opening a bag of white potatoes we find some of them beginning to sprout. Usually this happens when the potatoes are left undisturbed for a time in a dark, warm place. White potatoes are swollen parts of underground stems, called *tubers*. The dark spots or "eyes" are buds, from which shoots grow. Farmers today seldom, if ever, use potato seeds in growing crops. Instead, they cut potatoes into several bud-bearing parts and plant these. Each bud grows into a new plant which produces more potatoes.

Occasionally, we see shoots growing from onion bulbs stored in the home pantry. Bulbs, too, are modified stems. All contain thick, fleshy leaves wrapped tightly around a small, immature stem. Tulips and gladioli are typical flowers which may be grown from both bulbs and seeds.

Even leaves may develop into whole plants. If the rex begonia leaf suggested for a forthcoming lesson is unobtainable, a leaf from an African violet, echeveria, or bryophyllum plant may be substituted. Techniques for using these substitutes follow.

Use a fresh African violet leaf with attached petiole (leaf stalk). Put the stalk into an inch of water in a drinking glass. For better support of the leaf, use a card with a hole punched in it placed across the glass rim. Insert the leaf petiole through the hole and into the water.

An echeveria leaf will usually root by merely laying it flat on dry sand. It is a thick leaf which contains much food and water. After it roots, water sparingly. Like most desert plants, this one thrives in semiarid soil.

The bryophyllum leaf is sometimes sold in variety stores under the name "magic leaf." This title is only a slight exaggeration. To propagate, pin it down flat on damp sand with several toothpicks or straight pins. Tiny plants should grow from several of the notches around the leaf rim. A variation of this method is to pin the leaf to a curtain! When some plantlets start growing, cut them out with scissors and plant in damp sand.

Sometimes children ask, "If plants can grow from seeds, why are the other ways used?"

There are several reasons. All of these methods result in whole plants in far less time. Also, some things cannot be grown from seed—seedless oranges, for example. In this case branches of seedless oranges are grafted onto an orange tree grown from seed.

But most important is the reason of quality control. We can never be sure of the results when we plant seeds of some plants. Vegetative reproduction carries the assurance that the new plant will be very much like the parent plant. If large, healthy potatoes are cut up and planted, for example, we probably can harvest near-identical specimens.

All the foregoing methods of vegetative reproduction are asexual. In other words, reproduction does not require involvement of plant sex organs. Certain lower animal forms also can reproduce themselves asexually. In another exposition, we shall review sexual reproduction in flowering plants; that is, how fertile seeds are produced.

BASIC GENERALIZATION II: Some plants can grow from roots, stems, and leaves

Contributing idea A. Root parts from some plants can grow into whole new plants.

1. *Materials:* two fresh carrots with stems and leaves intact; two quart milk cartons with tops removed, containing clean sand; knife; large cardboard carton.

Hold up a carrot before the class. Elicit that the part we eat is a *tap root*, or main root. Let the children observe the smaller roots, if any, trailing away from the tap root. They will be able to identify the stems and leaves. Bring out that the orange-colored tap root grows just beneath the ground surface. Now develop a problem.

Carrot plants are usually dug up out of the ground when the part we eat is well developed. If a carrot plant is not dug up, all parts of the plant above ground die in winter, when the weather turns cold. In spring, as the weather gets warmer, new stems and leaves grow above the ground. Where does the

suggest
otheses
carrot plant get the energy needed to grow new stems and leaves? Draw out at least three possibilities:

a. From water in the ground.
b. From the soil.
c. From the tap root.

Which of these three seems likeliest? (Tap root. Since seeds store plant food, maybe a tap root works the same way.) Challenge the class to develop an experiment that will test this hypothesis and also tend to rule out the other two at the same time. Give a hint, if needed: We found that a small seed did not have as much energy as a larger seed. Another hint: How large and healthy will the stems and leaves be if only part of the tap root is planted?

select
edures
Most likely, children will suggest an experiment. (Plant a carrot top and a whole carrot in the same amount of sand. The top of each should be just below the sand surface. Give each carrot the same amount of water.)

Make sure some holes are punched in the cartons for drainage. Cartons should be placed on saucers to catch any excess water. If no one mentions it, suggest that these plantings be covered with a box to prevent sunlight from possibly affecting results.

draw
usions
Within two weeks, results should be obvious. Foliage of the whole carrot will be thicker than that of the carrot top.

2. *Materials:* milk cartons of sand; assorted beets, parsnips, turnips; any additional materials from home children may think they need.

Explain that beets, turnips, and parsnips are also tap roots. Encourage a "What will happen if . . ." session. Let the children suggest all the ideas they wish in varying the conditions under which plant stems and leaves might be grown from these roots. Then let them screen and develop tests for their ideas.

suggest
theses

select
edures

Here are some variables one class tried: (1) different kinds of soil; (2) water only, with the tops of these vegetables imbedded in gravel; (3) different solutions in water, such as salt, sugar, and ink; (4) different positions and depths in planting root tops; (5) different temperatures; and (6) different parts of the tap root (top, middle, and bottom).

Contributing idea B. Stems of some plants can grow into whole plants.

1. *Materials:* nearby outdoor planted area containing grass, strawberry plant, or ivy ground cover.

Begin this activity in class through discussion. Get pupils to recall that a grass lawn is usually planted from seed. Even a few weeks after the seeds have sprouted the grass is sparse. But several months later there is a thick grass cover. How is this possible? Some children may say some kinds of grass "spread." Try to pin down what they mean. If they know what ivy is, ask how it also "spreads" from a sparse planting.

define
problems

Take pupils to a nearby outdoor location. Have them examine closely the underground or above ground grass runners (stems) that gradually branch out and take root. Let them note that ivy and strawberry plants propagate themselves through the extension of stems above ground which take root. When leaves and roots are developed, these new plants also send out stems.

draw
conclusions

2. *Materials:* cuttings from a geranium, coleus, begonia, or philodendron plant; waterproof containers; water. (Cuttings should be about 4 or 5 inches long. Cut with a sharp knife just below a place where leaves join the stem. This place is called a "node." Remove any leaves from the lower halves of cuttings.)

Ask the children if they have seen their parents plant *cuttings* from a geranium or other plant. It may be necessary to define the term. Explain that, when placed in water or soil, cuttings from some plants may grow roots after a period; under proper conditions these grow into whole plants. Will any of these cuttings grow roots? We shall put them in jars containing several inches of water and find out.

Encourage children to bring in cuttings from other plants to learn if they will grow. Instruct them how to cut below the node.

draw conclusions

(Children should do this only in the presence of an adult.) Cuttings may need about two weeks in water for good results. They may be planted in rich soil when roots are well developed.

Contributing idea C. Leaves of some plants can grow into whole plants.

Materials: rex begonia leaf; container of moist sand; sharp knife or single-edged razor; large, wide-mouthed glass jar.

Demonstrate how a leaf may grow new plants. Take a healthy rex begonia leaf and place it underside up. Make one cross cut with the knife across each of the leaf's main veins. Lay the leaf flat, underside down, on moist sand. Press the leaf down gently. If needed, put a few pebbles on top to keep it flat. It will be necessary for the cut parts to be in direct contact with the moist sand. Invert a wide-mouthed glass jar over the leaf to reduce evaporation. Place the container on a window sill or other well-lighted place. In about two weeks, small plants will probably grow at the cross cuts.

Extending activities

1. Leave a healthy white potato in a dark place until shoots begin to sprout from the "eyes" or buds. Show it to your pupils. Explain that a white potato is a swollen part of an underground stem of the potato plant. Food for the plant is stored in this stem. Develop that farmers usually do not plant potato seeds to grow new potatoes. Instead, they cut up whole potatoes into several parts and plant them. Which parts are likeliest to grow into potato plants? (The parts with eyes or *buds.*) Have pupils plant potato parts that contain buds and some that do not. These should be planted in damp sand just below the surface. After two weeks, have the children dig up these parts and compare them. Growth will have occurred only in the parts with buds.

evaluate critically

2. Show the children an onion bulb. Cut it in half, lengthwise. Show the thick leaves and tiny stem. Explain that food in some plants, such as the onion, tulip, and gladiola is stored in a *bulb*. This is a swollen stemlike portion just below the ground surface. Mention that most gardeners prefer to plant a bulb rather than a seed. Can they guess why? (Maybe it will grow faster.)

suggest hypoth

Let them experiment. Several small onion bulbs may be planted in a container of moist sand and several onion seeds in another. Bulb tops should be just beneath the soil surface. The bulbs should grow faster and be much more vigorous. Bring out also that a healthy bulb usually produces a healthy plant. When only the seed is inspected, it is more difficult to determine if a plant will be healthy, or even grow.

select proced

draw conclus

3. Let some children find out how to grow a sweet potato vine. Place a sweet potato into a jar of water, pointed end down. Only about half of the potato should be immersed. If the jar rim is too large to support the potato, stick several toothpicks horizontally into its sides. Set the jar in a warm, dark location until roots and stems grow (about one week). Then place it in sunlight. A large sweet potato may grow for several months in water. At the end of that time, its food supply should be gone. Unless planted in soil or given liquid fertilizer, it will die.

Sometimes sweet potatoes purchased at the grocery store fail to grow because they have been heat treated prior to shipping.

4. Have pupils read or view a filmstrip to verify and extend their understanding of how plants may be grown from roots, stems, and leaves.

The next sequence of activities will help teach that green plants flourish only under proper conditions of water, light, temperature, minerals, and more indirectly, space. As such, these experiences should extend some ideas about growing conditions already developed with seeds.

Children will find that soil-watering requirements for plants are similar to those for germinating seeds. Overwatering causes the plant to die of oxygen deprivation or disease. Underwatering usually results in a droopy, malnourished plant. The absence of vital soil minerals and extremes in temperature also have a weakening, or even fatal, effect on plants.

Crowding of plants is harmful to growth largely because individual plants are deprived of enough of what they need for good growth through competition. Even the hardiest plants develop to less than normal size under crowded conditions.

Green plants need light energy to manufacture their own food, but not necessarily sunshine. Electric lights may be substituted. Many commercial flower growers take advantage of this fact to regulate the growth rates or blooming times of their flowers to coincide with different holidays. Plants generally grow faster when exposed to light for increased time periods. However, overexposure retards growth and delays normal blooming times.

Light color is also a factor in speed of growth. You remember that white light is composed of several different colors. Each color has a different wavelength. At various stages of growth, from seedling to adult plant, wavelengths of certain colors stimulate more growth than others. But generally of all colors, red seems to stimulate seedlings to grow fastest. (Perhaps the word "grow" is misleading. The plant becomes elongated or taller than normal, but not necessarily thicker and heavier.) Exposure to white light usually results in the best overall growth patterns.

Strange as it seems, recent experiments show that sound energy may also stimulate plant growth. Sounds of various types are generated near the plant. Some vibration frequencies appear to be more stimulating to growth than others.

BASIC GENERALIZATION III: To grow well, green plants need water, light, proper temperature, minerals, and space

Contributing idea A. Green plants need water, light, and the proper temperature to grow.

1. *Materials:* twelve healthy, young Lima bean plants potted in good soil; five cardboard shoe boxes; five pieces of cellophane—clear, red, green, blue, and yellow; cellophane tape; large cardboard box.

Review with the children the conditions that were needed for their seeds to germinate. Do plants need the same conditions to grow? Focus on water, light, and temperature at present. This can lead into the next three activities.

Most, if not all, children will realize their bean plants need water. But how much? What happens to a plant when it receives only a small amount of water? How do its parts grow, if at all? What does the plant look like? What happens if it is given a very large amount of water? How will this plant compare with a plant watered properly?

Have children plan some experiments to find out the effect of varying a plant's water supply. For example, use three healthy young plants in need of watering. Give one a sparse surface watering once every two days. Give a second plant a "normal" amount of water; that is, water it briefly until no more soaks into the soil. Rewater this plant only when the surface is slightly dry. Saturate the third plant's soil several times a day. Whenever definite results begin to appear (in a week or so) let the children remove the plants from their pots and closely examine roots, stems, and leaves. Both the overwatered and underwatered plants should be yellowish and doing poorly. If not, allow more time. Roots should be somewhat shallow in the underwatered plant. Roots should be unhealthy and in the first stages of decay in the overwatered plant. *select procedures*

draw conclusions

2. Pupils will recall that bean seeds sprouted and grew just as well or better for a time in the dark as in sunlight. What about plants that are no longer dependent upon the food in their seeds? Do they need sunlight? Let the class plan a test. One plant can be placed under an inverted cardboard box and a second placed nearby in a well-lighted place. (Or, a small patch of lawn can be covered with black construction paper for several days and then compared with adjacent grass.) *select procedures*

Cellophane taped over opening

Cardboard end removed

FIGURE 10-6

draw conclusions After about three days, results will be obvious. Call attention to the plant's yellowing leaves and droopy appearance. Confirm that a bean plant needs light. But what kind? Is sunlight the only kind of light energy that will work? Will an electric light do? How about colored light? Have the children plan some *select procedures* tests. For experiments to see how filtered light affects the growth of plants, children can use shoeboxes whose openings are covered with clear and different-colored pieces of cellophane. (The clear cellophane is the control.) Unless the plants are large, they will fit nicely in shoeboxes placed on end. Arrange five boxes, each with a different cellophane color, as in Figure 10-6. Punch holes in the sides of each box—near the bottom—for adequate air circulation.

reason quantitatively Boxes can be slipped off quickly for plant measurements and watering once a day. A graph might be kept of any changes in growth *draw conclusions* rates. The plant with the red cellophane covering will probably grow fastest.

Some children might like to try growing plants under artificial light at home. A dark basement will be useful. A gooseneck lamp with 50-watt bulb works well as a light source. This may be placed on books and positioned directly over the plant. There should be a distance of at least 24 inches between the light and plant to avoid overheating the plant. For safety, stress that an adult must be present when this experiment is set up. If the *draw conclu* bulb is left on twenty-four hours a day, children may discover that plant growth slows down.

When results are in, develop that once the food material in a seed is gone, a plant is completely dependent upon the food it makes for itself. Through the use of light energy, a plant can manufacture the food it needs from water, materials in the soil, and air. Mention that the class will soon learn more about how this is done.

3. Encourage pupils to think of ways to test *select proced* the effect of temperature on bean plants. Let everyone carefully evaluate suggestions. For *evalua* example, placing a plant in the refrigerator is *critical* not a valid suggestion unless the light stays on. We want to test temperature alone.

It may be difficult to test the effect of coldness unless the temperature outdoors is sufficiently low during the day. Excessive heat is more easily tested by placing a plant over or near a radiator or hot plate.

Contributing idea B. Green plants need sufficient minerals and space in which to grow.

1. *Materials:* small bottle of liquid plant fertilizer; six closely matched, young bean plants, a pair potted in rich garden soil, and a pair in each of two separate pots of moist sand.

Exhibit the six plants. Explain that they are entirely dependent upon the food they make for themselves. In which soil will these plants grow best? Garden soil or sand? (Garden soil.) Have children back up their answers by references to what they may have observed or read. Or, if desired, experiment with plants growing in sand and soil.

Bring out that sand generally lacks the decaying vegetable and animal matter called *humus*, found in good garden soil. This material is soaked by rain, partly dissolved, and taken up by plant roots in the water they absorb. Develop that *fertilizers* of various kinds are often put into poor soil to provide the same kinds of minerals naturally furnished

select cedures
by dissolved humus and rock particles. Hold up the bottle of fertilizer. Ask the children to plan a controlled experiment to determine if beans planted in sand with fertilizer added will grow as well as beans planted in rich garden soil.

A satisfactory plan might be as follows. Water each of the three pots the same every day, but add fertilizer to one pot of sand. Follow directions on the bottle label. Leave one pot of sand without fertilizer for comparison of its plants with those in the fertilized sand and garden soil. This is a control.

draw lusions
In about a week, some results should be visible. With proper fertilizing, the treated sand pot plants should compare favorably with those in humus soil. The untreated sand pot plants should be noticeably declining in vigor.

Point out, however, that sandy soil may present a watering problem under normal outdoor conditions. Sand is so porous water may drain too quickly, leaving the roots dry. Humus soil retains moisture to a greater extent. (This would be an excellent time to correlate the material on topsoil found in Unit 7, page 277.)

2. *Materials:* about twenty radish seeds; quart milk carton; damp garden soil. (Place the carton down lengthwise, and cut out one of its long sides. Fill the carton with garden soil.)

This activity can help teach that plants need space to grow if they are to develop properly.

uggest theses

select edures
Mention that instructions on seed packages usually recommend spacing planted seeds several inches apart, rather than closer together. Why is this done? (They may not grow as well when they are crowded together.) Let the children plan how they will test the effect of crowding on growing plants, using the available materials. (Plant several seeds 1 inch apart in a straight row at one end of the carton; plant all the rest closely together in a row at the opposite end.)

Within a week the stunting effect of crowding will be apparent. Let some children follow through on this experiment by thinning out some crowded plants in the second week after planting. This should cause the remaining plants at that end of the carton to grow faster.

draw conclusions

Extending activities

select procedures
1. If an outdoor garden plot is available, encourage the children to plan a class garden. They should know enough by now to apply their knowledge and do most of the planning themselves. Quick-growing plants will enable them to take home their harvest in a month or so. Radishes, lettuce, beets, peas, and turnips are all excellent for them to raise.

evaluate critically
2. Perhaps a study trip can be taken to a nearby plant nursery or greenhouse. Nurserymen are usually happy to pass on a few tips to eager young gardeners. In addition, there will be opportunities to learn how professionals handle the same problems of lighting, watering, germinating, and so on, that the children themselves have encountered.

Children are usually surprised to learn that, besides fruits and vegetables, all the meat they eat has originally been derived from green plants. Flesh-eating animals are dependent upon plant-eating animals. This is true in the ocean as well as on land. Everything alive basically depends upon food synthesized from raw materials in the leaves of green plants. The plant itself is dependent upon the proper functioning of its several parts to produce this food. In this section, we shall examine how these parts work. We begin with plant roots.

The experience of weeding a garden makes us very conscious of one principal function of roots—they anchor the plant. In addition, we know that food storage in roots enables the plant to survive when food-making cannot occur. Another function of roots is the absorption of soil water.

Plants that are transplanted sometimes grow poorly for a while, or even die. This is usually due to damage done to tiny, very delicate root hairs which grow from the older

FIGURE 10-7   A seedling has many root hairs.

root tissue. It is the root hairs which absorb nearly all the water, rather than the older, fibrous material. There may be billions of root hairs on a single plant, enough to stretch hundreds of miles if laid end-to-end. If laid side-by-side, in rows, they would occupy the floor area of an average-size home. Root hairs are so small that they are able to grow in the tiny spaces between soil particles and make direct contact with water and air trapped therein.

Growth takes place very largely at the tip of a root. A tough root cap protects the sensitive growing portion as it pushes through the soil. Since the soil is abrasive, the root cap tissue is continually worn off and replaced by new tissue.

Water absorbed by the roots goes into the stems, through which it is transported by narrow tubes to all parts of the plant. Dissolved minerals in the water are deposited within the cells of these parts. When water reaches the leaves, some of it evaporates into the air. Exactly how this continual movement of water occurs in the plant has been a mystery until recent times. Modern molecular theory provides an answer.

As we know, molecules that are alike have an attractive force which binds them together (cohesion). These molecules may also be attracted to unlike molecules (adhesion). The thin tubes that transport water in a plant run from root to stem to leaf. Adhesion of water molecules to the tube walls helps to support the tiny water column. Cohesion causes the water molecules to stick together. As water molecules evaporate into the air, they "tug" slightly at the molecules below because of cohesive attraction. Because of cohesion, all the other molecules rise in a kind of chain reaction.

Should an air bubble get into the tube, the chain reaction is broken. The bubble separates some molecules to a distance beyond their effective cohesive attraction. We shall suggest a way to prevent this from happening in an activity with stems.

A leaf seems thin and simple in structure from the outside. Yet the intricate mechanisms within it, which produce the world's food supply, have never been fully duplicated by man. Inside the leaf cells is a green-pigmented chemical, *chlorophyll*. Chlorophyll enables a leaf to combine carbon dioxide chemically from air and water into a simple sugar. The energy needed to power this chemical synthesis in the leaf comes primarily from sunlight, which is absorbed by the chlorophyll. *Photosynthesis*, as the process is called, literally means "to put together with light."

From the sugar it manufactures, the plant cells make starch, which may be stored in all parts of the plant. With additional compounds received from the soil and through soil bacteria, plant cells can manufacture proteins and vitamins.

While carbon dioxide is taken up in photosynthesis, oxygen is released as a waste product. However, as a plant consumes the food stored in its cells, it takes up oxygen and gives off carbon dioxide as a waste product, as does man. Fortunately for us, much more oxygen is released to the air through photosynthesis than is used by plants in oxidizing their stored food. In fact, green plants comprise the chief source of the world's present oxygen supply.

How do these gases enter and leave the leaf? Thousands of microscopic openings, called *stomata*, may be found in a green leaf.

These are largely, but not exclusively, located in the leaf's underneath surface. Each *stoma* is surrounded by special cells which regulate the size of the opening. Since water in the leaf evaporates into the air through the stomata, regulation of these openings has great survival value. In dry spells and at night, the stomata stay closed, thereby preventing any appreciable loss of water.

Interestingly, most of the photosynthesis on earth occurs in the ocean, within uncountable numbers of microscopic algae which float on and near the water surface. We have not yet learned to use the tremendous food supply this source potentially affords to a hungry world.

The flower is the reproductive system of a flowering plant. Its two principal organs are the *pistil*, which contain unfertilized egg cells, and *stamens*, which produce dustlike *pollen* cells. (See Figure 10-9.) When a pollen grain lands on the sticky end of a pistil, it begins to grow a tube which "eats" its way down to the pistil base or *ovary*. There it joins onto an egg cell or *ovule*. A sperm cell released from the pollen grain travels down the tube and unites with the ovule. Other ovules in the ovary may be fertilized by additional pollen in the same way.

The ovules, now fertilized, begin growing into seeds. The entire ovary begins to swell as a fleshy fruit begins to grow around the seeds. As the ovary becomes larger, parts of the flower drop off. In time, a whole fruit forms, such as an apple. It is the flower's ripened ovary. When eating an apple, look at the core end opposite the fruit stem. Quite likely tiny, dried-up remains of the pistil and stamens will be visible.

When examining flowers with children in a forthcoming activity, use single flowers, such as tulips and sweetpeas, rather than composite flowers, such as daisies and sunflowers. The centers of these composite types consist of many tiny flowers, each complete with pistil and stamens. They are too small to be readily observed and may be confusing to the children.

Self-pollination occurs when pollen from a flower's own stamens fertilize the ovules. *Cross-pollination* occurs when pollen from another flower perform this function. However, pollen must be from the same type of flower for fertilization to take place.

Much pollination is effected through gravity, as when pollen simply fall from tall stamens onto a shorter pistil. Or pollen may fall from a flower high up on a stem to one lower down. Insects are also primary distributors of pollen. As they sip nectar from flowers, pollen grains rub off onto their bodies. In visiting other flowers, these grains may become dislodged. It is interesting to note that bright colored and fragrant flowers are visited by the most insects. Wind is also an important distributor of pollen. In spring, the air contains billions of pollen grains, bringing pollination to plants and hay fever to many people.

Many garden flowers and vegetables grow from seed, then blossom, produce seeds, and die in one growing season. These are known as *annuals*. Examples are petunias, zinnias, beans, and tomatoes. Those that live two seasons are *biennials*. Examples are hollyhocks, forget-me-nots, carrots, and turnips. Plants that live more than two growing seasons are *perennials*. Trees and most shrubs fit into this classification.

BASIC GENERALIZATION IV: The special ways in which the several parts of a plant function keep the plant alive and growing

Ask the class members to name the several parts of most green plants. (Roots, stems, leaves, and flowers.) Briefly elicit comments about the functions of these parts to learn how much the children already know. Make no comments on their accuracy at this time. However, you might mention that now they will be doing experiments and other activities to find out more about the interesting, special ways in which these parts function.

Contributing idea A. Roots absorb water, anchor the plant, and store food.

1. *Materials:* three closely matched, vigorous bean seedlings, growing in separate pots; aluminum kitchen foil; a large tray or pan; hand water sprinkler (A substitute may be made by punching holes in the bottom of a quart milk carton. If the hinged cap on top is secure, water flow may be stopped by inverting the carton.)

If asked about the functions of roots, almost all intermediate-grade children will mention that roots take up or absorb water. Invite your pupils to cite evidence which might back up this belief. Most will mention that an unwatered house plant dies. But now ask them to think about natural watering—rainfall. Rain falls on the leaves before it soaks the ground. How do we know that the leaves do not take in water? Could it be that leaves also *select* take in water? How could we find out? Chal *procedures* lenge the class to think of an experiment with available materials.

(Use the two closely matched plants. Water the soil of one plant as usual. Keep track of how much water is used. Water only the leaves of the second plant with the same amount of water. To prevent water from dripping onto the soil, waterproof the pot opening. Carefully wrap waterproof foil around the base of the plant and extend it out over the sides of the pot. A tray underneath will contain water runoff.)

Within several days, results should be fairly conclusive. The plant whose leaves only were *draw* watered will be drooping. The soil-watered *conclusions* plant should be thriving as usual.

evaluate Evaluate for overgeneralizing from this ex *critically* periment. Some water absorption might take place in some leaves. In this case water absorption, if any, is not enough to maintain the plant. For further evidence encourage duplicate experiments at home with beans and other plants.

2. *Materials:* a dozen sprouting radish seeds, about three to four days old, with visible root hairs (Prepare by sprinkling the seeds on paper toweling or a sponge placed in a saucer of water. Cover with a moist paper towel.); hand magnifying lenses; two closely matched, potted, healthy bean plants; two pots of gar-

den soil; small flat stick; large, wide-mouthed glass jar containing water.

Exhibit some sprouting radish seeds. A background of black paper will permit easy viewing, as will hand lenses. Have everyone note the root structure. Point out that the tiny root hairs take in water and minerals from the soil. Mention that all the root hairs of a single radish seedling would stretch for miles if placed end to end.

Now develop a problem. Many gardeners have trouble when they dig up plants and replant them somewhere else. Even if the gardeners water carefully and apply fertilizer, the plants may do poorly. Sometimes they die. *sugges* Why? *hypot.*

When possible root-hair destruction is mentioned, indicate the two bean plants and ask pupils to think of an experiment. Help them to think this through. One plant might be *select* pulled roughly out of the soil and the other *proce* gently lifted out after the soil has been loosened and watered. Roots of both plants can be soaked gently in a container of water to remove any remaining soil. An examination with a hand lens will reveal more root hairs on the gently treated roots. Replant both. The plant with fewer root hairs should not be as vigorous as the other until it grows new root hairs.

Bring out other functions of roots. They store food, children should remember, in the carrot, beet, and sweet potato plant, and in other plants, too. Roots also anchor the plant to the ground. Have children dig up some *evalua* weeds of various kinds and bring them to *critica* school to examine and compare their root systems.

Contributing idea B. Stems conduct liquids and support leaves.

1. *Materials:* fresh, firm, celery stalk with many green leaves intact; red and blue food coloring or ink; freshly cut white carnation with 5-inch stem; razor or knife; two glasses containing water.

Mention that we usually water a house plant only at the roots. Yet all parts of the plant seem to contain some water. Why?

(The stem carries it from the roots to the plant's other parts.) Show the celery stalk.[2] How could the pupils use it to see how water is transported? (Put it in a glass of water.) But how will they tell if water is moving up the stalk? This is fresh celery. Discuss. Guide toward the use of colored water as an indicator.

select cedures

Make a new cut across the stalk base to open any clogged tubes. Immerse in colored water and place in strong sunlight for several hours. Water should rise in the stalk and enter the leaf veins, leaving a spidery network of colored lines. Pull apart the stalk and have children examine the individual tubes.

2. Bring out that sometimes florists color their white carnations green for St. Patrick's Day. Can the class guess how this is done? (Place a carnation with stem in green-colored water.) How might a florist prepare a carnation with *two* colors? (Maybe the stem can be split in two with each part placed in a glass of different-colored water.) Make a new cut just above the stem base to open any clogged tubes. Now split the stem carefully down the middle. Place the carnation in sunlight. In several hours, the flower should exhibit both colors.

select edures

Occasionally this demonstration does not work because the stem tubes contain air bubbles which block passage of the water. To prevent this, snip off a small piece of the stem end with scissors while it is underwater.

draw usions

Develop other stem functions. Some stems store plant food, as with asparagus, celery, and white potatoes. Stems also hold up leaves.

Contributing idea C. Leaves can make plant food; they also store some plant food.

1. *Materials:* hot plate, two tinned cans, one large, one small; water; alcohol; iodine; drinking glass; tweezers; fresh green leaf; a spoonful of sugar and one of powdered starch.

Get children to recall that a green plant turns yellow when left in the dark. Carefully develop the following ideas:

a. The green material in a plant is *chloro-*

phyll. It is made by the leaf, but only in the presence of light. If a plant is placed in darkness it turns yellowish in about three days because the plant's chlorophyll disappears.

b. Chlorophyll is very important. It enables the leaf to make its own food from the air and water that enter the leaf. Sunlight provides the energy for this to happen.

c. The food that is made is stored in different parts of the plant. Some of the stored food is starch. (Show some dried starch. Explain that a potato is mostly starch. When we eat a potato, we use as food what would have been used by the potato plant in its further growth.)

d. Of all living things, only green plants can make their own food. This process is called *photosynthesis*.

Now lead into a demonstration. Mention that leaves also store starch. Hold up the green leaf. This leaf has been taken from a tree (or bush) outside the classroom. Will it contain starch? You will demonstrate a way to find out.

First, show that iodine can indicate the presence of starch. Put a drop on some powdered starch. It will turn purple-black. Put a drop on some sugar. The iodine will largely remain its original color. Iodine changes to a purple-black only with starch. Develop that the iodine test can be used to see if a leaf contains starch, but first the green chlorophyll must be removed.

Boil out the green chlorophyll in the leaf with alcohol. *Since alcohol is flammable, do not boil it directly over a hot plate. Never use an open flame.* A safe method is as follows. Half fill a large can with water, and place on a hot plate. Half fill a small can with alcohol and drop a green leaf into it. Place the smaller can inside the larger one. Turn on the hot plate. The leaf should be almost pale white after about ten minutes in boiling alcohol.

Remove the leaf with tweezers after turning off the hot plate. It will look pale green or near-white. Explain that the boiling alcohol has removed most of the chlorophyll. However, if there was starch in the leaf it should still be there. Put a dozen drops of

---

[2] The celery stalk is a leaf petiole which functions like a stem.

iodine into a glass of water. If starch is present, the leaf's color will turn purple-black when the leaf is dropped into this solution. Drop in the leaf. It should change to that color.

2. *Materials:* small tree or shrub near the classroom; leaf-boiling materials used in preceding activity; glass of diluted iodine; two 2- by 2-inch squares of heavy tagboard or cardboard; paper clip.

select procedures

Tell pupils that they now have enough knowledge to find out about the importance of chlorophyll for themselves. Any part of a green leaf that does not receive light loses its chlorophyll in about three days. Challenge the class to plan an experiment to answer this question: Will starch be found in a leaf or part of leaf that does not have chlorophyll? If needed, hold up the cardboard squares and paper clip. How could these be used on a shrub leaf outdoors? What experiment can the children design?

(Place the squares on the top and bottom of a growing leaf outdoors. The squares will cover only part of the leaf. In about three days, the covered parts should have no chlorophyll. These sections will probably have used all the starch available to them. Test for starch by boiling the leaf in alcohol and then putting it into diluted iodine.)

draw conclusions

Children will be pleased to discover that uncovered portions of the leaf will appear blue-black, showing that starch is present. The previously covered portions will be light brown, indicating no starch is present. It will be interesting to test variegated ivy and pit-

tosporum, silver leaf geranium, and other plant leaves with parts that are not green. These parts generally will not contain starch.

3. *Materials:* microprojector or microscope; razor; fresh leaf; glass slide and cover slip; eye-dropper containing water; tweezers.

How does air move into and out of a leaf? The following demonstration will show children the tiny openings in a leaf's underside (stomata). (As an alternative to this demonstration, a colored drawing can be enlarged by an opaque projector.)

Only a small piece of leaf is needed for this demonstration, but it must be very thin for light to shine through. Carefully tear the leaf at an angle. Cut out a small section from a torn edge. This must be from the leaf's lower surface. With tweezers, place it on the glass slide. Put a drop of water on it and cover with a glass cover slip. Press the slip down slightly to remove air bubbles. With the microprojector, use a low power objective to locate some stomata. Then switch to a higher magnification, if desired.

Point out that these openings permit air to enter and leave the leaf. Each opening is called a *stoma.* Emphasize that the *stomata* are almost entirely on the bottom, not the top surface, of a leaf. Why is this an advantage? (Dust in the air might settle on the leaf and clog the stomata.) What might happen to a plant if the stomata became clogged? (It might die.)

draw concl

Continue with questions and ideas. Some plants, like 'the water lily, have leaves that float on top of water. On which surface of the leaf would stomata probably be found? (Top surface because there is more air.)

draw concl

4. *Materials:* four large, identical water glasses, two containing water; two identical pieces of cardboard, about 5 inches by 5 inches; large, fresh leaf with petiole (leaf stalk) intact; vaseline or soft modeling clay. (Arrange half of these materials as in Figure 10-8. A small hole for the leaf petiole can be punched in the card with a pencil. Be sure to seal around this opening with clay or vaseline.)

Mention that a plant takes in much more

FIGURE 10-8   A transpiration test.

Seal hole with clay or vaseline

Water

water than it can use. What happens to all the extra water when it reaches the leaves? (It may evaporate into the air.) Show the assembled materials. If the leaf gives off moisture what may happen to the inside of the top glass? (Water drops should appear.) Why is the cardboard placed between the two glasses? Why is there vaseline around the opening? (To prevent water evaporation from below reaching the top glass.)

select edures Raise the need for a further control, if no one else does. How shall we know if the water comes from the leaf? It might come from the air. Have pupils recall the many occasions when they have seen condensed water vapor on window panes, bathroom mirrors, and so on. How can the remaining materials help? (Put a cardboard over the second glass of water and an empty inverted glass on top. If water does not appear in this glass, and it does in the glass containing the leaf, we shall know that the leaf has given off moisture.)

After several hours in a well-lighted place water droplets should appear only or largely in the glass enclosing the leaf. Develop that, in addition to taking in and releasing air, water evaporates through a leaf's stomata. Mention that a stoma can open and close. *draw usions* Help children reason when a stoma would shrink in size or close. (Hot weather. This would help to preserve the water supply.)

This experiment can also be done with two leaves, one of which is coated with vaseline to clog the stomata.

Contributing idea D. Flowers make seeds under certain conditions.

1. *Materials:* any large single flower, such as a tulip, lily, snapdragon, petunia, or sweetpea; newspapers, if flowers are available for pupils; large chalkboard sketch of Figure 10-9; single-edge razor.

Raise conjecture as to how seeds are developed. Some children may know seeds are formed in a flower, but press for details. Invite pupils to use the chalkboard sketch as *uggest theses* they offer explanations. Mention that it shows the inside parts of a simple flower. If or when it becomes apparent they need more informa-

tion, let them search for it in books or other sources and then use the sketch.

Bring out the following ideas slowly and carefully through the drawing and related discussion:

a. A flowering plant usually has two parts —a male and a female part. The female part is called a *pistil*. The male part is the *stamen*. Some flowers have many stamens. The sketch flower has only two.

b. Tiny bits of dustlike material called *pollen* grow on the end of the stamen. These may be shaken off into the air. If a pollen grain lands on the sticky tip of the pistil it stays there. Soon it begins to grow a narrow tube. It grows until it reaches an *ovule*—a tiny bit of material which may become a seed. Ovules are always found in a place at the bottom of the pistil called the *ovary*.

c. As soon as the pollen tube joins an ovule, a tiny bit of pollen material travels down the tube. When it touches the ovule, the ovule begins growing. We say that the ovule is *fertilized*.

d. A fertilized ovule grows and forms a seed. Inside the seed is a baby plant.

e. When the flower dies and falls to the ground, the seed may grow into another plant, if it has the right conditions of water, heat, and so on.

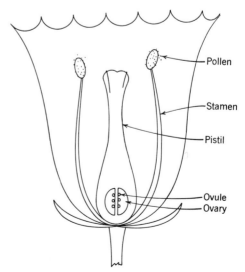

FIGURE 10-9 Parts of a flower.

evaluate critically

2. If flowers are available, distribute them now. Have pupils carefully pull away the leaves and identify the several parts. Let them feel the sticky end of the pistil and touch the pollen-bearing part, found at the ends of the stamens. Split and cut away with the razor the pistil wall protecting the ovary. Ovules should be visible.

3. *Materials:* microprojector or microscope; pollen-bearing flowers; glass slides, black construction paper; hand lenses.

Shake off some pollen onto black paper for visibility. Let pupils examine with a hand lens. Use a microprojector to show some pollen grains greatly magnified. An opaque projector may be used, with more limited success, if you shake some pollen onto cellophane tape, sticky side up. Grains will adhere strongly enough not to be blown away.

4. *Materials:* sugar; six small bowls; spoons; water; pollen grains; hand lenses.

Invite the children to try growing some pollen tubes from pollen grains. Explain that a pistil's sticky end is sugary, and hence a pollen grain may grow a tube if placed in a sugary solution. But it is somewhat difficult, because the amount of sugar in the sticky part of a plant depends on the kind of plant it is. A pollen tube grows only when the solution is about right for a particular pollen grain. Can they find the right amount of sugar needed?

select procedures

Have children plan. A record should be kept of the amount of sugar in each solution —1 teaspoon, 2 teaspoons, and so on. They will also want to use the same amount of water. Perhaps six or more small bowls of sugary water can be used. Pollen grains sprinkled into the right solutions should start growing tubes in about three days at normal room temperature. Examine with hand lenses or microscope.

Summarize children's learnings. Emphasize that they have studied the reproduction method of flowering plants, which includes most trees. However, flowerless plants reproduce in other ways. They will find out more about such plants in future studies.

Extending activities

1. Encourage some children to find out the several ways in which pollen can travel from one flower to another: wind, insects, water, and gravity.

draw conclu

Have children carefully observe the kinds of flowers visited by insects. These will be mostly fragrant flowers with bright colors.

2. Develop a bulletin board on the parts of plants we eat, from pictures brought in by the children. Let them work out a classification scheme, such as:

select proced

Seeds—oats, barley, beans, etc.
Fruits—peach, pear, apple, etc.
Leaves—lettuce, cabbage, spinach, etc.
Stems—asparagus, celery, white potato, etc.
Roots—sweet potato, carrot, radish, etc.

3. Initiate a discussion about what the earth would be like without green plants. Focus on food. What difference would it make to a meat eater who doesn't like vegetables, anyhow? Bring out food chains.

evalua critica

If you were asked to invent a plant, what adaptive characteristics would you want it to have for survival value? Whatever your design, it would be wise to have your plant regulate itself to some extent according to its needs. Assume it has the same needs as other plants. Since it requires water, and water soaks down into the soil, you would want the plant roots to grow downward. But what if there were no water below the roots? You would want roots that could overcome the pull of gravity and grow toward a water source, even if the source were to one side or above the roots.

Since the plant needs light, you would want the stem to be able to grow toward a light source if light became blocked or dimmed. At the same time it would be desirable to design the leaf petiole to accord maximum exposure of the leaf to sunlight. An efficient petiole should be able to grow longer if another leaf blocks its light. It might also turn the leaf perpendicular to the sun's rays as the sun appears at different positions in the sky.

You would also want to consider the obstructions which the plant might encounter in its growth both above and below the ground. It would be helpful for survival if the plant roots and stem could grow around these obstacles to some extent when they touch them.

Of course, there is no need to invent plants like this, as they exist now everywhere around us. Most green plants are responsive to gravity, water, light, and touch. These responses are called plant *tropisms*. Let us see why tropisms occur.

Figure 10-10 shows a radish seedling growing on wet blotting paper inside a water glass. The glass has been placed on its side for twenty-four hours. Notice that the seedling shoot or stem is beginning to curve upward, while the root is starting to grow downward. *Both* reactions are responses to gravity.

Why the opposite directions? Check the magnified sections of the seedling. Gravity causes a concentration of plant hormones (*auxins*) all along the bottom cells from the beginning of the stem to the root tip. The cells along the bottom of the stem are stimulated by the hormones to grow faster than cells above. Growth of these cells is fastest by the stem tip (left inset). As these bottom cells become elongated, the stem begins to curve upward. Root cells, however, are much more sensitive than stem cells. Therefore, the concentration of hormones along the bottom root cells has the opposite effect; it inhibits cell growth. Top cells are least affected and elongate faster, so that the root tip begins to curve downward. Cell growth is fastest by the tip (right inset).

All tropistic responses seem to be the result of plant hormones that concentrate in various parts of the plant. As we have seen, this causes some cells to grow faster than others. Such responses can occur only in growing tissue.

It is always easy and tempting to think of plants and animals as responding to stimuli the way man does. (Remember the discussion

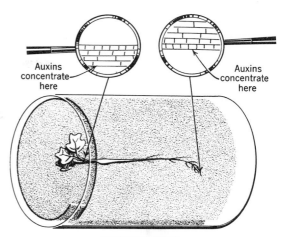

FIGURE 10-10

of anthropomorphism in Chapter 2.) When we are thirsty, we consciously seek water. Does the plant? The literature on living things contains thousands of references to plant and animal behavior that suggest anthropomorphism. Although most of the time no harm is done, anthropomorphism does encourage loose thinking. Perhaps the best reason we should be aware of anthropomorphic statements is because they are usually unwarranted inferences from a set of facts. It seems sensible to discourage faulty inferences wherever or whenever they occur.

BASIC GENERALIZATION V: Plants respond to gravity, light, water, and touch

Contributing idea A. Gravity influences plant roots to grow down and stems up.

Materials: small, potted geranium or bean plant; six-day-old radish seedling growing between a moist paper towel and side of a drinking glass.

Show the children a chalkboard sketch of Figure 10-11. Can they solve this problem? A man wants to plant some trees and shrubs on a steep, bare hill to hold the soil in place and prevent landslides. He has planted one young tree in A. Before he can plant any more, it rains hard and the loose earth on the hill shifts downward. The tree and roots now look

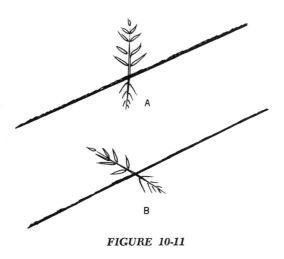

FIGURE 10-11

Contributing idea B. Plant stems above ground grow toward light.

Materials: quart milk carton; garden soil; six radish seeds; large shoebox; razor. (Slice the milk carton in half lengthwise. Discard one-half unless you wish to have two experiments going at one time. Place the remaining half down flat and fill with garden soil. Plant six seeds in a straight row, about an inch apart. In about five days, they will be sufficiently grown for this experiment. Take the large bottom section of the shoebox and invert it. With a razor, cut a narrow slot one-fourth inch wide running the length of the box. The slot should be about one inch from the top of the box. Except for the slot cutting, let children prepare these materials, preferably well in advance of need.)

You might begin with this bridge: "When we buy a house plant to put on a window ledge, sometimes we are told to turn the plant halfway around every two or three days. Why is this advice given?"

Guide the discussion as needed. Let the class investigate classroom plants and note how the leaves are oriented, and so on. Help the children to focus on the light factor. If a plant grows toward the light, its stem will become curved rather than straight. How could the materials be used to find out if plants grow toward the light? (Place the seedlings on a table in a well-lighted location. Put the inverted shoebox over the seedlings with the slotted side opposite the window. Seedlings should bend and grow toward the slot.) *suggest hypothe* *select procedu*

A definite bending toward the light source will be noticeable within a day or two. Let children evaluate their data. What makes it seem likely that the light was responsible? (All six seedlings are bent the same way.) What could we do to make sure? (Reverse the box. See if the plants start growing the opposite way.) To be as evident, the reversal will take somewhat longer than the initial experiment. *evaluate criticall* *select procedu* *draw conclus*

Let all the children try their own light experiment, if possible. This can be done with a radish seed planted in soil contained in a

suggest hypotheses

select procedures

like sketch B. If there are no further landslides, will this tree and its roots continue to grow in a slanty way? Raise conjecture.

Some children may recall that bean seedling roots grow down and the shoots grow up no matter how the seed is positioned. Will growing plants do the same? Hold up the growing radish seedling. How could it be used to find out what might happen to the farmer's slanted tree? (Put the glass on its side. The stem will change direction and grow up; roots will change direction and grow down.) The paper towel should be moistened several times a day. Let a fast-dripping faucet drip onto the inside surface of the toweling. When it is moist, quickly put the glass on its side again.

select procedures

How could the potted geranium be used in a substitute experiment? (Place it on one side, except for watering once a day. Notice the new direction the stem takes. Take the plant out of the pot to examine its roots.) Good results should be visible in both experiments within four or five days.

draw conclusions

Develop that gravity influences plant roots to grow down. Stems are influenced in the opposite way. Encourage pupils to apply their findings in observing foliage on hills and bluffs around the neighborhood. Generally, roots grow down and standing stems grow vertically, relative to the earth's horizontal surface.

small paper cup. Cover with a larger, inverted paper cup that has a small hole punched in the side with a pencil. Should there be inconsistencies in results, get pupils to analyze why. If other seeds are used, conclusions can be broadened. Otherwise, have everyone read for further confirmation.

evaluate critically

draw conclusions

Contributing idea C. Plant roots grow toward their source of water.

Materials: aquarium tank or substitute containing soil; three soaked Lima beans.

Tell the pupils they will find it interesting to learn more about how roots grow. Invite them to consider a problem that happens occasionally with underground pipes. Develop briefly how some large underground pipes near the children's homes are used to transport water and sewage. Some of these pipes are made of clay and some of iron. Occasionally, the clay pipes get clogged or broken from tree roots growing in and around them. This may happen even if the pipe is 30 or 40 feet away to one side of the tree. Yet almost never does this happen to iron pipes, even if they are closer. What causes the roots to grow in and around the clay pipes?

suggest hypotheses

Hint about the porosity of clay, if needed. When water is mentioned as the attraction, ask the children about gravity. Doesn't gravity cause plant roots to grow down? If water does "attract" roots, it would have to pull against gravity to some extent in this case. Can it do this? Develop a discussion.

select procedures

Divide the class into six "task forces." Ask the groups to design an experiment with available materials to see if water will cause plant roots to grow sideways. If necessary, mention that the glass tank could be used to make root growth visible. But give as few hints as are necessary to keep the children thinking. Let the chairmen present their groups' strategies. The whole class can screen these ideas and choose the one that seems best. Focus on the logic of all "arguments" for one or another strategy. Now is the time when "if-then" thinking can flourish with guidance.

evaluate critically

An experimental setup like the following

should work well. Plant three soaked Lima beans close to one end of the tank. They should be planted 1 inch apart, and against the glass, about 2 inches below the soil surface. Water directly over the seeds until they sprout and are growing well. From then on water only slightly and in the far opposite corner. In about a week, there should be a noticeable change in root direction, particularly with the roots nearest to the water. To hasten this experiment, have the seedlings already growing.

After children have drawn some limited conclusions, develop that clay pipes are often still used for sewage, for example, because iron pipes tend to corrode and rust. Someday, plastic pipes may be used. Perhaps then we shall seldom hear of a pipe getting clogged or broken by tree roots.

draw conclusions

Contributing idea D. Plants respond to touch.

1. *Materials:* large glass jar of soil in which a bean seedling is growing (The seed should have been planted next to the glass, so that the roots are currently visible.); several stones or sticks.

Mention that there is another problem with roots which the children can think about. What does the ground look like below the first few inches of topsoil? (It becomes rockier.) What happens to a root when a rock or something else gets in its way? (It may go around the rock.) Will roots move around something that gets in their way? Invite a test. (Put some rocks or sticks under the root tip. We shall see whether the root moves around or through these things.)

select procedures

Unless many obstructions are used, the root should go around or through them and continue to grow. Bring out that the root seems to be sensitive to touch.

Since this is another potential open-end experiment, encourage children to try individual tests, varying seedlings and obstructions. Tall glass jars or paper cups might be used. If paper cups are used, have children examine roots by cutting the cups in two and gently picking at the soil with pencils.

select procedures

FIGURE 10-12

2. *Materials:* vigorous, potted bean seedling; two rulers; a dozen or so books.

What would happen if there were something in the way of a growing plant *above* ground? Say a plant is growing directly under a railing. What would happen when it touches the railing? (It might go around.) Let the children suggest an experiment to find out. Perhaps it will look like Figure 10-12. (Put the seedling between two stacks of books. Lay two rulers close together across the stacks. The seedling tip should almost touch the rulers' undersides. Adjust stack heights as needed.)

select procedures

The seedling should grow around the obstacle. However, it might push the rulers aside unless they are weighted down. What if four rulers are used? What if different obstacles are used? Different plants? There are many possibilities for open-end, individual experiments and subsequent reports.

select procedures

Summarize by discussing the survival value of all four tropisms studied.

draw conclusions

Extending activities

1. For a dramatic example of a plant's sensitivity to touch, borrow a mimosa plant from a nurseryman. Touch the narrow leaves with a pencil. They will suddenly contract or fold together. This will not harm the plant, although it may take several hours for the leaves to return to their former position.

2. Have pupils grow a climbing plant, such as a sweetpea or morning glory. The narrow tendrils of these plants will curl around a stick or string and "lead" the rest of the plant. If a tendril's sensitive underside is stroked, it will curl within minutes.

3. Take the class on a study trip around the school or neighborhood to observe leaf arrangements of trees and bushes. Have the children notice how branches and even leaf petioles vary in length. This permits almost every leaf to have direct exposure to sunlight. Discuss how useful this is for survival.

draw conclus.

4. Show a film which features time-lapse photography of plant tropisms and other plant movements.

5. Help children become sensitive to anthropomorphic statements. Is it accurate to say that plant roots are "searching" for water? Why or why not? They should realize that a conscious purpose is probably not involved. Have them compose a more desirable statement. Let them search for such expressions in trade books, make reports on their findings, and discuss how these expressions could be rewritten. Sharp thinkers will particularly enjoy and profit from this activity.

evaluate criticall

UNIT 11

Animal Groups

(*Primary*)

This unit can help children learn how to observe and classify animals. But our intention goes beyond identification alone. Children should discover that despite their tremendous diversity, animals share certain characteristics and needs. Careful observation of how animals are built enables us to place them into common groups. These groupings permit us to learn many of the interesting adaptations and ways of animals without the need to study every individual group member.

The unit will particularly interest and teach children if several live animals are kept in the classroom. We shall provide a variety of suggestions for doing so in the pages which follow. To take full advantage of the teaching possibilities, begin this unit in the spring.

BASIC GENERALIZATIONS

I. There are many kinds of animals; they may be grouped in different ways.

II. Mammals are warm blooded, have some fur or hair, and milk glands.

III. Birds are warm blooded, have feathers, and two wings.

IV. Reptiles are cold blooded, and have a dry, scaly skin; some have a shell.

V. Amphibians are cold blooded, and have either a smooth or bumpy skin; most hatch from jellylike eggs laid in water.

VI. Fishes are cold blooded, live and breathe in water, and are usually covered with scales.

VII. There are many animals without backbones; insects make up the largest group.

Of some 1 million 250 thousand different forms of living things, animals make up almost 1 million. They run, walk, crawl, fly, slither, and swim. They range in size from a microscopic protozoan to the blue whale, 100 feet long. Their colors embrace all shades of the spectrum. In almost any way one can imagine, the diversity of animals is truly amazing. How do scientists keep track of them? A system developed by the great Swedish naturalist, *Carolus Linnaeus* (1707–1778), provided the base for modern classification. Fundamentally, it takes into account the physical structure of the living thing. Six main categories are used, which range from the general to the particular description of group characteristics. For example, let us classify a dog. Parenthetical remarks refer to the general meaning of each category.

Kingdom—Animalia (The subject belongs to the animal, not the plant kingdom.)
Phylum—Chordata (It has a backbone or a notochord.)
Class—Mammalia (It is a mammal.)
Order—Carnivora (It eats meat.)
Family—Canidae (It belongs to a group with doglike characteristics.)
Genus—Canis (It is a coyote, wolf, or dog.)
Species—Familiaris (It is a common dog.)

Such a system has important advantages to biologists. It is possible to pinpoint most living things and to note relationships which otherwise might be easy to miss. Since the system is accepted by scientists the world over, accuracy of communication is realized.

For elementary-school science, however, you will want to work with a more simplified classification scheme. The following one should be useful, and will fit nicely into any more formal structure the child may develop later in high school and college. Although in this unit children will not study all the groups described, seeing the overall classification scheme should be helpful.

We shall divide the entire animal kingdom into two huge groups, each with a manageably small number of subgroups:

Animals with Backbones (Vertebrates)
Mammals (man, dog, horse, etc.)
Birds (sparrow, penguin, eagle, etc.)
Reptiles (turtle, lizard, snake, etc.)
Amphibians (frog, toad, salamander, etc.)
Fishes (carp, bass, minnow, etc.)

Animals without Backbones (Invertebrates)
Echinoderms—animals with spiny skins (sand dollar, starfish, sea urchin, etc.)
Arthropods—animals with jointed legs
  insects (fly, moth, grasshopper, etc.)
  arachnids (spider, scorpion, tick, etc.)
  crustaceans (crab, lobster, crayfish, etc.)
  myriapods (millipede and centipede)
Mollusks—animals with soft bodies (clam, snail, octopus, etc.)
Worms (flatworm, roundworm, segmented worm, etc.)
Sponges and Jellyfish (sponge, jellyfish, sea anemone, coral, etc.)
Protozoa—one-celled animals (paramecium, ameba, foraminifera, etc.)

When primary children use the term "animal," they are inclined to mean mammal, or at best, another animal with a backbone. Yet the five main vertebrates make up a scant 5 per cent of the animals in existence. Insects, which make up 70 per cent of all animals, represent by far the largest class of inverte-

brates. There are more than 700,000 species. (A species is a group whose members can generally reproduce only among themselves.)

In daily contact and interest, the vertebrates and insects compose most of the animal world for primary children. Therefore, we shall concentrate in this unit on making children more aware of these particular animal groups and their fascinating adaptations.

Some of the forthcoming activities will require about twenty colored pictures of animals. Most, if not all, can be gathered by the children. One primary teacher who worked with this unit reported that over two hundred pictures had been brought in by the class! Children's trade books represent an additional source. Moreover, any children's encyclopedia is sure to have many animal pictures, located in one convenient section. These can be exhibited with an opaque projector.

The *Golden Nature Guides* (see page 72), contain outstanding pictures of animals in color. In addition, helpful descriptions and other data accompany each picture. These, too, can be used with an opaque projector. Both readers and nonreaders can thumb through these guides and classify specimens.

All of the animals mentioned in this unit's activities can be furnished through the children, pet shops, or biological supply houses. The unit contains many suggestions for maintaining these animals in the classroom. But you may wish to have even more detailed and comprehensive directions than can be provided in this book. One biological supply house offers many excellent leaflets[1] on the care of living things in the classroom.

---

[1] Turtox Service Leaflets: No. 5, *Starting & Maintaining a Fresh-Water Aquarium;* No. 11, *Plants for the Fresh-Water Aquarium;* No. 23, *Feeding Aquarium & Terrarium Animals;* No. 48, *Aquarium Troubles: Their Prevention & Cure;* No. 10, *The School Terrarium;* No. 40, *The Care of Rats, Mice, Hamsters & Guinea Pigs;* No. 28, *Reptiles in the School Laboratory;* No. 7, *The Care of Frogs & Other Amphibians;* No. 34, *The Care of Living Insects in the School Laboratory;* No. 35, *Studying Ants in Observation Nests;* No. 13, *Rearing the Silkworm Moth.* Employed teachers can obtain all these and several more

If there is a natural history museum nearby, don't overlook the possibility of borrowing preserved animal specimens. In addition, some museums arrange free guided tours and consultant services for individual classes.

The intent of the first sequence is to make pupils more aware that there is much diversity among animals, and that animals may be classified in many ways. We shall provide opportunity for children to invent their own classifications—pets, farm animals, and the like. From there they will move gradually into the more involved scheme of classification by body structure, with its consequent relationships to adaptation and life needs. Help pupils realize that we classify things according to our purposes. Different purposes may demand different classification schemes.

BASIC GENERALIZATION I: There are many kinds of animals; they may be grouped in different ways

1. *Materials:* 18 to 24 cut-out, colored magazine pictures, including several from each of these groups—mammals, birds, reptiles, amphibians, fishes, insects. (Place all pictures on a large bulletin board. Arrange in even rows and columns, but not in definite groups at this time. Put a different numeral on a small white card under each picture, for quick reference. Have this question mounted at the top of the board: *Which animals make good pets?*)

Mention that the children are going to find out many interesting things about animals during this unit. There will be many chances to work with different animals in the classroom. But first, they will want to find out the kinds of animals that are easy to work with and fun to observe.

Ask for the hands of those who have animal pets at home. Invite these pupils to name

leaflets free-of-charge. On school stationery simply request the *Turtox Elementary School Leaflet Set* from the General Biological Supply House, 8200 South Hoyne Ave., Chicago, Illinois 60620.

and describe their animals, and how they take care of them. Try to have a variety of pet animals described. Bring out some reasons why these animals make good pets: tameness, size, interesting habits, and so on. *draw conclusions*

After some discussion, direct attention to the bulletin board and caption. Are there any animals pictured here which make good pets? Ask pupils to use the picture numbers for handy reference, and the animal's name, if known. Get the class to screen each suggestion according to the pet criteria just established. Develop that some animals are too wild, large, difficult to feed, or have other characteristics which make them undesirable as pets. *evaluate critically*

To summarize, write "Good for pets" and "Not good for pets" on the chalkboard. Draw out appropriate numbers of the animal pictures for each heading and list them in columns. Include animal names, if known. *draw conclusions*

2. Develop that the class has divided the bulletin board animals into two large *groups*, according to their usefulness as pets. A group is a collection of things. Animals in the pet group belong together because they are alike in some ways. Elicit that there are many other ways the children can group animals. One other way is by size. Invite them to group the animals on the bulletin board according to size: *small, middle-size,* and *large.*

Be alert for chances to establish operational definitions. What is a "small" animal? A bear is small compared to an elephant. A bear is large compared to a mouse. Guide toward the use of three representative animals on the bulletin board to establish a workable definition for each of the three sizes. *define problems*

Encourage suggestions for other classifications of animals; for example, how they move. Some fly, swim, walk, or run. *evaluate critically*

3. *Materials:* pictures of two different birds, and two different fishes.

Now lay the groundwork for further study. Hold up a picture of a small fish and another of a bird. Tell the class about a boy who owned these animals. Establish that he probably kept the fish in a fish tank and the bird in a cage. One day the boy thought these animals must be tired of living in the same old places, so he decided to change things around. He thought he would put his bird in the fish tank and his fish in the cage. Is this a good idea? What would happen?

The boy found out from a friend that the bird would drown and the fish would die, so he did not switch them. But he had two other pets. (Show the second pair of pictures.) Could he switch *these* two around—bird in the tank and fish in the cage? (No!)

Develop that although the boy's two fishes are somewhat different in appearance, they are built in much the same way and have many of the same life requirements. This is also true of his birds. Point out that there are many different kinds of animals; more kinds of animals than there are children in the school, or in the whole neighborhood, or for many miles around. We will never be able to study each and every animal alive. There are too many. But we can study groups of animals. Although animals may look different at first, their bodies are often much the same. Animals with similar bodies often act and live in similar ways.

Extending activities

1. Through use of many picture books of animals, have children look up and determine common names for any animals not identified on the bulletin board: panther, alligator, salamander, and so on.

select procedures

2. Encourage pupils to invent additional ways to group the bulletin board pictures. Some classifications commonly used by primary pupils are farm animals, skin covering, number of feet, and kind of food eaten—animal or plant.

Look around long enough, and you will find animals everywhere: below the ground (mole, gopher, woodchuck); on the ground (man, giraffe, elephant); in trees above the ground (monkey, sloth, tree squirrel); in the air (bat); and in the water (whale, seal, dolphin). What can such a diverse collection of creatures have in common? All of these are *mammals*. That is, all have some fur or hair; all have milk glands. To be sure, you will not find much hair on a whale or seal—only a few bristles on the snout. And sometimes fur or hair is greatly modified, as with the porcupine's quills. But look closely enough, and, if it is a mammal, it has hair.

Both male and female mammals have mammary, or milk glands. (You can see how the term "mammals" originated.) Ordinarily, of course, only the female produces milk used in suckling the young.

Another distinction of mammals is their intelligence, the highest of all animal groups. But other unique characteristics are few and subtle.

Mammals are usually born alive. The embryo develops within the mother from a tiny egg fertilized by a sperm cell from a male of the same species. During its development the embryo is attached to the female by a placenta, or membranous tissue. Water, oxygen, and food pass from female to embryo through this tissue. In turn, liquefied waste materials flow the other way. These are absorbed into the female's blood stream, sent to the kidneys, and eliminated. The navel pit in the abdomen of humans is a reminder of this early stage of our development.

The two known exceptions to this reproductive pattern are the spiny anteater and duck-billed platypus, both of Australia. Each lays eggs. The hatched young, however, are cared for and suckled by the female much in the manner of other mammals.

Mammals are warm blooded and have efficient hearts with four chambers. These characteristics are shared by only one other group, the birds. Their blood temperatures stay at relatively the same level, whether the air warms or cools. Animals of lesser complexity are cold blooded. That is, their blood temperature changes as their environmental temperature changes.

It is both an advantage and disadvantage to be warm blooded. Vigorous activity is possible within most air temperature ranges. But the body heat of mammals must be conserved, else death occurs. In cold climates, thick blubber or fur performs this function, as does hibernation, and, in some cases, migration. In warm climates, humans perspire. Some animals estivate, becoming relatively inactive for a period in whatever suitably cool refuge can be found.

Some cold-blooded animals can withstand great cold or heat, but most are dependent on a narrow temperature range for normal activity or survival. We shall go into more detail later with several specific animals.

Although the terms are still relative, it is more accurate to say "constant temperatured" and "variable temperatured," rather than "warm blooded" and "cold blooded," when we refer to animals. In hot weather, for example, a "cold-blooded" animal might have a higher body temperature than a "warm-blooded" one.

The teeth of mammals are particularly interesting to observe, since they are apparently adapted to specific functions. We can see the four main kinds of teeth by examining our own in a mirror. In front are the chisel-like incisors. On both sides of these teeth are the conelike canines. Farther back are the front molars, and last, the back molars. Now let us note how these teeth are used by several kinds of mammals.

Prominent, sharp incisors are characteristic of gnawing mammals—rats, mice, guinea pigs, hamsters, muskrats, beavers, and rabbits. The incisors of these rodents grow continuously at the root, and are worn down at the opposite end by gnawing. When prevented from gnawing, incisors may grow so long the animal cannot close its mouth, and so starves to death.

The flesh eaters (carnivores), such as cats, dogs, and seals, have small incisors and prominent canines, sometimes called "fangs." Their molars have curved, sharp edges. The canines are useful for tearing meat. The molars are suited for chopping it into parts small enough to swallow.

Plant eaters (herbivores), such as the horse, goat, and sheep, have wide, closely spaced incisors, and large, flat-surfaced molars.

Canines do not appear. The incisors work well in clipping off grasses and plant stems. The molars grind this material prior to swallowing.

Since man is an omnivore, that is, capable of eating both plant and animal matter, human teeth include all four types.

A forthcoming activity suggests that children examine a dog's teeth. Besides this, they might look at a trade book that shows pictures of teeth of other animals.

An extending activity suggests the breeding of white rats or mice in the classroom. This is an interesting experience for youngsters, and furnishes the basis for a wholesome and intelligent attitude toward reproduction in all animals, including man. We recommend use of white rats or mice over such common classroom animals as hamsters and guinea pigs. Mating is more uncertain to come about with captive hamsters. They are also more inclined to bite, although this is less likely with young, well-handled hamsters. Guinea pigs are a bit large for small classroom cages, and their comparatively long gestation period (63 days after mating) is inconvenient.

Although simple cages for rodents can be homemade from strong screening material, a commercial cage is usually more secure and better suited to the animals' needs. Rodents are typically quite active and may deteriorate in health unless an exercise wheel is provided. A small, inverted water bottle with tube, affixed to the cage, will present a clean, long

FIGURE 11-1

lasting water supply. A commercial cage, like that in Figure 11-1, should serve well and last indefinitely. It may be purchased at most pet stores and scientific supply houses, as can white rats and mice.

One last point. Never house a rodent in a wood or cardboard container. Remember those incisors!

BASIC GENERALIZATION II: Mammals are warm blooded, have some fur or hair, and milk glands

1. *Materials:* several pictures of mammals, such as a seal, dog, rat, and horse; pictures of a cow with full udder of milk, and any animal suckling its young; several pictures of different birds, with one showing a parent bird feeding its young, if possible. (Affix these illustrations in no apparent order on a flannel or bulletin board.)

Call attention to the pictures. Mention that all the animals shown may be divided into two large groups. Challenge the children *evaluate* to note likenesses and differences. Let them *critically* separate the pictures. Discuss reasons for their choices. Bring out that one group has feathers and is made up of *birds.* Have pupils note carefully that the remaining animals all possess some fur or hair. If a picture of a cow is available, draw out that the udder is a milk gland used by the cow to nurse its young. This is also where the milk we drink comes from, before it is put into cartons or bottles.

Develop that all the animals on the bulletin board which are not birds are called *mammals.* All have some fur or hair. Mother mammals have live babies and feed their babies milk from their milk glands.

2. *Materials:* gentle female dog, preferably one that has had puppies; dog owner.

Have the child lift his dog's front feet up from behind so the class can see the dog's milk glands. Let him describe how his dog feeds its puppies, how often, and how long. Perhaps he can tell some other ways in which the dog takes care of its young. Encourage

other children to describe pups or kittens born to their pets—number in the litter, how the newborn animals looked, when they were able to walk around, and so on.

Have several children feel the dog's skin and note its warmth. Establish that mammals have warm blood in their bodies. Whether the air gets hot or cold, the blood of mammals stays at about the same warm temperature. Mention that this is true of only one other group of animals, which they will study shortly. In all other animal groups, we find cold-blooded animals. That is, the temperature of their blood is usually about the same as the air temperature around them. As the air gets warmer, their blood gets warmer. As the air gets colder, their blood gets colder.

Elicit that the dog needs air, food, and water. Then let its owner open the dog's mouth. Discuss how the teeth are well suited for chewing meat. Bring out how the fur coat keeps the dog warm.

Summarize on a chart how to identify a *draw* mammal: warm blooded, fur or hair, and milk *conclu* glands. Have pupils use these criteria to test *evalua* if man is a mammal. *critica*

Extending activities

1. Inform pupils that they can raise mammals in class. Tell them two white rats (or mice) are available; a *male* ("He will become the father"), and a *female* ("She will become the mother"). Demonstrate how to prepare the cage and care for the animals. If some children have raised small mammals, let them contribute suggestions. Be sure pupils understand the reason for each action taken whenever possible.

Cage—Use a commercially produced cage with exercise wheel and inverted water bottle as recommended in the exposition. Cover the floor with a double thickness of newspaper. Distribute a generous covering of sawdust, wood shavings, peat moss, or shredded newspaper over the paper. Remove the floor covering and replace with fresh materials twice a week, or oftener if a pronounced odor develops. The cage should be in a draft-free location, as rodents are quite susceptible to colds. The temperature should not fall below 60°F. However, a deep floor covering usually provides some insulation of heat energy since the animals will burrow into it.

Food—Dry pellets for small laboratory animals, including rats, are obtainable at most pet and feed stores. In addition, feed bits of carrots, lettuce, and bread. Avoid feeding rats raw meat as sometimes this makes them vicious. A constant supply of pellets and other nonperishable food may be left in a small, flat container in the cage. However, remove any perishable food within an hour after offered. A fresh bottle of water and tray of pellets should last over weekends, but provisions for feeding will need to be taken for longer periods.

Handling—White rats and mice are typically very gentle, likable creatures. They should be handled daily for a short period. This tames them and accustoms them to being around children. If a tiny bit of peanut butter or carrot is offered on the tip of a toothpick, they can be enticed into the children's hands. Although there is virtually no chance of the animals biting if treated gently, caution children to wear gloves when handling rats, mice, or hamsters. (Notify the school nurse immediately if *any* classroom animal should bite a child. Although the bite itself is usually very minor, germs the animal may harbor in its mouth may cause infection unless the wound is promptly treated.)

Breeding—Rats and mice usually breed within a few days. Provide some loose cotton or shredded newspaper which the female can use in preparing a nest. Remove the male rat from the cage after it appears obvious that the female is pregnant. It may eat the young or agitate the female to do the same. Return the male to the pet store, or give it to the Humane Society, or confine it to a separate cage until the young are a month old. About three weeks after mating, the female will give birth to six or more young in the nest. Do not disturb the female for several days after this event.

The newborn young will be blind and hairless. They may be weaned gradually to a regular diet after they are about two weeks old. Feed them milk which contains soft bread crumbs for a week, and adult food thereafter.

All rats should be given to a responsible source for disposal after completion of this activity. Abandoned rodents become wild and add prolifically to the local pest population within a short time.

During the seven or eight weeks of working with this activity, be sure to provide opportunity for frequent, short, class discussions about the behavior and habits of the caged rats. Particular emphasis should be placed on the birth, appearance, care, feeding, and physical development of the young. You may note rapid day-to-day improvement in children's oral reporting skills as they tell the latest news about their rats.

Use a chart with rotating names for assigning such tasks as replacement of water, paper, and food. Most primary children are delighted to serve. This may be an excellent opportunity to motivate a problem child or help him achieve a greater sense of responsibility.

2. Encourage the class to bring in pictures of as many different kinds of mammals as it can. Pictures should be screened by class members for accuracy of classification. If disputes arise about whether an animal is a mammal, have them use picture books and illustrated identification books for verification. Let an able class committee plan a bulletin board featuring unusual mammals and where they come from.

evaluate critically

"A bird is an animal with feathers." This is a primary child's definition, but really cannot be much improved. Almost all other characteristics we see in birds may be found here and there among other animal groups, though not in the same combinations. The coloring and construction of their feathers vary tremendously, from the luxuriant plumage of a peacock to the scruffy covering of a New Zealand kiwi.

Although we ordinarily think of birds as fliers, chickens and road runners seldom fly, and some birds—the ostrich, penguin, and kiwi, for example—cannot fly at all.

"He eats like a bird." How often we have heard a person who eats sparingly described this way. It is hardly fitting. Few other animals possess such voracious appetites for their size. Many birds must eat their weight in food each day just to stay alive.

To see why this is so, examine a small, flying bird closely. Notice that its body volume is relatively small when compared to the large surface area of its skin. As body volume decreases in size, the relative size of skin surface increases. If this seems unclear, inspect a pint and quart milk carton. The small carton holds only half as much, but clearly has more than one-half the surface area of the larger carton. A large skin surface area causes heat energy to radiate rapidly away from the body. This is bad when the body volume is small because the heat generating capacity is also small. To generate enough heat energy for normal functioning when heat energy is quickly being radiated away, a high metabolic rate (the rate at which food is oxidized and assimilated) must be maintained. The rapid burning of fuel causes body temperatures in birds of 102° to 110°F, highest of any animal group.

Mammals are also affected in this way. Smaller mammals usually eat more for their size than larger ones. As we travel toward the earth's polar regions, we can observe a general increase in mammals' body size. As body volume increases, the relative size of skin surface decreases. Comparatively less heat energy is radiated away.

The bodies of most birds are well suited for flight. Inside are several air sacs connected to the lungs. Many bones are hollow, or nearly so, and further reduce body weight. Even a chicken has relatively little marrow in its longer bones. It is said that the great evolutionist Charles Darwin had a pipe stem made from a wing bone of an albatross.

The body of a bird is streamlined and closely fitted with three kinds of feathers.

Next to the skin are fluffy, soft, down feathers. These contain numerous "dead-air" pockets which help conserve body heat. Contour feathers hug the body closely, and large flight feathers help to propel and steer the bird as it flies.

Most birds continually preen their feathers. This is done by using the bill to press a drop of oil from a gland located just above the tail, and then spreading it over the feathers. A shiny, waterproof coating results. It is so effective that a duck can float for many hours without becoming waterlogged. If the oil were removed, a swimming duck would disappear into the water like a slowly submerging submarine. If you can locate a large, recently molted feather, dip it in water before and after washing in soap or detergent. Let the children notice how water soaks in after the washing.

The thick white meat or breast section on poultry is partly the result of selective breeding by man. But virtually all birds have their largest and strongest muscles in this section, since they control the major wing movements. We shall provide an activity to help children realize how important these muscles are for this function.

The remarkably keen eyesight of birds has been well advertised. Less known is that they have three eyelids. Two shut the eye, and the third—a transparent membrane—sweeps back and forth, cleaning away dust or other foreign matter without need for blinking. Eyes of most birds are located on the sides of the head. Thus, they must continually cock the head to one side to see directly forward. Their hearing is also acute despite the lack of outer ears. But birds do not appear to discriminate well among various odors or tastes.

Most birds have horny beaks, whose various shapes show great diversity of function. Although all known modern birds are toothless, fossil records indicate that a variety of toothed birds lived in ancient times. The feet of birds are equally diverse in form. On the legs we find scales, which indicate their evolutionary connection to the reptiles.

As in mammals, sexual reproduction begins

FIGURE 11-2 **Children enjoy the chick-hatching activity.**

with an egg cell fertilized within the female by a sperm cell. However, fertilization is not necessary for an egg to be laid. Many chicken hens lay an egg every day. We eat these unfertilized eggs.

An egg acquires its hard shell in the lower part of the hen's oviduct, or egg-conducting tube. Glands produce a limy secretion which gradually hardens over a period of hours before the egg is laid. The shell is porous and permits both oxygen to enter and carbon dioxide to leave. In a fertilized egg, this is essential for life in the developing chick embryo.

Your pupils will thoroughly enjoy a chick-hatching activity, described later in some detail. You will need fertilized eggs and an incubator. Get the eggs from a hatchery or farmer. Buy a small incubator, usually priced at several dollars and up, from a pet shop or scientific supply house. Although it is possible to make an incubator with a glowing light bulb and insulated cardboard container, few seem to work satisfactorily. It is essential to success that a near-constant temperature of

101–103°F be maintained for the 21-day incubation period. Homemade incubators typically fluctuate in temperature well beyond permissible limits.

BASIC GENERALIZATION III: Birds are warm blooded, have feathers, and two wings

1. *Materials:* five or six pictures of birds. (Place on flannel or bulletin board.)

Ask the children to note several ways in which the pictured birds differ in coloring, marking, size, shape, and so on. Now ask them to note at least three ways in which they are the same. Develop that all have *draw conclusions* feathers, two wings, two legs and feet. Children may also observe that all have *bills*.

Probably some class members have handled chicks, parakeets, or ducks. Draw out that these animals feel warm to the touch. What might this tell us about their blood? (They are warm blooded, like mammals.) Draw out that their feathers can also keep them warm in cold weather. Perhaps some child has a blanket at home filled with downy feathers. Let him describe how warm it is.

Many children will be aware that young are hatched from eggs, laid by the mother bird in some kind of nest. If they become curious and interested about this at the present time, you may want to start immediately on a chick hatching activity (extending activity 1).

2. *Materials:* large stuffed bird specimen (or a large picture of a bird); several clean, dry, long bones from a chicken.

Ask for the hands of pupils who like to eat chicken. Who likes the dark meat? Light meat? Point to the bird specimen or picture. Where would most of the light meat be found on this bird? (Breast.) Let someone indicate this area.

Bring out that the light meat section on a bird is the thickest part of its body, and is made up of chest muscles. But why are the muscles so thick and large here? Encourage speculation briefly. Ask the children to stand and hold their arms out to the side, parallel to the floor. Arms should be straight-

FIGURE 11-3 (A) Duck, (B) woodpecker, (C) sparrow, (D) hawk.

ened and elbows locked. Have all rapidly move their arms forward and back, no more than a foot or so. In less than half a minute pupils will feel a tightening and slightly strained effect on their upper chest muscles (pectorals) and shoulders. Draw out that the bird's wings are moved mainly by the chest muscles. The exercise of pushing against the air develops strong, large chest muscles. *draw conclu*

Break open a few long bones from a chicken. Let the children closely examine them. Develop that the bones are relatively hollow, in contrast with mammal bones, which are thicker and filled with a heavy marrow. Mention that a few kinds of birds have some bones which are completely hollow. Help pupils reason that the lightness of hollow bones is an advantage in flying. Mention that many flying birds have several air pockets inside their bodies, which also help to make birds light for their size.

Ask the children to speculate why a bird cocks its head to one side as it looks at something directly ahead. Why doesn't it stare straight ahead? Have children examine the specimen and available pictures. Develop that most birds' eyes are located on the sides of their heads. This makes it difficult or impossible to see something directly in front. Let the class discover through pictures that owls are the commonest exception. *sugges hypoth* *draw conclu* *evalua critica*

Point out the eyelids on the stuffed specimen. There is an upper and lower lid, like on humans. Explain that, in addition there is a third eyelid which is clear (transparent). It sweeps from the back to the front of the eye, and wipes away dust.

Does a bird have ears? Ask a child to take a pencil and probe gently around the stuffed specimen's head. He should find an opening on each side of the skull. Explain that a bird does not have outside (external) ears, but does have hearing organs inside that work very well. The outside holes help to let in sounds.

3. *Materials:* opaque projector; Figure 11-3.

This is an appropriate time to develop adaptations of bills and feet of birds. Project Figure 11-3 onto a screen. Have the third column masked with some black paper at present. It can be revealed later to verify pupil hypotheses. Ask the children to study the first and second columns, and then to guess the kind of food each bird eats. To make this easier, you might slowly say, "One of these birds cracks open seeds; another eats small mammals; another scoops up plants of tiny fish from water; another punches holes in the bark of trees and digs out insects."

suggest hypotheses

Bring out the following ideas:

draw conclusions

a. The bill of bird A is useful in scooping up plants and small fish in water, because it is like a little shovel. The scooped-up water spills out through the uneven sides of the bill, but the food remains inside.

draw conclusions

b. The bill of bird B is like a large, pointed nail. It can dig into tough tree bark and catch insects. (Point out that the bills of most other insect eaters are slenderer.)

draw conclusions

c. The bill of bird C is small but strong. It can crack open seeds and some nuts. (A child may have a pet canary whose seed-cracking ways might be described.)

draw conclusions

d. The bill of bird D is like a sharp hook. It can tear the meat from bones of small mammals.

suggest hypotheses

Let children speculate how specialized feet help the birds. After some discussion, reveal the third column of Figure 11-3. Identify the birds: duck (A), woodpecker (B), sparrow (C), and hawk (D). Develop these ideas: Webbed feet of the duck are useful for paddling in water. The woodpecker's feet can dig securely into a vertical tree trunk. The

draw conclusions

sparrow's feet are useful for perching. They automatically close around a tree limb or similar perch. It requires no effort and the bird may sleep in this position without danger of falling. The owl's feet are useful for grasping an animal and holding it securely.

Extending activities

1. Have a chick-hatching activity. Get several fertilized eggs from a hatchery or farmer, and an egg incubator. Discuss the fact that birds hatch from eggs. Describe the behavior of a hen after it lays one or more eggs. The hen settles over the egg and keeps it warm.

Several times a day it turns the egg. This keeps the growing chick from sticking to the shell. After twenty-one days, the chick breaks open the shell and comes out.

Show the incubator. It can keep the eggs warm, too. We can turn the eggs twice a day —once in the morning, and once at dismissal time. Will chicks hatch? We shall see. Help the children to realize that a mark placed on the egg will assist in keeping track of egg positions.

select procedures

In twenty-one days, or sooner if the eggs have not been freshly laid, the hatching will take place. Let the children observe how a chick breaks out of its shell by using a tiny "egg tooth" on top of its beak. This drops off shortly after the chick emerges. The chick will look wet and scraggly until its downy feathers dry. No food is necessary for at least twenty-four hours as it will have digested the egg yolk and some egg white before breaking out of the shell. (Many children have the misconception that an egg yolk *is* the undeveloped embryo, rather than its principal food.)

Chicks need constant warmth. This is furnished by a brooder, or warm box. An incubator can be used temporarily if the lid is raised, but may be too confining after a few days. If the chicks are to be kept for more than several days, use a cardboard box with a shielded, goose-neck lamp shining into it. Chick feed may be purchased at a pet store. Leave some feed and clean water in dishes within the brooder at all times. A fresh newspaper floor cover each day will keep the brooder clean. Give the chicks to a farmer or hatchery after a week or two. Proper conditions become increasingly difficult to provide in a classroom as chicks become older.

2. Invite pupils to bring in pictures of various birds. On the basis of the bills, let the children tentatively divide the birds into such categories as "seed eaters," "insect eaters," and "meat eaters." Picture book research will confirm how accurate they are. Let the class discover that some birds cannot be classified in just one category.

suggest hypotheses

evaluate critically

Many children know that snakes are reptiles, but are unaware that the term also includes turtles, lizards, alligators, and crocodiles. What do these animals have in common? All typically have dry, scaly skin. Those with feet have five toes, which bear claws. All are lung breathers, which means that even an aquatic turtle will drown if placed underwater for an extended time period.

Reptiles have well developed hearts with three chambers—one less chamber than we find in mammals and birds. Like these two more complex groups, all reptiles are cold blooded. In winter, reptiles in relatively cold climates hibernate below ground; they become unable to move when the temperature drops very low. It is no accident that reptiles are rare in regions beyond the temperate zones, and grow prolifically in the tropics.

Reproduction in reptiles begins with internal fertilization of an egg, similarly to mammals and birds. But the process thereafter is different enough to warrant our attention. All of the turtles and most of the lizards and snakes lay eggs in secluded areas on land. The eggs have tough, leathery covers, and for the most part are dependent upon the sun's warmth for effective incubation. Some snakes and lizards retain the egg internally until the incubation period is complete. The young are then born alive. However, the process should not be equated with the development of mammalian young. In mammals, as we noted, the embryo is attached to the female and nourished directly through a placental membrane. In the case of reptiles, there is no internal attachment. The egg incubates until the growing embryo inside is sufficiently developed to hatch and so leave the female.

Turtles and most lizards have three eyelids, as do birds. Snakes have no eyelids. A transparent, horny cover over the eye protects it from injury as the animal moves among sticks and vegetation. Just before a snake sheds its skin—up to several times a year—the transparent eye cover becomes milky in color. Interestingly, the only easy way to tell the difference between the several species of legless lizards and snakes is to note if the eyes blink.

Children may bring lizards to class, often "swifts." In the southwestern United States, it is common for them to bring horned "toads." (Horned lizards.) Nearly all lizards may be housed satisfactorily in a terrarium containing some sand, placed where it is sunny. (*Caution: leave the top open to avoid excessive building of heat.*) The anole, or American chameleon—the kind often bought at fairs and pet shops—is more suited to a woodland terrarium, described on page 85.

Chameleons are fun for children to observe. Like many lizards, they change body color under different conditions of light, temperature, and excitation. However, the color change is greater in chameleons than in most other lizards. It is brought about by dilation and contraction of blood vessels in the skin. To distinguish the male, look for a loose fold of skin at its throat.

Many lizards have fragile tails which break off easily when seized. In some species, the broken-off tail part wriggles about animatedly, thereby often distracting the attention of a would-be captor until the lizard escapes. Lizards can grow back (regenerate) new tails.

If possible, try to obtain a small, tame snake for at least a short period during this unit. Let the children touch it and learn that it has a dry, cool skin, rather than a slimy coating. Children should be taught that nearly all snakes in this country are highly beneficial to man, that snakes consume many thousands of destructive rodent and insect pests each year. At the same time pupils should learn an intelligent respect for snakes. If poisonous snakes appear locally, show pictures of what they are like. Caution the class never to hunt for snakes unless accompanied by a responsible and informed older person. In the continental United States only the rattlesnake, copperhead, water moccasin, and coral snake are dangerous to man.

BASIC GENERALIZATION IV: Reptiles are cold blooded, and have a dry, scaly skin; some have a shell

1. *Materials*: two small aquatic turtles; deep, glass baking dish or dishpan; gravel. (To make a suitable home for the turtles, put some gravel in the container. Pile it gradually at one end to form a slope. Pour in several inches of water. The turtles will now have a pond for swimming and a land surface to crawl onto for resting.)

Show the children the turtles. Write *turtle* on the chalkboard when children mention the word. Place the turtles on a low table top and have everyone observe the way they walk. Touch their heads gently with a pencil. Draw out that withdrawal of the head and legs into a shell is a form of protection. Pass the turtles around for close examination. If each is first placed in a small dish, it will *evaluate critically* aid observation and handling. Have pupils describe what they see. Bring out these features: four webbed feet, bearing tiny claws; hard shell, no teeth, eyelids, and scaly dry skin. Emphasize the scaly skin appearance. Turn over the turtles. Have everyone observe how they achieve a right side up position. Ask why turtles feel cool to the touch. (They are cold blooded.) Their blood is as warm or cold as the air around them.

If some pupils have had turtle pets, invite them to tell how these may be cared for. Establish the following procedures:

Feeding—Once a day; commercial turtle food, bits of raw meat and lettuce, dropped into the water. These turtles feed under water. Remove all uneaten food from the tank after 15 minutes to keep the water clean. (Or, *suggest hypotheses* present this as a problem: How can we keep the water clean? The best solution is to re- *select procedures* move the turtles from the tank and put them into a deep glass dish of water. After 15 minutes for feeding, return them to the tank.)

Care of tank—Change the water twice a week. Wash off the gravel each time.

Sunshine—Most turtles are healthiest where they can get several hours of sunshine each day. But if they become too warm, they may die. Part of the container should be in the shade.

Ask the children why the gravel is slanted in the container. Develop that turtles are air breathers, like humans. They must be able to crawl out of the water to rest.

2. *Materials*: American chameleon; hand magnifying lens; woodland terrarium (The one described on page 85 is ideal for this lizard.)

Introduce this animal as a "mystery guest." It is an animal, but we will need to find out more about it before we can say for sure what it is. If a child calls it a lizard, ask him how *evaluate critically* he knows. Suggest personal observations if authority alone is cited. Let the children observe that its skin is dry and consists of tiny scales. The feet bear tiny claws on five toes. Draw out that the small holes on the head are ear openings. A hand lens will aid observations.

Put the animal into the terrarium. Ask pupils to observe its behavior during their individual free-time periods and occasionally during the day. Feed it some live insects or a mealworm daily. After several days, ask pupils what they have found out. (The animal changes color sometimes. It can climb on a branch very well with its padded feet. It laps water drops from the plants. We can see it breathing. It has a flap under the throat which swells up sometimes. And so on.) Encourage use of picture books to find its identity. Guide children to compare critically the *evaluate critically* data they have gathered through observation with data accompanying the picture. Let them locate pictures of other *lizards*.

3. *Materials*: various pictures of turtles, lizards, and snakes.

Invite the children to name these animals. Explain that all belong to the same group, called *reptiles*. There are many different kinds of turtles, snakes, and lizards. All reptiles have a dry, scaly skin. All are cold blooded and breathe air. Nearly all hatch from eggs which are laid on land by the female (mother) reptiles.

If a film is available which goes into the characteristics of reptiles, it may assist in developing some ideas. But pose a few thought-provoking questions before showing it. For example, what happens to these cold-blooded animals when the weather gets freezing cold?

What happens when the weather gets too warm?

Extending activities

1. Use a glass tank to house a small, tame snake for a week. It will not be necessary to feed it. Put newspapers and a low pan of water on the tank floor. Arrange inside several rocks of various sizes and shapes and a strong, branched stick. The snake should be able to retreat under or between the rocks. The branch can be used in climbing. Put a fine-meshed screen over the tank top. Weigh it down at the four corners with bricks or heavy books.

Help the children to understand that nearly all snakes are beneficial to man because they eat mostly insect and rodent pests. In our country only four kinds are dangerous. Let them observe that the snake's skin is scaly, dry, and cool, like that of the other reptiles they handled. Permit them to handle or touch the snake gently, but only if they want to. The important thing at this level is to circumvent, or at least diminish, unreasoning fears about these reptiles.

2. Provide a variety of picture books on lizards, snakes, and turtles. Divide class members into three groups. Help each child to find an interesting picture and fact about one type of reptile. Let him show the picture and report the fact to the entire class.

Amphibians make up a small group of animals that typically spend part of their lives in water and part on land. The principal kinds are frogs, toads, and salamanders. Amphibians represent an interesting evolutionary link between fish and reptiles, and indeed have many characteristics of both groups. If animal life originally began and evolved in the sea, as is generally supposed, it is probable that early amphibians were the first vertebrates to emerge from the water and live successfully on land.

All amphibians are cold blooded, and have hearts with three chambers. Like other cold-blooded animals, they hibernate in cold weather, usually by burrowing in the ground or mud. The adults breathe through lungs, but are also able to absorb some oxygen through the skin. The latter method of breathing is especially useful in hibernation. But skin breathing is inadequate for sustained activity, and even a frog will drown eventually if forced to remain underwater.

Frogs and salamanders usually have moist, smooth skins which must remain moist if they are to survive. For this reason a bowl of water is a necessity in a terrarium that houses these creatures.

One day a child may show you a small amphibian and ask, "Is this a toad or a frog?" Although it is hard to distinguish between them all the time, a toad usually has dry, rough skin. Its body is broad and fat, and the eyes are more prominent than those of frogs. Another indicator is the location where it was caught. Frogs are likelier to live by water, whereas toads are mostly land dwellers.

Can toads cause warts? Many children think they can. The toad's warty-looking tubercules are glands which secrete a fluid that can sicken attacking animals. But the substance cannot cause warts. It may, however, irritate a child's eyes if he should rub them after handling a toad. Advise pupils to wash their hands after playing with a toad.

Salamanders are less common than frogs and toads; chances are that pupils will not have these as pets. Most have four legs of the same size, and long, tubular bodies with tails. Superficially, they resemble lizards and are often mistaken for them. They differ from lizards in several ways: the forelegs of salamanders have four toes instead of five; they have no claws; and the skin is smooth, rather than rough.

Perhaps the most striking difference of amphibians from the other groups we have examined is in their means of reproduction. Female amphibians lay their eggs in water, or in very moist places on land. The males fertilize the eggs immediately after they are laid by shedding sperm over them. Thus, fertilization is external, unlike that in higher animals.

A single female frog or toad may lay several thousand eggs at one time. The eggs are coated with a thick, jellylike substance which quickly absorbs water and swells in size. This substance protects the developing embryo and serves as an initial source of food.

The embryo hatches after one to two weeks as a tadpole or "polliwog" which looks completely unlike the adult. It is only after several months to several years, depending on the species, that tadpoles acquire the adult form. (See Figure 11-4.) This process of changing forms (metamorphosis), is another distinct departure from the growth and development pattern of higher animals.

In their initial growth stages, tadpoles breathe like fishes—they obtain oxygen from water through tiny gills. Therefore, be sure to "age" tap water for at least twenty-four hours to rid it of chlorine before adding it to the container in which they are kept.

BASIC GENERALIZATION V: Amphibians are cold blooded, and have either a smooth or bumpy skin; most hatch from jellylike eggs laid in water

1. *Materials:* small, live adult frog in a small glass jar; large glass jar half-filled with aged water; terrarium (described on page 85); dead insect; thread; live insect.

Let pupils identify their new visitor as a *frog.* Mention that there are many interesting things they can notice about a frog's body if they observe carefully. Have several children touch its skin. Let them describe it. How might a smooth, slippery skin help a frog get away from an enemy? (It is hard to hold onto.) Is the frog probably warm blooded or cold blooded? (The skin is cool; it is probably cold blooded.)

evaluate critically

Direct attention to the frog's eyes. A thin, transparent membrane will periodically come up from the lower eyelid, sweep the eye, and go down again. Slowly draw the eraser end of a pencil near one eye. An upper and lower lid will close the eye, and the frog may re-

FIGURE 11-4   Metamorphosis of the frog.

tract the eyeball somewhat into its head. Let children describe these behaviors.

evaluate critically

Explain that a frog can hear sounds, but it does not have ears like ours. Can anyone find the places which serve as outside ears for the frog? (The round-shaped piece of skin below and back of each eye.)

Let everyone examine the frog's legs. The forelegs are small and have four tiny toes, but no claws. The hind legs are larger and longer, with five webbed toes. Some pupils will remember that several birds have webbed feet. Draw out that the hind legs may be used more in swimming than the forelegs. They can see if this is so, shortly.

Does the frog breathe air? Challenge the children to find any indications of air breathing. (Tiny nostril vents near its snout, and throat movements.) Will it breathe underwater? Hold the frog securely by its hind legs and submerge it completely for a few seconds in a large jar of water. (The nose holes close, and throat movements stop.) Develop that while the frog cannot breathe air directly, some air in the water goes through its skin. However, it cannot keep alive for long on this tiny amount of air except during special times.

evaluate critically

draw conclusions

Release the frog. Wait briefly until it floats quietly. Children will observe that its nose vents are open and above water and the frog is again visibly breathing. They may also notice that the frog's eyes are above water as it floats. Help them reason that in this way it can see better what is going on above the

evaluate critically

water surface. Compare to the eyes of a floating hippopotamus and alligator if pictures are available.

Rap the jar sharply with a pencil. The frog probably will begin swimming. Have everyone observe how the powerful hind legs propel it along.

Take the amphibian out of the water and place it in a smaller jar. Drop in a live ant or other nonflying insect. Children will be astonished at how quickly the frog's tongue lashes out, catches the insect, and withdraws into its mouth. Several trials may be needed before everyone observes this action. Develop that the tongue is attached to the *front* of the lower mouth, unlike the tongues of other animals.

suggest hypotheses

Put a dead insect inside the jar. Why doesn't the frog eat it? Raise conjecture. Tie a piece of thread loosely around a leg of the dead insect. Swing it slowly in front of the

draw conclusions

frog. It may eat the insect. Bring out that frogs usually do not eat something unless it moves.

Place the frog in the woodland terrarium. Be sure there is a bowl of water inside. Explain that a frog's skin must be moist if it is to survive. Schedule volunteers to supply it with several live earthworms and insects each day.

2. *Materials:* pictures of a frog, toad, salamander, and lizard (or live animals, if possible).

Ask the children to compare a frog with a

evaluate critically

toad. How is the toad different? (Toad's skin is bumpy. Its legs are shorter. The body is wider.) How is it alike? (Same general appearance, same number of toes, no claws.) Mention here that both animals hatch from jellylike eggs laid in water. Stress that each is an *amphibian*—an animal that usually spends part of its life in water and part on land.

Show the salamander and lizard, but do not identify them at present. Mention that one is an amphibian—a member of the same group as the frog and toad. Another is a reptile. Which is which, and why? Children should determine that the salamander is more

evaluate critica[lly]

closely related to the frog and toad because it has the same number of toes, no claws, and a smooth skin. Identify the *salamander.* Explain that the salamander often hatches from jellylike eggs laid in ponds, or in moist places on land.

Extending activities

1. Encourage a few pupils who have their parent's approval to gather some eggs of frogs or toads. These can be found in spring and summer among the weeds in ponds and marshy places close to shore. Frog's eggs will be in jumbled clumps, often floating on or near the water surface. Toad's eggs will be laid in strings, often wrapped around some water plants.

Wide-mouth jars can be used to scoop up and contain the eggs. Stress that only several eggs should be taken—for two reasons. Many frogs and toads should grow from the remaining eggs and destroy insect pests. Also, a crowded container may prevent some eggs from hatching or cause some tadpoles to die. A few small water plants and some pond water should be taken at the same time. Microscopic, waterborne matter will serve as the tadpoles' food supply until they are developed enough to eat tiny bits of lettuce and fish food. The plants will furnish a place for the newly hatched tadpoles to cling to until they become strong enough to swim freely.

Tadpoles can be kept in large, open glass jars or in a fishless aquarium tank. It may be necessary to change most of the water every several weeks and clean out the container. If so, replace with more pond water or aged, chlorine-free water.

Encourage the children to observe and discuss tadpole development as it proceeds. You might record for them the unfolding sequence of events as they describe them: tadpoles with tiny gills emerging from the eggs;

evalua[te] critica[lly]

clinging to the plants; body and tail increasing in length; hind legs appearing; gills disappearing; front legs developing; tails shrinking; and so on. When the front legs appear, place the tadpoles in a semiaquatic environment, like that recommended for the aquatic turtle. As its gills disappear, the tadpole develops lungs. Rest periods out of the water become increasingly necessary or the tadpoles may drown.

Since the time period for complete metamorphosis varies with each species, the tadpoles may not have grown into adult form when the school term ends. If so, let some responsible children take the tadpoles home, or release them where the eggs originally were found.

2. If the preceding activity cannot be done, show a film on the metamorphosis of amphibians. Develop some speculation first, before running the film, about the possible physical development of a frog or toad from egg to adult.

suggest *otheses*

Next to mammals, fishes are the vertebrates that present the greatest diversity in appearance, adaptations, and habits. Certainly fishes are most numerous, both as individuals and in numbers of species. (When only one species is referred to, "fish" is both singular and plural. "Fishes" means those of several species.) Fossil records indicate that these creatures were the first animals with true backbones.

Fishes are cold blooded and have hearts of only two chambers. Only they among the adult vertebrates breathe through gills, instead of lungs. Gills are composed of thousands of blood vessels contained in hairlike filaments, located in back of the head on both sides. We cannot easily see these filaments on a live fish, as gill covers conceal them.

A fish breathes by opening and closing its mouth. In the process, water is taken in and then forced out of the gill openings. As water passes over the gills, oxygen dissolved in the water filters into the filaments and blood vessels, then circulates throughout the body. At the same time, carbon dioxide passes out of the filaments and is swept away.

One of the advantages in carefully classifying living things by structure is that it enables us to see relationships we might otherwise miss. In fishes, for example, an organ called the "air bladder" appears to be a forerunner of the lung. The bladder is an air-filled sac usually located in the middle of a fish, between its kidney and stomach. By compressing and expanding its air bladder, a fish can rise and descend in the water.

In the curious lungfish, this organ has been modified into a crude lung, enabling it to breathe air directly, in addition to gill breathing. A lungfish typically lives in a muddy pond or marsh, which may dry up in summer. It survives by burrowing into the mud and breathing air supplied through a hole in the mud cover. When its pond fills again with seasonal rainfall, the lungfish resumes the behavior we are accustomed to expect of fish.

The lungfish is found in Africa, South America, and Australia, and is of no commercial importance. But to a student of evolution, it is a most interesting animal. The lungfish appears to be a clear link between fishes and amphibians in the long evolutionary march of vertebrates from the sea.

The body of a fish is well suited for its environment. Its streamlined contours offer a minimum of resistance to the water. A slimy, mucuslike secretion that exudes between the overlapping body scales further reduces friction and insulates the skin from attack by microorganisms. A large tail fin, wagged from side to side, propels it through the water. Vertical fins on top and bottom keep the fish on an even keel while it is moving. Two pairs of side fins, one pair near the gills (pectoral fins), and the other pair farther back (pelvic fins), balance the fish when it is stationary. These fins are also used to assist turning, in the manner of oars, and for swimming backward. When held out laterally, they brake the swimming fish to a stop. Pectoral fins correspond to forelegs, and pelvic fins to hind legs, in other animals.

The eyes of a fish are always open since it has no eyelids. Focusing is accomplished by shifting the pupil forward and back, rather than changing the lens shape, as in humans. Although there are no external ears, fish hear with auditory capsules deep within the head. In many fishes, a lateral line of sensory scales extends along both sides of the body from head to tail. These scales are particularly sensitive to sounds of low pitch. Some expert fishermen claim that a fish can hear heavy footsteps (Always of other, inexpert fishermen, of course!) on a nearby bank. The taste sense appears to be mostly lacking, but a fish is sensitive to smells. Nostril pits on the snout lead to organs of smell just below. The whole body seems to be sensitive to touch, especially the lips. In species like the catfish, extra touch organs are found in the form of "whiskers."

Reproduction of fishes is accomplished by either external or internal fertilization of the egg, depending on the species. The female goldfish, for example, lays eggs on aquatic plants. The male fertilizes the eggs by shedding sperm cells over them. Goldfish usually reproduce only in large tanks or ponds.

Guppies and many other tropical varieties use internal fertilization. The male has a modified anal fin which caries sperm. The fin is inserted into a small opening below the female's abdomen and sperm cells released. Fertilized eggs remain in the female's body until the embryos hatch and are "born." Many of the young guppies are eaten by the adult fish, unless sufficient plant growth makes it difficult to detect them.

To raise as many guppies as possible, place the pregnant female and some plants in a separate container. After the young are born, remove the mother. The young may join the adult guppies safely in about one month. Try not to be too efficient in breeding guppies, however. Someone good at arithmetic has calculated that a single pair will become three million guppies in a year, assuming all generations and offspring stay alive. A female guppy may produce several dozen young every four to six weeks at a water temperature of 70° to 80°F.

Male guppies are readily distinguishable from the females in several ways. They are about half the size (exclusive of the tails), much narrower in body, and more brilliant in color.

BASIC GENERALIZATION VI: Fishes are cold blooded, live and breathe in water, and are usually covered with scales

1. *Materials:* three quart jars of aged water, each containing a live goldfish.

Cluster one-third of the class around each jar, so each child can closely observe a fish. Ask some questions to determine pupil knowledge and to guide observations. What are these animals? How do we know? Seize any opportunity to improve reasoning. For example, someone may mention that these animals swim in water. Don't some of the other animals we studied? How do fish differ?

Have the children observe the overlapping body scales. Bring out that fish scales differ from reptile scales in that they overlap like house roof shingles; reptile scales do not overlap in this way.

Continue with other observations. How does a fish get its air? Draw attention to the related movements of the mouth and *gills.* Develop that a fish takes in water through its mouth. The water goes out through gill openings on each side of the head. Gills remove air from the water and also expel used air the fish exhales. Emphasize that, of all full-grown animals, only fish can breathe in this way.

Some children may observe two tiny nostrils in the snout. Raise conjecture about their use. Children might find out through a film shown later that these openings are used in smelling rather than breathing. Let them search in vain for external ears. Perhaps the same film may reveal that fish do not have ears as such, but that they can sense some sounds.

Pupils will observe that the fish do not close their eyes. Draw out that there are no visible eyelids. Challenge them to determine how they might discover whether a fish sleeps. After some discussion, tell them that there is no perfect way to know at this time. Scientists are still working on the problem.

evaluate critically

Raise questions about how the fish propel themselves in the water; also, how they turn and stop. Why doesn't the fish turn partly over on one side when it stops swimming? For a clue have a child stand balanced on one foot. Bring out how he uses his arms laterally to stabilize himself. What does the fish use? Develop that the side fins are employed in somewhat the same way, but that they push against the water.

draw conclusions

Perhaps some children have handled live fish. Let them recall how cool and slippery the skin feels. Develop that fish, too, are cold-blooded animals. Caution everyone not to handle a live fish with dry hands, since this rubs off the scales' protective, slippery coating.

2. *Materials:* pictures of a variety of fishes; simple film which shows some fish adaptations.

Exhibit many pictures of fishes in identification books or trade books. Let children discuss the many ways in which these fishes are different—in coloring, marking, probable size, shape, and so on. Develop how they are alike in several body parts.

evaluate critically

Use a film to confirm earlier observations and to furnish information for unanswered questions. Emphasize that fishes are usually covered with scales, breathe and live in water, and are cold-blooded animals.

Extending activity

Help children set up several small aquaria for observation at school or home. For each aquarium they will need a wide-mouth glass jar of at least one-quart capacity, two guppies (a male and female), an aquatic snail, a small water plant, and a large-size soda straw. If a child or another teacher has a large guppy aquarium, chances are they will gladly give up a dozen or more guppies to reduce the rapidly

increasing population, and some plants to thin out the thickening aquarium foliage. Use a small dip net or glass to scoop out the guppies. Transfer them to a jar containing water taken from their present home.

Show pupils what to use for their aquaria. Develop why these materials are used, when possible:

a. A wide-mouth glass jar, of at least one-quart capacity. A wide-mouth jar will let more air into the jar than a narrower one.

b. Water that is "aged" (left standing for one or two days). This warms the water to room temperature. Cold water may kill the fish. Also, this lets out chemicals that are put into the water to kill germs. Sometimes these chemicals kill the fish.

c. Two guppies (a male and a female, identify by size and coloring). They may have young and we can see how baby guppies are born.

d. A small, rootless water plant. When baby guppies stay among the plant leaves, the big fish cannot see them and eat them. (Also, the plant helps to provide extra air; this will be meaningless, however, at the primary level.)

e. A water snail. It will help to keep the jar clean. (Establish that the fish should be given only a tiny pinch of fish food, three or four times a week. Explain that uneaten food spoils the water after a while.)

f. A straw dip tube. Show how it is used to remove debris from an aquarium. Drop a small crumb into a glass of water; it should sink quickly. Place the bottom opening of the straw over the crumb. Close the straw's opposite, open end with your forefinger. Withdraw the straw and captured crumb. Release your finger; the crumb and water will rush out of the straw.

Encourage the children to observe their guppies and snails carefully, and to report any interesting events. When some baby guppies appear, develop that some fishes are born alive while others hatch from eggs laid in the water. Guide pupils to transfer some guppies when an overcrowded condition appears. Occasionally observe pupils' fish jars to prevent

FIGURE 11-5 There is nothing like telling a friend about events happening in one's own, personal aquarium.

other unsatisfactory conditions from developing. (See page 85.)

Insects

They eat our carpets and munch our clothes,
Spread disease and damage our homes,
Spoil our picnics and wreck our fun,
I'd like to get rid of every single one!
(Sandra, age 11)

This brief verse sums up the opinion of many persons about insects. But it is only one side of the story. "Get rid of" all insects and some very undesirable consequences take place. Here are only a few: Probably half of all the flowering plants on earth would disappear—bees, flies, moths, and butterflies help to pol-

linate them. Most of the land birds would vanish—their principal source of food is insects. Biological research would be hampered—the short life cycles of insects are ideal for quick results in medical and hereditary studies.

As mentioned, insects make up an astounding 70 per cent of all animal species. Hundreds of new species are discovered each year. They are found virtually everywhere on earth. What makes them so successful? How do we tell a "real" insect from a pseudo insect?

The first thing we might note about insects is that they have jointed legs. Instead of an internal skeleton, such as we find in vertebrates, they have an external skeleton, made of a crusty substance called chitin. Muscles and other body parts are attached inside to this semirigid exterior. To continue growing, an immature insect must molt or shed its outside covering from time to time. We can see that the need for molting greatly limits insect size. A heavy body would collapse before the soft, new covering hardened. These two characteristics—jointed legs and external skeleton—are also typical of the several other classes which make up the arthropods. (See page 388.)

The easiest way to distinguish an adult insect is to look for six legs and three body parts: head, thorax, and abdomen. The head contains a primitive "brain," and mouth parts which vary considerably among insect orders. Most insects have two compound eyes, which are aggregates of many lenses, and several simple eyes as well, each of which has only one lens. The eyes are always open, since there are no eyelids. Two hairlike antennae, sensitive to touch and sometimes smell, are also found on most insect heads. The middle section or thorax is where the six legs and wings are attached. Some insects have two wings, others four; a few have none. The abdomen contains the organs of digestion, excretion, and reproduction. Tiny holes (spiracles) in the thorax and abdomen furnish air for breathing. The air is piped into the internal organs by a network of connected tubes.

There are several reasons why insects have survived so successfully. Most are capable of flight. This provides a great range for potential food. Insects typically have very sensitive nervous systems; they are particularly sensitive to odors related to their food. The thorax of an insect may be packed with striated muscles—the kind that contract immediately upon signal. This makes many insects difficult to catch. The compound eyes add to this difficulty because they cover a wide-angle view. Although insects are cold blooded, as are all known invertebrates, their small size often permits them to secure adequate shelter when the weather becomes cold. Many pass through the winter months in a resting or inactive stage. Perhaps most important for their survival as a group is the rapidity with which they produce new generations.

The life cycles of insects are most interesting. Eggs are fertilized internally and hatched externally. In most species the insect goes through a complete metamorphosis of four stages as it matures: egg, larva, pupa, and adult. The hatched larva (caterpillar) eats almost continually, and sheds its skin several times as it grows. Then it either spins a cocoon (moth larva, for example) or encases itself in a leaflike chrysalid (a butterfly larva, for example) and enters the pupa stage. The body tissues change during this "resting" period. Sometime later—it varies with the species—an adult insect emerges.

Some insects, such as the grasshopper, cricket, termite, and aphid, go through an incomplete metamorphosis of three stages: egg, nymph, and adult. The hatched young, or nymphs, resemble the adult except that they appear out of proportion and lack wings. As they grow, molting takes place at least several times. There is no pupa stage. (See Figure 11-6.)

Pupils will relish observing some insects go through several stages of their life cycles and will learn from this procedure. They will not be able to locate eggs, as these are usually too small to see, but they should be able to find and bring in caterpillars, cocoons, and chrysalids. Remind them to take several leaves

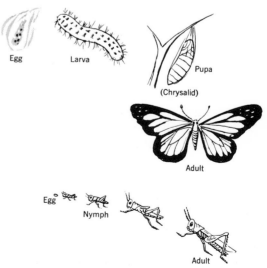

FIGURE 11-6 **Grasshopper and butterfly metamorphoses.**

from the plant on which the caterpillar was feeding when captured. A fresh supply may be needed every few days. Use a glass jar or similar container to house each of these specimens. Place some soil inside, and an upright twig from which the larva might suspend its chrysalid. Either a cheesecloth lid secured with an elastic band, or a perforated jar top, should provide enough air. Moisten the soil occasionally for cocoons and chrysalids, as they may dry up without sufficient humidity.

To show the entire life cycle of an insect from egg to egg, raise some silkworm moths in class. Within about eight weeks, children will see larvae hatch from the eggs, feed busily for a time, spin cocoons and pupate, emerge from the cocoons as adult moths, mate, lay eggs, and die. Eggs and specific instructions can be purchased inexpensively from a biological supply house. (See page 389.) The mulberry leaves on which the larvae feed are found in most parts of the continental United States.

BASIC GENERALIZATION VII: There are many animals without backbones; insects make up the largest group

1. *Materials:* 18 to 24 colored, magazine illustrations, featuring members of the five animal groups with backbones, and several insects (Use the same pictures suggested for activity 1 of the first generalization if others are unattainable. Scatter pictures in no apparent order on the right half of a large bulletin board. Put numbered white cards under each, so they may be quickly located. On the left side of the bulletin board space, place five cards in a column, bearing the titles *Mammals, Birds, Reptiles, Amphibians, Fishes.*)

evaluate critically   Challenge pupils to classify the animal pictures according to the five listed groups. Each child can do this individually by writing the numerals on a piece of paper. Walk around and note how successful they are. After an appropriate time interval, initiate a discussion. Encourage class members to evaluate

their choices with reasons. Place pictures in rows next to their corresponding headings.

Mention that there seems to be disagreement and hesitation about several pictures (indicate the insects). In which group do these animals belong? Raise conjecture. Many *suggest hypoth* children will know that these are insects or "bugs," but will be unaware that they belong in a group as yet unstudied. Develop that these animals—*insects*—do not seem to fit into any of the five classifications. Does anyone know why? Give some hints: There is something inside children's bodies which all the animals studied have, but not insects. After we eat chicken, what is left on the plate? Continue with meals of lamb chops, rabbits, and fish. Do reptiles and amphibians have bones, too? (Yes.) How about ants and flies? (No.)

Develop that the five groups of animals *draw conclus* they have studied all have bones inside their bodies. Many bones of each animal are joined to a *backbone*, which runs along the animal's back. Let each child feel his own backbone. Let some children recall feeling a pet's backbone.

Emphasize that all animals may be divided into two very large groups, those with and without backbones. They have studied the five kinds of animals with backbones. Now the class will find out about some animals which do not have backbones. Mention that study will begin with insects, which make up the largest group of animals without backbones. Later, the class will find out about some others.

Encourage children to bring to school the next day any dead animals in good condition which they think are insects. Suggest use of tin cans or paper sacks for containers, rather than breakable glass jars. Advise everyone to scoop up the insects with a small card or stiff piece of paper, rather than handle them with their fingers.

2. *Materials:* large sketch of Figure 11-7 (Keep concealed until needed for use.); a quantity of different dead insects and pseudo insects; toothpicks; white paper; three- by five-inch cards; hand magnifying lenses. (Dis-

tribute equal quantities of materials among several or more groups, so each child can actively participate. Insects should be on white paper for easy observation, with a hand magnifying lens alongside. Several toothpicks and small cards will permit insect handling without direct contact.)

Mention that of the many different animals on the white papers most are insects. What is an insect? (Answers will probably *define* vary considerably.) Capitalize on disagreements to arouse need for an operational definition. Develop that, although there are many kinds of insects, they mostly have the *evaluate* same body parts. Can the class find out what *critically* these parts are? Give hints, if needed. Let pupils carefully study their specimens for a time to note common characteristics.

Guide discussion about their findings. Note how close they are to an accurate description of insects as a group. Try to guide further observations as needed, without directly telling the children what to look for. Summarize their findings on a chart or chalkboard:

draw We think an insect has:
clusions
    6 legs;
    3 body parts;
    2 feelers;
    (add others as given)

How close did we come to finding out what an insect really is? Exhibit the sketch of Figure *evaluate* ure 11-7. Let the class evaluate agreements *critically* and disagreements. Emphasize that grownup (mature) insects have three body parts, six legs, and usually, two feelers. The feelers are sometimes used for smelling as well as touching. Many insects have two kinds of eyes— point out the simple eye and compound eye. Many, but not all, have wings. Point to the spiracles in the sketch. Mention that these are air holes, through which an insect breathes. State that the sketch shows a simplified grasshopper.

If a microprojector is available, show some enlarged body parts—wings, antennae, and so on. If a dead bee is in the collection, children will find it interesting to examine the stinger.

This can be removed by pushing down on the abdomen with a pencil eraser and pulling lightly on the stinger with tweezers.

Perhaps a child can bring in a live grasshopper. Let him hold it steadily in front of a filmstrip projector shining on a screen. Have children observe closely the abdomen's greatly enlarged silhouette. It will expand and contract visibly as the insect breathes.

3. *Materials:* two pint-size, identical, loosely capped jars; four recently captured, live flies (two enclosed in each jar); deep pan containing ice water and ice cubes.

Bring out that we see very few, if any, flies in the winter. But there are many flies around in spring and summer. Arouse conjecture as to why. Bring out that the weather is usually *suggest* colder in the winter and that this may affect *hypotheses* flies. How does coldness affect a fly? Point to the materials. How can we find out? (Put *select* one jar in the ice water for a while. Leave the *procedures* other jar alone for the same time. Then take off the caps and see how the flies in both jars act.)

Use a book to weigh down the immersed jar. If the jar is left in ice water for about ten minutes, the flies inside should become noticeably sluggish and unable to escape. Flies in the warm jar should escape immediately. Will the cold flies be able to fly away if they get warm again? Remove the jar from the pan. Within a short time, they will probably fly away.

Develop that flies are cold-blooded animals, as are all animals without backbones. When *draw* they get cold, flies move more slowly or not *conclusions*

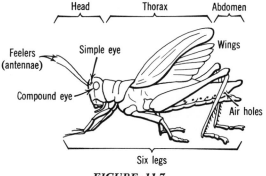

FIGURE 11-7

at all. Many cold-blooded animals die when the weather gets very cold.

Extending activities

1. Let pupils observe the life cycle of the silkworm moth, or stages in the life cycles of other insects. See the preceding exposition for details.

2. Encourage pupils to locate pictures of some common invertebrates other than insects. It may be desirable to check out from the school or district library some picture books containing illustrations of snails, earthworms, spiders, crabs, starfish, clams, jellyfish, and so on. Let small committees of pupils do the initial locating and screening of what they think are animals without backbones. Then have the entire class evaluate their selections. *evaluat critical*

3. Plan a trip to a local zoo or natural history museum as a culminating activity for this unit. Through consultation with a zoo official, concentrate class attention on only several of the most diverse animals within each of the five vertebrate groups. This will be more effective than trying to observe everything.

Human Growth and Nutrition

(Upper)

Many nutrition specialists claim that between the ages of 12 and 20 young Americans have the poorest diets of their lives. Significantly, this is the time of increasing personal independence and freedom of choice. How do we educate children to make intelligent decisions about their health? One way is to begin teaching good health habits early, when receptivity is high and "sophistication" low. Health and nutrition lessons are often begun in the primary grades. Another way to reach children is to develop scientific reasons for actions—reasons that can be discovered and demonstrated in ways that make sense to young minds.

A unit on growth and nutrition can be doubly rewarding to teach. There are many opportunities to involve children in science processes. In addition, one may make a contribution to children's health which will last throughout their lives.

BASIC GENERALIZATIONS

I. Growth takes place as living cells divide or enlarge; the amount of growth children have depends upon several things.

II. Several food nutrients are needed for health and growth of body cells; tests can be used to identify them.

III. Food is digested in the alimentary canal and then transported to cells, where it is oxidized, changed into body materials, or stored.

IV. For a healthful diet, one should choose wisely from a variety of foods.

One day in 1665 an English botanist named *Robert Hooke* examined a very thin section of cork under his crude microscope. To his surprise he saw what appeared to be tiny, empty compartments with thick walls. Since they resembled cells, this is what he named them. He learned through subsequent investigations of many other materials that living things are composed of cells. He soon realized that, unlike dried cork, these cells are filled with a fluidlike substance. We know today that this substance is the cell's living material, *protoplasm.*

Most children are unaware that their bodies and most other living matter are composed of cells, and that growth itself is a result of cell division and enlargement. It will be instructive for them to examine cells with a microprojector or microscope.

For examination of plant cells, the inside skin of an onion will suffice. Cut the onion in half, and peel off a bit of thin skin from one of the inside layers. Put a water drop on a slide and lay a piece of skin section in it. To make cell details clear, stain the specimen by putting a drop of diluted iodine on it with an eye-dropper. Cover with a cover slip. Leaves of elodea, a very common aquarium plant, are also thin enough for cell study. No stain is necessary.

413

Onion cells

A group of Human Epithelial Cells

A Leaf of the Water

Paramecia

FIGURE 12-1 Cells.

Human skin cells—*epithelial* cells—are interesting to show for contrast. These may be gotten by gently scraping the inside of a cheek with a blunt toothpick. Spread the whitish material on a slide and put a drop of diluted iodine on it. Cover with a glass cover slip.

Pupils will find that the most obvious difference between animal and plant cells is in the material enclosing these cells. Plant cells are enclosed by a wall composed chiefly of cellulose. This is tough, fibrous, nonliving substance indigestible to man. A thin membrane within the wall is almost invisible. Animal cells are enclosed by only a thin, living membrane, permeable to some fluids and gases. Both animal and plant cells contain a dense spot called the *nucleus*, which controls the cell's vital activities.

Children are usually very interested in examining single-celled animals, or protozoa. These tiny creatures carry on all the vital activities of living things: food taking, digestion, oxidation, excretion, responses to stimuli, growth and reproduction. The *paramecium*, one of the larger, easily observed protozoa, is especially interesting to watch. Children may note how hairlike cilia propel it through the water. (Ciliated cells within the human respiratory system sweep up irritants to where they can be coughed out.) The class may see an occasional paramecium divide, and become two paramecia. Growth by cell division is also characteristic of human cells. However, some human cells, such as those that compose nerve and muscle tissue, may merely enlarge somewhat or grow longer.

A culture of protozoa may be developed if desired by making a *hay infusion*. Drop a handful of dry grass, hay, or leaves into a quart glass jar of cool, previously boiled or aged water. Avoid direct sunlight. Within several days, protozoa of several varieties should appear.

Where do they come from? Protozoa are found almost everywhere there is moisture. When dry conditions occur, these animals lose much water. The cell membrane dries into a hard, cystlike cover. The animals may

Light

FIGURE 12-2   A waterdrop microscope.

survive this dormant condition for years until at last there is sufficient water to soften the cell cover and resume usual functions.

If regular microscopes are not available, let each pupil make his own water-drop microscope, as in Figure 12-2. Basic materials needed are a glass slide, strip cut from a tinned can, and a small mirror. For the lens, use a nail to punch a small hole in the strip. A drilled hole is superior, but not essential. Put a water drop in the hole with an eyedropper. If the hole is perfectly round, the water-drop lens may magnify up to 100 times. This is sufficient for viewing gross features of the cells previously described. Focusing is accomplished by slightly bending the strip up or down. For best viewing, the eye must be very close to the lens. For the best light conditions, adjust the mirror so light reflects upward through the lens. Then lean the mirror at the proper angle against an eraser.

Although children's cells are growing continually, they should realize that rates of growth—really, the speeds at which different cells divide—vary greatly at various periods of childhood. It is natural for upper-grade children to be concerned about their heights. From about age 10, this is a period when girls begin to grow faster than boys. Several years later the boys start to catch up, and by age 14, usually exceed the girls in height.

Pupils will be interested in a table of average heights, from age 5 to 17, presented in a forthcoming activity. (See Figure 12-3.) The table is based on data released in 1953 by the United States Office of Education. Figures are averages of almost 300,000 students then living in 17 states and the District of Columbia. Be sure to bring out that these figures are averages. Individual pupils may be taller or shorter. Get the children to understand that they inherit many characteristics of their parents, including height tendencies.

The graph on page 417 (Figure 12-4) is an estimate of the increasing heights of young adults in succeeding generations. It is based on a composite of several studies, old and new. Children seem to be growing taller than their parents, almost 1 inch taller every 25 years. Unfortunately, growth of feet and hips appears to be keeping pace with overall gains in height. Besides medical evidence, shoe manufacturers report increased sales of extra-large shoes. Theater owners now must install seats which are several inches wider than those designed twenty or so years ago.

What are the reasons for increased stature and size? It is difficult to know precisely, although some general factors seem clear. We know that better living conditions and reduced illness help children to attain better growth. Some persons claim that increased size is an evolutionary tendency. Certainly, a main factor is improved nutrition. Studies in England and France before, during, and after the Second World War clearly show that improved nutrition results in increased growth. There are many other researches which reveal the same evidence.

BASIC GENERALIZATION I: Growth takes place as living cells divide or enlarge; children's growth depends upon several things

Contributing idea A. Living things are composed of cells; growth takes place as cells divide or enlarge.

Materials: baby picture of a class member; microprojector or several microscopes; prepared slides of onion skin, elodea, epithelial cells, and protozoa (See preceding exposition for details.)

Ask for the hands of children who have at some time cut or scraped their skin. Discuss the varying lengths of time these wounds required to heal.

Show the baby picture. Ask the child whose

picture it is to stand. Look at the difference!

Develop the wondrous quality of these events. What causes wounds to heal? What makes a baby increase in size? Arouse conjecture. After some discussion, mention that observation of some microprojector slides will be useful in finding out.

Exhibit a stained onion skin slide. Children will immediately notice the cell-like structure. Explain that they are looking at a very small and thin section taken from a living thing. The small compartments are called *cells*. Point out the *cell wall* and *nucleus*. Have the children try to guess for a moment the living thing from which the slide specimen was taken. Now let them see how the slide was prepared. Show an unstained onion skin slide briefly for contrast, and then replace it with the stained slide. Lay a single human hair across the specimen so pupils can estimate cell size.

Follow with a projection of elodea leaf cells. Children will immediately note the contrast in size and color of the cells.

Do animals also have cells? Show slides of epithelial cells, stained and unstained. Have pupils try to guess their origin. Develop that these cells are like plant cells except that in place of a thick cell wall there is a thin, *cell membrane*. This is true of most animal cells, although they have many different shapes and sizes. Demonstrate how to prepare these slides.

Now project a slide of living *protozoa*. Mention that they are looking at some of the world's smallest animals. Each is made up of only one cell. Try to isolate a *paramecium*. Children may be able to detect how it uses its hairlike *cilia* for locomotion. Develop that there are many cells with cilia in our lung passages. The cilia brush irritating particles into the throat where they can be coughed out. (However, stress that ciliated cells in the respiratory tract are not protozoa.)

If there are many paramecia, some may divide as the children are observing. State that most growth in animals and plants takes place when cells divide. Food material dis-

Boys	43.9	46.1	48.2	50.4	52.4	54.3	56.2	58.2	60.5	63.0	65.6	67.3	68.2
Girls	43.6	45.8	47.9	50.0	52.0	54.2	56.5	59.0	60.6	62.3	63.2	63.5	63.6
Age:	5	6	7	8	9	10	11	12	13	14	15	16	17

FIGURE 12-3 Average height in inches of students in fifteen states.

solved in water enters through the thin cell membrane. Some of the food material is changed into part of the cell itself. The cell grows a little larger, then divides into two cells. Each new cell looks like the old cell but is a little smaller for a while. Some cells do not divide in this way, but just grow larger or longer. Mention that new cells continually replace old, injured, and worn-out cells.

Contributing idea B. Growth varies with age, sex, heredity, and nutrition.

1. *Materials:* opaque projection or chart of Figure 12-3. (Reveal when appropriate.)

Help children realize the significance of cell division: wounds heal; worn cells are replaced; physical growth results. Now ask them to think carefully. Do body cells always grow at the same rate when we are children, or do they slow down and speed up at times? What evidence can they point to which might help *evaluate* answer this question? Bring out that their *critically* shoes and clothing sizes often change radically in a short time period, after a long period of no change. Some children may observe that lately several boys and girls are growing taller than their classmates. Mention that it is a usual thing for growth to speed up and slow down. By looking at a chart the class will be able to find out more about the time periods when this happens to most children.

Reveal the projection or chart of Figure 12-3. Mention that these are the average heights of thousands of children of 17 states in our country. Invite the children to study the chart carefully for five minutes. What can they observe about amounts of growth and *reason* growth rates? Ask them to write down all the *tatively* important things they think the data reveal.

In the discussion, bring out three of the more important generalizations: (1) Until

the age of 10, boys and girls are about the *draw* same height. (2) Beginning just before age *conclusions* 11 until age 13, most girls grow faster than boys. (3) From 13 on most boys grow faster than girls.

Stress the average nature of these figures. Does this mean *all* girls are taller than *all* boys at age 12? Develop further the idea of deviations. Children of tall parents will tend to be taller than average. Children of short parents will tend to be shorter. These tendencies run in families; that is, we *inherit* the qualities of tallness and shortness, just as we inherit dark eyes or hair color. These tendencies are determined by *heredity*. Clarify this term as needed.

2. *Materials:* opaque projection or chart of Figure 12-4.

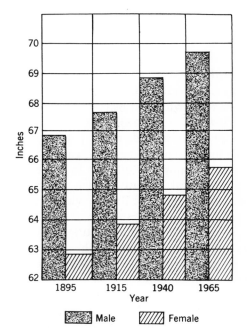

FIGURE 12-4 Estimated average heights of 21-year-olds in the United States.

Ask the children to look at Figure 12-4. There is something odd here. These are the average heights of young adults. What seems to be happening with each new group as the years go on? (The average 21-year-old is becoming taller; about 1 inch every 25 years.) Arouse conjecture as to why. Gradually draw out the concept of better, more healthful living conditions. Contrast the great variety of modern, nutritious foods with the limited, less nutritious foods of years past. Emphasize that healthful foods can help bring out the most that is passed on to each person through heredity. In this unit class members will find out a great deal about foods which will be useful for their growth and health throughout their lives.

define problems

suggest hypotheses

Extending activities

1. Invite pupils to look in trade books and encyclopedias for pictures of cells of different human tissues. If microscopes are available, let them bring in plant and animal cell materials to examine.

2. Let some children make a line graph from all or part of the data in Figure 12-3. (Ages 9 through 14 are particularly interesting.) Heights should appear along the vertical axis, ages along the horizontal axis. Or have them measure and arrange in graphic form the average heights of boys and girls in any grade or grades in the school. Their measurements might then be compared with those of Figure 12-3. Since all the children probably cannot be measured, guide pupils to reason how they could select a representative sample. A perfect sample is difficult to achieve without statistical analysis, which, of course, is beyond the children. But the idea of sampling itself they can understand.

reason quantitatively

3. Exhibit a motion picture film on the topic of cells and cell growth.

4. Encourage each child to bring in several pictures of himself taken at various ages. The set of pictures for each person might be arranged in a row, from younger to older, in a pocket chart. For an interesting "Guess Who?" arrangement, reverse all pictures in each set but the first. The object is to guess

evaluate critically

the child's identity while turning over the fewest pictures.

We may eat hundreds of foods, combined in thousands of ways. But nutritionally speaking, there are but seven kinds: sugars, starches, fats, proteins, vitamins, minerals, and water. These nutrients may be combined further into three groups:

(1) Foods for energy—sugars, starches, and fats.
(2) Foods for growth and repair of cells—proteins.
(3) Foods for regulation of body processes—vitamins, minerals, and water.

If we heat table sugar in a test tube, the sugar gradually turns black and water vapor is driven off. The black material is carbon. The water is formed as hydrogen and oxygen atoms given off by individual sugar molecules combine. Heat some starch, and again carbon and water appear. Both sugar and starch are *carbohydrates*, a name that means "carbon and water."

Although sugar and starches are composed of the same elements, these elements may appear in various combinations, and form relatively small to large molecules. "Simple" sugar molecules, for example, are the smallest carbohydrate molecules. They may be found in grapes and many other fruits. When two simple sugar molecules become attached, a complex sugar is formed, such as table sugar. A starch molecule is nothing more than a long chain of sugar molecules tightly attached to one another.

In digestion all carbohydrates are broken down into simple sugars. Only in this form are these molecules small enough to pass through cell membranes into the cells, where they "burn" and release energy. The "burning" is a result of *oxidation*, a process where oxygen chemically combines with fuel—in this case sugar—and releases heat energy. (Rusting is a form of slow oxidation; fire is very rapid oxidation.) The oxygen comes from the air we breathe.

Fats are also composed of carbon, hydrogen, and oxygen. But fat molecules have relatively fewer oxygen atoms than carbohydrates. Since they are oxygen "poor," fat molecules can combine with more oxygen atoms and yield about twice as much energy as carbohydrates.

Foods rich in carbohydrates and fats provide our principal source of energy. But when we eat more than we need of these materials the cells store any excess in the form of fat. Fat storage does not occur uniformly throughout all body cells, as every figure-conscious person knows. In another exposition, we shall discuss the different energy needs of persons.

Proteins are extremely complex, large molecules. A single molecule may contain thousands of atoms. Like the preceding nutrients, proteins are composed of carbon, hydrogen, and oxygen. But in addition, proteins contain nitrogen, and typically, sulphur. Proteins are the main source of materials (amino acids) needed for growth and repair of body cells. Excess proteins are oxidized in cells and provide energy.

Though all animal and some plant foods (mainly beans, peas, nuts) contain proteins, only animal proteins contain sufficient amino acids for complete growth and repair of body cells. This causes many vegetarians to supplement their diets with such animal products as milk, cheese, and eggs.

Vitamins are essential because they regulate cell activities. These chemicals are not digested or used directly, but permit biochemical processes to take place. We can get all the vitamins we need from a balanced diet (see page 428), without extra vitamin pills or capsules.

Minerals are essential because they also help to regulate cell activities. In addition, some minerals are incorporated into body tissue. Calcium and phosphorus form the hard portions of our bones and teeth. Milk is especially rich in these two minerals. Iron and copper help form red blood cells. A proper amount of iodine is needed in the thyroid gland for normal oxidation to take place in cells. Salt is often iodized to prevent goiter, an iodine deficiency. Some minerals cannot be used by cells unless specific vitamins are present. Most fruits and vegetables are rich in vitamins and minerals.

There are many reasons why water is essential to life and good nutrition. It changes chemically to form part of protoplasm. Water is the chief component of blood. It cools the body and carries away accumulated poisons. It is important to digestion and excretion. About two-thirds of the body itself is composed of water.

Besides drinking water directly, we take in much water in the food we eat. For example, celery is about 95 per cent water, fresh bread about 35 per cent water. Pupils can learn how to determine the proportion of water present in a food. To do this properly, they will need a sensitive balance.

A sensitive, handmade balance is shown in Figure 12-5. Materials needed for its construction are a soda straw, straight pin, small clip of staples, drinking glass, cellophane tape, thread, two bottle caps, and a small piece of modeling clay. First, affix with cellophane tape a small clip of stuck-together staples to the bottom of an upturned drinking glass. Then push a straight pin through the center of a straw and place it on the clip as shown. The straw should almost balance if it is well-centered. Next, suspend two bottle caps from the straw ends with thread. Use cellophane tape to secure the thread on both caps and straw ends. To correct any slight imbalance, place a tiny bit of modeling clay at some point near the pivot.

FIGURE 12-5 A soda straw balance.

To find the fraction of water in food, put into one bottle cap ten light, identical objects. Pins work well, but washers, brads, etc. may be used instead. Put into the other bottle cap several small, thin slices of food. Remove bits of food until there is a perfect balance. The food should now be taken off and dried. Also remove the pins (or substitute objects) from the second cap. When completely dry, place the food back into a cap. Carefully, drop one pin at a time into the opposite cap until there is a balance. If three pins balance the food, for example, you will know that seven-tenths (70 per cent) of the food originally was water.

Of course, if more precision is desired, you can use more pin units to balance larger quantities of food. If your class understands percentages, use 100 pin units. However, the counting of many small units takes time. One way to speed this up is to fasten a tiny bit of cellophane tape around each group of ten pins, brads, or other weight unit used. The tape's extra weight should be negligible.

In forthcoming activities we shall present other ways in which pupils may test foods. Encourage everyone to bring materials from home. This will permit all to participate.

BASIC GENERALIZATION II: Several food nutrients are needed for health and growth of body cells; tests can be used to identify them

Contributing idea A. Starches, sugars, and fats are needed for energy.

Materials: Benedict's solution (sold in drug stores); iodine; spoons; brown wrapping paper; eye-droppers; candles and matches; test tubes; small drinking glasses and paper cups; variety of foods brought in by the children—starches, sugars, fats.

Write on the chalkboard the words, "You are what you eat." Ask for interpretations of this idea. Develop that the body cells convert food into more living cells, and energy. How well body cells are constructed depends upon the materials that go into them. Persons who lack pep often do not eat the right foods.

What specific foods give us most of our energy? Start a discussion but withhold verification of children's guesses at this time. Develop that foods rich in *starches, sugars,* and *fats* are needed for energy. The children can discover for themselves which specific foods are rich in these substances by several simple tests. Demonstrate these now.

Starch test: Put a few drops of iodine on some dry cornstarch and on a sugar cube. Which contains starch? Bring out that iodine changes into a blue-black color when much starch is present.

Show how to test liquids for starch content. Mix some starch in a little water; dissolve some sugar in another glass containing water. Place a few drops of iodine in each glass. Which contains the starch? Emphasize that either technique can be used for a starch indicator.

Sugar test: Dissolve some brown sugar in a test tube one-third filled with water. Place inside several drops of Benedict's solution. Heat over a candle until the solution boils. (Demonstrate the proper method of holding a test tube over a flame. Grip the tube with tongs or pliers and point the open end away from you and the children.) The solution will gradually turn a brick-red color; this indicates the presence of a simple sugar.

This test does not work with complex sugars. Point out to the children that some sugar molecules are arranged in such a way that this test does not affect them. Table sugar and the sugar in pineapples are examples of foods which do not react to this test. Demonstrate with table sugar. If someone suggests tasting substances to detect sugar, bring out that some poisons look perfectly harmless.

Fat test: Rub a bit of margarine and a small piece of carrot on brown paper. Explain that the shiny, translucent spot made by the margarine came from oil, or melted fat. The wet spot made by the carrot will quickly dry and look as it did before the test.

In a second test crush a peanut into a fine

powder, and pour this into a glass containing some water. Have children notice the oil film on the water surface.

Which foods contain starches, sugars, and fats? Either of two ways may be used to organize the class for finding out. For example, have the entire class test only for starches, then sugars, then fats. Or let them test for all three at one time. This is more complex to administer, but more fun for the children. In either case, divide the class into several groups. Let each group chairman carefully record data on the chalkboard. When results are in, have children evaluate results by cross-checking all data. Where there are disagreements among groups ("Does bread really have starch in it?") let the groups run retests.

evaluate critically

Pupils might summarize their findings in three columns on a large butcher-paper chart. Of course, their notations may differ from the following according to the foods they bring and test:

draw conclusions

Has Starch	Has Sugar	Has Fat
potato	prune	bacon
white bread	raisin	peanut
spaghetti	grape	lard
corn	corn syrup	salt pork
soda cracker	fresh orange	olive
oatmeal	juice	mayonnaise
rice	honey	milk
	onion	

Have some children consult encyclopedias and trade books to check their food classifications. Encourage them to add to the chart names of other foods rich in starch, sugar, or fat as they are found.

Contributing idea B. Proteins are needed for growth and repair of body cells.

Materials: household ammonia; copper sulphate (sold in drug stores); drinking glasses and paper cups; spoons; eye-droppers; protein and nonprotein foods brought in by the children (Encourage the children to bring small portions of hard-boiled egg white, cheese,

milk, cooked lean meat, gelatin, almonds, beans, and peas—all are rich in proteins. Also have them bring sugar, oil, salt, carrots, baking soda, and other nonprotein foods. Do not indicate at this time which foods are proteins.)

Point out that athletes eat foods containing sugar and starch for energy, but that they are especially likely to eat many foods that are rich in *proteins*. Develop that proteins are food materials which enable the body to build new cells and replace worn-out cells. This is particularly important for athletes because they need to build strong muscles. Help pupils to reason why it is important for them to eat proteins. A growing child needs this food material to build tissue. Explain that surplus proteins may also be stored in the body in another form and later converted into energy.

Demonstrate a simple protein test. The two principal chemicals needed are copper sulphate and household ammonia. (*Caution children not to taste these poisonous substances.*) Dissolve a teaspoonful of copper sulphate in a half-glass of water. Put several drops of diluted copper sulphate and several drops of ammonia into a glass containing a little milk. A purple color should form. Try it with plain water for contrast. Bulk foods—cheese, beans, meat, and so on—can be tested in the same way except that they should first be thoroughly pulverized and stirred into a little water to attain a semiliquid state.

Let children speculate as to which foods are rich in proteins. Discourage blind guessing. To aid their thinking encourage wise use of clues they already know. Which foods are athletes likeliest to eat? Which foods are often recommended for children? Which foods tend to be alike? If one kind of food is rich in proteins, perhaps similar ones also are.

suggest hypotheses

Should there be enough materials available, divide the class into groups as before, and let them cross-check their results. Encourage them to make a chart of findings on which they agree. Results can be verified by consulting books. Other high-protein foods may be added to the list as discovered.

evaluate critically

draw conclusions

Contributing idea C. Minerals and vitamins regulate body processes; some minerals are used in growth and repair of cells.

1. *Materials:* a clean, chicken leg bone; capped fruit or peanut-butter jar containing fresh vinegar. (Prepare materials in advance of this lesson. Place the chicken bone in the jar and cap tightly. In about a week, acetic acid in the vinegar will dissolve most of the hard mineral structure of the bone.)

Write on the chalkboard: *Energy foods, Proteins, Minerals.* Review briefly why energy foods and proteins are essential to health. Point out that minerals in the diet are also essential to good health. Discuss with the class what minerals are—the materials of which rocks and soil are made. But we don't eat rocks. How could minerals get into our bodies? *suggest hypotheses* Develop that some minerals dissolve in rainwater and are taken into plants as they soak up the water. We eat plants and some animals which feed on plants.

Ask, "Can anyone think of one reason why our bodies need these materials?" For a clue remind the class that rocks are hard. When bones are mentioned, produce the vinegar jar and bone. Rinse the bone in water and dry it. Explain that the bone has been placed in a mild acid for a week. Acid dissolves much of the mineral matter in a bone. Can the children guess what has happened to the bone? Show them how flexible it is now. Bend it, or tie it in a knot!

Explain that, in addition to helping build bones and teeth, tiny amounts of minerals aid in the formation of blood and many other substances in the body. Some minerals are needed for body cells to work properly.

Point out that *calcium* is one of the most important minerals for building bones. Challenge the class to locate in books names of *evaluate critically* foods rich in calcium. In addition, mention that salt is often iodized—that is, the mineral element iodine is added. Invite several volunteers to find out why.

2. Add the word *vitamins* to the several nutrients already listed on the chalkboard. Develop that, like minerals, these chemical substances also help to promote health and growth of body cells. Mention that one of the most important of these substances is vitamin C. During the lengthy voyages of slow sailing ships long ago, many sailors suffered badly from a disease called scurvy. Their body joints would swell painfully, gums bleed, and teeth fall out. Yet once again on land, the sailors usually recovered quickly.

Which foods were probably missing on *suggest hypoth-* these ships? Invite hypotheses. Develop that fresh vegetables and fruits were lacking in sailors' diets soon after putting out to sea. Mention that British naval doctors discovered 200 years ago that a daily ration of juice from limes or lemons would prevent scurvy. Gradually, scurvy ceased to be a problem to sailors.

Contributing idea D. About two-thirds of the human body is composed of water; most foods we eat contain water.

Materials: soda-straw balances (see preceding exposition); a variety of fresh, thinly sliced foods—apple, orange, tomato, potato, bread, bologna, etc.; goose-neck lamp; metal kitchen foil.

Ask pupils to imagine themselves on a small desert island. There will be no rescue for three weeks. They can have either 1 pint of water each day, or a slice of bread each day; nothing else. Which would they choose, and *evaluat- critical-* why?

During discussion, establish that water is the wiser choice. The body can draw upon stored fat for energy, and even use up muscle or organ tissue if necessary. The average person might survive for three or four weeks without food. But water is needed within several days.

Stress reasons why water is so important. It makes up most of our blood. It cools the body, most noticeably as we perspire. Water permits the body to get rid of poisons that accumulate. It is essential for cells to function properly. There are other important reasons they will find in later study.

Back to the desert island. What if the children had a choice of three fresh apples a day or a daily pint of water? Establish that apples are a better choice because they contain sugar,

reason
tatively minerals, vitamins—and water, too. How much water? Encourage children to express their guesses in either percentages or tenths, depending upon their knowledge of arithmetic. Hold up some of the other food samples. List the foods and estimated percentages of water on the chalkboard. Ask how they think the water content can be found. Draw out that the foods can be weighed, then dried, and weighed again.

Demonstrate how to use the soda-straw balances. Divide children into as many groups as there are balances. This will allow much pupil participation, and permit later cross-checking of results. Group chairmen should carefully record weights of various food slices.

Thin food slices may be dried satisfactorily overnight with a goose-neck lamp. Put the slices on some kitchen foil and position the lamp shade about 18 inches away. If no lamp is available, just leave food slices exposed to air and sunshine for three or four days.

reason
tatively After the materials are dry they should be weighed again. The difference between before-and-after-drying weights will represent water loss.

valuate
itically Have children cross-check their results. Then let them compare their results with findings for the same foods recorded in nutrition books or trade books. Encourage them to analyze why differences appear. Guide them to treat their theories as hypotheses which can be tested.

Extending activities

1. Ask able pupils to look up the major diseases that result from vitamin deficiencies and how these diseases are prevented.

2. Encourage at-home testing of additional valuate
itically foods for starch or other nutritive materials. Have children make reports on their findings.

We can eat food, but when is it within the body? The answer to this seemingly simple question depends upon whose point of view we take. Most of us would say that food is inside the body once it is swallowed. To bio-chemists, however, any food still within the 30-foot digestive tube they call the *alimentary canal* is considered outside the body. This underlines the uselessness of foods we eat until they are digested—that is, chemically broken down and dissolved into a form that can be used in the cells. The digestive system is marvelously suited to this function. Let us examine how it works. (See Figure 12-6 for an illustration.)

The digestive process begins when we start chewing food. Our front teeth (incisors and canines) cut and tear the food. Back teeth (molars) crush it into small particles. At the same time, saliva pours into the food from six salivary glands in and near the mouth. Saliva softens the food and begins the chemical breakdown of starches. A gradual, sweetening flavor is experienced when we chew starchy foods, such as cooked potato, soda cracker, or bread. The saliva contains an enzyme called ptyalin, which reduces large starch molecules into simple sugar molecules. (An enzyme is a chemical that brings about or speeds up chemical reactions without being changed itself.) In addition to ptyalin, several other enzymes in the body's digestive system play important roles in the reduction of food to usable form.

Swallowed food passes into the esophagus, or food tube. It is squeezed down into the stomach by regular, wavelike contractions of smooth muscles which surround the esophagus. Similar muscles are located all along the alimentary canal. Since it is muscle action (peristalsis), not gravity, which moves the food inside the canal, it is possible to eat and swallow while standing on our heads.

Peristaltic motions continue in the stomach. The food is churned slowly in gastric juices secreted from the stomach lining. Several enzymes and diluted hydrochloric acid break down most of the proteins. Digestion of starch stops, because acid prevents ptyalin from working. Some fats are broken down, but for the most part fats go through the stomach undigested.

The stomach's hydrochloric acid is powerful indeed. (Almost every television viewer has seen at least one drug advertisement in which hydrochloric acid burns holes in a handkerchief!) Why doesn't this corrosive liquid digest the stomach itself? Only in recent years have researchers pinpointed the reason. A small amount of ammonia—this is an alkali or base—is secreted in the lining of the stomach. It effectively neutralizes acid next to the lining without interfering with the acid's digestive action elsewhere in the stomach. We use the same principle of neutralizing an acid when we drink seltzer or soda water to settle a "sour" stomach.

After about two to six hours in the stomach, depending upon what and how much has been eaten, the partially digested food materials are pushed into the small intestine. Here, glands within intestinal walls produce digestive juices with enzymes which· begin working on the food. Additional digestive juices are secreted into the intestine from small tubes connected to the liver and pancreas.

Throughout the small intestine, peristaltic motion continues as digestive juices complete

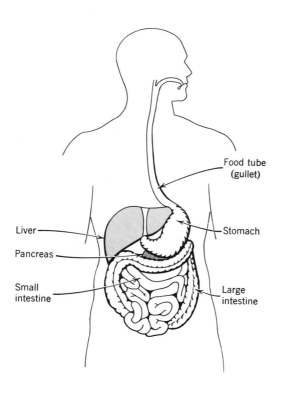

Liver

Pancreas

Small intestine

Food tube (gullet)

Stomach

Large intestine

the breakdown of carbohydrates into simple sugars, proteins into amino acids, and fats into fatty acids and glycerine. At various portions of the small intestine the sugars and amino acids are absorbed into blood vessels within its lining. Digested fats are first absorbed into the lymph system and then later transported into the blood stream.

Nondigestible material or waste, composed chiefly of cellulose, passes into the large intestine. Much of the water contained in waste material is absorbed into the intestinal walls. The remaining substance is eliminated from the body.

Food products dissolved in the blood are distributed to cells after they are processed by the liver. In the cells these products are oxidized, changed into protoplasm, or stored as fat. Many children find it difficult to believe that oxidation ("burning") takes place in cells. We shall provide several activities to aid their understanding.

BASIC GENERALIZATION III: Food is digested in the alimentary canal and then transported to the cells, where it is oxidized, changed into body materials, or stored

Contributing idea A. Digestion begins in the mouth, continues in the stomach, and is completed in the intestine.

1. *Materials:* model of human torso, or chart of human digestive system, or opaque projection of Figure 12-6.

Begin with a quick summary of digestion to help pupils grasp the big picture. Point out that although we can enjoy eating a delicious hamburger or peanut-butter sandwich, these foods cannot reach our body cells and give us energy until they are changed in form. Before food can be used, it must be in a *dissolved* form that can pass through the cell membranes. (Dissolve some salt in a glass of water if pupils are unacquainted with the term.) Indicate the chart or substitute material. Who can describe what happens when food is broken down or *digested* in the body?

Briefly develop the course of food in the

alimentary canal: Digestion begins in the mouth. Chewing breaks food into small particles. Saliva from the mouth is added to the food and it is swallowed. The swallowed food passes through the *gullet* into the stomach. From there it goes to the *small intestine* where digestion is completed. Some water and solid wastes go into the *large intestine*. Much of the water is absorbed into the body. The remaining waste matter is passed from the body.

Mention that, in the next several activities, the children will look more closely at what happens during digestion.

2. *Materials:* sugarless soda crackers; iodine; several test tubes; test tube holder; Benedict's solution; candle and matches.

This activity should help pupils learn that saliva changes starch into sugar. They should be already aware that soda crackers contain starch. If this has not been discovered in preceding activities, test some crackers for starch before starting the following lesson.

Ask several children to chew some soda crackers, but not to swallow them for at least one minute. Do they notice any change in taste as they chew? Draw out that the taste gradually becomes sweeter. Is there sugar in a chewed cracker or do they just imagine that *select* it is sweet? How can it be tested for sugar? *ocedures* (Put part of a chewed cracker with saliva in a test tube. Place inside several drops of Benedict's solution and heat over a candle. If the mixture turns brick-red it contains sugar.)

After sugar is identified, continue. Have pupils recall that at first there was no sugar taste. Where did the sugar come from? Some pupils will say from saliva, others, from the cracker itself. How can we find out if saliva contains sugar? (Put some by itself in a test *select* tube and test for sugar.) How can a cracker *ocedures* be tested for sugar? (Crush part of a cracker in a little water, put into a test tube, and once again heat with a few drops of Benedict's *evaluate* solution.) Raise an objection, if no one else *critically* does: How will we know if the *water* is sugar-free? (Water can first be tested by itself.)

Children will be puzzled by negative results of all three tests. Where does the sugar

come from? Have them speculate. Some chil- *suggest* dren may reason that there is something in *hypotheses* saliva that changes the starch to sugar. Develop this idea. There is a chemical in saliva which changes large starch molecules into smaller, simple sugar molecules. As they have found out, the chemical itself does not contain sugar.

3. *Materials:* two glasses; water; dry cornstarch; sugar; spoon.

Remind pupils that before food can be used by body cells, it must be in a dissolved form. Does changing a starch into a sugar help the dissolving process? Which of the two dissolves more completely in water? Indicate the materials. How can they be used to find out? (Put one spoonful each of sugar and starch *select* in separate glasses. Add the same amount of *procedures* water to each glass and stir the same number of times.)

Pupils will find that no matter how long the *draw* starch is stirred it will not dissolve. Help them *conclusions* to understand that starch must be broken down into a soluble form before it is usable. This is accomplished when it is changed to sugar.

4. *Materials:* two balloons; water; four small cubes of sugar; two empty glasses.

Have the class recall that swallowed food goes down the gullet or food tube to the stomach. There, further digestive juices, including a strong acid, break down proteins that may be in the chewed food. Also muscles in the stomach cause it to churn the food inside. Does the churning motion help to break down food?

Point to the materials. We will pretend the balloons are stomachs. We can use water for digestive juice. Sugar cubes can be the food to be digested. Can anyone think of a controlled experiment to see if churning helps to *select* break down food? (Put two sugar cubes in *procedures* each balloon with equal amounts of water. Squeeze and unsqueeze one balloon continually to imitate churning action. Leave the second balloon alone. After a few minutes, pour the contents of each balloon into separate glasses and check which sugar cubes have dissolved the most.)

Children will learn that the churning action results in faster dissolving. But this is an analogy. Let them read before conclusions are drawn. Bring out, too, that thorough chewing of food in the first place would speed up digestive action in the stomach.

evaluate critically

5. *Materials:* red and blue litmus paper (sold in drug stores); ammonia; vinegar; eyedropper; salt water solution in a glass; two empty glasses.

Explain that digestive acid released from the lining of the stomach is so powerful that it may break down meat into a semiliquid form within an hour or two after eating. Let pupils recall how even a weak acid in vinegar dissolved bone minerals in an early experiment. Why isn't the stomach itself digested by this powerful acid? Allow some speculation, then give further information for the children's thinking. Scientists have discovered that, besides the acid, a tiny amount of ammonia is released all along the stomach lining. Point out that ammonia is one of a group of chemicals called *bases*. Mention that a strong *basic* chemical is also very corrosive. Children may recall that their mothers use ammonia for dissolving thick grease spots.

Show children how to identify an acid. Dip blue litmus paper into the acid. It will turn red. Try it with red paper and it remains unchanged. Now demonstrate how to identify a base. Dip red litmus paper in some ammonia and it will turn blue. Try blue paper; it will remain blue. Hold up and identify the salt water. Is it an acid or a base? Dip in both red and blue litmus paper. Both will remain unchanged. Explain that salt water is one of many *neutral* materials. It is neither an acid nor a base, but a substance "between" these two.

Refer to the original question. Does anyone now have an idea why the stomach is not digested by its own acid? (Maybe the ammonia neutralizes the acid.) How can we test this? (Add ammonia drops to some vinegar a little at a time. Keep testing with both red and blue litmus paper. Neither should change color when or if the mixture becomes neutral.)

suggest hypotheses

select procedures

draw conclusions

Follow through by pointing out that the neutralizing effect takes place chiefly at the stomach lining. It does not materially weaken the acid's digestive action on the food itself.

6. *Materials:* yardstick.

Explain that digestion is completed in the small intestine by additional digestive juices released there. Remind children that the small intestine is coiled. Invite speculation as to its length in an adult. Reveal that it is about 22 feet long while the large intestine is about 5 feet in length. Have several children measure off these lengths to provide accurate, visible referents.

reason quanti

Contributing idea B. Digested food is transported by the blood to the cells, where it is oxidized, changed into body materials, or stored.

1. *Materials:* several straws; pocket mirror; limewater (sold in drug stores); two jars with caps; two small candles and matches. (Prepare materials beforehand. Drip some melted wax from a burning candle onto the inside base of two uncapped jars. Blow out the candle and attach it upright to the inside base of one jar before the wax hardens. Attach a second candle similarly inside the other jar. Pour about an inch of limewater into each jar and cap securely.)

Through pupil reading or your exposition, reveal that dissolved, digested food molecules seep through the walls of the small intestine and enter the blood stream. There the food, and oxygen picked up from the lungs, are transported to body cells. Inside the cells, the oxygen combines with the food molecules and releases heat energy. This process is called *oxidation*; it is a very slow kind of burning. A waste product, *carbon dioxide* gas, is given off by the cells and absorbed by the blood. The blood circulates back to the lungs and releases it. We then breathe out the carbon dioxide. You may have to go over the steps in this process several times before it seems reasonably clear.

Mention that many children find it hard to believe oxidation takes place in their bodies.

Several demonstrations may help to convince them.

Hold up the two capped jars containing candles. Remind pupils that a burning object releases carbon dioxide. Explain that there is a special kind of liquid called *limewater* inside the jars. When carbon dioxide dissolves in limewater, something happens. Ask the children to look carefully at the limewater— and also the jar—to see if any changes take place when one candle is lighted. Draw out *select* why only one candle should be lit. (The sec- *cedures* ond setup will serve as a control.)

Uncap one jar, light the candle, and quickly recap the jar. Shortly the flame will die. Children may notice that the limewater becomes whitish in appearance. Sharp observers may see a few water droplets condense inside on the glass. The control jar will remain unchanged. If the limewater reaction is slow, shake both jars gently for a few seconds. Establish that limewater turns milky white when carbon dioxide is dissolved in it.

Say, "If oxidation is taking place in our bodies, we should be breathing out some carbon dioxide. How can we find out?" (Blow *select* through a straw into clear limewater; see if it *cedures* turns white.) Results will be positive and obvious within a minute.

Now lead into a problem. If we are breathing carbon dioxide into the air, the air should contain carbon dioxide. Hold up the clear *define* limewater. There is something strange here. *roblems* What is the problem? (Why doesn't the limewater turn white *without* blowing into *suggest* it?) Encourage a reasonable hypothesis. *otheses* (Maybe there is only a tiny amount.) Let *select* the class develop a long-range test, such as *cedures* leaving some limewater in a wide-mouthed container for a week. It should change ap- *draw* pearance within this time. A second tightly *clusions* capped jar of limewater can serve as a control.

Bring out that some water droplets condensed in the jar after the candle went out. Explain that another product of burning is *water vapor*—that is, water in gaseous form that condenses into liquid water again when it strikes a cool object. Do we give off water vapor, too? What available material could we

use to find out? (Blow warm breath against a *select* mirror surface.) Have the class recall how *procedures* water vapor in the breath condenses in air on cold days.

2. *Materials:* clinical thermometer; alcohol; water.

The following activity can be used to demonstrate that exercise increases body temperature.

Press for additional evidence that slow burning may be going on in our bodies. Draw out that a warm body temperature is a strong indication. Develop that when we blow air on a fire, the increased oxygen makes the fire burn hotter and fuel is consumed faster. Explain that when we exercise we breathe harder and take in more oxygen than usual. Hard exercise uses up energy fast. Oxidation of food in cells should therefore take place faster than usual. Can the children think of any *evaluate* evidence that this happens when they engage *critically* in hard exercise? For example, how do they feel after running hard?

Hold up the thermometer. How can we *select* find out if exercise does increase body tem- *procedures* perature? (Measure temperatures of someone before and after a few minutes of hard exercise.) Guide pupils to see the wisdom of *reason* taking temperatures of several persons and *quantitatively* averaging them.

Help the class understand that increased activity requires increased food consumption. Explain, however, that eating more food than is required results in fat storage in the cells. How the children can select the right foods, in proper amounts, they shall consider shortly.

Extending activities

1. Children will enjoy discovering for themselves places on their tongues which give the four chief sensations of taste: sweet, sour, salt, and bitter. Each child will need a paper towel; a pocket mirror (unless he works with a partner); several cotton swabs; and four accessible containers of solutions to be tasted. There should be one container each of salt water, sugar water, diluted vinegar, and a bitter solution prepared by dissolving half of an aspirin tablet in a half-glass of water.

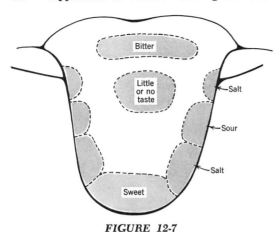

FIGURE 12-7

Each group of four containers can be shared by several or more children, provided they do not reuse a swab that has been placed in the mouth. To simplify charting of taste spots on the tongue, you might put a sketch of Figure 12-7 on the chalkboard. However, do not write in labels until children have revealed their results. Direct pupils to use only a tiny bit of solution on the swab, and to touch lightly various parts of the tongue. To promote accuracy of taste, tongues should be wiped dry with a paper towel before each time a different solution is tried.

draw conclus.

2. Pupils will recall how tasteless foods seem when they have colds. Develop a controlled experiment with them to determine how well they can detect the names of foods without use of their noses. Use tiny cubes of apple, carrot, potato, onion, and other common foods of about the same consistency. Pupils should try first to identify the foods by taste with noses pinched, and then with noses free. Eyes should be closed during both series of trials.

select procedu

A variation of this test is interesting and reveals how much we rely on smells to "taste" things. With eyes shut, have a pupil chew a tiny cube of one kind of food (apple) while a large piece of another food (pear) is held close to his nose. Most pupils will be misled about what they are tasting.

3. Exhibit a film on the digestive process in humans to help summarize the preceding ideas.

Does an apple a day keep the doctor away? It helps—but it had better be included in a balanced diet. No single food contains all the essential nutrients for good health. A balanced diet consists of carbohydrates, fats, proteins, vitamins, minerals, and water, in proper amounts. Even milk falls a bit short in several of these essentials.

It is desirable for persons to know that balanced nutrients are needed. But how is this knowledge transferred into action? For instance, can we rely on taste alone to be the guide? Try asking your class what they would prefer eating for a steady diet. As you might suspect, a list of their preferences usually resembles a chronicle of gastronomical horrors.

Even adults who want to may have some difficulty in selecting balanced foods. For this

FIGURE 12-8   The daily food guide.

reason, the federal government years ago asked nutrition specialists to prepare a simple Daily Food Guide. The guide originally contained seven basic food groups. Recently, these have been consolidated to form the "Basic 4," consisting of a meat group, vegetable-fruit group, bread-cereal group, and milk group. When eaten in suggested quantities and with sufficient water, these foods constitute a healthful diet for normal persons.

By "healthful diet for normal persons" we mean nothing else is needed for optimum health—no yogurt, vinegar and honey, organically grown vegetables, vitamin pills, brewer's yeast, or the other nutrients advertised as special health foods.

Will knowledge of the "Basic 4" really improve children's diets? Sometimes the objection is raised that there is not much value in teaching nutrition to children. After all, what they eat is controlled by their parents. How valid is this reasoning? Admittedly, the home does exercise control to a great degree. But no one can completely control a normal child—in food habits, or anything else—as many parents will ruefully testify. Even in homes where good diets are found, securing children's cooperation through understanding is usually more effective than the admonitory, eat-it-because-it-is-good-for-you approach. And most children do have some influence on food purchases, even in households with low budgets. Balanced meals can be prepared inexpensively. Finally, as children grow, they have more opportunity to exert their increasing independence in food selection. How wisely this is done is influenced by their knowledge, attitudes, and previous habits.

Although a balanced diet is essential to good health, care should be taken to eat only the amount of food that maintains proper bodyweight. People feel better and seem to live longer when their bodyweights are reasonably close to those recommended in height-weight tables.

How fat or thin we are largely depends on the amounts of carbohydrates, fats, and proteins we eat. These are the only nutrients that "burn" in our cells and provide energy.

FIGURE 12-9 A calorimeter.

When we take in more of these materials than the body can burn most of the excess is stored as fat in various cells.

The amount of heat energy that any food can produce is measured in *calories*. You may remember from another unit (page 118) that a food calorie is the amount of heat required to raise the temperature of 1000 grams of water 1 degree centigrade. In more familiar terms, 1 calorie will raise the temperature of a quart of water almost 2 degrees Fahrenheit.

The caloric value of a food is determined by burning it in an enclosed, insulated container called a *calorimeter*. A small, known weight of food is placed inside an oxygen-filled chamber surrounded by water. An electrically heated wire ignites the food and it burns completely. The heat given off raises the water temperature. The amount of rise indicates how many calories are in the burned food.

In a forthcoming activity, children can burn a peanut or other flammable food under a container of water to determine calories. Of course, their test will be inaccurate because of heat loss—possibly 25 to 50 per cent. Use this opportunity to have them reason why their results conflict with listed caloric values of foods.

How many calories should people have

daily? The proper number of calories for each of us is a highly individual matter, since it depends on several varying factors: age, size, physical activity, and environmental temperature. Temperature is included because we lose more body heat as the weather becomes colder. Recent evidence indicates that heavy work performed in hot temperatures also requires many additional calories. Apparently, the body works so hard at keeping cool a vast expenditure of energy occurs.

We shall close our last sequence with an activity to help pupils reason how the several factors combine to determine the amount of food one should eat.

BASIC GENERALIZATION IV: For a healthful diet, one should choose wisely from a variety of foods

Contributing idea A. Nutrients from the four basic food groups can provide a balanced diet.

1. Use the following activity to make pupils aware that food preferences alone are likely to be an unsatisfactory guide for healthful nutrition.

Begin by saying, "Boys and girls, suppose you had the chance to select all the kinds of food you wanted to eat, each day for the next five years. What would you choose?" Rapidly write on the chalkboard food preferences as they are given. One or two class secretaries might assist in chalkboard writing to speed up recordings.

After several moments, stop and have the pupils assess their choices. These foods would taste very good. But how good would they be *evaluate critically* for their health? Draw out the several nutrients needed for sound health: carbohydrates, fats, proteins, vitamins, and minerals. Do the foods selected have all the required nutrients? (Probably not.) Develop that a *balanced diet* includes all these nutrients and sufficient water.

Challenge the children to plan three meals —breakfast, lunch, and dinner—which together might contain all the essential nutri-

ents. Provide a few minutes for them to think about this task. Most children will realize the assignment is too difficult without reference to a guide of some kind. Bring out this need during discussion. Mention that many adults also are often uncertain about how to plan meals or select proper foods in the absence of a nutrition guide.

2. *Materials:* large chart of basic foods as follows:

A Daily Food Guide

I. *Meat Group:* two or more servings.
(Lean meats, poultry, fish, and eggs. Peas, beans, and nuts may be substituted sometimes.)
II. *Vegetable-Fruit Group:* two vegetables and two fruits.
(Green, yellow, and leafy vegetables. Fruits, including one citrus fruit daily.)
III. *Bread-Cereal Group:* four or more servings.
(Breads, cereals, and other grain products.)
IV. *Milk Group:* four glasses of milk or equivalent.
(Milk, butter, cheese, ice cream, and other dairy products.)

Exhibit the chart. Explain that it is based on recommendations of nutrition experts to help people select a balanced diet more easily. Let pupils analyze briefly the main nutrients *evaluate critically* of each group. The meat group is mostly rich in proteins. The vegetable-fruit group is richest in vitamins and minerals. Bring out that starches predominate in the bread-cereal group. Develop that milk is probably the most complete of these foods. It is rich in fat, has some protein, sugar, and several important minerals.

Remind pupils that the guide was developed to make food selection easier. Will it help them plan a nutritious breakfast, lunch, and dinner? Invite them to write down a balanced menu for one day. Walk around and help individual students. Suggest to the faster workers that they plan for several days, with as great a variety of foods as possible.

evaluate critically

When appropriate, organize the class into small groups to make possible specific evaluations of each pupil's plans. However, provide sufficient time for pupils to evaluate their own plans before further appraisal.

3. Ask children to collect and bring in colored, cutout, magazine pictures of foods *evaluate critically* belonging to the four basic groups. Have them sift through and classify the pictures according to basic groups. This can be done first within small committees, and then with the entire class for a final check. Let pupils plan a bulletin board to show the variety of foods within each broad category.

Contributing idea B. People need different amounts of food, depending on age, body size, physical activity, and temperature.

1. *Materials:* several peanuts, Brazil nuts, or substitutes; ice cube tongs; open, half-gallon can; Fahrenheit thermometer; two bricks; matches.

Have pupils recall that the basic food guide recommends a certain number of food portions, as well as food types, for daily meals. Raise the question: If a person has a balanced diet, what difference does it make if he eats a great deal, or very little? Bring out that overweight or underweight may result.

Mention that many persons, especially those placed on strict diets by their doctors, watch carefully the number of *calories* in foods they eat. Define a food calorie in familiar terms: One food calorie will raise the temperature of a quart of water almost 2 degrees Fahrenheit.

Hold up a peanut. Review that it releases heat energy in the body after it is digested and then oxidized in cells. How many calories does it have? Explain that it can be burned to find out. Pour slightly more than a quart of water into a half-gallon can. Place the can on two bricks spread apart several inches. Help children to realize what must be done. *select cedures* Water temperature will be taken before and after the burning peanut is held under the can of water.

Have someone take the first temperature reading. Then take hold of the peanut with tongs, and set it aflame. Several matches may be required. Keep the burning peanut a few inches below the water can until it is consumed; this may take about five minutes. Have someone stir the water briefly before taking the second thermometer reading. Let pupils calculate how many calories the peanut had. (For example, if the water temperature *reason quantitatively* rose 8 degrees, the peanut contained about 4 calories of heat energy.)

Look puzzled. According to calorie tables, the peanut should have had at least 6 calories. Why did we get only 4? Invite hypotheses. Some pupils may suggest that the peanut used was too small. Or perhaps temperatures were misread. Some may say that some of the heat energy probably did not go into heating the water. Assist them to think *select procedures* through what might be done in each case. Show them a picture of a calorimeter and explain how it works.

2. *Materials:* large chart of Figure 12-10.

Use this activity to bring out several factors which determine how many calories different persons need. Write the following data on the chalkboard before beginning this lesson:

Person	Age (yrs.)	Weight (lbs.)	Where Lives
(1) Boy or girl	2	27	Iowa
(2) Male lumberjack	40	175	Alaska
(3) High-school boy	16	150	New York
(4) Boy or girl	11	72	Texas
(5) Female office worker	25	110	Wisconsin
(6) Male office worker	26	175	California

Pin up the graph next to the preceding data. Inform children that the graph shows the number of calories needed by the six persons described. But there is a problem here. Before the graph can be used, something will *define problems* need to be done. (To which column in the graph does each of the six belong?) How can this be determined?

Have pupils speculate about the relative importance of the several factors described. Would a heavy, older man need more energy *evaluate critically* than a child? And so on. If some simple nutrition books are available, or an appropriate film, this would be an excellent time for

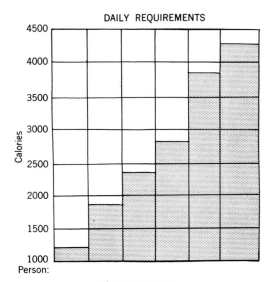

FIGURE 12-10

suggest hypotheses

draw conclusions

pupils to gather more data. After some study and discussion, challenge pupils to write the numerals of persons in the order in which they should probably appear on the graph. When this assignment is . completed, reveal the most probable order: (1), (5), (4), (6), (3), (2).

Help pupils to reason through the factors involved. Age, body size, amount of physical activity, and environmental temperature all would have some bearing on total calories needed. Stress that for most healthy children, their own appetite is an excellent guide as to how many calories must be consumed. Calorie watching is mostly for persons who are trying to gain or lose weight according to doctors' instructions.

Extending activities

define problems

select procedure

1. Introduce the idea that many persons believe certain foods increase their intelligence. Challenge pupils to criticize and set up an imaginary experiment to test this statement: "Fish food will make you smarter." Draw out that an operational definition is needed for "smarter." Also elicit that smarter implies a comparison—but to whom? to what? After these ideas have been explored, let the children design an imaginary, controlled experiment. This activity can stimulate deep thought if given a chance.

2. Invite the school nurse to discuss with the class how proper nutrition, exercise, and rest are the foundations upon which growing bodies depend for maximum growth and health.

3. Encourage class artists to design a free-hanging art mobile in which the four basic food groups form a "balanced" diet.

Bibliography

PROFESSIONAL BOOKS

Blough, Glenn O., and Julius Schwartz, *Elementary School Science and How To Teach It,* third edition, New York: Holt, Rinehart and Winston, 1964, 655 pp. Includes science subject matter and methods. The subject matter is exceptionally well written and comprehensive in scope.

Brandwein, Paul F., *Elements in a Strategy for Teaching Science in The Elementary School,* New York: Harcourt, Brace and World, 1962, 40 pp. This is the Burton Lecture of 1961, delivered at Harvard University by the author. He proposes that elementary science be organized according to major "conceptual schemes."

Burnett, R. Will, *Teaching Science in The Elementary School,* New York: Holt, Rinehart and Winston, 1953, 542 pp. Contains science subject matter and methods. Material in Chapter 4 on aesthetic contributions of science is pure gold.

Carin, Arthur, and Robert B. Sund, *Teaching Science Through Discovery,* Columbus, Ohio: Charles E. Merrill, 1964, 514 pp. Describes methods and materials for elementary science. Includes lesson plans grouped by basic science areas.

Craig, Gerald S., *Science for the Elementary-School Teacher,* new edition, Boston: Ginn, 1958, 894 pp. The most comprehensive book available on elementary science education. Good reference volume.

Fitzpatrick, Frederick L. (editor), *Policies for Science Education,* New York: Teachers College, Columbia University, 1960, 219 pp. Various authorities suggest policies for the improvement of science education at all levels.

Hone, Elizabeth B., Alexander Joseph, and Edward Victor, *A Sourcebook for Elementary Science,* New York: Harcourt, Brace and World, 1962, 552 pp. Very extensive collection of classroom activities, with specific accompanying instructions.

Hubler, Clark, *Working with Children in Science,* Boston: Houghton Mifflin, 1957, 425 pp. Particularly helpful on methods of teaching elementary-school science.

Jacobson, Willard L., and Harold E. Tannenbaum, *Modern Elementary-School Science: A Recommended Sequence,* New York: Teachers College, Columbia University, 1961, 194 pp. Gives specific recommendations for scope and sequence. Useful for curriculum workers.

Kambly, Paul E., and John E. Suttle, *Teaching Elementary-School Science,* New York: Ronald Press, 1963, 492 pp. Includes methods, comprehensive resource units, and a detailed listing of source materials.

Lewis, June E., and Irene C. Potter, *The Teaching of Science in the Elementary School*, Englewood Cliffs, N.J.: Prentice-Hall, 1961, 381 pp. Subject matter and activities for elementary science. Activities are arranged by questions within topic areas.

National Society for the Study of Education, *Re-Thinking Science Education, Fifty-Ninth Yearbook*, Part I, Chicago: University of Chicago Press, 1960, 338 pp. Directions and designs of modern thinking in science education.

Navarra, John G., and Joseph Zafforoni, *Science Today for The Elementary-School Teacher*, New York: Harper and Row, 470 pp. Contains material on methods of teaching and science subject matter.

Tannenbaum, Harold E., Nathan Stillman, and Albert Piltz, *Science Education for Elementary-School Teachers*, second edition, Boston: Allyn & Bacon, 1965, 349 pp. Focuses mainly on methods of science teaching. Excellent material on relation of child development to science education.

Vessel, Matthew F., *Elementary-School Science Teaching*, New York: Center for Applied Research in Education, 1963, 119 pp. A monograph on the organization and improvement of programs in elementary science.

Victor, Edward, *Science for the Elementary School*, New York: Macmillan, 1965, 772 pp. Methods and activities for teaching science. Features an extensive presentation of subject matter in outline form.

PAMPHLETS

Ashley, Tracy H., and others, *An Administrator's Guide to the Elementary-School Science Program*, Association of Public School Systems, 525 W. 120th St., New York, N.Y., 1958, 30 pp. Helpful suggestions for administrators who want to improve science programs.

Blackwood, Paul E., *Science Teaching in The Elementary Schools, A Survey of Practices*, U.S. Office of Education Publication 29059, Washington, D.C.: Government Printing Office, 1965, 104 pp. A thorough report of science teaching in elementary schools of the United States.

Craig, Gerald S., *Science in the Elementary School: What Research Says to the Teacher Series*, Washington, D.C.: Department of Classroom Teachers, National Education Association, 1957, 33 pp. Recommends teaching practices indicated by research.

Dunfee, Maxine, and Julian Greenlee, *Elementary-School Science: Research, Theory, and Practice*, Washington, D.C.: Association for Supervision and Curriculum Development, National Education Association, 1957, 67 pp. Sets forth research findings and recommended practices in elementary science.

Zafforoni, Joseph, *New Developments in Elementary-School Science*, Washington, D.C.: National Science Teachers Association, National Education Association, 1963, 52 pp. A survey report on emerging programs of science in the elementary school.

PERIODICALS

Journal of Research in Science Teaching (Official journal of the National Association for Research in Science Teaching), John Wiley and Sons, Inc., 605 Third Ave., New York, N.Y. (Quarterly). Scholarly articles on research and practice at all levels of science education.

School Science and Mathematics, Central Association of Science and Mathematics Teachers, 450 Ahnsip St., Menasha, Wisconsin (9 issues a year). Frequently contains articles on elementary science.

Science and Children, National Science Teachers Association, 1201 Sixteenth St., N.W., Washington, D.C. (8 issues a year). Journal articles of interest and value to elementary-school teachers. $4.00 subscription includes elementary membership in NSTA with voting privileges, and periodic receipt of materials packets.

Science Education, Clarence M. Pruitt, Editor, University of Tampa, Tampa, Florida (5 issues a year). Articles on science education at all levels.

Science News Letter, Science Service, 1719 N Street, N.W., Washington, D.C. (Weekly). Useful reports on current research findings. Articles are short and fairly easy to read.

Scientific American, Scientific American Company, 415 Madison Ave., New York, N.Y. (Monthly). Interesting, thorough reports on recent scientific developments. Requires some science background of the reader.

CURRICULUM IMPROVEMENT PROJECTS

American Association for the Advancement of Science—Commission on Science Education, American Association for the Advancement of Science, 1515 Massachusetts Avenue, N.W., Washington, D.C. 20005.

Educational Services Incorporated—Elementary Science Study, 108 Water Street, Watertown, Massachusetts 02172.

State University of New York (Stony Brook)—Quantitative Approach in Elementary-School Science, Department of Physics, State University of New York, Stony Brook, New York 11790.

University of California (Berkeley)—Elementary-School Science Project, 2232 Piedmont Avenue, University of California, Berkeley, California 94720.

University of California (Berkeley)—Science Curriculum Improvement Study, University of California, Berkeley, California 94720.

University of Illinois—Elementary-School Science Project, 805 West Pennsylvania Avenue, Urbana, Illinois 61801.

University of Illinois—School Science Curriculum Project, 805 West Pennsylvania Avenue, Urbana, Illinois 61801.

University of Minnesota—Mathematics and Science Teaching Project, University of Minnesota, Minneapolis, Minnesota 55455.

Utah State University—Elementary-School Science Project, Utah State University, Logan, Utah 84321.

Index